LINEAR ANALYSIS

LINEAR ANALYSIS

By

RALPH HENSTOCK, M.A., Ph.D.

Reader in Mathematics
The University of Lancaster

NEW YORK
PLENUM PRESS
LONDON
BUTTERWORTHS

Published in the U.S.A. by
PLENUM PRESS
a division of
PLENUM PUBLISHING CORPORATION
227 West 17th Street, New York N.Y. 10011

First published by
Butterworth & Co. (Publishers) Ltd.

QA 320
· H384
1967A

Suggested U.D.C. number: 517
Library of Congress Catalog Card Number 67–31097

Printed in Hungary
Franklin Printing House

PREFACE

THE analytic topology of the 1870's resulted in two new subjects: on the one hand the theory of measure and Lebesgue integration, and on the other, the apparatus of functional analysis. Many references to early results are given in the book, to counteract a student impression that Lebesgue integration, topology, and functional analysis began in the 1940's or even later. Naturally, however, most papers are fairly recent. My own research has been in integration and summability theory, and particularly in problems that use both. In Henstock (1963c) can be found a simple outline of a new integration theory. The present book fills a gap in existing literature by containing details of that part of functional analysis in which summability theory is imbedded. In the main the integration can be Lebesgue's, or the new kind.

I wish to acknowledge with gratitude the help given by the lectures and notes mentioned in the first book, together with the following:

(i) Lectures on infinite matrices and functional analysis by Cooke (1944–46)

(ii) Lectures on divergent series and Tauberian theorems by Ingham (1947)

(iii) The books of Bourbaki, Cooke (1950, 1953), Dunford and Schwartz (1958, 1963), Kuratowski (1952), Loomis (1953), Zaanen (1953).

The present book can serve as an introduction to larger or more specialized books, such as the ones of Dunford and Schwartz.

Dr. R. G. Cooke and Professor P. Dienes are no longer with us. I would therefore like to add my tribute to those of the many research students they stimulated and encouraged, for an unveiling of a most interesting section of mathematics, summability theory.

v

PREFACE

The Library staff at Lancaster University have been most cooperative in obtaining periodicals not contained in the Library.

Professor H. B. Griffiths and Dr. I. J. Maddox have read the manuscript, and Dr. T. T. McGrotty and Dr. P. Y. Lee the proofs, and I am most grateful for their comments, which have improved the presentation.

Finally I would like to express my thanks to Messrs. Butterworth & Co. for their helpfulness throughout the preparation of both books.

Lancaster   R. H.

CONTENTS

CONTENTS

CONTENTS

CONTENTS

1

LOGIC AND SET THEORY

1. Introduction

A DISTINGUISHING feature of modern mathematics is the establishment of patterns of behaviour in mathematical systems. For example, connections have been established between a heterogeneous collection of theorems in classical analysis by the methods of functional analysis, so that a flood of light has been thrown on them, stimulating research.

It has transpired that three principles are involved. The first, the *Hahn–Banach theorem*, is concerned with the existence of extensions of a linear functional to regions over which it was not originally defined, and it can be thought of as belonging to the algebraic side of functional analysis. The second is known as the *principle of uniform boundedness*, and often leads to the proof that, under certain conditions, the limit of a sequence of continuous linear operations is continuous. In the form often given, it could more exactly be called the *principle of uniform convergence*. The third principle is called the *interior mapping principle*, and states that continuous linear mappings between certain types of spaces, map open sets onto open sets.

Only the first principle is usually given in elementary textbooks, the other two being considered too difficult for inclusion. Here we shall consider the first two principles, concentrating mainly on the second, and using it to prove parts of many theorems of convergence-factor or summability type.

This book grew out of the idea of presenting summability theorems for integrals to parallel the accounts of summability theorems for series as given, for example, in Hardy (1949) and Cooke (1950). One can do much by using the ideas of elementary analysis and Lebesgue integral theory, but this book contains two unifications. First, as many proofs as possible are based on theorems of the Banach–Stein-haus–Sargent type, in which we need the ideas of first and second category sets, and β-groups, so that clearly one needs at least the beginnings of general topology and topological groups. On examining other results it became clear that the uniform boundedness principle is a unifying influence that extends beyond the classical Banach–Steinhaus result. Secondly, when considering integral summability theorems I have had to use several kinds of integrals, often three or four in one chain of argument. This situation can now be avoided by the use of the systems of generalized Riemann integration, which now extend to cover, for example, the Haar integral in locally compact topological groups. Because the system outlined in Henstock (1963c) is only one of many systems, it was necessary to include a chapter on the new integration, to explain the different systems, and to advance the theory from the position in the earlier book. Those interested only in Lebesgue integration theory can find most of the necessary theorems in Saks (1937), though sometimes the Lebesgue integral is not powerful enough to cope with the problems.

The book begins with elementary logic and the theory of sets, and then gives the upper boundedness theorem in a form that uses no topology. Then we sweep quickly through elementary topology, including pseudometrizability, for which I am grateful to Kelley (1955) for the ideas and notation. We then deal with category and Baire's theorem, Borel and analytic sets, and Baire functions, and round off this section of the book with an account of the upper boundedness theorem in topological spaces.

A group structure is then introduced and the Hahn–Banach theorem proved, and we quickly move to topological groups. The β-groups are a generalization of Sargent's β-spaces, and we consider bounded sets and continuity, an important section being that on sequences of bounded multiplicative functions. A very brief account is given of more complicated algebraic structures, and Gál's unsymmetrical theory is given. Then Riemann and generalized Riemann integration, the existence of a Haar measure, and the Kolmogoroff 'law of the iterated logarithm', which is needed for results concerning sequences. For our special spaces we consider n-dimensional vector spaces, and then sequence spaces and summability theorems. Here I could have included far more material, but have concentrated on topics on which I could say a little more than is given in Cooke (1950). Questions of category and measure, for example the Borel property, are studied in the next chapter, followed by spaces of continuous functions and (continuous) Denjoy integrals. Then, using the early part of the book as a foundation, we study spaces of integrable functions, including Lebesgue, Orlicz, and Denjoy spaces, and give a representative collection of summability theorems for integrals.

Much more could have been included, but considerations of space have prevented this, and the attention of the reader is directed to the larger or more specialized works on functional analysis. I include no results on special matrices nor on special integrals; these can be found in Hardy (1949) and in the periodical literature.

2. Notations for Sets, Functions, Relations

We begin this section informally, since a more systematic approach would lead to difficult logic beyond the province of this book. First, an object often has several descriptions, which we can symbolize as $x, y, \ldots$, and then we write $x = y$. If an object is a collection of other objects, it is called a *set*, or a *family*. Two interchangeable terms are used in the interests of readability. A finite and not too large set can be described by enumeration. But sometimes there is a property common to all objects of a set, even an infinite set, that is not satisfied by any other object. For example, the set 1, 2, 3, 4, 5 is also the set of all positive integers less than 6. The enumeration of the set of all positive integers less than 100,000 would take up space that could be put to better use. In this sense one cannot enumerate the set of all integers, nor the set of all pairs (x, y) of real numbers satisfying

(2.1) $$x^2 + y^2 < 1$$

We write this last set symbolically as

(2.2) $$\{(x, y) : x, y \text{ are real and } x^2 + y^2 < 1\}$$

The words and symbols to the right of the colon form a *propositional*

3

function that includes arbitrary objects x, y, such that if we replace both x, y by particular objects we obtain a *proposition* that is either true or false. If $P(z)$ is a propositional function of an arbitrary object z, we denote the more general set of all objects z for which $P(z)$ (i.e. $P(z)$ *is true*) by

$$\{z : P(z)\}$$

In (2.2), $z = (x, y)$ where x, y are the first and second parts of z, and (2.1) can be written as a propositional function of z. For more details on propositional functions the reader is directed to treatises on logic.

In defining a set (or family) X, we only need to know which objects x are in X, and which are not. If x is *in X* (or *of X*, or a *member* or *element* of X) we write

(2.3) $x \in X$

If x is not in X, we write

(2.4) $x \notin X$,   or $x \overline{\in} X$

An *empty set* $\varnothing$ is a set X with (2.3) false, (2.4) true, for all objects x.

If $x \in Y$ when $x \in X$, we write $X \subseteq Y$, $Y \supseteq X$, saying that X is a *subset of Y*, that *X is contained in Y*, and that *Y contains X*. If $X \subseteq Y$, $Y \subseteq X$, so that each member of X is a member of Y, and conversely, we write $X = Y$. For example, the set of a, a, b is the set of a, b; we do not recognize the multiplicity of occurrence of an object in a set. Also, if X, Y are empty sets, then $X = Y$. If $X = Y$ is false, we write $X \neq Y$, saying that X, Y are *distinct*. If $X \subseteq Y$, $X \neq Y$, we write $X \subset Y$, $Y \supset X$, saying that X is a *proper subset of Y*, that *X is contained in Y properly*, and that *Y contains X properly*.

We cannot handle logically with safety the collection of all x satisfying (2.4). However, we can suppose a universal set U given, and then say that the *complement $U \backslash X$* of a set X, relative to U, is the set of all $x \in U$ that satisfy (2.4). For example, if in a particular theory all our X consist of sets of real (or complex) numbers, we can allow U to be the real line (respectively, the complex plane). If U is understood, it can be omitted from $U \backslash X$, and we can write $\backslash X$.

4

If x, y are objects let sing (x), pair (x, y) be the respective sets of x alone, and x, y alone, i.e.

$x \in$ sing (x), $x \in$ pair (x, y), $y \in$ pair (x, y);

if $z \in$ sing (x) then $z = x$;

if $z \in$ pair (x, y) then $z = x$ or $z = y$

The *ordered pair of x and y* is

$$(x, y) = \text{pair } \big(\text{sing } (x), \text{ pair } (x, y)\big)$$

A *relation R* is a set of ordered pairs (x, y). We write xRy if (x, y) is in the set. Further, R is an *equivalence relation* if it is *reflexive* (i.e. xRx if xRy), *symmetric* (i.e. yRx if xRy), and *transitive* (i.e. if xRy and yRz, then xRz). Then the *R-coset* (or *R-equivalence class*) $R(x)$ is the set

$$\{y : xRy\}$$

The *Cartesian product* $X \times Y$ of sets X, Y, is the family of ordered pairs (x, y), for all $x \in X$, all $y \in Y$, i.e.

if $\quad x \in X, y \in Y, \quad$ then $\quad (x, y) \in X \times Y$

if $\quad z \in X \times Y, \quad$ then $\quad z = (x, y), \quad x \in X, \quad y \in Y$.

A *function (mapping, operator) f on a set X to a set Y*, is a subset Z of $X \times Y$ with the properties that if $x \in X$, there is a $y \in Y$ with $(x, y) \in Z$, and that if $(x, z) \in Z$ for some $z \in Y$, then $z = y$. We write $f : X \to Y$, and $y = f(x)$. Also, if $X^* \subseteq X$, $Y^* \subseteq Y$, we write

$$f(X^*) = \{y : y = f(x), x \in X^*\}, \quad f^{-1}(Y^*) = \{x : y = f(x), y \in Y^*, x \in X\}.$$

We call $f(X^*)$ the *image* of X^*, and $f^{-1}(Y^*)$ the *inverse image* of Y^*.

A more general definition of a Cartesian product can now be given. For each $a \in A$ let $Y_a \subseteq Y$. Then the *Cartesian product*

(2.5) $$\times_A Y_a$$

is the set of all $f : A \to Y$ for which $f(a) \in Y_a$ when $a \in A$. If $Y_a = Y$ for all $a \in A$, we write (2.5) as Y^A, so that if $f \in Y^A$ then $f : A \to Y$, and conversely. Later, when cardinal numbers have been defined, we can write

$$\underset{j=1}{\overset{n}{\times}} Y_j = Y_1 \times Y_2 \times \ldots \times Y_n.$$

Ex. 2.1. If $x = y$, show that pair $(x, y) = $ sing (x), $(x, y) = $ sing $(\text{sing }(x))$.

Ex. 2.2. If $(x, y) = (u, v)$, prove that $x = u, y = v$.

Ex. 2.3. Show that equality of objects is an equivalence relation.

Ex. 2.4. Let R be an equivalence relation and $R(x)$ the R-coset of x. Prove that if xRy then

$$x \in R(x), \quad x \in R(y), \quad y \in R(x), \quad R(x) = R(y).$$

Ex. 2.5. Let $f: X \to Y$, with $X_* \subseteq X^* \subseteq X$, $Y_* \subseteq Y^* \subseteq Y$. Show that

$$f(X_*) \subseteq f(X^*), \quad f^{-1}(Y_*) \subseteq f^{-1}(Y^*).$$

Ex. 2.6. Let $f: X \to Y$, with $X^* \subseteq X$, $Y^* \subseteq Y$. Show that

$$f(f^{-1}(Y^*)) \subseteq Y^*, \quad f^{-1}(f(X^*)) \supseteq X^*.$$

Ex. 2.7. Let $f: X \to Y$, with $Y_* \subseteq Y$, $Y^* \subseteq Y$. If Y_*, Y^* are *disjoint* (i.e. there is no object $y \in Y_*$ that satisfies $y \in Y^*$), show that $f^{-1}(Y_*)$ and $f^{-1}(Y^*)$ are disjoint.

3. The Union, Intersection and Symmetric Difference of Sets

Let $P(X)$ be a propositional function of sets X. The *union* (*join*, *sum*) of those X for which $P(X)$, is the set of all objects, each of which is in *some set* X for which $P(X)$, and we write

$$(3.1) \qquad \bigcup \{X : P(X)\} = \{x : x \in X, P(X)\}$$

The *intersection* (*meet, product*) of those X for which $P(X)$, is the set of all objects, each of which lies in *all* X for which $P(X)$, and we write

$$(3.2) \qquad \bigcap \{X : P(X)\}$$

Variations of this notation occur, e.g. if $\mathcal{H}$ is a family of sets X, then

$$\bigcup_{\mathcal{H}} X = \bigcup \{X : X \in \mathcal{H}\}, \quad \bigcap_{\mathcal{H}} X = \bigcap \{X : X \in \mathcal{H}\}$$

are the union and intersection, respectively, of sets of $\mathcal{H}$. If A is a family of suffixes a, then

$$\bigcup_{A} X_a = \bigcup \{X_a : a \in A\}, \quad \bigcap_{A} X_a = \bigcap \{X_a : a \in A\}$$

are the union and intersection, respectively, of sets X_a, for $a \in A$. In the special case when A is the set of all positive integers (when defined), or a subset, we use the more explicit notation

$$\bigcup_{j=1}^{\infty} X_j, \quad \bigcap_{j=1}^{\infty} X_j, \quad \bigcup_{j=1}^{n} X_j, \quad \bigcap_{j=1}^{n} X_j$$

The union and intersection of two sets X, Y are written, respectively, as

$$X \cup Y = Y \cup X \quad \text{and} \quad X \cap Y = Y \cap X$$

Two sets with no common member, so that their intersection is empty, are called *disjoint*. If each pair of distinct sets from a family $\mathcal{H}$ of sets is disjoint, we say that the sets of $\mathcal{H}$ are *mutually disjoint*. The *symmetric difference* of two sets X, Y, is the set

$$d(X, Y) = (X \backslash Y) \cup (Y \backslash X)$$

A non-empty family $\mathcal{M}$ of subsets of a set U, is called a *module* if

(3.3) $\qquad Y \in \mathcal{M}$ when $Y \subseteq X$ and $X \in \mathcal{M}$

(3.4) $\qquad$ if $X \in \mathcal{M}$, $Y \in \mathcal{M}$, then $X \cup Y \in \mathcal{M}$

In the notation of Chapter 2, the property of being in $\mathcal{M}$ is *shrinkable* and *finitely additive*. If it is also *countably additive*, i.e. the union of a sequence of sets of $\mathcal{M}$ belongs to $\mathcal{M}$, then $\mathcal{M}$ is called a *σ-module*. Every module contains the empty set. The module is *trivial* if it contains no other set. Two sets X, Y are *congruent modulo* $\mathcal{M}$, $X \equiv Y(\mathcal{M})$, if $d(X, Y) \in \mathcal{M}$.

Ex. 3.1. If $Y \supseteq X$ for all X satisfying $P(X)$, then

$$Y \supseteq \bigcup \{X : P(X)\}$$

Ex. 3.2. If $Y \subseteq X$ for all X satisfying $P(X)$, then

$$Y \subseteq \bigcap \{X : P(X)\}$$

Ex. 3.3.
$$\bigcup \{X : P(X)\} \cap \bigcup \{Y : P^*(Y)\}$$
$$= \bigcup \{X \cap Y : P(X), P^*(Y)\}$$

Ex. 3.4.
$$\bigcap \{X : P(X)\} \cup \bigcap \{Y : P^*(Y)\}$$
$$= \bigcap \{X \cup Y : P(X), P^*(Y)\}$$

Ex. 3.5. More generally, if the set $X(a, b) \subseteq U$ is a function of the ordered pair (a, b), for $a \in A$, $b \in B$, and if $P(a)$, $Q(b)$ are propositional functions of a and b, respectively, show that

$$\bigcap_B \left\{ \bigcup_A \{X(a, b) : P(a)\} : Q(b) \right\}$$

$$= \bigcup_{A^B} \left\{ \bigcap_B \{X(a(b), b) : Q(b)\} : P(a(b)), Q(b) \right\}$$

Ex. 3.6. Taking complements relative to U, if $X \subseteq U$ then $X \cup \backslash X = U$, $X \cap \backslash X$ is empty.

Ex. 3.7. The complement of the complement of X, relative to Z, is $X \cap Z$, whether or not X is contained in Z.

Ex. 3.8. If $X \subseteq U$, $Y \subseteq U$, then $X \backslash Y = X \cap (U \backslash Y)$

Ex. 3.9, 3.10 give the rules of de Morgan.

Ex. 3.9.
$$U \backslash \bigcup \{X : P(X)\} = \bigcap \{U \backslash X : P(X)\}$$

Ex. 3.10.
$$U \backslash \bigcap \{X : P(X)\} = \bigcup \{U \backslash X : P(X)\}$$

Ex. 3.11.
$$\bigcup \{X : P(X)\} \backslash Y = \bigcup \{X \backslash Y : P(X)\}$$

Ex. 3.12.
$$\bigcap \{X : P(X)\} \backslash Y = \bigcap \{X \backslash Y : P(X)\}$$

Ex. 3.13.
$$\bigcup_A \{X_a : P(a)\} \backslash \bigcup_A \{Y_b : P(b)\}$$
$$\subseteq \bigcup_A \{X_a \backslash Y_a : P(a)\} \quad \text{(Use } Ex. 3.11.\text{)}$$

8

Ex. 3.14.
$$d\left(\bigcup_A \{X_a : P(a)\},\ \bigcup_A \{Y_b : P(b)\}\right)$$
$$\subseteq \bigcup_A \{d(X_a, Y_a) : P(a)\}$$

Ex. 3.15. Taking complements relative to a U that contains X, Y,
$$d(\backslash X, \backslash Y) = d(X, Y)$$

Ex. 3.16. If all X_a, Y_a lie in a fixed set U,
$$d\left(\bigcap_A \{X_a : P(a)\},\ \bigcap_A \{Y_b : P(b)\}\right) \subseteq \bigcup_A \{d(X_a, Y_a) : P(a)\}$$

Ex. 3.17.
$$d(W, X) \cup d(X, Y) \supseteq d(W, Y)$$

Ex. 3.18. If $\mathcal{M}$ is a module, show that 'congruence modulo $\mathcal{M}$' is an equivalence relation.

Ex. 3.19. Let f be a function in X to Y. Show that
$$f\left(\bigcup \{X^* : X^* \subseteq X, P(X^*)\}\right) = \bigcup \{f(X^*) : X^* \subseteq X, P(X^*)\}$$

Ex. 3.20. Let f be a function in X to Y. Show that
$$f\left(\bigcap \{X^* : X^* \subseteq X, P(X^*)\}\right) \subseteq \bigcap \{f(X^*) : X^* \subseteq X, P(X^*)\}$$

Ex. 3.21. Let $f(x) = 0(x > 0)$, $X = (0, \infty)$, and let $P(X^*)$ denote that $X^* = (0, \varepsilon)$ for some $\varepsilon > 0$. Then in *Ex. 3.20* the left side is empty, while the right side contains the point 0.

Ex. 3.22. Let *proj* denote the projection function $f : X \times Y \to X$ that sends (x, y) into x. Let A be a set of suffixes, and for each $a \in A$ let $X_a \subseteq X$, $Y_a \subseteq Y$, the intersection of the Y_a containing an element $y \in Y$. By proving that

$$\left(\bigcap_A X_a\right) \times \text{sing}\,(y) \subseteq X_b \times Y_b \qquad (each\ b \in A);$$

show that in this case *Ex. 3.20* becomes

$$\text{proj}\left(\bigcap_A X_a \times Y_a\right) = \bigcap_A X_a = \bigcap_A \text{proj}\,(X_a \times Y_a)$$

Ex. 3.23. There is equality in *Ex. 3.20* when both f and f^{-1} are functions. Note that proj^{-1} is not a function.

Ex. 3.24. If f is a function in X to Y, then

$$f^{-1}\left(\bigcup Y^*\right) = \bigcup f^{-1}(Y^*)$$

$$f^{-1}\left(\bigcap Y^*\right) = \bigcap f^{-1}(Y^*)$$

4. Bijections and Cardinal Numbers

We now have to define the positive integers to explain the latter part of section 3. Let X, Y be sets, and let f be a function in X to Y. Then f is an *injection* if, for each $x \in X$, $x' \in X$ with a $y \in Y$ for which $y = f(x)$ and $y = f(x')$, we have $x = x'$. If also to each $y \in Y$ there is an $x \in X$ with $y = f(x)$, we say that f is a *bijection (one-one or biuniform correspondence) from X to Y*. In this case, if $x \in X$, there is a $y \in Y$ such that $y = f(x)$; if $y' \in Y$ satisfies $y' = f(x)$ then $y' = y$; if $y \in Y$, there is an $x \in X$ such that $y = f(x)$; if $x' \in X$ satisfies $y = f(x')$ then $x' = x$. Further, we have $f^{-1}: Y \to X$, the *inverse function (mapping, operator) of f*, and $Y = f(X)$, and we say that X, Y are *similar*, writing $X \sim Y$. Similarity of subsets of the universal set U, is an equivalence relation. The corresponding coset of X is called the *cardinal number*, card (X), of X, i.e. card (X) *is the family of all sets $Y \subseteq U$ that satisfy $Y \sim X$*.

If $\emptyset$ is empty, $X \sim \emptyset$, $x \in X$, there are $f: X \to \emptyset$ and $y \in \emptyset$, with $y = f(x)$. But $y \notin \emptyset$. Hence $x \notin X$, for all x, and $X = \emptyset$. Putting 0 for card $(\emptyset)$,

$$(4.1) \qquad\qquad 0 = \text{card } (\emptyset) = \text{sing } (\emptyset)$$

Each sing $(x) \sim$ sing (y); put $X = \text{sing } (x)$, $Y = \text{sing } (y)$, and (x, y) as the only point of the subset of $X \times Y$ that defines f. If $Y \sim \text{sing } (x)$ there are $f: \text{sing } (x) \to Y$ and $y \in Y$, such that $y = f(x)$. If $y' \in Y$, there is an $x' \in \text{sing } (x)$ with $f(x') = y'$. But $x' = x$, $f(x) = y'$, $y' = y$, $Y = \text{sing } (y)$, proving that card $\left(\text{sing } (x)\right)$ is the set of all sing(y), and we denote this by 1. It is different from $0 = \text{sing } (\emptyset)$, since 1 has sing $(\emptyset)$ as a member, a non-empty set, whereas 0 has only the empty set as a member. Thus $0 \neq 1$.

10

If X is similar to a proper subset of itself, we call X an *infinite set;* other sets are *finite.* As $\emptyset$ has no proper subsets, and as the only proper subset of sing (x) is $\emptyset$, $\emptyset$ and sing (x) are finite sets.

We can put some cardinal numbers in order. If

$$X \subseteq Y, \quad a = \text{card}(X), \quad b = \text{card}(Y), \quad \text{we write} \quad a \leqslant b, \quad b \geqslant a$$

THEOREM 4.1. *If $a \leqslant b$, $b \leqslant a$, then $a = b$.*

Proof. There are sets $X^* \sim X$, $X_* \sim X$, $Y^* \sim Y$, $Y_* \sim Y$, that satisfy $X^* \subseteq Y^*$, $X_* \supseteq Y_*$. As similarity is an equivalence relation, $Y^* \sim Y_*$ by an $f : Y^* \to Y_*$. Hence, for the same f, there is a set X' with $X' \subseteq Y_* \subseteq X_*$, such that $f(X^*) = X'$, and

$$X' \sim X^* \sim X \sim X_*, \quad X' \sim X_*$$

For finite X_*, $X' = X_*$, so that $X_* = Y_*$, $a = b$. Otherwise, if $X_* \sim Y_*$ then

$$X \sim X_* \sim Y_* \sim Y, \quad X \sim Y, \quad a = b$$

Thus we need only prove that if $W \subseteq X \subseteq Y$, $W \sim Y$, then $X \sim Y$. Let $V = X \backslash W$, $g : Y \to W$ be a bijection, and let us denote by D any set satisfying $D \supseteq g(D) \cup V$. Then Y is a D, so that the intersection T of all D's exists. Since $V \subseteq D$, for all D, then $V \subseteq T$. Also by *Ex. 3.20*,

$$g(T) \subseteq \bigcap g(D) \subseteq g(D) \subseteq D, \quad g(T) \subseteq \bigcap D = T$$

Hence T is a D. Further, as Y is a D, and by *Ex. 2.2*, with $g(T) \subseteq T$,

$$T \subseteq Y, \quad g(T) \subseteq g(Y) = W, \quad g(T) \cap V \text{ empty}, \quad g(T) \subseteq T \backslash V.$$

To prove that

(4.2) $$g(T) = T \backslash V$$

let $x \in T \backslash V$. Then $x \notin V$. If $x \notin g(T)$, let $S = T \backslash \text{sing}(x)$. As $g(T) \subseteq T$ and $x \notin g(T)$, then $g(T) \subseteq S$, $S \subset T$, $g(S) \subseteq g(T)$, $g(S) \subseteq S$. Again, $x \notin V \subseteq T$, so that $V \subseteq S$, and S is a D. Hence $S \supseteq T$, a contradiction. Hence we prove (4.2), which shows that $T = g(T) \cup V$. Since $g(T) \subseteq W$, we have

$$X = W \cup V = \{W \backslash g(T)\} \cup \{V \cup g(T)\}$$

11

the bracketed sets being disjoint, and the latter being T. The former is similar to itself, and $T \sim g(T)$, so that $X \sim W$, giving the result.

Let $X_0 \sim X$, $Y_1 \sim Y$, with X_0, Y_1 disjoint, e.g.

$$X_0 = \{(x, 0) : x \in X\}, \quad Y_1 = \{(y, 1) : y \in Y\}$$

Then card (X)+card (Y) is defined to be card $(X_0 \cup Y_1)$. Ex. 4.2 shows that this is a valid definition. By using it we can define the positive integers 1, $2 = 1+1$, $3 = 2+1$, ... Cardinal multiplication and exponentiation can also be defined. First,

$$\text{card } (X) \cdot \text{card } (Y) = \text{card } (X \times Y)$$

while if $c = $ card (A), with card $(Y_a) = b$, independent of $a \in A$, then

$$b^c = \text{card } \left(\underset{A}{\times} Y_a \right)$$

If X is not empty, then card $(X) \geq 0$, card $(X) \neq 0$, so that we write card $(X) > 0$. If X is also a finite set, it can be shown that its cardinal is obtained in a 'finite' number of steps from 1 by cardinal addition, i. e. card (X) is a positive integer. If I is the set of all finite cardinals it can be shown that all infinite cardinals are greater than or equal to card (I), which is denoted by $\aleph_0$. Thus a proper subset of I is a finite set. The set I can be ordered in the given way, so that if a, $b \in I$, then either $a < b$, or $a = b$, or $a > b$. We say that a set X is *countable*, if it is similar to I, or to a proper subset of I.

If X is a set, a *sequence* $\{x_n\}$ in X is a function $f : I \to X$ with $f(n) = x_n$ for each $n \in I$. For example, if $x \in X$ we can have $x_n = x(n \in I)$. If $\mathscr{X}$ is a family of sets, and $\{X_n\}$ a sequence of sets in $\mathscr{X}$, we define

$$\lim_{n \to \infty} \sup X_n = \bigcap_{n=1}^{\infty} \bigcup_{j=n}^{\infty} X_j, \quad \lim_{n \to \infty} \inf X_n = \bigcup_{n=1}^{\infty} \bigcap_{j=n}^{\infty} X_j$$

and if they are equal we write the set as $\lim_{n \to \infty} X_n$.

Note: Theorem 4.1 is the Schroeder–Bernstein theorem, see F. Bernstein in Borel (1898), p. 103.

Ex. 4.1. Prove that similarity is an equivalence relation.

Ex. 4.2. If X, Y are disjoint, if X_0, Y_1 are disjoint, and if $X \sim X_0$, $Y \sim Y_1$, then prove that $X \cup Y \sim X_0 \cup Y_1$.

Ex. 4.3. Prove that if a is a cardinal number, $0 + a = a + 0 = a$.

Ex. 4.4. In *Ex. 4.3* prove that $0 \cdot a = a \cdot 0 = 0$.

Ex. 4.5. If a, b are cardinal numbers, prove that $a + b = b + a$, $a \cdot b = b \cdot a$.

Ex. 4.6. $\displaystyle\bigcup_{j=1}^{\infty} \bigcup_{k=1}^{\infty} X_{jk} = \bigcup_{l=2}^{\infty} \bigcup_{j+k=l} X_{jk}, \quad \bigcap_{j=1}^{\infty} \bigcap_{k=1}^{\infty} X_{jk} = \bigcap_{l=2}^{\infty} \bigcap_{j+k=l} X_{jk}.$

Ex. 4.7. Prove that the union of a countable number of sets, each of which is countable, is also countable.

Ex. 4.8. Let S be a collection of positive real numbers, and $N > 0$ a real number, such that the sum of numbers in any finite subset from S, is less than N. Prove that the number of real numbers in S that are greater than $1/n$, is less than nN, and hence prove that S is countable.

Ex. 4.9. Prove that the rational numbers in $0 \leqslant x \leqslant 1$ are countable.

Ex. 4.10. Let S be the set of all finite sequences $(n_1, \ldots, n_j)$, where each $n_k (1 \leqslant k \leqslant j)$ is a positive integer. Show by repeated use of Cantor's diagonal process in the form of *Ex. 4.6*, that S is countable.

Ex. 4.11. Prove that the real numbers in $0 \leqslant x < 1$ are not countable. More generally, let S be the set of all sequences $\{n_j\}$, where each n_j is a positive integer; or we could even restrict n_j to take values out of the space $Y = $ pair $(0,1)$. Show that S is not countable.

Each number in $0 \leqslant x < 1$ has a binary decimal form, those with repeated 1's after a certain stage being positive multiples of negative of powers of 2. Thus those real numbers with a double representation are countable and so can be neglected, and we reduce the first problem to the second. Then if $\{n_j^1\}$, $\{n_j^2\}, \ldots$ is a sequence of sequences we can find a sequence of S different from them all by putting

$$n_j = 1 - n_j^j \quad (j = 1, 2, \ldots)$$

13

Ex. 4.12. If $\{X_n\}$ is a sequence of sets, then

$$\liminf_{n \to \infty} X_n \subseteq \limsup_{n \to \infty} X_n$$

Ex. 4.13. Prove that $\lim_{n \to \infty} X_n$ exists, if $\{X_n\}$ is either monotone increasing or monotone decreasing, and find the limit in each case.

Ex. 4.14. The *characteristic function* $\mathrm{ch}(X_1; x)$ of a set $X_1 \subseteq X$, is the function that is 1 if $x \in X_1$, and is 0 if $x \notin X_1$. Find properties of characteristic functions that correspond to the complements, unions, and intersections of sets.

2

THE PRINCIPLE OF UPPER BOUNDEDNESS

5. The Upper Boundedness Theorem

MANY proofs in analysis and functional analysis hinge on the principle of *uniform convergence*, namely, that the limit of a sequence of continuous linear operators is continuous, under conditions special to each problem. This principle depends on a principle of *upper boundedness* of the following type. From the upper boundedness of a function in a subset X of a space T, we obtain the upper boundedness at all points of T, or a substantial part of T, by using a relation similar to convexity. The very simple pattern of proof is given in this chapter.

(To the knowledgeable reader it may be pointed out that this pattern is useful in classifying most proofs of the principles, and in the recognition of other applications of them, see Henstock (1963a). Since then I have found a connection with convex functions and with results in Mehdi (1964), see section 32.)

In a normed linear space (section 37), the norm $\|x\|$ satisfies

(5.1) $$\|x-y\| \leqslant \|x\|+\|y\|.$$

The norm $N(x)$ in a normed group (section 30) satisfies

(5.2) $$N(x \cdot y^{-1}) \leqslant N(x)+N(y).$$

If $\{f_n(x)\}$ is a sequence of additive functionals on a group (section 25),

$$N(x) \equiv \sup_n |f_n(x)|$$

satisfies (5.2) since

$$|f_n(x \cdot y^{-1})| = |f_n(x)-f_n(y)| \leqslant |f_n(x)|+|f_n(y)| \leqslant N(x)+N(y).$$

15

If N is convex in an additive group with division by 2, it satisfies

(5.3) $$N(\tfrac{1}{2}(x+y)) \leqslant \tfrac{1}{2}(N(x)+N(y))$$

These special cases lead to the following general theory.)

Let T be a space of points, and $\theta(x, y)$ a function in $T \times T$ to T. As in section 2, if $t \in T$, $X \subseteq T$, $Y \subseteq T$, we write

$$\theta(X, t) = \{\theta(x, t) : x \in X\}, \quad \theta(X, Y) = \{\theta(x, y) : x \in X, y \in Y\}$$

Given $X \subseteq T$, a sequence $\{Th_n\}$ of sets of T is a θ-*sequence* if

(5.4) $$Th_{n+1} \supseteq \theta(Th_n, Th_n) \quad (n \geqslant 0), \quad Th_0 = X$$

We put Th for the union of the Th_n $(n \geqslant 1)$. If equality holds in (5.4) for each n, we say that $\{Th_n\}$ is a *minimal* θ-sequence, putting $Th_n(X)$ for Th_n $(n \geqslant 0)$, and $Th(X)$ for Th. We call $Th_n(X)$ the Th_n-*set from* X, and $Th(X)$ the θ-*sub-union from* X. If $Th(X) = T$, we say that X is a θ-*base for* T, and that T is a θ-*union*.

We do not include X in Th, since X is sometimes anomalous. See *Ex. 24.1*.

Let $L(\lambda)$ be a finite real function monotone increasing in $\lambda \geqslant 0$, with a conventional $L(+\infty) = +\infty$. For convenience we can allow

(5.5) $$L(\lambda) \geqslant L_0(\lambda) \equiv \lambda, \quad L_{n+1}(\lambda) \equiv L(L_n(\lambda)) \geqslant L_n(\lambda) \geqslant 0 \quad (n \geqslant 0)$$

A function $N(x)$ on T to the extended real line (i.e. conventional values $+\infty$ are allowed) is a $\theta - L$ *convex function*, generalizing (5.1; 5.2; 5.3), if

(5.6) $$N(\theta(x, y)) \leqslant L(\sup \{N(x); N(y); 0\}) \quad (x, y \in T)$$

A special case is when

(5.7) $$N(\theta(x, y)) \leqslant N(x)+N(y)$$

where we can take $L(\lambda) = 2\lambda$

The pattern of proof of the upper boundedness principle begins in the following way.

THEOREM 5.1. *If N is a $\theta - L$ convex function, and if, for real $\lambda \geqslant 0$, $P(\lambda)$ is the set of $x \in T$ with $N(x) \leqslant \lambda$, then*

(5.8) $$Th_n(P(\lambda)) \subseteq P(L_n(\lambda))$$

16

(5.9)   *and for each $\lambda \geqslant 0$, $N < +\infty$ in $P(\lambda) \cup Th(P(\lambda))$.*

(5.10)   *If X is the set where $N(x) < +\infty$, then $X \supseteq Th(X)$.*

(5.11) *If, for some $\lambda \geqslant 0$, $P(\lambda)$ is a θ-base for T, then $N < +\infty$ in T.*

(5.12) *If $L(0) = 0$, and if $N(x) \leqslant 0$ in X, then $N(x) \leqslant 0$ in $Th(X)$.*

Result (5.11) is often the conclusion of the upper boundedness principle, while in other cases, $P(\lambda) \cup Th(P(\lambda))$ is often a substantial and useful part of T.

Proof. To prove (5.8) we use (5.5; 5.6) repeatedly. The rest follow easily.

A similar theorem holds if N is on T to a partially ordered space, such as a space of sets of points, generalizing Henstock (1963a (29; 30; 31), p. 310). Further results are given in Chapter 5.

THEOREM 5.2. *If, for each integer n, $N(n, x)$ satisfies (5.6), with L independent of n, and if, for some sequence $\{x_n\}$ of points of T,*

(5.13) $N(n, x_n) = +\infty \qquad (n = 1, 2, \ldots)$

then the set X of points where

(5.14) $N(n, x) = +\infty \qquad (x \in X, \text{ and all } n = 1, 2, \ldots)$

is such that $\backslash X$ is a countable union of sets none of which is a θ-base for T. The complement is taken relative to T.

The conclusion sometimes shows that X is a substantial part of T.

Proof. For each n let X_n be the maximal set of points x for which $N(n, x) < +\infty$. By Theorem 5.1(5.10), $x_n \notin Th(X_n)$, and X_n cannot be a θ-base for T. In $\backslash X$, (5.14) is false, so that $N(n, x) < +\infty$ for at least one n, and

$$\backslash X = \bigcup_{n=1}^{\infty} X_n$$

Hence the result.

The scope of Theorems 5.1, 5.2 can be extended by the following theorem.

17

THEOREM 5.3 *For each $a \in A$ let $N(a, x)$ satisfy (5.7). Then so do*

$$(5.15) \qquad \sup_{a \in A} N(a, x)$$

$$(5.16) \qquad \lim_{a \to \infty} N(a, x) \quad \text{where it exists (when } a \geqslant 0 \text{ in } A\text{)};$$

$$(5.17) \qquad \limsup_{a \to \infty} N(a, x) \quad (\text{when } a \geqslant 0 \text{ in } A)$$

$$(5.18) \qquad \sum_{a \in A} N(a, x) \quad (\text{for countable } A)$$

$$(5.19) \qquad \int_A N(a, x)\, ds(a)$$

for a as a continuous variable, and $s(a)$ a monotone increasing point function, and an appropriate integration.

(5.20) *If, for each $a \in A$, $N(a, x)$ satisfies (5.6) for an L independent of a, then so does (5.15), while (5.16; 5.17) do so if L is also continuous to the right.*

Let $P_a(\lambda)$, $P^\circ(\lambda)$, $P^1(\lambda)$, be the respective sets where $N(a, x) \leqslant \lambda$, $\sup\limits_{a \in A} N(a, x) \leqslant \lambda$, $\limsup\limits_{a \to \infty} N(a, x) \leqslant \lambda$ ($a \geqslant 0$ in A). Then

$$(5.21) \quad P^\circ(\lambda) = \bigcap_{a \in A} P_a(\lambda), \quad P^1(\lambda) = \bigcap_{\varepsilon > 0} \bigcup_{m > 0} \bigcap_{a \in A \cap [m, \infty)} P_a(\lambda + \varepsilon)$$

Proof. If (5.7) is true for $N(a, x)$, for each $a \in A$, then

$$(5.22) \quad N(a, \theta(x, y)) \leqslant N(a, x) + N(a, y) \leqslant \sup_{a \in A} N(a, x) + \sup_{a \in A} N(a, y)$$

This gives (5.7) for (5.15) on taking the supremum of the first term in (5.22). For (5.16) we take the limit of the first inequality in (5.22). Then for (5.17) we use (5.15; 5.16) since

$$(5.23) \qquad \limsup_{a \to \infty} N(a, x) = \lim_{b \to \infty} \left\{ \sup_{a \geqslant b} N(a, x) \right\}$$

For (5.18) we sum the first inequality in (5.22), for $a \in A$; while for (5.19) we integrate the inequality relative to $s(a)$.

If $N(a, x)$ satisfies (5.6) for each $a \in A$ and an L independent of a, (5.22) is replaced by

$$(5.24) \qquad N(a, \theta(x, y)) \le L(\sup \{N(a, x); N(a, y); 0\})$$
$$\le L\left(\sup \left\{\sup_{a \in A} N(a, x); \sup_{a \in A} N(a, y); 0\right\}\right)$$

the last result following since L is monotone increasing. Then (5.6) for (5.15) follows by taking the supremum of the first term in (5.24). For (5.16) we use (5.24) and the monotonicity of L. For each $\varepsilon > 0$,

$$N(a, \theta(x, y)) \le L\left(\sup \left\{\lim_{a \to \infty} N(a, x)+\varepsilon; \lim_{a \to \infty} N(a, y)+\varepsilon; 0\right\}\right)$$
$$(a \ge a_0(\varepsilon), \ a \in A)$$

If L is also continuous on the right we let $a \to \infty$ in the first term, and then $\varepsilon \to 0$ in the rest, to obtain (5.6) for (5.16). For the same continuity assumption on L, (5.23) shows that (5.6) is true for (5.17).

The first result of (5.21) is obvious. For the second, take $\varepsilon > 0$.

$$\text{If } \limsup_{a \to \infty} N(a, x) \le \lambda \quad \text{then} \quad \sup_{a \in A \cap [m, \infty)} N(a, x) \le \lambda+\varepsilon$$

for some m depending on x, ε, and

$$P^1(\lambda) \subseteq \bigcap_{\varepsilon > 0} \bigcup_{m > 0} \bigcap_{a \in A \cap [m, \infty)} P_a(\lambda+\varepsilon)$$

Conversely, if x is in the right side, then for each $\varepsilon > 0$, and for some m depending on ε and x,

$$N(a, x) \le \lambda+\varepsilon(a \in A \cap [m, \infty)), \quad \limsup_{a \to \infty} N(a, x) \le \lambda+\varepsilon$$

This is true for each $\varepsilon > 0$, so that $x \in P^1(\lambda)$, completing (5.21).

THEOREM 5.4. *For each integer n let $N(n, x)$ satisfy* (5.6), *with L independent of n and continuous on the right. If, for some $X \subseteq T$,*

$$(5.25) \qquad \limsup_{n \to \infty} N(n, x) < \infty \qquad (x \in X)$$

then (5.25) *is true for all $x \in Th(X)$.*

If also $L(0) = 0$, and if, for some $X \subseteq T$,

$$(5.26) \qquad \limsup_{n \to \infty} N(n, x) \le 0 \qquad (x \in X)$$

then (5.26) *is true for all $x \in Th(X)$.*

19

Proof. Using Theorem 5.3, (5.20) for (5.17), then (5.25) is true in $\theta(X, X)$, and the first result follows by induction. Similarly for the second.

Usually $N(n, x) \geqslant 0$, and then the *lim sup* in (5.26) can be replaced by *lim*. As we shall see later, an example is given by a fundamental sequence of functions $f_j(x)$ for $x \in X$, with values in a metric space, and with

$$N(n, x) = \sup_{j > k \geqslant n} \varrho(f_j(x), f_k(x))$$

The following is a generalization of the condensation of singularities theorem of Banach and Steinhaus (1927), p. 54.

THEOREM 5.5. *If, for each pair (m, n) of integers, $N(m, n, x)$ satisfies (5.6), with L independent of (m, n) and continuous on the right, and if, for some sequence $\{x_m\}$ of points of T,*

(5.27) $\lim\limits_{n \to \infty} \sup N(m, n, x_m) = +\infty \qquad (m = 1, 2, \ldots)$

then the set X of points where

(5.28) $\lim\limits_{n \to \infty} \sup N(m, n, x) = +\infty \qquad (x \in X, \text{ and all } m = 1, 2, \ldots)$

is such that $\backslash X$ is a countable union of sets none of which is a θ-base for T.

(5.29)   *If also $L(0) = 0$, we can replace ' $= +\infty$' in (5.27; 5.28)*

by '> 0'.

Proof. We use the method of proof of Theorem 5.2 with the results of Theorem 5.4.

6. The θ-Sub-unions and θ-Bases for T

The study of Th_n-sets is important for the principle of upper boundedness and for the discovery of θ-bases for T. Given θ, the question of whether or not a particular set X is a θ-base for T, or is such that $Th(X)$ is a substantial part of T, depends in some sense how 'thick' the set X is. In other chapters we shall specify 'thickness' in terms of sets of the second category, the β-sets of Sargent (1950, 1953), and sets of positive measure. Here we give a few general results.

The sequence $\{Th_n\}$ is *monotone increasing* if $Th_{n+1} \supseteq Th_n$ $(n \geqslant 1)$. The set $X \subseteq T$ is *pinned* if X is non-empty, and if $x \in \theta\,(x, X)$ (all $x \in X$), where

$$\theta(x, X) = \{\theta(x, y) : y \in X\}$$

Further, complements of sets are taken relative to the space T, unless otherwise written.

THEOREM 6.1.

(6.1) If $X \subseteq Y$ then $Th_n(X) \subseteq Th_n(Y)\,(n \geqslant 1)$, $Th(X) \subseteq Th(Y)$

(6.2) $Th_m(Th_n(X)) = Th_{m+n}(X)$, $Th(Th_n(X)) \subseteq Th(X)$

$$(m \geqslant 1,\, n \geqslant 1)$$

(6.3) $\{Th_n(X)\}$ *is monotone increasing if X is pinned, if $X \subseteq Th_1(X)$, and if and only if $Th_1(X) \subseteq Th_2(X)$. Then*

(6.4) $Th(Th_n(X)) = Th(X) = Th_n(Th(X))$ $(n \geqslant 1)$

Proof. (6.1) is obvious, and (6.2) follows by induction. Further, if X is pinned,

$$x \in \theta(x, X) \subseteq \theta(X, X)\,(x \in X), \quad X \subseteq Th_1(X),$$

$$Th_1(X) = \theta(X, X) \subseteq \theta(Th_1(X), Th_1(X)) = Th_2(X),$$

$$Th_n(X) = Th_{n-1}(Th_1(X)) \subseteq Th_{n-1}(Th_2(X)) = Th_{n+1}(X)\,(n > 1)$$

The 'only if' part is obvious. From (6.3), monotonicity, and (6.2),

$$Th(Th_n(X)) \supseteq Th_m(Th_n(X)) = Th_{m+n}(X), \quad Th(Th_n(X)) \supseteq Th(X),$$

$$Th(Th_n(X)) = Th(X)$$

For the second equality in (6.4), if

$$z \in Th_1(Th(X)) \quad \text{then} \quad z = \theta(x, y) \quad \text{with} \quad x, y \in Th(X)$$

21

Thus for certain integers m, n, and by monotonicity, with $r = \max(m, n)$,

$$x \in Th_m(X), \quad y \in Th_n(X); \quad x, y \in Th_r(X);$$

$$z \in Th_{r+1}(X) \subseteq Th(X); \quad Th_1(Th(X)) \subseteq Th(X)$$

By (6.1; 6.2) and monotonicity,

$$Th_1(Th(X)) \supseteq Th_1(Th_m(X)) = Th_{m+1}(X), \quad Th_1(Th(X)) \supseteq Th(X)$$

Hence the second equality in (6.4), by induction from $n = 1$.

For each fixed y let

$$\theta^{-1}(v, y) \equiv \theta_x^{-1} \left(\text{sing}\,(v), y\right)$$

be the inverse image relative to x of $\text{sing}(v)$, for $v = \theta(x, y)$. Also let

$$\theta^{-1}(v, X) \equiv \bigcup \{\theta^{-1}(v, y) : y \in X\} \qquad (v \in T, \quad X \subseteq T)$$

Then X is pinned, if and only if $x \in \theta^{-1}(x, X)$ (all $x \in X$).

We use $\mathcal{O}$ as a standard notation for a known family of pinned sets V that are θ-bases for T, or have $Th(V)$ of substantial size, comparing other sets E with the sets V by using auxiliary sets X that may possibly vary as a certain point v varies in V. By this means we aim to widen $\mathcal{O}$ to a family $\mathcal{E}$ with the same properties relative to the $Th(E)$ as has $\mathcal{O}$, using $\mathcal{E}$ as a standard notation also.

THEOREM 6.2. *Let* E, $V \subseteq T$ *be connected in the following way. If* $v \in V$, *there is an* $X \subseteq T$, *depending on* v, E, *such that*

(6.5) $X^v \nsubseteq X_v$, *where* $X^v \equiv X \cap \theta^{-1}(v, X)$, $X_v \equiv (X \backslash E) \cup \theta^{-1}(v, X \backslash E)$

(6.6) *Then* $V \subseteq \theta(E, E)$, $Th(V) \subseteq Th(E)$

(6.7) *In particular, if* $Th(V) = T$ *then* $Th(E) = T$

(6.8) *If* $\mathcal{O}$ *is a family of pinned sets, let* $\mathcal{E}$ *be the family of sets* E *with the given property relative to* $V \in \mathcal{O}$. *Then* $\mathcal{O} \subseteq \mathcal{E}$.

Proof. By (6.5) there is a $z \in X^v$, $z \notin X_v$. Thus z is in X and $\theta^{-1}(v, X)$, but not in $X \backslash E$ nor in $\theta^{-1}(v, X \backslash E)$. Hence for some $e \in E$, and by (6.1; 6.2),

$$z \in E \cap \theta^{-1}(v, E), \quad z \in \theta^{-1}(v, e), \quad v = \theta(z, e) \in \theta(E, E),$$

$$V \subseteq \theta(E, E)$$

22

giving (6.6; 6.7). For (6.8) we take $X = E = V$, X_v empty. But the pinned set V is not empty, and for $v \in V$ we have

$$v \in \theta^{-1}(v, V), \quad v \in X^v \nsubseteq X_v, \quad V \in \mathcal{E}, \quad \mathcal{O} \subseteq \mathcal{E}$$

The crux of this method of widening the family $\mathcal{O}$ lies in proving (6.5), by showing that X_v is one kind of set, and X^v is a larger kind. It is here where we need the idea of the 'thickness' of a set that was mentioned at the beginning of the section. Alternatively we can replace the descriptive notion of 'thinness' by the use of a property p, saying that the set is 'thin', if it has the property p, and is 'thick' otherwise. We can denote by $\mathcal{P}$ the family of 'thin' sets. As we shall see subsequently, we can use a variety of properties depending on the particular problem in hand, for example, the properties of being nowhere dense, or of the first category, or of measure zero, etc.

However, it is not at the moment necessary to know of any one of these particular properties. Here we consider which properties of the p are necessary, and which are useful, in order that we can prove that the relation $X^v \subseteq X_v$ is false. We are going to arrange that X^v is 'thick' and X_v 'thin', so that the final step can be taken if every subset of a 'thin' set is 'thin'. It then follows that every set containing a 'thick' set is also 'thick'. The allied property of p is contained in the following definition.

A property p of sets $X \subseteq T$ is *shrinkable*, if $Y \in \mathcal{P}$ when $Y \subseteq X$ for some $X \in \mathcal{P}$

We now move one stage further back, noting that X^v is to be 'thick', and X_v 'thin', and assuming for simplicity that X is independent of the $v \in V$. We say that a set $X \in T$ is *strongly-$\bar{p}$*, if there is a $V \in \mathcal{O}$ such that $X^v \notin \mathcal{P}$ for each $v \in V$. A useful related definition is that a set $X \subseteq T$ is a *strong θ-base for T*, if there is a $V \in \mathcal{O}$ such that $Th(X^v) = T$ for each $v \in V$.

If p is shrinkable and $X_v \in \mathcal{P}$, then $X \backslash E \in \mathcal{P}$, $\theta^{-1}(v, X \backslash E) \in \mathcal{P}$. Hence also assuming X independent of v, it is necessary that E is a p-Baire set. A set $E \subseteq T$ is a *p-Baire set*, if $X \backslash E \in \mathcal{P}$ for some strongly-$\bar{p}$ set X. Note that if p is shrinkable and $T \in \mathcal{P}$, then p is useless for proving (6.5), and no strongly-$\bar{p}$ sets, and so no p-Baire sets, can occur.

Considering the property $\theta^{-1}(v, X \backslash E) \in \mathcal{P}$, the points v are restricted to lie in V, while $X \backslash E$ need not be the most general set of $\mathcal{P}$. Thus it is useful, but need not be necessary, to assume that p is θ^{-1}-invariant.

A property p is θ^{-1}-*invariant*, if $\theta^{-1}(v, X) \in \mathcal{P}$ when $X \in \mathcal{P}$, $v \in T$. Collecting the definitions together, we assume that p is

(6.9)   *shrinkable* $(Y \in \mathcal{P}$ when $Y \subseteq X$ for some $X \in \mathcal{P})$ and

(6.10) θ^{-1}-*invariant* $(\theta^{-1}(v, X) \in \mathcal{P}$ when $X \in \mathcal{P}$, $v \in T)$.

(6.11) Also a set $X \subseteq T$ is *strongly-$\bar{p}$*, if there is a $V \in \mathcal{U}$ for which

$$X^v \equiv X \cap \theta^{-1}(v, X) \notin \mathcal{P} \qquad (v \in V).$$

(6.12) A set $X \subseteq T$ is a *strong θ-base* for T, if there is a $V \in \mathcal{U}$ with

$$Th(X^v) = T(v \in V)$$

(6.13) A set $E \subseteq T$ is a *p-Baire set*, if $X \backslash E \in \mathcal{P}$ for some strongly-$\bar{p}$ set X.

In the reverse direction, to pass from

$$X \backslash E \in \mathcal{P} \quad \text{and} \quad \theta^{-1}(v, X \backslash E) \in \mathcal{P} \quad \text{to}$$
$$X_v \equiv (X \backslash E) \cup \theta^{-1}(v, X \backslash E) \in \mathcal{P}$$

we sometimes assume that

(6.14) p is *finitely additive* $(X \cup Y \in \mathcal{P}$ when $X, Y \in \mathcal{P})$.

The following theorem underlies parts of many proofs of the principles of uniform convergence and upper boundedness. The preceding discussion explains how far the conditions are necessary for the final result.

THEOREM 6.3. *If p is shrinkable, θ^{-1}-invariant, and finitely additive, then each p-Baire set $E \in \mathcal{E}$.*

Proof. A strongly-$\bar{p}$ set X exists with $X \backslash E \in \mathcal{P}$. Then, for all v,

$$\theta^{-1}(v, X \backslash E) \in \mathcal{P}, \quad X_v \in \mathcal{P}, \quad X_v \cap X^v \in \mathcal{P}$$

But $X^v \notin \mathcal{P}(v \in V)$, for some $V \in \mathcal{U}$. Hence (6.5) is true, and $E \in \mathcal{E}$. Not every useful property p is finitely additive. But in two cases

24

involving measure and β-sets (see later) we shall avoid the use of (6.14).

In other arguments we use Th_n-sets directly. It is convenient when

(6.15) p is *hereditary* $(Th_1(X) \in \mathcal{P}$ when $X \in \mathcal{P})$.

Then we say that $Th(X)$ *has the property* p^σ, $Th(X) \in \mathcal{P}^\sigma$.

(6.16) An $X \subseteq T$ has the *property* $h(p)$, or is an $\alpha(p)$-*set*, if
$Th_n(X) \in \mathcal{P}(n \geqslant 0)$. Other sets are called $\beta(p)$-*sets*.

If p is hereditary then $h(p) = p$. Also $h(p)$ is hereditary from (6.2), whatever the p. Further,

(6.17) the set $X \subseteq T$ is said to have the property $th(p)$, if $X \subseteq Th(E)$ for some $E \in \mathcal{P}_1$, the family of all sets with the property $h(p) \equiv p_1$.

Clearly $p_2 \equiv th(p)$ is shrinkable. If, for a given θ, we can always choose the E so that $\{Th_n(E)\}$ is monotone increasing, then $th(p)$ is hereditary by Theorem 6.1 (6.4). We use $th(p)$ with special θ in Chapter 6, Theorem 24.3, and Chapter 7, Theorems 29.7, 32.3. It would be difficult to give results involving $th(p)$ with general θ.

THEOREM 6.4. (6.18) *If p is hereditary,* $X \in \mathcal{P}$, $T \notin \mathcal{P}^\sigma$, *then* $Th(X) \neq T$

(6.19) *If* $p_1 \equiv h(p)$, $Th(X) = T \notin \mathcal{P}_1^\sigma$, *then* $Th_n(X) \notin \mathcal{P}$ *for some* $n \geqslant 0$.

(6.20) *If p is hereditary, with* $T \notin \mathcal{P}^\sigma$, *then a strong θ-base for T is strongly-$\bar{p}$.*

These results are obvious, and the pattern of proof is similar to that of Chapter 3, Theorem 12.2.

With $p_1 \equiv h(p)$, $p_2 \equiv th(p)$, we shall consider properties p_3 (of being nowhere dense), p_4 (of being of the first category), $p_5 = h(p_3)$, $p_6 = h(p_4)$, $p_7 = th(p_3)$, $p_8 = th(p_4)$, $p_9(\delta)$ (involving measure), and p_{10} (involving cardinal number). Properties p_3, p_4, p_5, $p_9(\delta)$ are considered in Chapter 5, while p_3 to p_{10} are considered for special θ in Chapter 7.

Historical Note: The $\alpha(p)$-sets and $\beta(p)$-sets generalize the α-sets and β-sets of Sargent (1950, 1953), and those of Henstock (1963a), p. 314.

3

TOPOLOGICAL STRUCTURE

7. Topologies and Product Topologies

WE now impose an analytic structure, that of a topology, on the space T of Chapter 2. As a result, in Chapter 5 we can consider properties that involve topological density, and can give the connection between the principles of upper boundedness and uniform convergence.

The essential idea behind that of the limit x of a sequence $\{x_n\}$, is that of 'nearness', i.e. x_n is as 'near' as we like to x, for all sufficiently large integers n. To measure the 'nearness' we surround x by 'open neighbourhoods', and a collection of such sets, for all $x \in T$, leads us to the definition of a topological space.

A family $\mathcal{G}$ of subsets $G \subseteq T$, is called a *topology in T*, if

(7.1)   the empty set and T are in $\mathcal{G}$;

(7.2)   if $\mathcal{H} \subseteq \mathcal{G}$, then $\bigcup_{\mathcal{H}} G \in \mathcal{G}$;

(7.3)   if $G_1, G_2 \in \mathcal{G}$, then $G_1 \cap G_2 \in \mathcal{G}$.

Each $G \in \mathcal{G}$ is called an *open set*, relative to $\mathcal{G}$, or a $\mathcal{G}$-set, and $(T, \mathcal{G})$, or T itself if $\mathcal{G}$ is understood, is called a *topological space*. A *neighbourhood* of $x \in T$, is any $G \in \mathcal{G}$ with $x \in G$, and a *neighbourhood* of $X \subseteq T$, is any $G \in \mathcal{G}$ with $X \subseteq G$. *Note that all our neighbourhoods are open neighbourhoods.*

THEOREM 7.1. *A set in T is a $\mathcal{G}$-set if and only if it contains a neighbourhood of each of its points.*

Proof. If $G \in \mathcal{G}$, then G is a neighbourhood of all its points. Conversely, if G contains a neighbourhood, say $G(x)$, of each $x \in G$, then

26

G contains the union of the $G(x)$, and so it is the union. By (7.2), $G \in \mathcal{G}$.

The *interior* of a set $X \subseteq T$, is

$$X° = \bigcup \{G : G \in \mathcal{G}, \ G \subseteq X\}$$

By (7.2), $X°$ is the largest $\mathcal{G}$-set contained in X. Thus $X = X°$ if and only if X is a $\mathcal{G}$-set.

A subfamily $\mathcal{C} \subseteq \mathcal{G}$ is a *cover* of a set X, if each point of X lies in at least one member of $\mathcal{C}$. A cover $\mathcal{C}'$ of X is a *refinement* of $\mathcal{C}$, if each member of $\mathcal{C}'$ lies in a member of $\mathcal{C}$.

The construction of a topology is helped by the following theorem.

THEOREM 7.2. *Let $\mathcal{A}$ be a family of sets $A_1 \subseteq T$. Then the family $\mathcal{B}$ of all unions of subfamilies of $\mathcal{A}$, with the empty set, is a topology in T if and only if*

(7.4) *for each $A_1, A_2 \in \mathcal{A}$ and each $x \in A_1 \cap A_2$, there is an $A_3 \in \mathcal{A}$ such that*

$$x \in A_3 \subseteq A_1 \cap A_2; \quad and$$

(7.5) $$T = \bigcup_{\mathcal{A}} A_1$$

Proof. Using (7.5), $\mathcal{B}$ satisfies (7.1; 7.2). From (7.4), if $A_1, A_2 \in \mathcal{A}$ then

$$A_1 \cap A_2 = \bigcup \{A_3 : all \ x \in A_1 \cap A_2\} \in \mathcal{B}$$

By *Ex. 3.3*, if $B_1, B_2 \in \mathcal{B}$ then $B_1 \cap B_2 \in \mathcal{B}$. Hence (7.3) holds.

Conversely, if $\mathcal{B}$ is a topology then (7.1) gives (7.5), while A_1, $A_2 \in \mathcal{A}$ and (7.3) imply that $A_1 \cap A_2 \in \mathcal{B}$, so that (7.4) is true.

A family $\mathcal{A}$ of subsets of T is a *base* for a topology $\mathcal{G}$, if $\mathcal{A} \subseteq \mathcal{G}$, and if for each $x \in T$ and each open set G with $x \in G$, there is an $A \in \mathcal{A}$ with $x \in A \subseteq G$. Further, $\mathcal{A}$ is a *sub-base* for $\mathcal{G}$, if the family of finite intersections of members of $\mathcal{A}$ is a base for $\mathcal{G}$. Thus in Theorem 7.2, $\mathcal{A}$ is a base for $\mathcal{B}$.

We now construct a topology for a Cartesian product T. Let A be a set of suffixes, and for each $a \in A$ let $(Y_a, \mathcal{G}_a)$ be a topological space. We put Y as the union of the spaces Y_a, so that $Y_a \subseteq Y (a \in A)$ and we construct

$$T = \bigtimes_A Y_a, \quad C = \bigtimes_A X_a.$$

27

The family $\mathcal{C}$ of all C with $X_a = Y_a$, except for a single a for which $X_a \in \mathcal{G}_a$, is a sub base for the required topology. A base is the family $\mathcal{A}$ of all finite intersections of members of $\mathcal{C}$, i.e. the family of all C with $X_a = Y_a$ except for a finite number of a for which $X_a \in \mathcal{G}_a$. Clearly $\mathcal{A}$ satisfies (7.4; 7.5), so that the $\mathcal{B}$ of Theorem 7.2 is a topology for T, called the *product topology*.

Historical Notes: The idea of an open set is due to Lebesgue (1902), p. 242. The product topology in a Cartesian product originated in Tychonoff (1935), p. 763.

Ex. 7.1. If T is the space of real or complex numbers, show that we can construct a topology for T from the modulus, called the *modulus topology.*

Ex. 7.2. If $T_1 \subseteq T$, show that the family $\mathcal{G}_1$ of sets $G \cap T_1$, for all $G \in \mathcal{G}$, is a topology in T_1. It is called the *relative topology of T_1 from $\mathcal{G}$.*

Ex. 7.3. The $\mathcal{G}$ containing only T and the empty set, is a topology. It is called the *trivial* (or *indiscrete*) *topology.*

Ex. 7.4. The $\mathcal{G}$ containing T and all subsets of T, including the empty set, is a topology. It is called the *discrete topology.*

Ex. 7.5. A family $\mathcal{A}$ of sets $A_1 \subseteq T$, is a sub base for a topology for T, if and only if the union of all the A_1 is T.

Ex. 7.6. If $\mathcal{A}$ is a base for the topology $\mathcal{G}$ of T, show that the topology $\mathcal{B}$ of Theorem 7.2 is $\mathcal{G}$ itself.

Ex. 7.7. If A is an index set, and if for each $a \in A$, $(Y_a, \mathcal{G}_a)$ is a topological space, so that we can construct the Cartesian product T and its product topology $\mathcal{G}$, using the union Y of the $Y_a (a \in A)$, let $f : A \to Y$ be such that $f \in G \in \mathcal{G}$. Show that in the notation used, there is a $C \subseteq G$ that has $X_a = Y_a$, except for a finite number of a for which

$$f(a) \in X_a \in \mathcal{G}_a$$

8. Closure, Closed Sets

A point $x \in T$ is called a *limit-point (cluster point)* of a set $X \subseteq T$, if each neighbourhood of x contains a point of X different from x. The set X' of all limit-points of X is called the *derived set of X*. A point

$x \in T$ is called a *contact-point of X*, if each neighbourhood of x contains a point of X. The set $\bar{X}$ of all contact-points of X is called the $\mathcal{G}$-*closure of X*, the $\mathcal{G}$ being dropped if understood; we sometimes write $\mathcal{G}X$ for $\bar{X}$.

THEOREM 8.1. (8.1) *If* $X \subseteq T$ *then* $\bar{X} = X \cup X'$

(8.2)   *For complements relative to* $T, \backslash \bar{X} = (\backslash X)^0$.

Proof. For (8.1) use the definitions. For (8.2), if $x \notin \bar{X}$, there is a neighbourhood of x free from points of X, and so lying in $\backslash X$, and $\backslash \bar{X} \subseteq (\backslash X)^\circ$. If $y \in (\backslash X)^\circ$, then y is in an open set contained in $\backslash X$ and so containing no point of X. Hence $y \in \backslash \bar{X}$, and (8.2) is true.

A set $F \subseteq T$ is $\mathcal{G}$-*closed*, or *closed* if $\mathcal{G}$ is understood, if $F' \subseteq F$, or, equivalently, if $\bar{F} = F$. Sometimes we call a closed set an $\mathcal{F}$-*set*.

THEOREM 8.2. *Let* $Y = \backslash X$. *If* X *is closed, then* $Y \in \mathcal{G}$. *If* $X \in \mathcal{G}$ *then* Y *is closed.*

The proof follows from Theorem 8.1 (8.2).

Thus closed sets ($\mathcal{F}$-sets) have the following properties.

(8.3)   The empty set and T are $\mathcal{F}$-sets.

(8.4)   The intersection of a family of $\mathcal{F}$-sets is an $\mathcal{F}$-set.

(8.5)   If F_1, F_2 are $\mathcal{F}$-sets, so is $F_1 \cup F_2$.

Conversely, if a family $\mathcal{F}$ has properties (8.3; 8.4; 8.5), then the family of complements is a topology.

THEOREM 8.3 *Let* $X, Y \subseteq T$. *Then*

(8.6) $\bar{X}$ *is an* $\mathcal{F}$-*set, so that* $\mathcal{G}\mathcal{G}X = \mathcal{G}X$,

(8.7)   *if* $X \subseteq Y$ *then* $X' \subseteq Y', \bar{X} \subseteq \bar{Y}$,

(8.8) $\bar{X}$ *is the smallest* $\mathcal{F}$-*set containing* X,

(8.9) $\overline{X \cup Y} = \bar{X} \cup \bar{Y}$,

(8.10) $(X \cup Y)' = X' \cup Y'$.

Proof. For (8.6), if $x \in (\bar{X})'$ then each neighbourhood G of x contains a point, say q, of $\bar{X}$. As G is also a neighbourhood of q, G contains a point r of X, where r can be x. Hence $x \in \bar{X}$, and (8.6) is

29

true. (8.7) is obvious. For (8.8) we use (8.6; 8.7). For if F is closed and $X \subseteq F \subseteq \bar{X}$, then $\mathcal{G}X \subseteq \mathcal{G}F = F \subseteq \mathcal{G}\mathcal{G}X = \mathcal{G}X, F = \bar{X}$. For (8.9) let $x \in \overline{X \cup Y}, x \notin \bar{X}$. Then there is a neighbourhood G of x containing no point of X. If G_1 is a neighbourhood of x, then by (7.3), $G \cap G_1$ is also a neighbourhood of x, and so contains a point g of $X \cup Y$. As $g \notin X$, then $g \in Y \cap G_1$ and $x \in \bar{Y}$. Hence $\overline{X \cup Y} \subseteq \bar{X} \cup \bar{Y}$. If $y \in \bar{X} \cup \bar{Y}$ then $y \in \bar{X}$ or $y \in \bar{Y}$, so that each neighbourhood of y contains a point of X or of Y, and so a point of $X \cup Y$, and $y \in \overline{X \cup Y}$. Hence (8.9). Similarly for (8.10), in the proof of which, $g \neq x$.

THEOREM 8.4. (8.11) *Let* $T_1 \subseteq T$, *and let* $\mathcal{G}_1$ *be the relative topology of* T_1 *from* $\mathcal{G}$. *If* $F \subseteq T_1$ *is closed under* $\mathcal{G}_1$, *then there is a set* F_1, *closed under* $\mathcal{G}$, *such that* $F = F_1 \cap T_1$.

(8.12) $\qquad$ *If* $X \subseteq T_1$, *then* $\quad \mathcal{G}_1 X = \mathcal{G}X \cap T_1$.

Proof. For (8.11) we take complements relative to T_1 in the definition of a $\mathcal{G}_1$-set and use Theorem 8.2. Then for (8.12) we also use (8.8).

Historical Note: Cantor defined the derived set of X in Cantor (1872), p. 129, and a closed set in Cantor (1883a), p. 51.

Ex. 8.1. The closure of the empty set is the empty set.

Ex. 8.2. $\overline{X \cap Y} \subseteq \bar{X} \cap \bar{Y}$ (use (8.7)).

Ex. 8.3. $\backslash \bar{X}$ is a $\mathcal{G}$-set.

Ex. 8.4. Let $\mathcal{H}$ be a family of subsets H of T. Show that

$$\mathcal{G} \bigcup_{\mathcal{H}} H \supseteq \bigcup_{\mathcal{H}} \bar{H}$$

Ex. 8.5. If in *Ex. 8.4* each $x \in T$ has a neighbourhood intersecting only a finite number of sets H, then

$$\mathcal{G} \bigcup_{\mathcal{H}} H = \bigcup_{\mathcal{H}} \bar{H}$$

Ex. 8.6. In *Ex. 7.7* show that if

$$X = \bigtimes_A X_a, \quad \text{then} \quad \bar{X} = \bigtimes_A \bar{X}_a$$

30

9. Continuity, Openness, Convergence, and Order

Let $(T_1, \mathcal{G}_1)$, $(T_2, \mathcal{G}_2)$ be topological spaces, with $X \subseteq T_1$ and $f: X \to T_2$. Then f is *continuous* (relative to $\mathcal{G}_1$, $\mathcal{G}_2$) *at* $x \in T_1$, if $x \in X$, and if, for $v = f(x)$, given a $\mathcal{G}_2$-neighbourhood G_2 of v, there is a $\mathcal{G}_1$-neighbourhood G_1 of x such that $G_1 \subseteq X$ and $f(G_1) \subseteq G_2$. If f is continuous at all $x \in X$, we say that f is *continuous on* X. Then by Theorem 7.1, $X \in \mathcal{G}_1$.

The function f is *open in* T_1 *to* T_2 (relative to $\mathcal{G}_1$, $\mathcal{G}_2$) if $f(G_1) \in \mathcal{G}_2$ for all $G_1 \in \mathcal{G}_1$. The inverse image f^{-1} is *open in* T_2 *to* T_1 (relative to $\mathcal{G}_2$, $\mathcal{G}_1$) if $f^{-1}(G_2) \in \mathcal{G}_1$ ($G_2 \in \mathcal{G}_2$).

THEOREM 9.1 *The function f is continuous on X if and only if*

$$(9.1) \qquad f^{-1} \text{ is open in } T_2 \text{ to } T_1, \quad \text{and only if}$$

$$(9.2) \qquad f(X \cap \mathcal{G}_1 Y) \subseteq \mathcal{G}_2 f(Y) \quad (Y \subseteq X).$$

If $X = T_1$ then f is continuous on T_1 if and only if any one of (9.2) and the following propositions is true.

$$(9.3) \qquad \text{If } F \text{ is } \mathcal{G}_2\text{-closed,} \quad \text{then} \quad f^{-1}(F) \text{ is } \mathcal{G}_1\text{-closed.}$$

$$(9.4) \qquad f^{-1}(\mathcal{G}_2 Y) \supseteq \mathcal{G}_1(f^{-1}(Y)) \quad (Y \subseteq T_2).$$

Proof. For (9.1), if f is continuous on X let $G_2 \in \mathcal{G}_2$, $x \in f^{-1}(G_2)$. Then $f(x) \in G_2$, and by continuity there is a $\mathcal{G}_1$-neighbourhood $G_1 \subseteq X$ of x with

$$f(G_1) \subseteq G_2, \quad G_1 \subseteq f^{-1}(G_2), \quad \text{and} \quad f^{-1}(G_2) \in \mathcal{G}_1 \quad \text{(Theorem 7.1).}$$

Conversely, if f^{-1} is open, with $x \in X$, let G_2 be a $\mathcal{G}_2$-neighbourhood of $f(x)$. Then $G_3 = f^{-1}(G_2)$ is a $\mathcal{G}_1$-neighbourhood of x with $f(G_3) \subseteq G_2$. Thus f is continuous at x, and so is continuous on X.

For (9.2) if f is continuous on X, let $v \in f(X \cap \mathcal{G}_1 Y)$. Then $v = f(x)$ for some $x \in \mathcal{G}_1 Y$. If $v \in G_2 \in \mathcal{G}_2$, there is a $\mathcal{G}_1$-neighbourhood $G_1 \subseteq X$ of x with $f(G_1) \subseteq G_2$. As $x \in \mathcal{G}_1 Y$, there is a $y \in Y \cap G_1 \subseteq X$, and $f(y) \in f(Y) \cap G_2$.

Assuming now that $X = T_1$, we use complements, *Ex. 2.7* with $Y_* = F$, $Y^* = \backslash F$, and Theorem 8.2. Then $f^{-1}(Y^*) = \backslash f^{-1}(Y_*)$, and (9.3) is equivalent to (9.1). Also (9.3) implies (9.4). For $Y \subseteq \mathcal{G}_2 Y$ implies $f^{-1}(Y) \subseteq f^{-1}(\mathcal{G}_2 Y)$, the latter being $\mathcal{G}_1$-closed by (9.3).

Taking $\mathcal{G}_1$-closures we have (9.4). Conversely, if (9.4) is true, and if F is $\mathcal{G}_2$-closed, then

$$f^{-1}(F) \supseteq \mathcal{G}_1(f^{-1}(F))$$

and $f^{-1}(F)$ is $\mathcal{G}_1$-closed, giving (9.3). Finally, if (9.2) holds, then for

$$Y \subseteq T_2, \quad f\big(\mathcal{G}_1(f^{-1}(Y))\big) \subseteq \mathcal{G}_2\big(f(f^{-1}(Y))\big) \subseteq \mathcal{G}_2 Y,$$
$$\mathcal{G}_1(f^{-1}(Y)) \subseteq f^{-1}(\mathcal{G}_2 Y)$$

using *Ex. 2.6*. Thus (9.4) is true and f is continuous on T_1.

A continuous open bijection on T_1 to T_2 is called a *homeomorphism*, and we say that T_1, T_2 are *homeomorphic*.

A sequence $\{x_n\}$ in T *converges to* $x \in T$ if, given an arbitrary neighbourhood G of x from the topology $\mathcal{G}$ of T, there is an integer m, depending on G, such that $x_n \in G$ for all $n \geqslant m$. Then x is the *limit of* $\{x_n\}$. Here we have changed $(T_2, \mathcal{G}_2)$ to $(T, \mathcal{G})$, while T_1 is the space of positive integers with a conventional $+\infty$, and with $f(n) = x_n$, $f(+\infty) = x$. The topology $\mathcal{G}_1$ reduces to neighbourhoods of $+\infty$ of the form $[m, +\infty)$.

Sometimes we use a partial order and Moore–Smith convergence.

A *partially ordered set* $(P, \leqslant)$ is a non-empty set P, and a relation $\leqslant$ in P, called an *order relation*, such that

(9.5)   if $a \leqslant b$ and $b \leqslant c$, then $a \leqslant c$;

(9.6) $a \leqslant a$.

We sometimes write $b \geqslant a$ when $a \leqslant b$. Let $X \subseteq P$. Then an $x \in P$ is an *upper bound of X*, if $y \leqslant x$ for every $y \in X$. An upper bound x of X is a *supremum of X*, denoted by *sup X*, if each upper bound z of X satisfies $x \leqslant z$. Similarly for the *lower bound* and *infimum, inf X*, of X.

A partially ordered set $(P, \leqslant)$ is *well ordered* if

(9.7) $a \leqslant b$ and $b \leqslant a$ imply $a = b$;

(9.8)   each non-empty set $X \subseteq P$ has a lower bound $x \in X$.

Theorem 4.1 (Schroeder-Bernstein) shows that the order defined between some cardinal numbers satisfies (9.7), but (9.8) need not be satisfied unless we assume a special axiom.

AXIOM 9.1. *Every set can be well ordered*, i.e. *given a set P, an order relation can be defined in P so that P is well ordered.*

THEOREM 9.2. *A subset of a well ordered set is well ordered.*

Proof. If $(P, \leqslant)$ is well ordered and $R \subseteq P$, let $a, b \in R$. Then $a, b \in P$. Using the same order in R as in P, then (9.5; 9.6; 9.7) are true in R. Further, if $X \subseteq R$ then $X \subseteq P$, and X has a lower bound $x \in X$, taking $X \subseteq P$. This x is also a lower bound for X when considered as a subset of R.

A partially ordered set $(P, \leqslant)$ is *directed*, if every finite subset X of P has an upper bound. In this case, $f : P \to T$ is called a *generalized sequence in T*. If $(T, \mathcal{G})$ is a topological space, the generalized sequence f *converges to a point* $t \in T$, if to each $G \in \mathcal{G}$ with $t \in G$, there is an $x \in P$ such that for all $y \in P$ with $x \leqslant y$ we have $f(y) \in G$. We then write

$$t = \lim_{P} f(y)$$

This Moore–Smith convergence will be used later for our integration. The reason for using a directed set, is that if for various purposes we consider a finite number of sets $y \geqslant x_1, \ldots, y \geqslant x_n$, then we can replace each x_n by an upper bound x of the $x_1, \ldots, x_n$, and consider the single set of $y \geqslant x$, in which the various purposes hold simultaneously.

Historical Notes: Axiom 9.1 is connected with Zermelo's axiom. The Moore–Smith convergence originated in Moore (1915; 1939) and Moore and Smith (1922).

Ex. 9.1. If $(T_j, \mathcal{G}_j)$ $(j = 1, 2, 3)$ are topological spaces, and if $f : T_1 \to T_2$, and $g : T_2 \to T_3$ are continuous, then $g(f(.)) : T_1 \to T_3$ is continuous.

Ex. 9.2. Let $(T, \mathcal{G})$ be a topological space, and let R be the real line or complex plane with the modulus topology. If $f : T \to R$ and $g : T \to R$ are continuous, and if $x \in R$, show that

$$|f|, \quad xf, \quad f+g, \quad fg$$

are continuous. If R is the real line show that

$$max\,(f, g), \quad min\,(f, g)$$

are continuous.

Ex. 9.3. Let T be the real line, containing a bounded open interval G and its complement F. If $f = 0$ in G, with f undefined in F, show that f is continuous on G, $\mathcal{G}$ being the modulus topology on T. But

$$f^{-1}(T) = G \subset \mathcal{G}G$$

showing that (9.3; 9.4) need not be true when $X \neq T_1$.

Ex. 9.4. Let T be the real line with modulus topology $\mathcal{G}$, and let $f = 0$ at the rationals, with f undefined at the irrationals. Show that (9.2) is true, but that f is not continuous.

Ex. 9.5. Show that the property, that two topological spaces are homeomorphic, is an equivalence relation. (Much topological theory consists of describing the corresponding cosets).

Ex. 9.6. Show that for the Cartesian product of section 7 with the product topology, the function *proj* $(a;.)$ is continuous, where

$$proj\,(a; H) = \{f(a) : f \in H\}\,(H \subseteq T)$$

10. Special Topological Spaces

At times we need additional assumptions on the topology, and an increasing sequence of specialization is provided by the $\mathcal{T}_j$-spaces, in the notation of Alexandroff and Hopf (1935).

A topological space T is a $\mathcal{T}_0$-*space* if, for each pair of distinct points $x, y \in T$, there is a neighbourhood of one that does not contain the other.

T is a $\mathcal{T}_1$-*space* if, for each pair of distinct points $x, y \in T$, there are a neighbourhood of x that does not contain y, and so a neighbourhood of y that does not contain x.

A $\mathcal{T}_1$-space is a $\mathcal{T}_0$-space, but the converse need not hold, see *Ex. 10.2.*

THEOREM 10.1. *In a $\mathcal{T}_1$-space, sing (x) and each derived set are closed.*

Proof. If $y \neq x$, there is a neighbourhood of y that contains no point of sing (x), so that y cannot be a limit-point of sing (x), which is, therefore, closed. To prove that X' is closed we replace X by X' in

34

the proof of Theorem 8.3 (8.6). Then we can take a neighbourhood of q that does not contain x, and its intersection with G is another neighbourhood of q, that contains r but not x. Thus $r \in G$, $r \neq x$, and $x \in X'$.

T is a $\mathcal{U}_2$-space (*Hausdorff space, Hausdorffian*), if for each pair of distinct points $x, y \in T$, there are disjoint neighbourhoods of x and y. A $\mathcal{U}_2$-space is a $\mathcal{U}_1$-space. *Ex. 10.3* gives a $\mathcal{U}_1$-space that is not a $\mathcal{U}_2$-space.

THEOREM 10.2. *In a $\mathcal{U}_2$-space, a sequence and a generalized sequence can have only one limit.*

Proof. Since a sequence is a special case of a generalized sequence, we assume that we have a directed set $(P, \preccurlyeq)$, and a function $f : P \to T$. Let $t, u \in T$ be such that for $t \in G(t) \in \mathcal{Q}$, $u \in G(u) \in \mathcal{Q}$, there are $x, y \in P$ such that for all $z \in P$ with $z \geqslant x$, we have $f(z) \in G(t)$, and for all $z \in P$ with $z \geqslant y$, we have $f(z) \in G(u)$. Then since P is directed, there is an upper bound w of x, y, so that for $z \geqslant w$, $f(z) \in G(t) \cap G(u)$. Thus at least one point $f(w)$ lies in the intersection. But since T is a $\mathcal{U}_2$-space we can choose $G(t)$, $G(u)$ so that the intersection is empty, if $t \neq u$. Hence $t = u$.

T is a *regular space* if, for each closed set $F \subseteq T$ and each $x \in T$, $x \notin F$, there are disjoint neighbourhoods of F and x.

THEOREM 10.3. *T is a regular space if, and only if, it has the property that if G is a neighbourhood of a point x, there is another neighbourhood of x with closure contained in G.*

Proof. If T is regular let $F = \backslash G$, closed by Theorem 8.2. Then there are disjoint sets G_1, $G_2 \in \mathcal{Q}$ with $\backslash G \subseteq G_1$, $x \in G_2$. By Theorem 8.2, $\backslash G_1$ is closed.

Hence $\qquad x \in G_2 \subseteq \backslash G_1$, $\quad \bar{G}_2 \subseteq \backslash G_1 \subseteq G$

and T has the property. Conversely, if T has the property, let F be a closed set and $x \notin F$. By Theorem 8.2, $\backslash F$ is a neighbourhood of x, which, therefore, contains the closure of a neighbourhood G of x. Hence F is contained in $\backslash \bar{G}$, a $\mathcal{Q}$-set by *Ex. 8.3*, that is disjoint from G, and T is regular.

For a non-regular $\mathcal{U}_2$-space see *Ex. 10.4*. A $\mathcal{U}_3$-*space* is a regular

$\mathcal{T}_1$-space. By Theorem 10.1, sing (x) is closed, so that if $y \neq x$ there are disjoint neighbourhoods of x and y i.e. a $\mathcal{T}_3$-space is a $\mathcal{T}_2$-space.

T is a *completely regular space* if, for each $x \in T$ and each neighbourhood G of x, there is a continuous function f on T to $[0,1]$ such that $f(x) = 0$, and $f = 1$ everywhere on $\backslash G$.

Each completely regular space is regular. For the set where $f < \frac{1}{2}$, is open, with closure contained in the set where $f \leqslant \frac{1}{2}$, and in turn this is contained in G. Hence the result by Theorem 10.3.

A completely regular $\mathcal{T}_1$-space, which is a $\mathcal{T}_3$-space, and so a $\mathcal{T}_2$-space, is called a *Tychonoff space*. See Tychonoff (1929), p. 545.

T is a *normal space* if, for each pair of disjoint closed sets F_1, F_2, there are disjoint neighbourhoods of F_1, F_2. A normal $\mathcal{T}_1$-space, which is then a $\mathcal{T}_2$-space and a $\mathcal{T}_3$-space by Theorem 10.1, is called a $\mathcal{T}_4$-*space*.

THEOREM 10.4. (*Urysohn* (1925), p. 292). *Let F_1, F_2 be disjoint closed sets in a normal space T. Then there is a continuous function f on T to $[0,1]$, with $f = 0$ on F_1, and $f = 1$ on F_2.*

Corollary. A $\mathcal{T}_4$-space is a Tychonoff space.

Proof. Since T is normal, and by Theorem 8.2, there are $G_{1/2}$, $G_{1/2}^* \in \mathcal{G}$ such that

$$F_1 \subseteq G_{1/2} \subseteq \bar{G}_{1/2} \subseteq \backslash G_{1/2}^* \subseteq \backslash F_2$$

As F_1 and $\backslash G_{1/2}$ are disjoint closed sets, and as $\backslash G_{1/2}^*$ and F_2 are disjoint closed sets, we apply the construction again to obtain $G_{1/4}$, $G_{3/4} \in \mathcal{G}$ with

$$F_1 \subseteq G_{1/4} \subseteq \bar{G}_{1/4} \subseteq G_{1/2} \subseteq \bar{G}_{1/2} \subseteq G_{3/4} \subseteq \bar{G}_{3/4} \subseteq \backslash F_2$$

and so on. By induction we define $G_r \in \mathcal{G}$ for each $r = m \cdot 2^{-n}$ ($m = 1, 3, 5, \ldots, 2^n - 1; n = 1, 2, \ldots$), such that if $r < s$ then

$$\bar{G}_r \subseteq G_s, \quad F_1 \subseteq G_r \subseteq \bar{G}_r \subseteq \backslash F_2$$

We put $f = 0$ in the intersection of all G_r, and otherwise put

$$f(x) = \sup \{r : x \notin G_r\}$$

Then $0 \leqslant f \leqslant 1$, with $f = 0$ on F_1, $f = 1$ on F_2. To show f continuous, let $y = f(x) > 0$. Let $0 < \eta < \varepsilon$ be arbitrarily small, with $y + \varepsilon$,

$y - \eta$ as $r's$. Then

$$x \in G_{y+\varepsilon} \cap \setminus \bar{G}_{y-\eta} \in \mathcal{G}$$

If z is also in this $\mathcal{G}$-set, then

$$|f(x) - f(z)| < 2\varepsilon$$

and f is continuous where $f(x) > 0$. If $f(x) = 0$ a similar proof holds. The corollary then follows by Theorem 10.1.

A *local base* at a point $x \in T$, is a family N of neighbourhoods of x such that each neighbourhood of x contains a member of N. Then T satisfies the *first axiom of countability*, if each $x \in T$ has a *countable* local base.

T satisfies the *second axiom of countability*, if its topology has a *countable* base. Then T also satisfies the first axiom of countability. *Ex. 10.7* is one in which the converse is false.

Ex. 10.1. If $x, y \in T$, and if each neighbourhood of x contains y, and each neighbourhood of y contains x, we say that x and y are *indistinguishable*. Prove that this is an equivalence relation, the cosets forming a $\mathcal{T}_0$-space.

Ex. 10.2. Let T be the set of positive reals, a neighbourhood of $x \in T$ being an open infinite interval (t, ∞), for some t in $(0, x)$. Then if $x < y$ and $x, y \in T$, we take $t = \frac{1}{2}(x+y)$ so that (t, ∞) contains y but not x. However, every neighbourhood of x contains y. Thus T is a $\mathcal{T}_0$-space but not a $\mathcal{T}_1$-space.

Ex. 10.3. Let T be the positive integers, with -1 and -2. Let neighbourhoods of a positive integer j be any subsets of T containing j. Let each neighbourhood of -1 contain -1 and all integers $j \geqslant N$, for some positive integer N, and similarly for -2. Show that T is a $\mathcal{T}_1$-space but not a $\mathcal{T}_2$-space.

Ex. 10.4. In $(0,1)$ let R be the set of rationals, and let $\mathcal{G}$-sets be constructed from open intervals I and all sets $R \cap I$. Show that the closure of an $R \cap I$ contains I, which is not in $R \cap G$, for any union G of open intervals. Hence show that we have a non-regular $\mathcal{T}_2$-space.

Ex. 10.5. Prove that a $\mathcal{T}_1$-space containing a finite number of points is a $\mathcal{T}_4$-space.

Ex. 10.6. Let $X \subset T$ be non-empty, and let $\mathcal{G}$ consist of X, $\setminus X$, T,

37

and the empty set. Show that T is then a normal space, that if $f = 0$ in $X, f = 1$ in $\backslash X$, then f is continuous.

Ex. 10.7. Let T be uncountable, such that every subset of T is a $\mathcal{G}$-set. Then sing (sing(x)) is a local base at x, so that T satisfies the first axiom of countability. But every base contains sing (x) for all $x \in T$, and so is uncountable, and T does not satisfy the second axiom of countability.

11. Pseudometric and Metric Spaces

The spaces of this section give simple examples of topological spaces. We say that T is a *pseudometric space* with *pseudometric* ϱ, if to each ordered pair $x, y \in T$ there corresponds a real number $\varrho(x, y)$ such that

(11.1) $\varrho(x, y) = 0$ if $x = y$ (*each* $x \in T$)

(11.2) $\varrho(x, y) \leqslant \varrho(x, z) + \varrho(y, z)$ (*each* $x, y, z \in T$)

A more usual set of axioms is given by (11.1) and the following.

(11.3) $0 \leqslant \varrho(x, y) = \varrho(y, x)$ (*each* $x, y \in T$)

(11.4) $\varrho(x, y) \leqslant \varrho(x, z) + \varrho(z, y)$ (*each* $x, y, z \in T$)

Axiom (11.4) [or (11.2)] is the *triangle axiom.*

THEOREM 11.1. *The two axiom systems are equivalent.*

Proof. Clearly (11.3; 11.4) imply (11.2). Conversely, taking $x = y$ in (11.2) and using (11.1), we obtain

$$\varrho(x, z) \geqslant 0 \quad (each\ x, z \in T)$$

Taking $x = z$ in (11.2) and using (11.1),

$$\varrho(x, y) \leqslant \varrho(y, x) \quad (each\ x, y \in T)$$

Interchanging x, y we have equality and (11.3). Then (11.4) follows from (11.2).

A few further results can be obtained. From (11.2),

$$\varrho(x, y) - \varrho(x, z) \leqslant \varrho(y, z)$$

so that if we interchange y and z and use (11.3),

(11.5) $\qquad |\varrho(x, y) - \varrho(x, z)| \leqslant \varrho(y, z) \qquad$ (each $x, y, z \in T$)

Further, we have

$$|\varrho(y, z) - \varrho(y', z')| \leqslant |\varrho(y, z) - \varrho(y', z)| + |\varrho(y', z) - \varrho(y', z')|$$

so that if we use (11.5) we obtain

(11.6) $\quad |\varrho(y, z) - \varrho(y', z')| \leqslant \varrho(y, y') + \varrho(z, z') \qquad$ (each $y, z, y', z' \in T$)

The pseudometric space T with a pseudometric ϱ, is a *metric space*, with *metric* ϱ, if also ϱ obeys the axiom

(11.7) $\qquad$ if $\quad \varrho(x, y) = 0 \quad$ then $\quad x = y \quad$ (each $x, y \in T$)

Given $\varepsilon > 0$, $x \in T$, the set $S(x; \varepsilon)$ of all $y \in T$ with $\varrho(x, y) < \varepsilon$, is called the *open sphere with centre x and radius ε*, the corresponding *closed sphere* being $CS(x; \varepsilon)$, the set of $y \in T$ with $\varrho(x, y) \leqslant \varepsilon$.

THEOREM 11.2. *The family* $\mathcal{G}$, *of the empty set and all unions of open spheres in T, is a topology, called the* pseudometric (*or* metric) topology *according as ϱ is a pseudometric (or a metric) in T.*

Proof. By Theorem 7.2 we need only prove (7.4; 7.5). For (7.4) let

$z \in S(x; \varepsilon_1) \cap S(y; \varepsilon_2)$. $\qquad$ Then $\qquad \varrho(x, z) < \varepsilon_1, \qquad \varrho(y, z) < \varepsilon_2$.

If $\quad \varepsilon_3 = \min \{\varepsilon_1 - \varrho(x, z); \quad \varepsilon_2 - \varrho(y, z)\} > 0$, $w \in S(z; \varepsilon_3)$

then by (11.4) we have

$$\varrho(x, w) \leqslant \varrho(x, z) + \varrho(z, w) < \varrho(x, z) + \varepsilon_3 \leqslant \varepsilon_1, \qquad w \in S(x; \varepsilon_1)$$

Similarly

$$w \in S(y; \varepsilon_2), \qquad S(z; \varepsilon_3) \subseteq S(x; \varepsilon_1) \cap S(y; \varepsilon_2)$$

Hence the result. (7.5) is obvious.

THEOREM 11.3. (11.8) *A set $G \subseteq T$ is a $\mathcal{G}$-set if, and only if, to each $x \in G$ there corresponds an $\varepsilon(x) > 0$ such that $S(x; \varepsilon(x)) \subseteq G$.*
(11.9) *In (11.8), for each $x \in T$, it is sufficient to take $\varepsilon(x)$ as one of a sequence $\{\varepsilon_n(x)\}$ of values of $\varepsilon > 0$ that tends to 0 as $n \to \infty$, so that T obeys the first axiom of countability.*

Proof. (11.8) follows from Theorem 7.1 and the fact that each $\mathcal{G}$-set is a union of sets $S(x; \varepsilon)$. For if $y \in S(x; \varepsilon)$ we can take $\varepsilon(y) = \varepsilon - \varrho(x, y)$.

For (11.9), each $\varepsilon_n(x)$ is an $\varepsilon(x)$, and if $\varepsilon(x) > 0$, there is an $\varepsilon_n(x) \leqslant \varepsilon(x)$.

THEOREM 11.4. *If $x \in T$, $\varepsilon > 0$, then $CS(x; \varepsilon)$ is closed and contains the closure of $S(x; \varepsilon)$, but there is not always equality.*

Proof. Suppose that

$$y \in \mathcal{G}CS(x; \varepsilon), \quad \varepsilon_1 > 0$$

Then there is a point z in

$$CS(x; \varepsilon) \cap S(y; \varepsilon_1), \quad \varrho(x, z) \leqslant \varepsilon, \varrho(y, z) < \varepsilon_1, \quad \varrho(x, y) < \varepsilon + \varepsilon_1$$

As $\varrho(x, y)$ is independent of $\varepsilon_1 > 0$, then $y \in CS(x; \varepsilon)$. Thus the set is closed. The second result then comes from

$$S(x; \varepsilon) \subseteq CS(x; \varepsilon)$$

Finally, if $T_1 \subseteq T$, then T_1 is also a pseudometric (or metric) space with the same ϱ. Let T contain x, y with $\varrho(x, y) > 0$, and let

$$T_1 = \{\backslash S(x; \varrho(x, y))\} \cup \text{sing}\,(x)$$

Then the open sphere in T_1 with centre x and radius $\varrho(x, y)$, is

$$S(x; \varrho(x, y)) \cap T_1 = \text{sing}\,(x)$$

Its closure is sing (x), while the corresponding closed sphere in T_1 contains x, y, and possibly other points.

THEOREM 11.5. (11.10) *If $x \notin F$, F closed, then $\varrho(x, F) \equiv \inf_{y \in F} \varrho(x, y) > 0$.*

(11.11) *The set of x where $\varrho(x, F) < \varepsilon$, is open.*

(11.12) *The set of x where $\varrho(x, F) \leqslant \varepsilon$, is closed.*

(11.13) *T is a regular and normal space.*

(11.14) *If ϱ is a metric, T is a Hausdorff $(\mathcal{C}_2\text{-})$space.*

40

Proof. For (11.10), by Theorem 8.2, $\backslash F \in \mathcal{G}$. As $x \in \backslash F$, then for some $\varepsilon > 0$,

$$S(x; \varepsilon) \subseteq \backslash F, \quad \varrho(x, F) \geqslant \varepsilon$$

For (11.11), the set is the union of spheres $S(y; \varepsilon)$ with $y \in F$. For (11.12), if z is in the closure of the set, there is a point of the set within δ of z, and so a point of F within $\varepsilon + 2\delta$ of z. Thus $\varrho(z, F) \leqslant \varepsilon + 2\delta$, for all $\delta > 0$, and z lies in the set, which is therefore closed. For (11.13), from Theorem 11.4, if x and the closed F are disjoint, with $\varepsilon = \varrho(x, F) > 0$,

$$\mathcal{G}S(x; \tfrac{1}{2}\varepsilon) \subseteq S(x; \varepsilon)$$

and $S(x; \tfrac{1}{2}\varepsilon)$ is a neighbourhood of x disjoint from

$$\backslash \mathcal{G}S(x; \tfrac{1}{2}\varepsilon) \supseteq F$$

Thus T is a regular space. Further, if F_1, F_2 are two disjoint closed sets, put

$$G(F_1, F_2) = \{x : \varrho(x, F_1) < \varrho(x, F_2)\}$$

If $x \in F_1$ then $x \in \backslash F_2$, and by (11.10), $x \in G(F_1, F_2)$. Further, if $x \in G(F_1, F_2)$ then

$$3\varepsilon_1 \equiv \varrho(y, F_2) - \varrho(y, F_1) > 0$$

while if $z \in S(y; \varepsilon_1)$ then

$$\varrho(z, F_2) - \varrho(z, F_1) > \varrho(y, F_2) - \varrho(y, F_1) - 2\varepsilon_1 = \varepsilon_1,$$
$$S(y; \varepsilon_1) \subseteq G(F_1, F_2)$$

Thus $G(F_1, F_2)$ is a $\mathcal{G}$-set containing F_1. It is disjoint from $G(F_2, F_1)$, a $\mathcal{G}$-set containing F_2. Hence T is a normal space.

Finally, if ϱ is a metric, and $x \neq y$ in T, then $\varrho(x, y) > 0$, so that if $\varepsilon_2 = \tfrac{1}{2}\varrho(x, y)$, $S(x; \varepsilon_2)$ and $S(y; \varepsilon_2)$ are disjoint neighbourhoods of x, y, respectively, and T is a $\mathcal{T}_2$-space.

Given a space T with topology $\mathcal{G}$, the question arises, can $\mathcal{G}$ be given by a pseudometric or a metric? In particular, proofs that certain T are Baire spaces use a pseudometric. Thus when generalizing known results it is vital to know how general a pseudometric space is. Note also that $\mathcal{G}$ is a metric topology if, and only if, $(T, \mathcal{G})$ is a

Hausdorff space and $\mathcal{Q}$ is a pseudometric topology, so that we restrict our examination to pseudometric topologies. If $\mathcal{Q}$ is a pseudometric topology we say that the pseudometric *pseudometrizes T*, and *T* is said to be *pseudometrizable*.

The problem needs a few more definitions. A family $\mathcal{H}$ of subsets of *T* is *locally finite* if each point of *T* has a neighbourhood that intersects only a finite number of sets of $\mathcal{H}$. Then *Ex. 8.5* holds, and the family of $\bar{H}$, for all $H \in \mathcal{H}$, is locally finite.

A family $\mathcal{H}$ of subsets of *T* is *discrete* if each point of *T* has a neighbourhood that intersects at most one member of $\mathcal{H}$. Then a discrete family is locally finite, and the corresponding family of H is discrete.

A family $\mathcal{H}$ is *σ-locally finite*, or *σ-discrete*, if it is the union of a countable number of families that are locally finite, or discrete, respectively.

THEOREM 11.6. *The following three conditions on T are equivalent.*

(11.15) *T is pseudometrizable.*

(11.16) *T is regular and $\mathcal{Q}$ has a σ-locally finite base.*

(11.17) *T is regular and $\mathcal{Q}$ has a σ-discrete base.*

For proof see Kelley (1955), pp. 126–129.

Ex. 11.1. If ϱ is a pseudometric in *T*, then ϱ is a metric in the cosets of *Ex. 10.1*, so that the cosets form a $\mathcal{U}_4$-space in this case.

Ex. 11.2 (Urysohn) A regular topology with a countable base is pseudometrizable. (For the base is σ-discrete.)

Notes: Theorem 11.1 is due to Lindenbaum (1926).

12. Density, Category, and Baire Sets

Given a topological space $(T, \mathcal{Q})$ we can define various densities relative to $\mathcal{Q}$. These were first defined for the real line with the modulus topology, and were then extended to more general spaces, so that it sometimes helps in comprehension to give the original version for the real line, as well as the abstract version.

If $X \subseteq T$, $G \in \mathcal{Q}$, with $G \cap X$ not empty, then $G \cap X$ is called a *portion of X.* A point x is an *isolated point of X*, if sing(x) is a portion of X, i.e. if $x \in X$ and if there is a neighbourhood of x that contains no other point of X. All non-isolated points of X lie in X'.

A set X is *dense* in a set X_1, if $\overline{X} \supseteq X_1$. i.e. if each point of X_1 is either in X or a limit-point of X. In the case of the real line, points of X approach arbitrarily closely to the points of X_1. See *Ex. 12.1.* Considering the first case of the definition we see that every set X is dense in X. The second case gives rise to another notion.

A set X is *dense-in-itself*, if $X' \supseteq X$. For the real line, each point of X is approached arbitrarily closely by other points of X. See *Ex. 12.3.*

A set P is *perfect*, if it is closed and dense-in-itself, so that $P = P'$. For the real line, all points of P, and no other points, are approached arbitrarily closely by other points of P. For example, a closed interval is a perfect set. Cantor's ternary set (*Ex. 12.6*) is another.

We now consider an opposite idea to that of density. If X is a set on the real line we can imagine that X has an infinity of 'holes' (intervals of the complement) that are scattered densely along the line. The generalization of this led to the following definitions. A set X is *nowhere dense (rare)* in a set X_1, if each $G \in \mathcal{G}$ with $G \cap X_1$ not empty, has $(G \cap X_1)\backslash\overline{X}$ not empty. Here, each portion of X_1 contains a point that has some neighbourhood free from points of X. See *Ex. 12.4.* Also note that Cantor's ternary set is closed and dense-in-itself, but is not dense in [0, 1], it is nowhere dense.

We can also say that a set X is *nowhere dense-in-itself*, if each portion of X contains a point that is not in X', and so is isolated.

In all these definitions, when $X_1 = T$ we omit the words 'in a set X_1'.

THEOREM 12.1 (12.1) *A set X is nowhere dense in a set X_1 if, and only if, each $G \in \mathcal{G}$ with $G \cap X_1$ not empty, contains a $G_1 \in \mathcal{G}$ with $G_1 \cap X_1$ not empty, but with $G_1 \cap \overline{X}$ empty.*

(12.2) *If X_2, X_3 are nowhere dense in X_1, so is $X_2 \cup X_3$.*

(12.3) *A set X is not nowhere dense in a set X_1 if, and only if, there is a portion of X_1 contained in $\overline{X}$.*

43

(12.4) *If* $G \in \mathcal{G}$ *then* $\bar{G} \backslash G$ *is nowhere dense.*

(12.5) *If F is closed, then* $F \backslash F^{\circ}$ *is nowhere dense.*

Proof. If X is nowhere dense in X_1, and if $G \in \mathcal{G}$ with $G \cap X_1$ not empty, then by *Ex. 8.3* and (7.3), $G \backslash \bar{X} = G_1 \in \mathcal{G}$, with $G_1 \cap X_1$ not empty. The converse is clear, giving (12.1). For (12.2), if $G \in \mathcal{G}$ with $G \cap X_1$ not empty, then by (12.1), G contains a $G_2 \in \mathcal{G}$ with $G_2 \cap X_1$ not empty but $G_2 \cap \bar{X}_2$ empty. In turn, G_2 contains a $G_3 \in \mathcal{G}$ with $G_3 \cap X_1$ not empty, but $G_3 \cap \bar{X}_3$ empty. Hence by Theorem 8.3 (8.9), $G_3 \cap (\overline{X_2 \cup X_3})$ is empty, proving (12.2). For (12.3) there is by definition a $G_4 \in \mathcal{G}$ with $G_4 \cap X_1$ not empty but $G_4 \cap X_1 \backslash \bar{X}$ empty. For (12.4), $\bar{G} \backslash G$ is closed by Theorems 8.3 (8.6), 8.2, and (8.4). By (12.3), if $\bar{G} \backslash G$ is not nowhere dense, there is a non-empty open set $G_5 \subseteq \bar{G} \backslash G$ so that $G_5 \subseteq \bar{G}$. Being a neighbourhood of each of its points, G_5 contains a point of G. This contradicts $G_5 \subseteq \bar{G} \backslash G$, so that (12.4) is true. For (12.5) we replace G by F°, $\bar{G}$ by F, and the argument gives $G_6 \subseteq F$. Then $G_6 \subseteq F^{\circ}$, giving a contradiction.

We now consider larger sets than those that are nowhere dense in X_1. A set X is of the *first category (meager)* in a set X_1, if X is a countable union of sets each of which is nowhere dense in X_1. Otherwise X is of the *second category (non-meager)* in X_1. We shall see later that a large family of spaces T are of the second category in T. In these cases, if X is of the first category then $\backslash X$ is called a *residual*, or *co-meager*.

THEOREM 12.2. *If the union of sets* $Y_1, Y_2, \ldots$ *is of the second category in* X_1 *then for an integer n,* Y_n *is dense in a portion of* X_1.

Proof. By definition there is at least one Y_n that is not nowhere dense in X_1, and Theorem 12.1 (12.3) gives the result.

THEOREM 12.3 (12.6) *Let X,* $X_1 \subseteq T$ *be fixed, and let K be the union of a family* $\mathcal{K}$ *of disjoint open sets G with X* $\cap$ *G nowhere dense in* X_1. *Then X* $\cap$ *K* $\cap$ *$\bar{X}_1$ is nowhere dense in* X_1.

(12.7) *For each* $G \in \mathcal{K}$ *let* Y_G *be nowhere dense in* X_1 *and* $Y_G \subseteq G$. *Then the union Y of the* $Y_G \cap \bar{X}_1$ ($G \in \mathcal{K}$) *is nowhere dense in* X_1.

(12.8) *In* (12.6) *we can change 'nowhere dense' to 'of the first category'.*

Proof. If in (12.6), $X \cap K \cap \bar{X}_1$ is not 'nowhere dense' in X_1, then by (12.3) there is a $G_1 \in \mathcal{G}$ with a non-empty

(12.9) $G_1 \cap X_1 \subseteq \mathcal{G}(X \cap K \cap \bar{X}_1).$

As G_1 is a neighbourhood of each point in $G_1 \cap X_1$, G_1 contains a point of $X \cap K \cap \bar{X}_1$, and so of K. Hence for some $G_2 \in \mathcal{X}$,

(12.10) $G_1 \cap G_2 \cap \bar{X}_1$ is not empty.

As the $G_2 \in \mathcal{X}$ are disjoint, and as $G_2 \in \mathcal{G}$, and by (12.9),

$$G_2 \cap \overline{X \cap G_2} = G_2 \cap \overline{X \cap K} \supseteq G_2 \cap G_1 \cap X_1$$

Since $G_1 \cap G_2 \in \mathcal{G}$, we see by (12.10) that $X \cap G_2$ is not 'nowhere dense' in X_1. This contradiction proves (12.6). Note that $X \cap K$ itself can be dense in X_1. For let X_1 be Cantor's ternary set, let X be the complement, and let the G of $\mathcal{X}$ be the separate intervals of X. Then an easy proof shows that $X \cap K = X$ is dense in $[0, 1]$, while the separate $X \cap G$ are nowhere dense in X_1.

(12.6) gives (12.7). For we can put X as the union of the Y_G, and then as the $G \in \mathcal{X}$ are disjoint, $X \cap G = Y_G$. Then for (12.8), each $X \cap G$ is a countable union of sets Y_G^j nowhere dense in X_1. Then if

$$Z^j = \bigcup_{\mathcal{X}} Y_G^j \qquad (j = 1, 2, \ldots),$$

$$X \cap K = \bigcup_{\mathcal{X}} X \cap G = \bigcup_{\mathcal{X}} \bigcup_{j=1}^{\infty} Y_G^j = \bigcup_{j=1}^{\infty} Z^j$$

As $Y_G^j \subseteq G$, (12.7) gives $Z^j \cap \bar{X}_1$ nowhere dense in $X_1 (j = 1, 2, \ldots)$, and (12.8).

Let $I(X)$ be the union of all $G \in \mathcal{G}$ with $X \cap G$ of the first category in T, and put $II(X) = \setminus I(X)$. Then $I(X)$ is open, $II(X)$ closed.

THEOREM 12.4 (12.11) $\setminus \bar{X} \subseteq I(X)$, $\bar{X} \supseteq II(X)$.

(12.12) $\overline{I(X)} \cap X$ *is of the first category.*

(12.13) $I(X)$ *is the interior of* $\overline{I(X)}$.

(12.14) $II(X)$ *is the closure of* $II(X)^{\circ}$.

(12.15) X *is of the second category, if and only if* $II(X)^{\circ}$ *is not empty.*

(12.16) *Let G be a non-empty open subset of the open set*

$$III(X) \equiv II(X)^\circ \cap I(\backslash X).$$

Then $G\backslash X$ and $G \cap X$ are respectively of the first and second category.

Proof. For (12.11), $\backslash \overline{X}$ is an open set disjoint from X, and so lying in $I(X)$. The second result follows by complements. For (12.12), $I(X)$ is the union of a family $\mathcal{K}$ of non-empty $G \in \mathcal{G}$ for which $X \cap G$ is of the first category, and we look for a corresponding family $\mathcal{K}_1$ of *disjoint G*. If the topology has a countable base, then $\mathcal{K}$ can be a sub-family of the base, and so countable and well ordered. Otherwise we use axiom 9.1 to well order $\mathcal{K}$.

In the well ordering, $\mathcal{K}$ has an infimum G_1. We put G_1 in $\mathcal{K}_1$ and take G_1 from $\mathcal{K}$, giving a family with infimum G_2^*. Let $G_2 = = (G_2^* \backslash G_1)^\circ$. If G_2 is not empty we put it in $\mathcal{K}_1$, and so on. After urther construction, if we have a sub-family $\mathcal{K}_2$ of $\mathcal{K}$, such that all $G \in \mathcal{K} \backslash \mathcal{K}_2$ have been used in constructing a sub-family $\mathcal{K}_1^*$ of $\mathcal{K}_1$, then $\mathcal{K}_2$ has an infimum G^*. With $\mathcal{K}_1^*$ we now put

$$\left(G^* \Big\backslash \bigcup_{\mathcal{K}_1 *} G \right)^\circ$$

if not empty, to continue the construction of $\mathcal{K}_1$. By the well ordering of $\mathcal{K}$ we have $\mathcal{K}_1$ a sub-family of a well ordered family, and $\mathcal{K}_1$ is well ordered by Theorem 9.2. By construction the sets of $\mathcal{K}_1$ are disjoint open sets, so that their union $K \subseteq I(X)$ by Theorem 12.3 (12.8). We now show that

(12.17) the closed set $K_1 \equiv \overline{I(X)} \backslash K$ is no-where dense.

If false, then K_1 is dense in, and so contains, a non-empty $G_3 \in \mathcal{G}$. Hence $I(X) \cap G_3$ is not empty, and so contains a $G_4 \in \mathcal{K}$. As G_4 is the infimum of the family of all $G_5 \in \mathcal{K}$ with $G_5 \geqslant G_4$ in the well ordering, a portion of G_4, and so of G_3, lies in a $G_6 \in \mathcal{K}_1$, and so in K, contradicting $\backslash K \supseteq K_1 \supseteq G_3$. Hence (12.17), and (12.12) now follows.

In (12.13) the first set is open and in the second. Conversely, by (12.12) the interior of $\overline{I(X)}$ is a $G_7 \in \mathcal{G}$ with $G_7 \cap X$ of the first category. Hence $G_7 \subseteq I(X)$ by definition of $I(X)$. By complements we have (12.14) and then (12.15). For (12.16), $G\backslash X \subseteq I(\backslash X)\backslash X$, and

(12.12) gives the first result. As G is non-empty and disjoint with $I(X)$, $G \cap X$ is of the second category.

A set $X \subseteq T$ is called a *Baire set relative to* X_1, if, for some $G \in \mathcal{G}$, $d(X, G) \equiv (X \backslash G) \cup (G \backslash X)$ is of the first category in X_1. If for σ-module we take sets of the first category, then in the language of section 3, a Baire set is one that is congruent to an open set, modulo sets of the first category.

THEOREM 12.5 (12.18) *Each set of the first category in X_1 is a Baire set relative to X_1.*

(12.19) *Each open set is a Baire set relative to X_1.*

(12.20) *Each closed set is a Baire set relative to T.*

(12.21) *If X, Y are Baire sets relative to X_1, so is $X \cap Y$.*

(12.22) *If X_n ($n = 2, 3, \ldots$) are Baire sets relative to X_1, so is the union.*

(12.23) *A set X is a Baire set if, and only if,*

$$II(X)^\circ \subseteq I(\backslash X), \quad \text{i.e.} \quad II(X)^\circ = III(X)$$

(12.24) *A set X contains a Baire set of the second category in X_1 if, and only if, there is a $G \in \mathcal{G}$ of the second category in X_1, such that $G \backslash X$ is of the first category in X_1.*

(12.25) *A set X contains a Baire set of the second category if, and only if, $III(X)$ is not empty.*

Proof. For (12.18) take G empty. In (12.19), $d(G, G)$ is empty. For (12.20) we take the closed set F and $G = F^\circ$, using (12.5). Then $F \backslash G$ is nowhere dense, while $G \backslash F$ is empty. For (12.21) let G_1, G_2 correspond to X, Y. As

$$d(X \cap Y, G_1 \cap G_2) \subseteq d(X, G_1) \cup d(Y, G_2)$$

from *Ex. 3.16*, the result follows. For (12.22) let G_n correspond to X_n.

$$d\left(\bigcup_{n=2}^{\infty} X_n, \bigcup_{n=2}^{\infty} G_n\right) \subseteq \bigcup_{n=2}^{\infty} d(X_n, G_n)$$

by *Ex. 3.14*, giving the result. For (12.23) we replace X by the corresponding G and use (12.4) and *Ex. 12.16*. Then

$$II(G) \subseteq (\bar{G})^{\circ}, \quad II(G) \subseteq G = \backslash \mathcal{G} \backslash G \subseteq I(\backslash G)$$

gives the relation. Conversely, we take

$$G = III(X) = II(X)^{\circ}, \quad X \backslash G = X \backslash II(X)^{\circ} = X \cap \overline{I(X)}$$

By Theorem 12.4 (12.12; 12.16), $X \backslash G$ and $G \backslash X$ are of the first category, and $d(X; G)$ is the same. (12.24) is obvious, while for (12.25), if X contains a Baire set Y of the second category, then by *Ex. 12.14*,

$$II(Y) \subseteq II(X), \quad I(\backslash Y) \subseteq I(\backslash X), \quad III(Y) \subseteq III(X)$$

By (12.23), $III(X)$ is not empty. Conversely, if $III(X)$ is not empty, then by Theorem 12.4 (12.16), $III(X) \cap X$ is the required Baire set of the second category.

THEOREM 12.6 (12.26). *If X and $Y \subset X$ are Baire sets with $I(X) = I(Y)$, then $X \backslash Y$ is of the first category.*

(12.27) *If X is a Baire set, with $Z \subset X$, there is a Baire set Y in $Z \subseteq Y \subseteq X$ with $I(Z) = I(Y)$.*

1 2.28) *If $\{X_n\}$ is a sequence of Baire sets, and if*

$$Z_n \subseteq X_n, \quad I(Z_n) = I(X_n) \quad (n = 0, 1, 2, \ldots),$$

$$Z_0 = \bigcup_{n=1}^{\infty} Z_n, \quad X = \bigcup_{n=1}^{\infty} X_n$$

then $R \equiv X_0 \backslash X$ is of the first category.

Proof. As in the proof of (12.23), with X, Y we associate open sets

$$G_1 \equiv III(X) \supseteq III(Y) \equiv G_2$$

By *Ex. 12.14*, (12.11), and as $\backslash G_2$ is closed, with $I(G_1) = I(G_2)$,

$$G_3 \equiv II(G_1 \backslash G_2) \subseteq II(\backslash G_2) \subseteq \backslash G_2, \quad G_3 \subseteq II(G_1) = II(G_2) \subseteq \bar{G}_2$$

Hence from (12.4) and $G_3 \subseteq \bar{G}_2 \backslash G_2$, G_3 is a nowhere dense open set, and so is empty, proving (12.26). For (12.27) let $F \equiv II(Z)$, a closed set, and so a Baire set by (12.20). Thus by hypothesis and (12.21), $X \cap F$ is a Baire set, while

$$Z \subseteq H \equiv (X \cap F) \cup Z \subseteq X, \quad Z \backslash (X \cap F) = Z \backslash F$$

Each point of the last set is in $Z \cap I(Z)$, so that by (12.12), $Z \backslash (X \cap F)$ is of the first category. Thus H is a Baire set associated with the same open set as $X \cap F$. Since $H \supseteq Z$, if a point $x \in II(Z)$, then $x \in II(H)$. On the other hand, if $x \in I(Z)$ then $x \notin F$, and there is an open neighbourhood G of x contained in $\backslash F$, and $H \cap G = Z \cap G$. Thus $x \in I(H)$, giving (12.27).

For (12.28) let

$$K = X_0 \backslash R = X_0 \cap X$$

Here X is a Baire set by (12.22), and X_0 is given to be one, so that by (12.21), K is a Baire set. Now we are given that

$$Z_0 \subseteq X_0, \quad Z_0 = \bigcup_{n=1}^{\infty} Z_n \subseteq \bigcup_{n=1}^{\infty} X_n = X,$$

$$Z_0 \subseteq X_0 \cap X = K \subseteq X_0$$

Also $I(Z_0) = I(X_0)$. Hence $I(K) = I(X_0)$. As K, X_0 are Baire sets,

$$R = X_0 \backslash X = X_0 \backslash (X_0 \cap X) = X_0 \backslash K$$

is of the first category by (12.26).

THEOREM 12.7(12.29). *If X is of the second category, then X is of the second category in the space X.*

(12.30) *Let $X \subset T$ be dense in T. If X is of the second category in the space X then X is of the second category in the space T.*

Proof. If the union X of X_m ($m = 1, 2, \ldots$) is of the second category, then for some m, and some $G \in \mathcal{G}$, X_m is dense in G. Hence if $\mathcal{G}_1$ is the relative topology of X from $\mathcal{G}$, X_m is $\mathcal{G}_1$-dense in $G \cap X$. This is true whatever the decomposition of X into sets X_m, so that X is of the second category in X, giving (12.29). For (12.30), *assuming $\mathcal{G}_1$ as the topology in X*, let X be of the second category in X, and be the union of X_m ($m = 1, 2, \ldots$). Then for some m, and some $G \in \mathcal{G}$, X_m is $\mathcal{G}_1$-dense in $G \cap X$. As X is dense in T, X_m is dense in G. Being true whatever the decomposition, X is of the second category in T.

Historical Notes: The definition of an isolated point occurred in Cantor (1872), p. 129, 'dense' occurred in Cantor (1879), p. 2, 'dense-in-itself' in Cantor (1884), p. 471, 'nowhere dense' in du

Bois-Reymond (1882), 'first and second category' in Baire (1899), p. 67, 'residual' in Denjoy (1915), pp. 123–125; and 'rare, meager, non-meager, co-meager' are Bourbaki terms. For Baire sets see, for example, Banach (1930), Kuratowski (1930). The proof of Theorem 12.4 is due to Banach (1930), that of Theorem 12.6 is in Nikodym (1925), and Theorem 12.7 is extracted from Adams and Morse (1937), p. 201, with a proof of a special case at the bottom of p. 199.

Ex. 12.1. Prove that the rationals are dense in $(-\infty, \infty)$, using the modulus topology.

Ex. 12.2. If $Y \supseteq X$, $Y_1 \subseteq X_1$, and X is dense in X_1, then Y is dense in Y_1.

Ex. 12.3. A set dense-in-itself cannot have an isolated point.

Ex. 12.4. There are non-empty nowhere dense closed sets. For example, put the rationals of $[0, 1]$ in a sequence $\{r_n\}$, and consider

$$G_m = \bigcup_{n=1}^{\infty} (r_n - 2^{-n-m}, \quad r_n + 2^{-n-m}), \quad F_m = [0, 1] \backslash G_m.$$

Ex. 12.5. In *Ex. 12.4* show that, for

$$X = \bigcup_{m=1}^{\infty} F_m, \quad Y = \bigcap_{m=1}^{\infty} G_m \cap (0, 1) = (0, 1) \backslash X,$$

X is of the first category and of measure 1, while Y is of the second category and of measure 0. (Note that $(0,1)$ is of the second category and of measure 1, and that G_m has measure not greater than 2^{-m+1}.)

Ex. 12.6. Cantor's ternary set (Cantor (1883b), p. 590). Let C be the set of all ternary decimals $0. x_1 x_2 \ldots x_n \ldots$ with $x_n \neq 1$ (*all n*). Show that in a repeated trisection of $[0, 1]$ the open middle interval in each trisection is missing from C. This is another example for *Ex. 12.4.*

Ex. 12.7. For $y_n = \frac{1}{2}x_n$, the binary decimal $0. y_1 y_2 \ldots$ corresponds to the decimal of *Ex. 12.6.* Show that there is a continuous monotone increasing $f: [0, 1] \to [0, 1]$, with f constant in each middle interval missing from C, and with $f(0) = 0, f(1) = 1$. Show also that C has the same cardinal number as $[0, 1]$.

Ex. 12.8. X is nowhere dense in X_1 if and only if $\bar{X}$ is nowhere dense in $\bar{X}_1$.

Ex. 12.9. If $Y \subseteq X$, with X nowhere dense in X_1, then Y is nowhere dense in X_1.

Ex. 12.10. Let X be nowhere dense in X_1, and let $G \in \mathcal{G}$, $G \subseteq \bar{X}$, G not empty, $G \cap X_1$ empty. For $Y_1 = X_1 \cup G \supset X_1$ show that X is *not* nowhere dense in Y_1. Thus Hausdorff (1957), p. 161, III, last part, is false.

Ex. 12.11. A countable union of sets of the first category in X_1, is of the first category in X_1.

Ex. 12.12. If $Y \subseteq X$, where X is of the first category in X_1, then Y is of the first category in X_1.

Ex. 12.13. If $Y \supseteq X$, and X is of the second category in X_1, then Y is of the second category in X_1.

Ex. 12.14. If $Y \subseteq X$ then $I(Y) \supseteq I(X)$ and $II(Y) \subseteq II(X)$.

Ex. 12.15. If $Y \subseteq X$ and $X \backslash Y$ is of the first category, prove that $I(Y) = I(X)$.

Ex. 12.16. If $d(X, Y) \equiv (X \backslash Y) \cup (Y \backslash X)$ is of the first category, prove that

$$I(X) = I(Y), \quad II(X) = II(Y), \quad I(\backslash X) = I(\backslash Y), \quad II(\backslash X) = II(\backslash Y).$$

Ex. 12.17. For each portion $G \cap II(X)$ $(G \in \mathcal{G})$, $G \cap X$ is of the second category.

Ex. 12.18. $II(II(X)) = II(X)$, $I(II(X)) = I(X)$.

Ex. 12.19. For $I(X; X_1)$ as the union of all $G \in \mathcal{G}$ with $G \cap X$ of the first category in X_1, let $II(X; X_1) = \backslash I(X; X_1)$, Prove *Exs. 12.14* to *12.17* true for $I(X; X_1)$, replacing 'category' by 'category in X_1'.

Ex. 12.20. Prove that $I(X; X_1) \supseteq \backslash(\bar{X} \cap \bar{X}_1)$, $II(X; X_1) \subseteq \bar{X} \cap \bar{X}_1$.

The analogue of Theorem 12.4 (12.12) is, that $\mathcal{G}\{I(X; X_1) \cap X \cap X_1\}$ is of the first category in X_1. The first half of the analogous proof follows the proof given. But the proof of (12.17) can fall into two parts, first the proof that $\overline{I(X)} = \bar{K}$, and then the use of (12.4). It appears that neither alternative proof of (12.17) can be generalized to complete the proof of the analogue of (12.12), so that the analogue remains a conjecture.

4

BAIRE SPACES, SETS AND FUNCTIONS

13. Compact Sets

IN the theory centred round upper boundedness we need criteria for the existence of $\bar{p}$-spaces. This chapter gives two known cases of Baire spaces, and a wide family of Baire sets in those spaces.

First, a sub-family $\mathcal{C}$ of the topology $\mathcal{G}$ of T is a *cover* of a set $X \subseteq T$, if the union of the sets of $\mathcal{C}$ contains X. If $\mathcal{C}$ has a finite cardinal (or cardinal $\aleph_0$) we say that the cover is *finite* (respectively, *countable*). An $X \subseteq T$ is *compact* (*in* $(T, \mathcal{G})$) if every cover of X contains a finite cover of X. We can allow $X = T$.

On the real line a closed bounded interval is compact, and for proof we can use Borel's covering theorem. There is a simple extension to a closed bounded set on the real line by using Young's covering theorem. The extension to a Euclidean n-dimensional space with closed bounded sets is proved by Goursat's lemma. However, we shall see that Theorems 13.3, 13.8 and the Borel covering theorem are enough to show that closed bounded sets on Cartesian products of real lines with the product topology are compact. Theorem 13.6 is also useful.

THEOREM 13.1 (13.1). *If X is compact in $(T, \mathcal{G})$, then X is compact in $(X, \mathcal{G}_1)$, where $\mathcal{G}_1$ is the relative topology of X from $\mathcal{G}$, and conversely.*

(13.2) *If $\mathcal{G}_2 \subseteq \mathcal{G}$ are two topologies for T, and if X is compact in $(T, \mathcal{G})$, then X is compact in $(T, \mathcal{G}_2)$.*

These are obvious results.

52

A family of sets has the *finite intersection property* if every finite non-empty sub-family has a non-empty intersection. A family of sets has the *finite intersection property relative to a set X*, if X contains a point of the intersection of each finite non-empty sub-family.

THEOREM 13.2 (13.3). *A set $X \subseteq T$ is compact if, and only if, every family of $\mathcal{Q}_1$-closed sets in X with the finite intersection property has a non-empty intersection.*

(13.4) *A set $X \subseteq T$ is compact if, and only if, every family of $\mathcal{Q}$-closed sets in T with the finite intersection property relative to X has an intersection containing a point of X.*

Proof. (13.4) follows from (13.1; 13.3) and Theorem 8.4 (8.11). To prove (13.3) we can, for simplicity, write $(T, \mathcal{Q})$ for $(X, \mathcal{Q}_1)$. If T is compact let $\mathcal{F}$ be a family of closed sets in T with the finite intersection property, and let $\mathcal{Q}_2$ be the family of their complements, open by Theorem 8.2. By the finite intersection property of $\mathcal{F}$, no finite union of sets of $\mathcal{Q}_2$ can cover T. As T is compact it follows that $\mathcal{Q}_2$ cannot be a cover of T, and $\mathcal{F}$ has a non-empty intersection. Conversely, if each family of closed sets in T with the finite intersection property has a non-empty intersection, let $\mathcal{Q}_3$ be a family of open sets no finite union of which covers T. Then the complements of members of $\mathcal{Q}_3$, closed by Theorem 8.2, have the finite intersection property, and so have a non-empty intersection that cannot lie in the union of the sets of $\mathcal{Q}_3$. Thus $\mathcal{Q}_3$ cannot be a cover of T, every cover of T contains a finite cover of T, and T is compact.

THEOREM 13.3 (13.5). *A closed subset of a compact set is compact.*
(13.6) *The union of a finite number of compact sets is compact.*

Proof. For (13.5) let X be compact, F closed, and $F \subseteq X$. By Theorem 8.2, $\backslash F$ is open, so that we put it with a cover of F to obtain a cover of X. As X is compact, there is a finite cover of X. Removing $\backslash F$ if in the finite cover, we have a finite cover of F from the original cover of F, and F is compact. For (13.6), a cover of the union of compact sets C_j $(j = 1, \ldots, n)$ contains a cover of each C_j, and so a finite cover of C_j. The finite union of the finite covers of the C_j $(j = 1, \ldots, n)$ is a finite cover of the union. Hence the result.

53

THEOREM 13.4 (13.7). *If $(T, \mathcal{Q})$ is a Hausdorff space, if X is compact, and if $y \notin X$, then y and X have disjoint neighbourhoods.*

If the conclusion of (13.7) *is true, then so are the following:*

(13.8) *a compact set is closed;*

(13.9) *if X, Y are disjoint and compact, there are disjoint neighbourhoods of X and Y.*

(13.10). *If T is compact, and Hausdorff or regular, it is normal.*

A mild generalization of (13.7; 13.8) is given in Weston (1957a), p. 349, Lemma 2.

Proof. For (13.7), if $x \in X$ then $x \neq y$, and as $(T, \mathcal{Q})$ is a Hausdorff space there are disjoint neighbourhoods $N(x)$, $N(y)$ of x, y, respectively. For all $x \in X$ the $N(x)$ are a cover of X, and so contain a finite cover with union $N(X)$. The intersection of the corresponding finite number of $N(y)$ is an open set containing y that does not meet $N(X)$, proving (13.7). For (13.8), if $y \notin X$ then $y \notin \bar{X}$, and X is closed. For (13.9) let $y \in Y$, so that $y \notin X$. By (13.7) there are disjoint neighbourhoods $N_1(y)$, $N(X)$ of y, X respectively. For all $y \in Y$ the $N_1(y)$ are a cover of Y, and so contain a finite cover of Y with union $N_1(Y)$. The intersection of the corresponding finite number of sets $N(X)$ is an open set containing X that does not meet $N_1(Y)$, proving (13.9). For (13.10), if X, Y are closed, they are compact by Theorem 13.3. As T is Hausdorffian it is regular by (13.7). If T is compact and regular it is normal by (13.9).

THEOREM 13.5. *If $\mathcal{Q} \subseteq \mathcal{Q}^*$ are topologies in T, where $\mathcal{Q}$ is Hausdorffian and $(T, \mathcal{Q}^*)$ compact, then $\mathcal{Q} = \mathcal{Q}^*$. Thus if a topology $\mathcal{Q}$ on T is properly contained in a topology for which T is compact, $\mathcal{Q}$ cannot be Hausdorffian.*

This cuts down the use of (13.2).

Proof. Let $F \subseteq T$ be $\mathcal{Q}^*$-closed. By Theorem 13.3 (13.5), F is $\mathcal{Q}^*$-compact. A $\mathcal{Q}$-cover $\mathcal{Q}_2$ of F is also a $\mathcal{Q}^*$-cover since $\mathcal{Q} \subseteq \mathcal{Q}^*$, so that $\mathcal{Q}_2$ contains a finite $\mathcal{Q}^*$-cover of F that is a finite $\mathcal{Q}$-cover of F, and F is $\mathcal{Q}$-compact. By Theorem 13.4 (13.8), since $\mathcal{Q}$ is Hausdorffian, F is $\mathcal{Q}$-closed. Hence by Theorem 8.2, $\mathcal{Q} = \mathcal{Q}^*$.

THEOREM 13.6. (13.11). *Let $(T_j, \mathcal{Q}_j)$ $(j = 1, 2)$ be topological spaces,* *and let* $f: T_1 \to T_2$ *be continuous. If* $F \subseteq T_1$ *is* $\mathcal{G}_1$-*compact, then* $f(F)$ *is* $\mathcal{G}_2$-*compact.*

(13.12) *If* $(T_2, \mathcal{G}_2)$ *is the real line with the modulus topology, if* F *is* $\mathcal{G}_1$-*compact, and if* $f: T_1 \to T_2$ *is continuous, then given* $\varepsilon > 0$, *there is a finite cover* $\mathcal{C}$ *of* F *such that if* $x, y \in G \in \mathcal{C}, z \in G^* \in \mathcal{C}$, *where* G, G^* *have a point in common, then*

$$|f(x)-f(y)| < 2\varepsilon, \quad |f(x)-f(z)| < 4\varepsilon$$

(13.13) *If in* (13.11), f *is a bijection and continuous,* $(T_1, \mathcal{G}_1)$ *compact, and* $T_2 = f(T_1)$ *is Hausdorffian, then* f^{-1} *is also continuous.*

(13.11) is a generalization of the theorem that a continuous real-valued function on the real line is bounded on each finite interval, while (13.12) is a generalization of the uniformity of continuity of such functions.

Proof. To prove (13.11) let $\mathcal{G}_3$ be a $\mathcal{G}_2$-cover of $f(F)$, and let $\mathcal{G}_4$ be the corresponding family of $f^{-1}(G)$, for all $G \in \mathcal{G}_3$. By Theorem 9.1 (9.1), $\mathcal{G}_4$ is a $\mathcal{G}_1$-cover of F, which is $\mathcal{G}_1$-compact. Hence $\mathcal{G}_4$ contains a finite $\mathcal{G}_1$-cover of F. The corresponding finite family from $\mathcal{G}_3$ is a $\mathcal{G}_2$-cover of $f(F)$, giving the result.

For (13.12), by definition of continuity there is a neighbourhood $N_1(x)$ of each $x \in F$ such that if $y \in N_1(x)$ then

$$|f(y)-f(x)| < \varepsilon$$

The neighbourhoods $N_1(x)$ form a cover of F, so that a finite number form a cover of F with the given properties.

For (13.13), if $F \subseteq T_1$ is $\mathcal{G}_1$-closed, then by Theorem 13.3 (13.5), F is $\mathcal{G}_1$-compact. By (13.11), $f(F)$ is $\mathcal{G}_2$-compact, so that it is $\mathcal{G}_2$-closed by Theorem 13.4 (13.8), since T_2 is Hausdorffian. As f is a bijection, if $G \in \mathcal{G}_1$ then $f(G) \in \mathcal{G}_2$, and f is open. Hence f^{-1} is continuous, by Theorem 9.1 (9.1).

A further result for pseudometric spaces comes from a property analogous to that of Theorem 13.4 (13.9).

THEOREM 13.7. (13.14) *If* T *is regular,* F *closed,* C *compact, and* F, C *disjoint, there are disjoint neighbourhoods of* F *and* C.

(13.15) *If in* (13.14) *the topology of T is given by a pseudometric ϱ,
then*

$$\varrho(F, C) \equiv \inf\{\varrho(x, y) : x \in F, y \in C\} > 0$$

Proof. For (13.14), as T is regular, given $x \in C$, then $x \notin F$, and
there are disjoint neighbourhoods $N(x)$, $N(F)$ of x and F. The $N(x)$
form a cover of C, so that a finite number, with union $N_1(C)$, cover
C, and the intersection of the corresponding finite number of
$N(F)$ is a neighbourhood of F disjoint from the neighbourhood
$N_1(C)$ of C.

For (13.15) we use Theorem 11.4 and the proof of Theorem
11.5 (11.10) to find suitable

$$N(x) = S(x; \tfrac{1}{2}\varepsilon) \subseteq \bar{S}(x; \tfrac{1}{2}\varepsilon) \subseteq S(x; \varepsilon) \subseteq \backslash F, N(F) = \backslash \bar{S}(x; \tfrac{1}{2}\varepsilon)$$

Taking $\delta = \min \tfrac{1}{2}\varepsilon$, for the $S(x; \tfrac{1}{2}\varepsilon)$ of the finite cover of C, we have

$$\varrho(F, C) \geqslant \delta > 0$$

which gives the result.

We now turn to the theorem of Tychonoff (1935) on the Cartesian
product of compact spaces.

THEOREM 13.8. *The Cartesian product of a collection of compact
topological spaces is compact relative to the product topology.*

When the Cartesian product is one of a countable number of
spaces, the theorem has much the same effect as a method of proof
as Cantor's diagonal process. But when the product is one of a non-
countable number of spaces, the theorem transcends Cantor's method.

Proof. We use a set A of suffixes a, a space Y, and coordinate
topological spaces $(Y_a, \mathcal{G}_a)$ that are compact, with $Y_a \subseteq Y$ for all
$a \in A$, and we put

$$T = \bigtimes_A Y_a, \quad C = \bigtimes_A X_a$$

If $X_a = Y_a$ for all $a \in A$, expect for $a = b$, when $X_b \subseteq Y_b$, we write
C as $C(b; X_b)$. Then the C for which $X_a = Y_a$ for all $a \in A$, except for
$a = b, c, \ldots, d$, is

$$C = C(b; X_b) \cap C(c; X_c) \cap \ldots \cap C(d; X_d)$$

Such sets C, with $X_a \in \mathcal{G}_a (a \in A)$, form a base for the product topology.

Let $\mathcal{B}$ be a family of sets in T with the finite intersection property, and let $\mathcal{F}$ be the family of all subsets of T that are not in $\mathcal{B}$. By axiom 9.1 we can well order $\mathcal{B}$, and then well order $\mathcal{F}$, putting the sets of $\mathcal{F}$ after those of $\mathcal{B}$. Let $\leqslant$ denote the well ordering relation. We construct a family $\mathcal{C}$ of subsets of T with the following property. A subset H of T is in $\mathcal{C}$ if, and only if, H, the sets of $\mathcal{B}$, and all $K \in \mathcal{C}$ with $K \leqslant H$, together have the finite intersection property. Clearly

$$(13.16) \qquad\qquad \mathcal{B} \subseteq \mathcal{C}$$

$$(13.17) \qquad If\ H_1,\quad H_2 \in \mathcal{C},\quad then\quad H_1 \cap H_2 \in \mathcal{C}$$

For let $H_3, \ldots, H_n \in \mathcal{C}$ be before $H_1 \cap H_2$ in the well ordering. Then of the sets $H_1, H_2, H_3, \ldots, H_n$, of $\mathcal{C}$, there is a last, say H_j. Then $H_j \in \mathcal{C}$ means in particular that

$$(H_1 \cap H_2) \cap H_3 \cap \ldots \cap H_n = H_1 \cap \ldots \cap H_n$$

is not empty. As $H_3, \ldots, H_n$ are arbitrary in $\mathcal{C}$ and before $H_1 \cap H_2$, then by construction (13.17) is true.

(13.18) If H has a point in common with each member of $\mathcal{C}$, then $H \in \mathcal{C}$. For by (13.17), H has a point in common with each intersection of a finite number of members of $\mathcal{C}$, so that by construction, $H \in \mathcal{C}$.

If $H \in \mathcal{C}$ let proj $(a; H)$ be the projection of H onto Y_a, i.e.

$$\text{proj}\ (a; H) = \{f(a) : all\ f \in H\}$$

Since $\mathcal{C}$ has the finite intersection property by construction, the family of proj $(a; H)$, for all $H \in \mathcal{C}$, has the property. Hence since $(Y_a, \mathcal{G}_a)$ is compact,

$$\bigcap_{e} \mathcal{G}_a\ \text{proj}\ (a; H)$$

is not empty, and so contains a point, say, $g(a)$. Being true for each $a \in A$, we can define a function $g : A \to Y$, such that g takes the value $g(a)$ for $a \in A$. Then each neighbourhood X_a of $g(a)$ has a non-empty intersection with proj $(a; H)$, for each $H \in \mathcal{C}$. Hence the set $C(a; X_a)$ has a non-empty intersection with each $H \in \mathcal{C}$, so that by

(13.18), $C(a; X_a) \in \mathcal{C}$. By (13.17) each set of the base for the product topology, that is a neighbourhood of g, lies in $\mathcal{C}$, and so has a non-empty intersection with each $H \in \mathcal{C}$. Hence by (13.18),

$$g \in \overline{H}(H \in \mathcal{C}), \quad g \in \bigcap_e \overline{H} \subseteq \bigcap_{\mathcal{B}} \overline{H}$$

Since $\mathcal{B}$ is an arbitrary family of sets in T with the finite intersection property, and since there is a point in the intersection of the closures, it follows that T is compact in its product topology, proving the theorem.

THEOREM 13.9. *If an infinite number of coordinate Hausdorff spaces of a Cartesian product are non-compact, then each compact subset of the product is nowhere dense.*

Proof. Let T have a compact subset D with an interior point f. Then D contains a neighbourhood H of f that is a member of the base for the product topology. Then for all but a finite number of suffixes we have proj $(a; H) = Y_a$, so that proj $(a; \overline{H}) = Y_a$. By *Ex. 9.6*, proj $(a;.)$ is continuous. Then by Theorems 13.6 (13.11) and 13.3 (13.5), $\overline{H} \subseteq D$ is compact, and Y_a is compact. Thus all but a finite number of the coordinate spaces are compact, contradicting the hypothesis. Hence the result.

Ex. 13.1. A single point forms a compact set.

Ex. 13.2. A compact set need not be closed. For if $\mathcal{Q}$ is the trivial topology, and if the non-empty $X \subset T$, then X is compact but not closed (Kelley (1955), p. 140).

Ex. 13.3. Theorem 13.7 (13.15) can be false if C is replaced by a closed set. For in the Euclidean plane consider the example of a hyperbola and its asymptotes.

Ex. 13.4. Let T be the space of real or complex sequences $\{x_n\}$ with $|x_n| \leqslant 1$ *(all n)*, or, more generally, the space of functions $f: A \to B$, where B is the real line or complex plane, with $|f(a)| \leqslant 1$ *(all $a \in A$)*. Beginning with the modulus topology on B, define a topology for T such that T is compact, Hausdorffian, and normal.

14. Locally Compact Sets

Not many spaces that are considered in practice are compact, but most, for example, the real line, are locally compact. A set $X \subseteq T$ is *locally compact* if for each $x \in X$ there is a neighbourhood $G(x)$ of x such that $\overline{G(x)} \cap X$ is compact.

A *discrete set* (i.e. a set having only isolated points) is locally compact.

A compact set is locally compact (take $G(x) = T$), and many results for compact sets can be extended to locally compact sets. We extend Theorem 13.2 (13.4) and omit for simplicity the extension of (13.3).

THEOREM 14.1. *A set $X \subseteq T$ is locally compact if, and only if, for each $x \in X$ there is a neighbourhood $G(x)$ of x such that every family of closed sets, with the finite intersection property relative to $\overline{G(x)} \cap X$, has an intersection containing a point of $\overline{G(x)} \cap X$.*

THEOREM 14.2. (14.1) *A closed subset of a locally compact set is locally compact.*

(14.2) *The union of a finite number of locally compact sets is locally compact.*

(14.3) *Let T be a locally compact Hausdorff space, and let X, Y be disjoint compact sets in T. Then there are disjoint neighbourhoods of X, Y that have compact closures.*

(14.4) *If T is locally compact, and Hausdorffian, then T is regular. If T is locally compact and regular, then the open sets with compact closures form a base for the topology.*

Proof. For (14.1), the intersection of $\overline{G(x)}$ and the closed set, is a closed subset of $\overline{G(x)} \cap X$, and so is compact by Theorem 13.3 (13.5). Hence the closed set is locally compact. For (14.2) we use Theorem 13.3 (13.6). For (14.3), we modify the proof of Theorem 13.4 (13.9), taking neighbourhoods $N(y)$, $N(x)$ that have compact closures. Then $N_1(Y)$ is a finite union of sets with compact closures, so that by Theorem 13.3 (13.6), the closure of $N_1(Y)$ is compact. Similarly the closure of the cover of X is compact. For (14.4) we use Theorem 10.3.

59

Let $x \in X$ and let $G(x)$ be a neighbourhood of x with compact closure. If G is an arbitrary neighbourhood of x, $C = \overline{G(x)}\backslash G$ is a closed subset of a compact set, and so is compact by Theorem 13.3 (13.5). Also $x \notin C$. By Theorem 13.4 (13.7) there are disjoint neighbourhoods of x, C, and we can take the neighbourhood of x to lie in $G(x)$; its closure will not intersect C, and so lies in G, proving that T is regular. If in turn T is locally compact and regular, there is a neighbourhood of x whose closure lies in $G(x) \cap G$, where G is an arbitrary neighbourhood of x. This proves the result.

The study of locally compact sets is made easier by the *one-point compactification* of Alexandroff. Let p be a point not contained in a topological space T. Then the compactification of T, is the topological space $(T \cup \mathrm{sing}\,(p), \mathcal{G}_1)$, where $\mathcal{G}_1$ is the family of G and $G_1 \cup \mathrm{sing}\,(p)$, for all $G \in \mathcal{G}$, and all $G_1 \in \mathcal{G}$ with $\backslash G_1 \mathcal{G}$-compact, where *complements are relative to* T.

THEOREM 14.3. (14.5) T_1 is $\mathcal{G}_1$-*compact*.

(14.6) $(T_1, \mathcal{G}_1)$ *is a Hausdorff space if, and only if,* $(T, \mathcal{G})$ *is locally compact and Hausdorffian*.

Proof. We first show that $\mathcal{G}_1$ is a topology. If the union H of members of $\mathcal{G}_1$ does not contain p, then H is a union of $\mathcal{G}$-sets, so that $H \in \mathcal{G}$, $H \in \mathcal{G}_1$. If $p \in H$, then for some $G_1 \in \mathcal{G}_1$, $p \in G_1$, and $G_1 = G \cup \mathrm{sing}\,(p)$ for some $G \in \mathcal{G}$ with $\backslash G$ $\mathcal{G}$-compact. Then $\backslash H$ s a $\mathcal{G}$-closed subset of $\backslash G$, and so is also $\mathcal{G}$-compact, and $H \in \mathcal{G}_1$ again. If H is the intersection of two members of $\mathcal{G}_1$, each containing p, then $p \in H$, and by Theorem 13.3 (13.6), $\backslash H$ is the union of two $\mathcal{G}$-compact sets, and so is $\mathcal{G}$-compact, and $H \in \mathcal{G}_1$. If at least one member of the intersection does not contain p, then $p \notin H$, and H is the intersection of two $\mathcal{G}$-sets, and so is in $\mathcal{G}$, and so in $\mathcal{G}_1$. Finally, $\backslash T$ is the empty set, compact, so that the empty set and T_1 are i,n $\mathcal{G}_1$

Now T_1 is $\mathcal{G}_1$-compact, for if $\mathcal{C}$ is a cover of T_1 from $\mathcal{G}_1$ then. one $G \in \mathcal{C}$ contains p, while $\backslash G$ is $\mathcal{G}$-compact, so that a finite famly from $\mathcal{C}$ covers $\backslash G$. This with G is a finite cover of T_1, proving (14.5)i.

For (14.6), if $(T_1, \mathcal{G}_1)$ is a Hausdorff space, then so is $(T, \mathcal{G})$. If $x \in T$, there are disjoint neighbourhoods of p and x, so that the neighbourhood $G(x)$ of x lies in the complement of the neighbourhood of p, which complement is a $\mathcal{G}$-compact set. Thus $\overline{G(x)}$ is also $\mathcal{G}$-compact, and T is locally $\mathcal{G}$-compact. Conversely, if T is a locally $\mathcal{G}$-compact Hausdorff space, then $(T_1, \mathcal{G}_1)$ is a Hausdorff space if we can show that there are disjoint $\mathcal{G}_1$-neighbourhoods of p and each $x \in T$. But sing $(p) \cup \backslash\overline{G(x)}$ and $G(x)$ will suffice, provided that $\overline{G(x)}$ is $\mathcal{G}$-compact. We can choose such a neighbourhood $G(x)$ of each $x \in T$ since T is locally $\mathcal{G}$-compact.

THEOREM 14.4. (14.7) *If* F_1 *is a* $\mathcal{G}_1$-*closed set, where* $(T, \mathcal{G})$ *is locally compact and* $(T_1, \mathcal{G}_1)$ *is the one-point compactification by using* p, *then either* $F_1 = F \cup$ *sing* (p) *for a* $\mathcal{G}$-*closed set* F, *or else* $F_1 = C$, $\mathcal{G}$-*compact.*

(14.8) *If* $(T, \mathcal{G})$ *is locally compact and Hausdorff, if* $C \subseteq T$ *is compact,* $F \subseteq T$ *is closed, and* C, F *disjoint, then there is a continuous function* f *on* T *to* $[0, 1]$, *such that* $f = 0$ *on* C *and* $f = 1$ *on* F.

Proof. For (14.7), a $\mathcal{G}_1$-set either lies in $\mathcal{G}$, or else is $G \cup$ sing (p), where $\backslash G$ is compact. Now taking complements relative to T_1, instead of T, we have (14.7). For (14.8) we use Theorem 14.3 to show that $(T_1, \mathcal{G}_1)$ is compact and Hausdorff. Thus it is normal by Theorem 13.4 (13.10). By Theorem 10.4 we have a result using two disjoint $\mathcal{G}_1$-closed sets. Both sets cannot include p, so that by (14.7) the best result is obtained when one is $\mathcal{G}$-closed and the other $\mathcal{G}$-compact, as written in (14.8). The other alternative is when both sets are $\mathcal{G}$-compact, and Theorem 13.4 (13.8) shows that this case is included in (14.8).

Ex. 14.1. An open set on the real line with the modulus topology is locally compact. Hence show that the analogues of Theorems 13.4 (13.7; 13.8) are false.

Ex. 14.2. Similarly show that an open set on the complex plane with the modulus topology, or on an n-dimensional space with the Euclidean metric, is locally compact.

15. Sequences, Completeness, and Semi-compact and Locally Semi-compact Sets

To build up the collection of known examples of Baire spaces we consider sequences, and in particular their convergence, defined in section 9. A most useful connected idea is that of the completeness of spaces.

If $\{x_n\}$ is a sequence of points of T, let

$$L_m \equiv L_m(\{x_n\}) = \{x_n : n \geqslant m\}, \quad L \equiv L(\{x_n\}) = \bigcap_{m=1}^{\infty} \bar{L}_m(\{x_n\})$$

Then $X \subseteq T$ is *semi-compact* (Bourbaki) if, for each sequence $\{x_n\}$ in X, $X \cap L(\{x_n\})$ is not empty. We can say that X is *locally semi-compact*, if each $x \in X$ has a neighbourhood $G(x)$ with $\overline{G(x)} \cap X$ semi-compact.

THEOREM 15.1. (15.1) $y \in L(\{x_n\})$, *if and only if each neighbourhood of y contains x_n for an infinity of n.*
(15.2) *If $\{x_n\}$ is a sequence of distinct points, with Y the derived set of $L_1(\{x_n\})$, then $L \subseteq Y$. If T is a $\mathcal{O}_1$-space then $L = Y$.*
(15.3) *If $\{x_n\}$ is convergent to x, then $x \in L(\{x_n\})$, and $\bar{L}_1(\{x_n\})$ is semi-compact. If T is a $\mathcal{O}_2$-space, then also $L(\{x_n\}) = \text{sing}(x)$, and a sequence cannot be convergent to more than one point of T.*
(15.4) *If $x_j \in X$ for an infinity of j, and if $\{x_n\}$ converges to x, then $x \in \bar{X}$.*
(15.5) *If $\{x_n\}$ contains an infinity of distinct points of X, and if $\{x_n\}$ converges to x, then $x \in X'$.*
(15.6) *Let $\mathcal{G}$ have a countable local base. If $\{x_n\}$ is a sequence of points of T, with $x \in L(\{x_n\})$, then a subsequence of the $\{x_n\}$ converges to x.*
(15.7) *Let $\mathcal{G}$ have a countable local base, and let $X \subseteq T$. Then to each $x \in X'$ there corresponds a sequence of points of X converging to x.*
(15.8) *Let $\mathcal{G}, \mathcal{G}^*$ be consistent topologies in T. i.e. for each $x \neq y$ in T, x has a $\mathcal{G}$-neighbourhood disjoint from a $\mathcal{G}^*$-neighbourhood of y. If $\{x_n\}$ has a $\mathcal{G}$-limit x, then the intersection of $\mathcal{G}^*$-closures*

of $L_m(\{x_n\})$ is either empty or contains x alone. In particular, if also $\{x_n\}$ has a $\mathcal{Q}^*$-limit y, then $x = y$.

Proof. (15.1) is obvious. For (15.2), let $y \in L$. As the x_n are distinct, there is possibly an integer m such that $x_m = y$, and for $n \neq m$, $x_n \neq y$. If G is a neighbourhood of y, there is an $n > m$ such that $x_n \in G$, $x_n \neq y$, so that $y \in Y$. Conversely, if T is a $\mathcal{C}_1$-space, and $y \in Y$, then for each n, where $n \neq m$ if $y = x_m$, there is a neighbourhood of y that does not contain x_n. By finite intersection there is a neighbourhood of y that does not contain $x_1, \ldots, x_n$, except possibly $x_m = y$, and so contains x_p, for some $p > n$. Hence $y \in \bar{L}_n$, $y \in L$.

Ex. 15.1 shows that sometimes $L \subset Y$.

The first part of (15.3) is clear. The second part, and (15.8), follow from the fact that if $x \neq y$, there is a $\mathcal{Q}$-neighbourhood of x disjoint from a $\mathcal{Q}$-(or $\mathcal{Q}^*$-)neighbourhood of y. In general the converse of (15.3) is false, for see *Ex. 15.3*. (15.4; 15.5) are obvious. For (15.6) we use (15.1). Let $G_n(x)$ ($n = 1, 2, \ldots$) form the countable local base at x. By taking finite intersections we can assume that

$$(15.9) \qquad G_1(x) \supseteq G_2(x) \supseteq \ldots$$

Then there are integers $m(j)$ with

$$m(0) = 1, \quad x_{m(j)} \in L_{m(j-1)}(\{x_n\}) \cap G_j(x)$$

$$(m(j) > m(j-1), \quad j = 1, 2, \ldots)$$

and $\{x_{m(j)}\}$ converges to x since the $G_n(x)$ form a local base at x. For (15.7) we choose $x_n \in X \cap G_n(x)$, and x is the limit of $\{x_n\}$.

THEOREM 15.2 (15.10) *A set $X \subseteq T$ is semi-compact, if, and only if, every countable family of closed sets, with the finite intersection property relative to X, has an intersection containing a point of X.*
(15.11) *If there is a neighbourhood of each $x \in X$ within the closure of which the closed sets property of* (15.10) *holds, then X is locally semi-compact, and conversely.*

The difference between Theorem 15.2 and Theorems 13.2, 14.1, is that here the family of closed sets is countable, instead of having an arbitrary cardinal number.

Proof. If X has the closed sets property of (15.10), and if $\{x_n\}$ is a sequence of points of X, then the family of closed sets $\bar{L}_m(\{x_n\})$ is countable and has the finite intersection property relative to X, so that $X \cap L(\{x_n\})$ is not empty. Hence X is semi-compact. Conversely, if X is semi-compact, and if $\{F_n\}$ is a sequence of closed sets with the finite intersection property relative to X, then the sequence

$$F_1, \quad F_1 \cdot F_2, \quad F_1 \cdot F_2 \cdot F_3, \quad \ldots, \quad \text{or} \quad \{F_m^*\}$$

is such that $F_m^* \cap X$ is not empty $(m = 1, 2, \ldots)$. Thus we can take

$$x_m \in F_m^* \cap X \quad (m = 1, 2, \ldots) \quad \text{and} \quad x_p \in F_m^* \quad (p \geqslant m)$$

(15.12) $$\bar{L}_m(\{x_n\}) \subseteq \bar{F}_m^* = F_m^*$$

The first sets in (15.12), and so the F_m^* and the F_m, have intersection containing a point of X. Thus (15.10) is proved. Then (15.11) follows since a local condition is imposed on hypothesis and conclusion, in both the direct result and the converse, and the proof is clear.

Result (15.13) gives an alternative definition of semi-compact sets. Also a set $X \subseteq T$ is *sequentially closed*, if each sequence $\{x_n\}$ of points of X contains a subsequence $\{x_{n(j)}\}$ convergent to a point $x \in X$.

THEOREM 15.3. (15.13) *A set $X \subseteq T$ is semi-compact, if, and only if, every countable cover of X contains a finite cover of x.*

(15.14) *A compact and a sequentially closed set are semi-compact.*

(15.15) *If $\mathcal{G}$ has a countable local base, then a semi-compact set is sequentially closed.*

(15.16) *If $\mathcal{G}$ has a countable base, a semi-compact set is compact.*

(15.17) *If $\mathcal{G}$ has a countable base and is Hausdorffian, then a semi-compact or sequentially closed or compact set is closed.*

Proof. The proof of (15.13) follows from Theorem 15.2 (15.10) in a similar way as Theorem 13.2 (13.4) is proved. From (15.13), every compact set is semi-compact, giving the first part of (15.14), (15.16) is a partial converse, for let $\mathcal{C}$ be a cover of the semi-compact set X, and let $\mathcal{G}$ have a countable base $\mathcal{B}$. Then each member of $\mathcal{C}$ is a union of members of $\mathcal{B}$, and there is a cover $\mathcal{C}_1$ of X that uses only members of $\mathcal{B}$, so that $\mathcal{C}_1$ is countable. Since X is semi-compact, $\mathcal{C}_1$ contains a finite cover of X by (15.13), so that X is compact. For the second part of (15.14), if X is sequentially closed, let $\{x_n\}$ be a sequence of points of X. Then a subsequence $\{x_{n(j)}\}$ converges to a point $x \in X$, so that by (15.3),

$$x \in L(\{x_{n(j)}\}) \subseteq L(\{x_n\})$$

and X is semi-compact. The partial converse here is (15.15), and it follows from (15.6). For (15.17) we use (15.14; 15.16) to show that the set is compact, and then Theorem 13.4 (13.8) shows that the set is closed.

In order to define a fundamental sequence we have to compare neighbourhoods at any two different points. An axiomatic theory of this comparison has been given by Weil (1937), who defines uniform spaces. However, the use of uniform spaces to prove such theorems as the Baire density theorem seems to be doubtful, since known conditions on the uniform space that give Baire's theorem also imply the existence of a pseudometric. I have therefore considered fundamental sequences only in pseudometric spaces and groups.

Let a pseudometric ϱ be defined in T, with the following connection with $\mathcal{G}$.

(15.18) Given $\varepsilon > 0$, $x \in T$, there is a neighbourhood G of x such that if $y \in G$ then $\varrho(x, y) < \varepsilon$.

An equivalent formulation is that

(15.19) each $\qquad\qquad S(x; \varepsilon) \in \mathcal{G}$

For (15.19) implies (15.18), while (15.18) implies that if $y \in S(x; \varepsilon)$, there are $\varepsilon_1 > 0$ and $G_1 \in \mathcal{G}$ satisfying

$$y \in G_1 \subseteq S(y; \varepsilon_1) \subseteq S(x; \varepsilon)$$

This proves (15.19).

In most of the work we need not assume that $\mathcal{G}$ is given by ϱ, but only that (15.18) holds. A sequence $\{x_n\}$ in T is *fundamental* if, given

65

$\varepsilon > 0$, there is an integer m, depending on ε, such that $\varrho(x_j, x_k) < \varepsilon$ $(j \geqslant m, k \geqslant m)$.

THEOREM 15.4. (15.20) *A subsequence of a fundamental sequence is fundamental.*

(15.21) *Assuming* (15.18), *a convergent sequence is fundamental.*

Proof. (15.20) is obvious. To prove (15.21) we use (15.19). Then, given $\varepsilon > 0$, there is by convergence an integer m such that if x is the limit,

$$x_n \in S(x; \tfrac{1}{2}\varepsilon)\,(all\ n \geqslant m), \quad \varrho(x_j, x_k) \leqslant \varrho(x_j, x) + \varrho(x, x_k) < \varepsilon$$

proving the result.

The space T is *complete*, if each fundamental sequence in T is convergent. The space T can be called *semi-complete*, if every fundamental sequence is a set with a semi-compact closure. By (15.20) and the definition of semi-compact sets, there is an alternative equivalent definition. The space T is *semi-complete*, if each fundamental sequence $\{x_n\}$ in T is such that $L(\{x_n\})$ is not empty. We can also say that T is *locally complete*, if to each $x \in T$ there corresponds a neighbourhood $G(x)$ within the closure of which, each fundamental sequence is convergent. T is *locally semi-complete*, if to each $x \in T$ there corresponds a neighbourhood $G(x)$ within the closure of which every fundamental sequence has a semi-compact closure.

THEOREM 15.5. (15.22) *A complete space is semi-complete. Let $\mathcal{G}$ be the pseudometric topology given by ϱ. Then*

(15.23) *a fundamental sequence with a semi-compact closure is convergent*

(15.24) *if T is semi-complete, it is complete.*

Proof. (15.22) follows from Theorem 15.1 (15.3), which shows that a convergent sequence has a semi-compact closure. For (15.23) let $\{x_n\}$ be a fundamental sequence with a semi-compact closure. Then, given $\varepsilon > 0$, there is an integer m such that

$$\varrho(x_j, x_k) < \tfrac{1}{2}\varepsilon \qquad (all\ j, k \geqslant m)$$

Also there is an $x \in L(\{x_n\})$. By Theorem 15.1 (15.1), an infinity

66

of terms of the sequence lie in $S(x; \frac{1}{2}\varepsilon)$, so that for some $k \geq m$,

$$\varrho(x, x_k) < \tfrac{1}{2}\varepsilon, \quad \varrho(x, x_j) \leq \varrho(x, x_k) + \varrho(x_k, x_j) < \varepsilon \quad (all\ j \geq m)$$

Hence $\{x_n\}$ is convergent to x, since $\mathcal{G}$ is given by ϱ. Then (15.24) follows. Thus the connection of completeness with semi-compactness is obscured if $\mathcal{G}$ is the pseudometric topology.

We can now give more results on the intersection of closed sets like those in Theorems 13.2, 14.1, 15.2. We shrink the family of closed sets with the finite intersection property and, as a result, the conditions imposed on the space are weakened.

THEOREM 15.6. (15.25) *Every monotone decreasing sequence* $\{F_n\}$ *of closed sets, with a fundamental sequence* $\{x_n\}$ *such that* $x_n \in F_n$ *($n = 1, 2, \ldots$), has a non-empty intersection if, and only if, T is semi-complete.*
(15.26) *If for each $x \in T$ there is a neighbourhood of x such that those* $\{F_n\}$ *in the closure of the neighbourhood and satisfying the conditions of* (15.25), *have non-empty intersections, then T is locally semi-complete, and conversely.*

Proof. Clearly we need only prove (15.25). First suppose that every such $\{F_n\}$ has the given property, and let $\{x_n\}$ be a fundamental sequence. Then

$$F_m = \bar{L}_m(\{x_n\}) \qquad (m = 1, 2, \ldots)$$

satisfies the given conditions, so that $\{x_n\}$ has a semi-compact closure, and T is semi-complete. Conversely, let T be semi-complete. The F_n are monotone decreasing with $x_n \in F_n$, so that $x_n \in F_m$ (*all* $n \geq m$),

(15.27) $$\bar{L}_m(\{x_n\}) \subseteq \bar{F}_m = F_m$$

By semi-completeness, the first sets in (15.27), and so the F_m, have a non-empty intersection, completing the proof of (15.25).

If T is semi-compact, the closure of each sequence $\{x_n\}$ of points of T, whether fundamental or not, is semi-compact, so that T is semi-complete for all pseudometrics ϱ. But if T is only locally semi-

67

compact, it need not be semi-complete, for see *Ex. 15.5*; of course such a T is *locally* semi-complete for every ϱ.

Ex. 15.1. Let $x \in T$ be such that for some $y \neq x$ in T, y is in every neighbourhood of x. If $x_1 = y$ then $x \in Y$. But if $x_2, x_3, \ldots$ is a sequence of points lying outside some neighbourhood of x, then $x \notin L$, and $L \subset Y$.

Ex. 15.2 (Kelley (1955), p. 163 (e)). Assuming the theory of ordinal numbers, let Ω_0 be the set of all ordinals less than the first uncountable ordinal Ω, with topology the family of all unions of open intervals $a < x < b$, where a, x, b are ordinal numbers. Then Ω cannot be the limit of any sequence of ordinals of Ω_0. If $\{x_n\}$ is a sequence of ordinals in Ω_0, show that the $\bar{L}_m(\{x_n\})$ have a common ordinal, so that Ω_0 is semi-compact. But show that Ω_0 is not compact by observing that it is not countable and that each open interval contains a countable number of ordinals only. This space is locally compact, Hausdorff, and its topology has a countable local base.

Ex. 15.3. Let $x_n = n\{1 + (-1)^n\}$. Find $L_m(\{x_n\})$, and show that $L(\{x_n\})$ contains 0 alone, but that $\{x_n\}$ is not convergent to 0 in the modulus topology.

Ex. 15.4. Prove that a convergent sequence and its limit form a compact set.

Ex. 15.5. Let T be the set of positive real numbers, with topology given by unions of open intervals (a, b) in T. If $x \in T$ show that $[\frac{1}{2}x, 2x]$ is semi-compact, so that T is locally semi-compact. For $\varrho(x, y) = |x - y|$, and $x_n = 1/n$ $(n = 1, 2, \ldots)$, show that $\{x_n\}$ is fundamental, but that the $\bar{L}_m(\{x_n\})$ have no common point, so that T is not semi-complete.

Ex. 15.6. Whatever the space T, we can define

$$\varrho_0(x, y) = \begin{cases} 0 & (x = y) \\ 1 & (x \neq y) \end{cases}$$

If $\{x_n\}$ is a fundamental sequence using ϱ_0, show that there is an integer N such that $x_N = x_n$ (*all* $n \geqslant N$), so that $\{x_n\}$ is convergent.

Ex. 15.7. Let s be the space of all sequences of complex numbers. If $\mathbf{x} = \{x_n\}$, $\mathbf{y} = \{y_n\}$, $\mathbf{x}, \mathbf{y} \in s$, let

$$\varrho(\mathbf{x}, \mathbf{y}) = \sum_{n=1}^{\infty} \frac{1}{2^n} \cdot \frac{|x_n - y_n|}{1 + |x_n - y_n|}$$

Show that ϱ is a metric for which s is complete.

Ex. 15.8. Let m be the space of bounded sequences of complex numbers, with

$$\varrho(x, y) = \sup_n |x_n - y_n|$$

Show that ϱ is a metric for which m is complete.

Ex. 15.9. Let c be the space of convergent sequences of complex numbers, with metric as in *Ex. 15.8.* Show that c is complete for this metric.

16. Contraction Maps

One of the first uses of functional analysis was to unify proofs of 'fixed point' theorems from various fields. One such result is an application of the property of completeness. Let T be a complete metric space with metric ϱ, and let $A : T \to T$. Then A is a *contraction map*, if there is a number $a < 1$ independent of $x, y \in T$, such that

(16.1) $\varrho\big(A(x), A(y)\big) \leqslant a \cdot \varrho(x, y)$ (*all* $x, y \in T$)

It follows that

(16.2)   if $y \to x$ then $A(y) \to A(x)$

THEOREM 16.1. *Each contraction map in a complete metric space T has one and only one fixed point, i.e. the equation $A(x) = x$ has one, and only one, solution.*

Proof. Let $x_0 \in T$ be arbitrary, and set $x_n = A(x_{n-1})$ $(n \geqslant 1)$, i.e. $x_n = A^n(x_0)$. Then $\{x_n\}$ is a fundamental sequence. For by (16.1),

69

if $m < n$,

$$\varrho(x_m, x_n) \leqslant \varrho(x_m, x_{m+1}) + \varrho(x_{m+1}, x_{m+2}) + \ldots + \varrho(x_{n-1}, x_n)$$
$$\leqslant a^m \cdot \varrho(x_0, x_1) + a^{m+1} \cdot \varrho(x_0, x_1) + \ldots + a^{n-1} \cdot \varrho(x_0, x_1)$$
$$\leqslant a^m \cdot \varrho(x_0, x_1)/(1-a) \to 0 \qquad (m \to \infty)$$

As T is complete, $\{x_n\}$ is convergent, say to x. Then by (16.2),

$$A(x) = A\left(\lim_{n \to \infty} x_n\right) = \lim_{n \to \infty} A(x_n) = \lim_{n \to \infty} x_{n+1} = x$$

To show that x is unique, if $A(x) = x$, $A(y) = y$, then by (16.1),

$$\varrho(x, y) = \varrho(A(x), A(y)) \leqslant a \cdot \varrho(x, y) \qquad (a < 1),$$
$$\varrho(x, y) = 0, \qquad x = y$$

There is a more general result.

THEOREM 16.2. *If A is a map of the complete metric space T into itself, with an integer n such that A^n is a contraction map, then $A(x) = x$ has one, and only one, solution.*

Proof. As before, there is an $a < 1$, independent of k, m, such that if $x_k = A^{kn}(x_0)$,

$$\varrho(x_k, x_m) \leqslant \varrho(x_0, x_1) a^k/(1-a) \qquad (k < m)$$

and $\{x_k\}$ has a limit x. Further,

$$\varrho\big(A^{kn}(A(x_0)), A^{kn}(x_0)\big) \leqslant a^k \cdot \varrho(A(x_0), x_0) \to 0 \qquad (k \to \infty)$$

so that by continuity,

$$A(x) = A\left(\lim_{k \to \infty} A^{kn}(x_0)\right) = \lim_{k \to \infty} A(A^{kn}(x_0)) = \lim_{k \to \infty} A^{kn}(A(x_0))$$
$$= \lim_{k \to \infty} A^{kn}(x_0) = \lim_{k \to \infty} x_k = x$$

Uniqueness follows from the previous theorem, since if

$$A(x) = x, \quad A(y) = y, \quad \text{then} \quad A^n(x) = x, \quad A^n(y) = y, \quad x = y$$

Note that by Theorem 15.5, semi-completeness gives us nothing new here. The results of this section are used in sections 52 and 64.

17. Baire and Second Category Spaces

If every non-empty open set of T is of the second category, then T is a *Baire space*. In the notation of the end of Chapter 2, if p_4 is the property of being of the first category, a Baire space is a $\bar{p}_4$-*space*.

Further, an intersection of a countable number of open sets is called a $\mathcal{G}_\delta$-set, so that a $\mathcal{G}$-set is a $\mathcal{G}_\delta$-set. If each non-empty $\mathcal{G}_\delta$-set is of the second category in itself, we say that T is a *second category space*. Clearly it is then also a Baire space.

We begin by giving equivalent conditions for T to be a Baire space, followed by properties of Baire and second category spaces, and then we show that many of the spaces mentioned in this chapter are second category spaces.

Bourbaki (1958), p. 109, lists three equivalent conditions.

THEOREM 17.1. *T is a Baire space if, and only if, any one of the following three conditions is true.*

(17.1) *Every countable intersection of open sets dense in T, is dense in T.*

(17.2) *Every countable union of closed sets nowhere dense in T, has no interior point.*

(17.3) *The complement of a first category set in T is dense in T.*

Proof. By complements, (17.1) is equivalent to (17.2). If T is a Baire space, then no non-empty $\mathcal{G}$-set can be contained in the union of a countable number of sets each nowhere dense in T, so that (17.2) is true. Conversely, if (17.2) is true, and if the non-empty $G \in \mathcal{G}$ is contained in the union of a countable number of sets X_n, then G is contained in the union of the $\bar{X}_n$, closed sets. By (17.2), an $\bar{X}_n$, and so X_n, is dense in a portion of G, and G is of the second category. Hence T is a Baire space. Further, if T is a Baire space, no non-empty $G \in \mathcal{G}$ can lie in a first category set, and (17.3) follows. Conversely, if (17.3) is true, each non-empty $G \in \mathcal{G}$ contains points of the complement of each first category set, so that the open set must be of the second category.

THEOREM 17.2. (17.4) *T is a second category space if, and only if, given any non-empty $\mathcal{G}_\delta$-set $H \subseteq T$, with any set X of the first category in H, then $H\backslash X$ is dense in H.*

(17.5) *If each $x \in T$ has a neighbourhood $G(x)$ that is a Baire (or second category) space under the relative topology of $G(x)$ from $\mathcal{G}$, then T is also a Baire (or second category) space.*

(17.6) *Let T be a Baire (or second category) space containing a non-empty $\mathcal{G}$-(or $\mathcal{G}_\delta$-) set D. Then D is a Baire (or second category) space under the relative topology $\mathcal{G}_1$ of D from $\mathcal{G}$.*

(17.7) *Let T be a Baire (or second category) space and let X be of the first category in T (or in each $\mathcal{G}_\delta$-set $H \subseteq T$). Then $\backslash X$ is a Baire (or second category) space.*

Proof. For (17.4) we follow the proof of the equivalence of (17.3) and the definition of a Baire space. For (17.5) let the union H of $X_m (m = 1, 2, \ldots)$ be a non-empty $\mathcal{G}$-(or $\mathcal{G}_\delta$-) set. If $x \in H$, then $G(x) \cap H$ is a non-empty $\mathcal{G}$-(or $\mathcal{G}_\delta$-) set, the union of $G(x) \cap X_m$. Hence for some integer m and some portion G_1 of $G(x)$, $G(x) \cap X_m$, and so X_m itself, are dense in $G_1 \cap H$, and H is of the second category, giving (17.5). For (17.6) let H be a non-empty $\mathcal{G}_1$-(or $\mathcal{G}_{1\delta}$-) set in D. Then H is a $\mathcal{G}$-(or $\mathcal{G}_\delta$-) set in T. (For the second case, H is the intersection of sets $G_n^1 \cap D$, for some $G_n^1 \in \mathcal{G} (n \geqslant 1)$, while D is a $\mathcal{G}_\delta$-set, so that H is a $\mathcal{G}_\delta$-set.) Hence H is of the second $\mathcal{G}$-category in T. If H is the union of sets $X_m (m \geqslant 1)$, then for some integer, m, and some $G_2 \in \mathcal{G}$, $X_m \cap G_2$ is $\mathcal{G}$-dense in the non-empty $H \cap G_2$. As $H \subseteq D$, $X_m \subseteq D$, then $X_m \cap G_2$ is $\mathcal{G}_1$-dense in $H \cap G_2$, and H is of the second $\mathcal{G}_1$-category in D. For (17.7) $\backslash X$ is dense in T. Let $Y \subseteq \backslash X$ be a first $\mathcal{G}_1$-category set in $\backslash X$ (or in a $\mathcal{G}_{1\delta}$-set $H \backslash X$, where H is a $\mathcal{G}_\delta$-set). Then Y is the union of sets nowhere $\mathcal{G}_1$-dense in $\backslash X$ (or $H \backslash X$), and so nowhere $\mathcal{G}$-dense in T (or H). (For the second case, if $x \in H \cap X$ and $x \in G \in \mathcal{G}$, then X is of the first $\mathcal{G}$-category in $G \cap H$, so that $G \cap (H \backslash X)$ is not empty. Thus each portion of H contains a portion of $H \backslash X$, so that for a further portion $G_3 \cap (H \backslash X)$, G_3 is free from points of the nowhere $\mathcal{G}_1$-dense set $\subseteq Y \subseteq \backslash X$.) Since X is of the first $\mathcal{G}$-category relative to T (or H), the same is true of $X \cup Y$. Hence by (17.3) or (17.4), $\backslash (X \cup Y)$ is $\mathcal{G}$-dense in T (or H), and so is $\mathcal{G}_1$-dense in $\backslash X$ (or $H \backslash X$). Then (17.3) or (17.4) completes the proof.

The known kinds of Baire spaces fall into two types, as (17.10) will show. First we can use a pseudometric ϱ with (15.19), i.e. each

$S(x; \varepsilon) \in \mathcal{G}$. We say that T is *locally half-complete*, if to each $x \in T$ there is a neighbourhood $G(x)$ such that every monotone decreasing sequence $\{\bar{G}_n\}$ of closures of open sets in $G(x)$, with a fundamental sequence $\{x_n\}$ such that $x_n \in \bar{G}_n$, has a non-empty intersection. Secondly, omitting ϱ and the requirement of a fundamental sequence, if the property is still true we say that T is *locally half-compact*.

THEOREM 17.3. (17.8) *A locally half-complete space is locally complete.*

(17.9) *A space T is locally half-compact, if for each $x \in T$ there is a neighbourhood $G(x)$ for which from every countable cover of $\overline{G(x)}$, of sets consisting of interiors of closed sets, we can select a finite cover of $\overline{G(x)}$.*

(17.10) *If T is compact, sequentially closed, semi-compact, locally compact, or locally semi-compact, then T is locally half-compact. If T is complete, semi-complete, locally complete, or locally semi-complete, then T is locally half-complete (and so locally complete).*

(17.11) *For a regular $\mathcal{G}$, if T is either locally half-compact, or locally half-complete for a pseudometric ϱ satisfying (15.19), then T is a second category space and so is a Baire space.*

Proof. For (17.8), if $\{x_n\}$ in $G(x)$ is a fundamental sequence that does not have $\varrho(x_m, x_n) = 0$ $(m, n \geq N)$, for some N, we take

$$G_n = G(x) \cap S\left(x_n, \sup_{m > n} \varrho(x_m, x_n)\right) \qquad (n = 1, 2, \ldots),$$

a sequence of open sets by (15.19). As T is locally half-complete, the intersection of the $\bar{G}_n$ contains a point z, and $\{x_n\}$ converges to z, for

$$\varrho(x_n, z) \leq \sup_{m > n} \varrho(x_m, x_n) \to 0 \qquad (n \to \infty).$$

(17.9) follows as in Theorem 13.2, and (17.10) from Theorems 13.2 (13.4), 14.1, 15.2 (15.10; 15.11), 15.6 (15.25; 15.26), and 15.3 (15.13) with (17.9).

It is curious that the construction of special sequences and series has been avoided in the proofs of many convergence factor theorems by an appeal to the Banach–Steinhaus theorem in a form that uses Theorem 17.3 (17.11) or Theorem 31.1 later. The construction of special sequences seems to be unavoidable in proving these results, however.

For (17.11) let a $\mathcal{G}_\delta$-set $H \subseteq T$, sets $G_{1,n} \in \mathcal{G}$, and sets $X_m \subseteq T$, satisfy

$$(17.12) \qquad H = \bigcap_{n=1}^{\infty} G_{1,n} = \bigcup_{m=1}^{\infty} X_m.$$

We look for a monotone decreasing sequence of $G_{2,n} \in \mathcal{G}(n = 1, 2, \ldots)$, lying in a neighbourhood $G(x)$ of some $x \in T$, and for $n = 1, 2, \ldots,$ with:

$$(17.13) \qquad G_{2,n} \cap H \text{ is not empty};$$

$$(17.14) \qquad \bar{G}_{2,n} \subseteq G_{1,n} \cap G(x);$$

$$(17.15) \qquad \bar{G}_{2,n} \cap \bigcup_{m=1}^{n} X_m \text{ is empty};$$

and when we have to use a pseudometric ϱ,

$$(17.16) \quad \varrho(x_n, y) < 1/n, \quad \text{for all} \quad y \in \bar{G}_{2,n}, \quad \text{and some} \quad x_n \in \bar{G}_{2,n}.$$

If T is locally half-complete, or locally half-compact, the $G(x)$ is that of the definitions. Then the $\bar{G}_{2,n}$ are monotone decreasing, and if they satisfy (17.13; ...; 17.16), by the definitions the $\bar{G}_{2,n}$ have a common point z. By (17.12; 17.14), $z \in H$. By (17.12; 17.15), $z \notin H$. Thus the construction is impossible for locally half-complete and half-compact spaces. To complete the proof of (17.11) we show that when T is a regular space that is not a second category space, the construction is possible.

If the non-empty $\mathcal{G}_\delta$-set H, and X_m each nowhere dense in H, satisfy (17.12), we choose $x \in H$, so that $G(x) \cap H$ is not empty. Let $G_{2n} \in \mathcal{G}(1 \leqslant n \leqslant N-1)$ have been defined, satisfying (17.13; ... 17.16). By (17.12), $H \subseteq G_{1n}(n \geqslant 1)$. Using $x \in H \cap G(x)$ if $N = 1$, and by (17.13) if $N > 1$, the open sets

$$(17.17) \quad G_{31} = G(x) \cap G_{11}, \quad G_{3N} = G_{2,N-1} \cap G_{1N} \ (N > 1)$$

contain a portion of H. By Theorem 12.1 (12.1; 12.2),

$$X^N \equiv \bigcup_{m=1}^{N} X_m$$

is nowhere dense in H, so that there is an open set $G_{4N} \subseteq G_{3N}$ with $G_{4N} \cap H$ not empty, but with $G_{4N} \cap X^N$ empty. We choose, by (17.17),

$$x_N \in G_{4N} \cap H \subseteq G_{3N} \subseteq G_{2, N-1}$$

if a pseudometric ϱ is involved. By (17.8) and Theorem 10.3, there is a G_{2N} satisfying

(17.18) $\quad x_N \in G_{2N} \in \mathcal{G}, \quad \bar{G}_{2N} \subseteq G_{4N} \cap S(x_N; 1/N) \subseteq G_{3N}, \quad x_N \in H,$
$H \cap G_{2N}$ not empty

which continues the sequence $\{G_{2n}\}$. When ϱ is not involved, or does not exist, we omit x_N and $S(x_N; 1/N)$. Clearly (17.13) is true, and (17.14) by definition of $G_{3, N}$ and (17.15) by (17.18), since $G_{4N} \cap X^N$ is empty. If necessary, (17.16) follows from (17.18).

Note that even if H is of the second category, it is conceivable that the sets X_m become dense so slowly in portions of H that the construction is still possible, so that it seems that the possibility of the construction, is not equivalent to T not being a second category space.

Ex. 17.1. A countable number of isolated points form a second category space.

Ex. 17.2. The set J of irrationals in $(0, 1)$ is a second category space with the modulus topology. (Each rational forms a closed set, so that J is a countable intersection of open sets, i.e. a $\mathcal{G}_\delta$-set. Now use Theorem 17.2 (17.6).) This is a second category space that is not locally half-complete.

Ex. 17.3. If T is a second category space, if D is open or a $\mathcal{G}_\delta$-set, and is not empty, and if X is of the first category in each $\mathcal{G}_\delta$-set of T, show that $D\backslash X$ is a second category space.

18. Borel and Analytic (Souslin) Sets

After Baire spaces there come Baire sets. In order to find which set operations leave the family of Baire sets invariant, we study general families of sets. First, if $\mathcal{E}$ is a family of sets of T, then $\mathcal{E}_\delta, \mathcal{E}_\sigma$ denote the respective families of intersections and unions of sequences $\{E_j\}$

of sets of $\mathcal{E}$. Taking $E_j = E$ for all j, we see that

$$\mathcal{E} \subseteq \mathcal{E}_\delta, \quad \mathcal{E} \subseteq \mathcal{E}_\sigma$$

Let $\mathcal{G}$, $\mathcal{F}$, $\mathcal{H}$, $\mathcal{H}_0$ be the respective families of open sets, closed sets, closures of open sets, and interiors of closed sets. By (7.2; 8.4),

$$\mathcal{G}_\sigma = \mathcal{G}, \quad \mathcal{F}_\delta = \mathcal{F}$$

But often we have $\mathcal{F} \subseteq \mathcal{G}_\delta$, and $\mathcal{G}_\delta \supset \mathcal{G}$, $\mathcal{F}_\sigma \supset \mathcal{F}$.

By the rules of de Morgan *(Exs. 3.9, 3.10)* and Theorem 8.1 (8.2),

$$\backslash \bigcap_{j=1}^{\infty} G_j = \bigcup_{j=1}^{\infty} \backslash G_j, \quad \backslash \bigcup_{j=1}^{\infty} F_j = \bigcap_{j=1}^{\infty} \backslash F_j, \quad \backslash \bar{G} = (\backslash G)^\circ$$

so that by Theorem 8.2, the complement of a set in $\mathcal{G}_\delta$ is a set in $\mathcal{F}_\sigma$, and vice versa; and the complement of a set in $\mathcal{H}$ is a set in $\mathcal{H}_0$, and vice versa.

By Ex. 4.6, $(\mathcal{E}_\delta)_\delta = \mathcal{E}_\delta$, $(\mathcal{E}_\sigma)_\sigma = \mathcal{E}_\sigma$. But in general the family $(\mathcal{E}_\delta)_\sigma$ written $\mathcal{E}_{\delta\sigma}$, and the family $(\mathcal{E}_\sigma)_\delta$, written $\mathcal{E}_{\sigma\delta}$, are wider than $\mathcal{E}_\delta, \mathcal{E}_\sigma$. Thus we are led to the family $\mathcal{B}(\mathcal{E})$ of *Borel sets* constructed from the family $\mathcal{E}$, the smallest family that contains $\mathcal{E}$, and the union and intersection of every sequence $\{E_j\}$ of sets of $\mathcal{B}(\mathcal{E})$. Compare Borel (1898), p. 46. Thus the families $\mathcal{E}_\delta$, $\mathcal{E}_\sigma$, $\mathcal{E}_{\delta\sigma}$, $\mathcal{E}_{\sigma\delta}$, $\mathcal{E}_{\delta\sigma\delta}$, ... are all contained in $\mathcal{B}(\mathcal{E})$.

THEOREM 18.1. (18.1) $\mathcal{B}(\mathcal{B}(\mathcal{E})) = \mathcal{B}(\mathcal{E})$

(18.2) *In order that* $\mathcal{B}(\mathcal{F}) = \mathcal{B}(\mathcal{G}) = \mathcal{B}(\mathcal{H}) = \mathcal{B}(\mathcal{H}_0)$, *it is necessary and sufficient that* $\mathcal{G} \subseteq \mathcal{B}(\mathcal{H})$.

(18.3) *If* $\mathcal{G}$ *is a pseudometric topology, then* $\mathcal{G} \subseteq \mathcal{H}_\sigma \subseteq \mathcal{B}(\mathcal{H})$.

(18.4) *Let* $\mathcal{G}$ *be regular with a countable base* $\mathcal{A}$, *and for each* $x \in T$ *let there be a neighbourhood* $G(x)$ *of* x. *Let* $\mathcal{H}_1$ *be the family of all* $\bar{G}$ *with* $G \in \mathcal{A}$, *and with an* $x \in T$ *such that* $x \in G \subseteq G(x)$. *Then* $\mathcal{G} \subseteq \mathcal{H}_{1\sigma}, \mathcal{B}(\mathcal{G}) = \mathcal{B}(\mathcal{H}_1)$.

(18.5) *If* $\mathcal{B}(\mathcal{F}) = \mathcal{B}(\mathcal{G})$ *and if* $X \in \mathcal{B}(\mathcal{F})$, *then* $\backslash X \in \mathcal{B}(\mathcal{F})$.

Proof. (18.1) and the necessity of $\mathcal{G} \subseteq \mathcal{B}(\mathcal{H})$ in (18.2) are obvious. For sufficiency, from $\mathcal{G} \subseteq \mathcal{B}(\mathcal{H})$ and complements, $\mathcal{F} \subseteq \mathcal{B}(\mathcal{H}_0)$.

Then by (18.1),

$$\mathcal{B}(\mathcal{F}) \subseteq \mathcal{B}(\mathcal{H}_0) \subseteq \mathcal{B}(\mathcal{G}) \subseteq \mathcal{B}(\mathcal{H}) \subseteq \mathcal{B}(\mathcal{F})$$

and all inclusions are equalities.

For (18.3), Theorem 11.5 (11.10) shows that if $x \in G$ then $\varrho(x, \backslash G) > 0$. Thus G is the union of $F_n(n = 1, 2, \ldots)$, where F_n is the set of points x for which $\varrho(x, \backslash G) \geqslant n^{-1}$. In $\backslash F_n$, $\varrho(x, \backslash G) < n^{-1}$, so that by Theorem 11.5 (11.11), $\backslash F_n$ is open and F_n closed. Further, if

$$G_n \equiv \{x : \varrho(x, \backslash G) > n^{-1}\}, \quad F_n \supseteq G_n \supseteq F_{n-1}, \quad F_n \supseteq \bar{G}_n \supseteq F_{n-1}$$

and $\backslash G_n$ is closed by Theorem 11.5 (11.12), so that G_n is open. Since G is the union of the F_n, then G is the union of the $\bar{G}_n$, giving (18.3). Note that if we use the alternative conditions that are given in Theorem 11.6, that correspond to $\mathcal{G}$ being given by ϱ, the proof of (18.3) is just as easy. For (18.4) let $\mathcal{A}_1$ be the family of all $G \in \mathcal{A}$ with an $x \in T$ such that $x \in G \subseteq G(x)$. By definition of a base we see that $\mathcal{A}_1$ is also a base. Since $\mathcal{A}_1 \subseteq \mathcal{A}$, then $\mathcal{A}_1$ is countable. By *Ex. 11.2* (Urysohn's theorem), $\mathcal{G}$ is pseudometrizable, and the proof follows as for (18.3). Alternatively we can omit *Ex. 11.2* and prove the result directly, for each $\mathcal{G}$-set G_1 is a countable union of $\bar{G} \subseteq G_1$, with $G \in \mathcal{A}_1$.

To prove (18.5) we need only note that complements change unions into intersections, intersections into unions, closed sets into open sets, and $\mathcal{B}(\mathcal{F})$ into $\mathcal{B}(\mathcal{G}) = \mathcal{B}(\mathcal{F})$.

The direct study of $\mathcal{B}(\mathcal{E})$ needs a succession of countable unions and intersections, and the use of a transfinite system of ordinal numbers as far as the first uncountable ordinal. To avoid this, Souslin (1917) used analytic sets. See Lusin (1927) also. Here a single operation defines all Borel sets, and often other sets too. Further, the continuous image of even a $\mathcal{G}_\delta$-set need not be a $\mathcal{B}(\mathcal{G})$ set, even with Euclidean metric topology. But the continuous image of a $\mathcal{B}(\mathcal{G})$ set is an analytic set, under simple conditions on the transformation. See section 19. Thus it is useful to study the family $\mathcal{A}(\mathcal{E})$ of analytic sets.

Let $\mathcal{I}$ be the family of all infinite sequences $\mathbf{n} \equiv \{n_j\}$ of positive integers. We write $n_1, \ldots, n_j$ as $(\mathbf{n}, j)$ and $n_1, \ldots, n_j, n$ as $(\mathbf{n}, j; n)$.

If $\mathbf{m} \in \mathcal{J}$, we write $n_1, \ldots, n_j, m_1, \ldots, m_k$ as $(\mathbf{n}, j; \mathbf{m}, k)$. There should be no confusion between the three types, as they have different numbers of letters.

If for every finite sequence $(\mathbf{n}; j)$ of positive integers there is an

$$X(n_1, \ldots, n_j) \equiv X(\mathbf{n}, j) \subseteq T,$$

the family of sets $X(\mathbf{n}, j)$ is called a *determining system* $\mathcal{DS}(X)$. The nucleus of $\mathcal{DS}(X)$ is the set

$$A(X) = \bigcup_{\mathcal{J}} \bigcap_{j=1}^{\infty} X(\mathbf{n}, j)$$

The step from $\mathcal{DS}(X)$ to $A(X)$, is called the *operation* $(\mathcal{A})$ of Souslin, and the family of $A(X)$ obtained from all $\mathcal{DS}(X) \subseteq \mathcal{E}$, is called the *family* $\mathcal{A}(\mathcal{E})$ *of analytic sets from* $\mathcal{E}$.

THEOREM 18.2. *The operation* $(\mathcal{A})$ *includes countable unions and intersections, so that* $\mathcal{A}(\mathcal{E}) \supseteq \mathcal{E}_\delta \cup \mathcal{E}_\sigma$.

Proof. We write in turn

$$X(\mathbf{n}, j) = Y(n_1), \quad A(X) = \bigcup_{j=1}^{\infty} Y(j);$$

$$X(\mathbf{n}, j) = Y(j), \quad A(X) = \bigcap_{j=1}^{\infty} Y(j)$$

THEOREM 18.3. $\mathcal{A}(\mathcal{A}(\mathcal{E})) = \mathcal{A}(\mathcal{E}), \mathcal{B}(\mathcal{E}) \subseteq \mathcal{A}(\mathcal{E}), \mathcal{A}(\mathcal{B}(\mathcal{E})) = \mathcal{A}(\mathcal{E})$
Proof. By Theorem 18.2,

$$\mathcal{A}(\mathcal{E}) \supseteq \mathcal{E}, \quad \mathcal{A}(\mathcal{A}(\mathcal{E})) \supseteq \mathcal{A}(\mathcal{E})$$

In the second case we prove the opposite inclusion. For each fixed $(\mathbf{m}, k)$ let $A(\mathbf{m}, k; X)$ be the nucleus of the determining system of sets $X(\mathbf{m}, k; \mathbf{n}, j)$, and let Y be the nucleus of the determining system of sets $A(\mathbf{m}, k; X)$. Then by *Ex. 3.5*,

$$Y = \bigcup_{\mathbf{m} \in \mathcal{J}} \bigcap_{k=1}^{\infty} A(\mathbf{m}, k; X) = \bigcup_{\mathbf{m} \in \mathcal{J}} \bigcap_{k=1}^{\infty} \bigcup_{\mathbf{n} \in \mathcal{J}} \bigcap_{j=1}^{\infty} X(\mathbf{m}, k; \mathbf{n}, j)$$

$$= \bigcup_{\mathbf{m} \in \mathcal{J}} \bigcup_{\mathbf{n}(k) \in \mathcal{J} \, (k=1, 2, \ldots)} \bigcap_{k=1}^{\infty} \bigcap_{j=1}^{\infty} X(\mathbf{m}, k; \mathbf{n}(k), j)$$

78

From sequences $\mathbf{m}$, $\mathbf{n}(k)$ $(k = 1, 2, \ldots)$ we construct $\mathbf{N} = \{N_l\}$, obtaining

$$m_1,\ n(1)_1,\ m_2,\ n(2)_1,\ n(1)_2,\ m_3,\ n(3)_1,\ n(2)_2,\ n(1)_3,\ m_4,\ \ldots$$

by Cantor's diagonal process. Then $\mathbf{N} \in \mathcal{A}$ if, and only if, $\mathbf{m} \in \mathcal{A}$, $\mathbf{n}(k) \in \mathcal{A}(k = 1, 2, \ldots)$, so that the two unions can be replaced by a single union for all $\mathbf{N} \in \mathcal{A}$. Further, we can define

$$Y(\mathbf{N}, l) = \begin{cases} X(\mathbf{m}, k; \mathbf{n}(k), j) & (N_l = n(k)_j) \\ T & (N_l = m_k) \end{cases}$$

Then for fixed $\mathbf{N}$, and so fixed $\mathbf{m}$, $\mathbf{n}(k)$ $(k = 1, 2, \ldots)$ $Y(\mathbf{N}, l)$ runs through all the sets $X(\mathbf{m}, k; \mathbf{n}(k), j)$ once and once only, with repetitions of T. Hence

$$\bigcap_{l=1}^{\infty} Y(\mathbf{N}, l) = \bigcap_{k=1}^{\infty} \bigcap_{j=1}^{\infty} X(\mathbf{m}, k; \mathbf{n}(k), j)$$

and Y is the nucleus of the determining system of sets $Y(\mathbf{N}, l)$, that are constructed from the $X(\mathbf{m}, k; \mathbf{n}, j)$, thus proving the first result. The others follow using Theorem 18.2, for

$$\mathcal{A}(\mathcal{E}) \supseteq \mathcal{E}_\delta \cup \mathcal{E}_\sigma, \quad \mathcal{A}(\mathcal{E}) = \mathcal{A}(\mathcal{A}(\mathcal{E})) \supseteq \mathcal{A}(\mathcal{E}_\delta \cup \mathcal{E}_\sigma)$$
$$\supseteq \mathcal{E}_\delta \cup \mathcal{E}_{\delta\sigma} \cup \mathcal{E}_{\sigma\delta} \cup \mathcal{E}_\sigma, \ldots,$$
$$\mathcal{A}(\mathcal{E}) \supseteq \mathcal{B}(\mathcal{E}), \quad \mathcal{A}(\mathcal{E}) = \mathcal{A}(\mathcal{A}(\mathcal{E})) \supseteq \mathcal{A}(\mathcal{B}(\mathcal{E})) \supseteq \mathcal{A}(\mathcal{E})$$

In many cases, $\mathcal{A}(\mathcal{E}) \supset \mathcal{B}(\mathcal{E})$.

THEOREM 18.4. (18.6) *In order that* $\mathcal{A}(\mathcal{F}) = \mathcal{A}(\mathcal{G}) = \mathcal{A}(\mathcal{H}) = \mathcal{A}(\mathcal{H}_0)$, *it is necessary and sufficient that* $\mathcal{G} \subseteq \mathcal{A}(\mathcal{H})$, $\mathcal{F} \subseteq \mathcal{A}(\mathcal{H}_0)$.

(18.7) *If* $\mathcal{G}$ *is a pseudometric topology, then* $\mathcal{G} \subseteq \mathcal{H}_\sigma \subseteq \mathcal{A}(\mathcal{H})$, $\mathcal{F} \subseteq \mathcal{H}_{0\delta} \subseteq \mathcal{A}(\mathcal{H}_0)$.

(18.8) *For the conditions of* (18.4), $\mathcal{G} \subseteq \mathcal{A}(\mathcal{H}_1)$, $\mathcal{A}(\mathcal{G}) = \mathcal{A}(\mathcal{H}_1) = \mathcal{A}(\mathcal{F})$.

Proof. The conditions in (18.6) are clearly necessary. We need two since the complement of a nucleus need not be another nucleus.

Sufficiency follows by using Theorem 18.3, and

$$\mathcal{A}(\mathcal{F}) \subseteq \mathcal{A}(\mathcal{A}(\mathcal{H}_0)) = \mathcal{A}(\mathcal{H}_0) \subseteq \mathcal{A}(\mathcal{G}) \subseteq \mathcal{A}(\mathcal{A}(\mathcal{H}))$$
$$= \mathcal{A}(\mathcal{H}) \subseteq \mathcal{A}(\mathcal{F})$$

Thus all inclusions are equalities. For (18.7) we use Theorems 18.1 (18.3), 18.3, and take complements, obtaining the conditions in (18.6),

$$\mathcal{G} \subseteq \mathcal{B}(\mathcal{H}) \subseteq \mathcal{A}(\mathcal{H}), \quad \mathcal{F} \subseteq \mathcal{B}(\mathcal{H}_0) \subseteq \mathcal{A}(\mathcal{H}_0)$$

For (18.8) we use Theorem 18.1 (18.4), putting $\mathcal{H}_2$ as the family of complements of sets of $\mathcal{H}_1$. Then

$$\mathcal{G} \subseteq \mathcal{H}_{1\sigma} \subseteq \mathcal{A}(\mathcal{H}_1) \subseteq \mathcal{A}(\mathcal{H}), \quad \mathcal{F} \subseteq \mathcal{H}_{2\delta} \subseteq \mathcal{A}(\mathcal{H}_0)$$

and the proof proceeds as usual.

We denote by $\mathcal{B}a(\mathcal{G})$ the family of Baire sets (relative to $\mathcal{G}$).

THEOREM 18.5 (Nikodym (1925)).

$$\mathcal{A}(\mathcal{B}a(\mathcal{G})) = \mathcal{B}(\mathcal{B}a(\mathcal{G})) = \mathcal{B}a(\mathcal{G})$$

Proof. If each $X(\mathbf{n}, j) \in \mathcal{B}a(\mathcal{G})$, we show that the same is true of the nucleus. By Theorem 12.5 (12.21) we can replace each $X(\mathbf{n}, j)$ by

$$\bigcap_{k=1}^{j} X(\mathbf{n}, k)$$

without altering $A(X)$. Thus we suppose that $\mathcal{DS}(X)$ satisfies

(18.9) $\qquad X(\mathbf{n}, j) \supseteq X(\mathbf{n}, j+1) \qquad (j = 1, 2, \ldots)$

Further, for each fixed $(\mathbf{m}, k)$ let $A(\mathbf{m}, k; X)$ be the nucleus of the determining system of sets $X(\mathbf{m}, k; \mathbf{n}, j)$. From (18.9),

(18.10) $\qquad A(\mathbf{m}, k; X) \subseteq X(\mathbf{m}, k)$

(18.11) $\qquad A(X) = \bigcup_{\mathbf{n} \in \mathcal{J}} \bigcap_{j=2}^{\infty} X(\mathbf{n}, j) = \bigcup_{n=1}^{\infty} A(n; X)$

(18.12) $\qquad A(\mathbf{m}, k; X) = \bigcup_{\mathbf{n} \in \mathcal{J}} \bigcap_{j=2}^{\infty} X(\mathbf{m}, k; \mathbf{n}, j) = \bigcup_{n=1}^{\infty} A(\mathbf{m}, k; n; X)$

By Theorem 12.6 (12.27) and $A(X) \subseteq T$, there is a Baire set Y such that

$$(18.13) \qquad A(X) \subseteq Y, \quad I(Y) = I(A(X))$$

The $X(\mathbf{m}, k)$ are Baire sets with (18.10), so that similarly for each $(\mathbf{m}, k)$ there is a Baire set $Y(\mathbf{m}, k)$ with

$$(18.14) \qquad A(\mathbf{m}, k; X) \subseteq Y(\mathbf{m}, k) \subseteq X(\mathbf{m}, k),$$

$$I(Y(\mathbf{m}, k)) = I(A(\mathbf{m}, k; X))$$

Let us now put

$$(18.15) \qquad Z = \bigcup_{n=1}^{\infty} Y(n), \quad W = Y \backslash Z$$

$$(18.16) \quad Z(\mathbf{m}, k) = \bigcup_{n=1}^{\infty} Y(\mathbf{m}, k; n), \quad W(\mathbf{m}, k) = Y(\mathbf{m}, k) \backslash Z(\mathbf{m}, k)$$

$$(18.17) \qquad V = W \cup \bigcup_{(\mathbf{m}, k)} W(\mathbf{m}, k)$$

By Theorem 12.5 (12.22), Z and $Z(\mathbf{m}, k)$ are Baire sets. As Y and $Y(\mathbf{m}, k)$ are Baire sets, then by (18.11; 18.13; 18.15) or (18.12; 18.14; 18.16), respectively, and Theorem 12.6 (12.28), W and $W(\mathbf{m}, k)$ are of the first category. Hence by (18.17) and *Ex. 4.10*, V is of the first category, so that $U \equiv Y \backslash V$ is a Baire set. We finally show that $U \subseteq A(X)$. For if $x \in U = Y \backslash V$, then $x \in Y$, $x \notin V$. Hence by (18.17) $x \notin W$. By (18.15) $x \in Z$, and there is an integer n_1 such that $x \in Y(n_1)$. By (18.17), $x \notin V$ gives $x \notin W(n_1)$. Using (18.16),

$$x \notin Y(n_1) \backslash Z(n_1), \quad x \in Y(n_1), \quad \text{imply} \quad x \in Z(n_1)$$

By (18.16) there is an n_2 such that $x \in Y(n_1, n_2)$, and so on. Hence for an $\mathbf{n} \in \mathcal{J}$, $x \in Y(\mathbf{n}, j)$ ($j = 1, 2, \ldots$). By (18.14),

$$x \in \bigcap_{j=1}^{\infty} X(\mathbf{n}, j) \subseteq A(X), \quad U \subseteq A(X) \subseteq Y, \quad A(X) \backslash U \subseteq Y \backslash U \subseteq V$$

Since V is of the first category, so is $A(X) \backslash U$, so that $A(X)$ is a Baire set since U is a Baire set.

Note that by *Ex. 4.11*, the set of $\mathbf{n} \in \mathcal{J}$ is not countable, which explains why the operation $(\mathcal{A})$ does not usually lead to Borel sets only. An example to the contrary is given in Theorem 18.6 (18.20) below.

We say that $\mathcal{DS}(X)$ is *degenerate*, if there is a fixed $\mathbf{m} \in \mathcal{J}$ such that $X(\mathbf{n}, j)$ is empty when $n_j > m_j$. Let us put

$$A^*(\mathbf{m}, k) = \bigcup_{n_l \leqslant m_l \, (l=1, 2, \ldots, k)} \bigcap_{j=1}^{k} X(\mathbf{n}, j)$$

THEOREM 18.6 (18.18) *If* $\mathcal{DS}(X) \subseteq \mathcal{E}$, *then* $A^*(\mathbf{m}, k) \in \mathcal{E}_{\delta\sigma}$

$$(18.19) \quad \bigcap_{k=1}^{\infty} A^*(\mathbf{m}, k) = \bigcup_{n_l \leqslant m_l \, (l=1,2, \ldots)} \bigcap_{j=1}^{\infty} X(\mathbf{n}, j) \subseteq A(X)$$

(18.20) *If* $\mathcal{DS}(X) \subseteq \mathcal{E}$ *and is degenerate, then for some* $\mathbf{m} \in \mathcal{J}$,

$$A(X) = \bigcap_{k=1}^{\infty} A^*(\mathbf{m}, k) \in \mathcal{E}_{\delta\sigma\delta}$$

This is due to Sierpinski (1929).

Proof. Clearly (18.18) is true, and the first term in (18.19) contains the second. To prove equality let x lie in the first term of (18.19). Then for a positive integer $h_1 \leqslant m_1$, and each $l \geqslant 2$,

$$(18.21) \qquad x \in \bigcap_{j=1}^{l} X(h_1, n_2, \ldots, n_j)$$

for some $n_j \leqslant m_j$ ($j = 2, 3, \ldots, l$). For if not, then for each $n \leqslant m_1$ we could define an integer $q(n) > 0$, such that x belongs to no intersection

$$\bigcap_{j=1}^{q(n)} X(n, n_2, \ldots, n_j)$$

for which $n_j \leqslant m_j$ ($j = 2, 3, \ldots, q(n)$). If $q = \max(q(1), q(2), \ldots, q(m_1))$, then

$$x \notin \bigcap_{j=1}^{q} X(\mathbf{n}, j) \qquad (n_j \leqslant m_j, j = 1, 2, \ldots, q), \qquad x \notin A^*(\mathbf{m}, q)$$

contrary to hypothesis. Hence (18.21) is true. Similarly there is an integer $h_2 \leqslant m_2$, such that, for each $l \geqslant 3$, and for some $n_j \leqslant m_j$, for $3 \leqslant j \leqslant l$,

$$x \in \bigcap_{j=1}^{l} X(h_1, h_2, n_3, \ldots, n_j)$$

And so on. We thus determine $\mathbf{h} \equiv \{h_j\} \in \mathcal{A}$ with $h_j \leqslant m_j$. $(j = 1, 2, \ldots)$, and

$$x \in \bigcap_{j=1}^{l} X(\mathbf{h}, j) \, (\text{all } l), \quad x \in \bigcap_{j=1}^{\infty} X(\mathbf{h}, j)$$

This proves the equality in (18.19), and so the enclosure. Then (18.20) follows by definition of a degenerate family.

We now show that each analytic set $A(X)$ is the projection of a set Y in the space $T \times (0, 1)$, where Y can often be chosen to be of a more simple kind of set than $A(X)$. Let J be the open interval $(0, 1)$ on the real line, and let $J(\mathbf{n}, j)$ be a determining system consisting of intervals contained in $(0, 1)$. Then the Y is defined to be

$$Y = \bigcap_{j=1}^{\infty} \bigcup_{\mathbf{n} \in \mathcal{A}} X(\mathbf{n}, j) \times J(\mathbf{n}, j)$$

We still have a choice of $J(\mathbf{n}, j)$, one such system being defined by

$$s(\mathbf{n}, j) = j + \sum_{k=1}^{j} n_k, \quad u(\mathbf{n}, j) = 2^{-s(\mathbf{n}, 1)} + 2^{-s(\mathbf{n}, 2)} + \ldots + 2^{-s(\mathbf{n}, j)}$$

$$J(\mathbf{n}, j) = \left(u(\mathbf{n}, j), \ u(\mathbf{n}, j) + 2^{-s(\mathbf{n}, j)} \right)$$

Let us say that a sequence $\{\mathbf{n}(j)\}$ of sequences of $\mathcal{A}$, is *tied* to a sequence $\mathbf{n} \in \mathcal{A}$, if $(\mathbf{n}(j), j) = (\mathbf{n}, j)$ $(j = 1, 2, \ldots)$, i.e. the first j terms of $\mathbf{n}(j)$ are the same as those of $\mathbf{n}$.

THEOREM 18.7. (18.22) *The given determining system of* $J(\mathbf{n}, j)$ *is such that, for points*

$$y = y(\mathbf{n}) = \sum_{j=1}^{\infty} 2^{-s(\mathbf{n}, j)} \in J$$

and for each sequence $\{\mathbf{n}(j)\}$ *of sequences of* $\mathcal{A}$,

$$K \equiv \bigcap_{j=1}^{\infty} J(\mathbf{n}(j), j)$$

contains $y(\mathbf{n})$ if $\{\mathbf{n}(j)\}$ is tied to $\mathbf{n}$, and otherwise, if $\{\mathbf{n}(j)\}$ is tied to no $\mathbf{n} \in \mathcal{J}$, then K is empty.

(18.23) *Let $J(\mathbf{n}, j)$ have the property of (18.22), except possibly the value of $y(\mathbf{n})$. Let* proj: $T \times J \rightarrow T$ *send* $(t, u) \in T \times J$ *into* $t \in T$. *Then*

$$\text{proj }(Y) = A(X)$$

(18.24) *Let $\mathcal{G}_1$ be the product topology from $\mathcal{G}$ in T and open intervals in J. If each $X(\mathbf{n}, j) \in \mathcal{G}$, then $Y \in \mathcal{G}_{1\delta}$.*

(18.25) *More generally, if $\mathcal{DS}(X) \subseteq \mathcal{E}$, and if $\mathcal{E}_1$ is the family of $X \times J_1$, for each $X \in \mathcal{E}$, each open interval $J_1 \subseteq (0, 1)$, then $Y \in \mathcal{E}_{1\sigma\delta}$.*

Proof. For (18.22),

$$n_j \geqslant 1 \quad (j = 1, 2, \ldots), \quad s(\mathbf{n}, 1) = 1 + n_1 \geqslant 2,$$

$$s(\mathbf{n}, j+1) - s(\mathbf{n}, j) = 1 + n_{j+1} \geqslant 2,$$

$$u(\mathbf{n}, j) < y(\mathbf{n}) < u(\mathbf{n}, j) + 2^{-s(\mathbf{n}, j)}, \quad y(\mathbf{n}) \in J(\mathbf{n}, j)$$

and the conditions on K are satisfied. For (18.23) we have to invert the order of the intersection and union signs in the definition of Y.

$$Y = \bigcup_{\mathbf{n}(j) \in \mathcal{J}, j=1, 2, \ldots} \bigcap_{j=1}^{\infty} X(\mathbf{n}(j), j) \times J(\mathbf{n}(j), j)$$

by *Ex. 3.5*. The inner intersection is contained in $T \times K$ and so is empty unless $\{\mathbf{n}(j)\}$ is tied to an $\mathbf{n} \in \mathcal{J}$, in which case we can replace $\mathbf{n}(j)$ by $\mathbf{n}$ in $X(\mathbf{n}(j), j)$ also, and we obtain Y as the nucleus of a determining system of sets $X(\mathbf{n}, j) \times J(\mathbf{n}, j)$. Since $y(\mathbf{n}) \in K$, we see that *Exs. 3.19, 3.22* apply, and

$$\text{proj }(Y) = \text{proj}\left(\bigcup_{\mathbf{n} \in \mathcal{J}} \bigcap_{j=1}^{\infty} X(\mathbf{n}, j) \times J(\mathbf{n}, j)\right)$$

$$= \bigcup_{\mathbf{n} \in \mathcal{J}} \text{proj}\left(\bigcap_{j=1}^{\infty} X(\mathbf{n}, j) \times J(\mathbf{n}, j)\right)$$

$$= \bigcup_{\mathbf{n} \in \mathcal{J}} \bigcap_{j=1}^{\infty} \text{proj}\,(X(\mathbf{n}, j) \times J(\mathbf{n}, j)) = A(X)$$

Further, (18.24) follows from (18.25), which is clear from the first definition of Y, since there the inner union is a countable union by

Ex. 4.10. Thus each analytic set in Euclidean n-dimensional space with the usual topology, is the projection of a $\mathcal{G}_\delta$-set in Euclidean $(n+1)$-dimensional space.

19. Baire Functions*

There are many ways of defining a limit function f of a sequence $\{f_n\}$ of functions. One simple way is as follows. Let T_1, T_2 be spaces, T_2 having a topology $\mathcal{G}_2$. Let $X \subseteq T_1$ and let $f_n : X \to T_2$ ($n = 1, 2, \ldots$). If the sequence $\{f_n(x)\}$ converges to a limit $f(x)$ in T_2, for each fixed $x \in X$, so that we have defined $f : X \to T_2$, we say that $\{f_n\}$ is *pointwise convergent to f in X*, and that f is the *pointwise limit of $\{f_n\}$ in X*. If we can define a fundamental sequence in T_2, e.g. by a pseudometric, and if $\{f_n(x)\}$ is fundamental in T_2 for each fixed $x \in X$, we say that $\{f_n\}$ is *pointwise fundamental in X*. When $X = T_1$ we can omit 'in X'.

If T_1 also has a topology $\mathcal{G}_1$, we define a family of functions analogous to the family of Borel sets. Let $\mathcal{C}(T_1)$ be the family of all continuous functions $f : T_1 \to T_2$. Then the family $\mathcal{BF}(T_1)$ of *Baire functions* (or *analytically representable functions*) is the smallest family of functions $f : T_1 \to T_2$ that contains all continuous functions (i.e. $\mathcal{C}(T_1) \subseteq \mathcal{BF}(T_1)$) and all pointwise limits of pointwise convergent sequences of functions of $\mathcal{BF}(T_1)$. (See Baire (1899)).

First we have conditions for which the pointwise limit of a convergent sequence of continuous functions is also continuous. The ideas are traceable to Ascoli (1883–4), pp. 545–9, and Arzelà (1889), (1895), pp. 56–60. See, for example, Dunford and Schwartz (1958), pp. 382–3.

Let $(T_1, \mathcal{G}_1)$ be a topological space, (T_2, ϱ_2) a pseudometric space. We say that $\{f_n\}$ *converges uniformly at $x \in T_1$* if, given $\varepsilon > 0$, there are an integer n and a $\mathcal{G}_1$-neighbourhood $G(x)$ of x with

$$(19.1) \qquad \varrho_2(f_n(y), f(y)) < \varepsilon \qquad (y \in G(x)).$$

* This section is very technical and need only be used for reference in a first reading.

The functions f of a family $\mathcal{D}$ of functions are *equicontinuous at the point* $x \in T_1$ if, given $\varepsilon > 0$, there is a $\mathcal{G}_1$-neighbourhood $G_1(x)$ of x such that $y \in G_1(x)$ implies

(19.2) $\qquad \varrho_2(f(x), f(y)) < \varepsilon \qquad$ (all $f \in \mathcal{D}$)

Then each $f \in \mathcal{D}$ is continuous at x. Such f are *equicontinuous in* $X \subseteq T_1$, if equicontinuous at each $x \in X$. If also a pseudo-metric ϱ_1 gives $\mathcal{G}_1$, if $G_1(x)$ is or includes the set of y with $\varrho_1(x, y) < \delta$, and if $\delta > 0$ can be chosen independently of $x \in X$, we say that the equicontinuity is *uniform in* X. If $X = T_1$, we omit 'in X'.

THEOREM 19.1 (19.3) *Let* $\{f_n\}$ *be pointwise convergent to* f, *and every* f_n *continuous at* $x \in T_1$. *Then* f *is continuous at* x *if and only if* $\{f_n\}$ *converges uniformly at* x.

(19.4) *The set of points of uniform convergence of* $\{f_n\}$ *is a* $\mathcal{G}_{1\delta}$-*set.*

(19.5) *Let* $\{f_n\}$ *be pointwise convergent to* f *in a* $\mathcal{G}_1$-*neighbourhood* $G_2(x)$ *of* $x \in T_1$. *Then* f *is continuous at* x *if, but* not *only if, the family of functions* f_n ($n = 1, 2, \dots$) *is equicontinuous at* x.

(19.6) *If in* (19.5) *the equicontinuity is uniform in a set* X, *then* f *is uniformly continuous in* X.

(19.7) *Let* $(T_1, \mathcal{G}_1)$ *be a topological space,* (T_2, ϱ_2) *a pseudometric space, let* $X \subseteq T_1$, $Y \subseteq T_1$, *and let* $\{f_n\}$ *be pointwise fundamental in* X, *a set* $\mathcal{G}_1$-*dense in* Y. *If the* $f_1, f_2, \dots$ *are equicontinuous in* Y, *then* $\{f_n\}$ *is pointwise fundamental in* Y.

(19.8) *Even for continuous* f_n *in* (19.7) *we cannot put* $\overline{Y}$ *for the final* Y.

(19.9) *If in* (19.7) *the* f_n *are continuous in* $\overline{Y}$ *and uniformly equicontinuous in* Y, *we can replace the final* Y *by* $\overline{Y}$.

Proof. If $\{f_n\}$ converges uniformly at x, we have (19.1) for suitable n, $G(x)$. As f_n is continuous at x we can choose $G(x)$ also to satisfy

$$\varrho_2(f_n(x), f_n(y)) < \varepsilon \qquad (y \in G(x)). \qquad \text{Then}$$

$$\varrho_2(f_n(x), f(x)) < \varepsilon, \qquad \varrho_2(f_n(y), f(y)) < \varepsilon, \qquad \varrho_2(f(x), f(y)) < 3\varepsilon$$
$$(y \in G(x))$$

and f is continuous at x. Conversely, if f is continuous at x we first choose n so that

$$\varrho_2(f_n(x), f(x)) < \varepsilon$$

Next, using the continuity of both f and f_n, we choose a $\mathcal{G}_1$-neighbourhood $G(x)$ of x for which

$$\varrho_2(f_n(x), f_n(y)) < \varepsilon, \quad \varrho_2(f(x), f(y)) < \varepsilon \quad (y \in G(x))$$

Hence (19.1) with 3ε for ε, proving (19.3).

For (19.4) let $G_3(\varepsilon)$ be the set of x for which (19.1) is true for some integer n and some $\mathcal{G}_1$-neighbourhood $G(x)$ of x. Then $G(x) \subseteq G_3(\varepsilon)$, so that $G_3(\varepsilon)$ is a $\mathcal{G}_1$-set. The set of points of uniform convergence is the intersection of the $G_3(1/j)$, for $j = 1, 2, \ldots$, giving (19.4).

(19.3) can be compared with (19.5), in which there is a $\mathcal{G}_1$-neighbourhood $G_1(x)$ of x with (19.2) for f replaced by f_n. Then letting $n \to \infty$,

$$\varrho_2(f(x), f(y)) \leqslant \varepsilon \quad (y \in G_1(x) \cap G_2(x))$$

which gives the continuity of f since $\varepsilon > 0$ is arbitrary. To show that equicontinuity at x is not necessary, let $T_1 = T_2 = [0,1]$, let $f_n(1/n) = 1$, $f_n(x) = 0$ for $x = 0$ and for $x \geqslant 2/n$, and let f_n be linear in $[0, 1/n]$ and in $[1/n, 2/n]$. Then $\{f_n\}$ is pointwise convergent to 0, but $\{f_n\}$ is not equicontinuous at 0.

After (19.5), then (19.6) is an obvious step. To prove (19.7), let $y \in Y$, $\varepsilon > 0$. By equicontinuity at y, there is a $\mathcal{G}_1$-neighbourhood G of y for which

$$\varrho_2(f_n(y), f_n(x)) < \varepsilon/3 \quad (x \in G, n = 1, 2, \ldots)$$

Since X is $\mathcal{G}_1$-dense in Y we can take $x \in X$, so that $\{f_n(x)\}$ is fundamental. Thus there is an N, depending on x, ε, such that

$$\varrho_2(f_m(x), f_n(x)) < \varepsilon/3 \quad (m > n \geqslant N),$$
$$\varrho_2(f_m(y), f_n(y)) < \varepsilon \quad (m > n \geqslant N)$$

and $\{f_n(y)\}$ is a fundamental sequence, proving (19.7). To prove (19.8) we need some care in the construction. We use the set G_2 of *Ex. 12.4* with measure or variation not greater than $\frac{1}{2}$, the intervals of which are dense in $(0,1)$, and we define a sequence of continuous functions constant in each interval, so that they are equicontinuous in

87

$X = G_2$. The constants converge to 0 in $Y = G_2$. But at one point in $(0,1)$ the sequence tends to infinity even though $\overline{Y}$ contains that point. This will prove (19.8).

Let $g(y) = V\{(0,y)\backslash G_2\}$, where V denotes the measure or variation. Then $g(0) = 0$, $g(1) \geqslant \frac{1}{2}$, and g is continuous, monotone increasing and constant over the intervals. The values $g(r_n)$ for the intervals are countable in number, and $(g(0), g(1))$ is not countable, so that we can choose a fixed η unequal to any $g(r_n)$, and so a fixed ξ that is not in G_2, but with $g(\xi) = \eta$. Let $\eta_j(N)$ $(j = 1, 2)$ be the two values $g(r_n)$ (or $g(0)$, $g(1)$ where necessary) for which $n \leqslant N$, that are nearest to η and satisfy

$$\eta_1(N) < \eta < \eta_2(N)$$

Let $f_N(y) = 0$ for $y \leqslant \eta_1(N)$, $y \geqslant \eta_2(N)$, let $f_N(\eta) = N$, and let f_N be linear in $[\eta_1(N),\eta]$ and in $[\eta, \eta_2(N)]$. Then the f_N are continuous, so that $f_N(g(x))$ is continuous, constant in the intervals of G_2, tends to 0 in G_2 as $N \to \infty$, but with

$$f_N(g(\xi)) = f_N(\eta) = N \to \infty$$

Finally, to prove (19.9) we need only observe that from the continuity of the separate f_n, and the uniform equicontinuity in Y, there follows the uniform equicontinuity in $\overline{Y}$, with the '$< \varepsilon$' in (19.2) replaced by '$\leqslant \varepsilon$'.

Result (19.8) was made necessary by statement (1.3) of Alexiewicz (1950), p. 5, which is as follows.

'The space Y being complete, suppose the sequence of operations $\{U_n(x)\}$ to be equicontinuous and convergent in a set D dense in the space X; then the sequence $\{U_n(x)\}$ converges in the whole of X.'

Through lack of punctuation this statement is ambiguous. If the equicontinuity is restricted to D, the statement is false by (19.8). If the equicontinuity is in all X, the statement is correct by (19.7). Uniform equicontinuity in D is probably too strong a requirement, it is enough to ensure convergence in X, by (19.9). Possibly Alexiewicz only needs the statement with equicontinuity in X.

Next we have two theorems on neighbourhoods of the graphs of f and f^{-1} in relation to the graphs of the f_n, f_n^{-1} $(n = 1, 2, \ldots)$.

THEOREM 19.2. *Let T_1 be a space and (T_2, ϱ_2) a pseudometric space. Let $f_n:T_1 \to T_2$ ($n = 1,2,...$), and let f be the pointwise limit of $\{f_n\}$ in T_1, which is supposed to exist. Then for each $\varepsilon > 0$,*

$$\{(x, y) : \varrho_2(f(x), y) < \varepsilon\} = \bigcup_{\delta>0} \bigcup_{m=1}^{\infty} \bigcap_{n=m}^{\infty} \{(x, y) : \varrho_2(f_n(x), y) < \varepsilon - \delta\}$$

Proof. For (x, y) in the left side, then for some $\delta > 0$,

$$\varrho_2\left(\lim_{n \to \infty} f_n(x), y\right) = \varrho_2(f(x), y) < \varepsilon - \delta$$

and there is an integer m with

$$\varrho_2(f_n(x), y) < \varepsilon - \delta \qquad (\text{all } n \geqslant m)$$

and (x, y) is in the right side. Conversely, if (x, y) is in the right side there are a $\delta > 0$ and an integer m, such that, for all $n \geqslant m$,

$$\varrho_2(f_n(x), y) < \varepsilon - \delta, \qquad \varrho_2(f(x), y) \leqslant \varepsilon - \delta < \varepsilon$$

by convergence, and (x, y) is in the left side.

THEOREM 19.3. *Let T_1 be a space and (T_2, ϱ_2) a pseudometric space. Let $f_n : T_1 \to T_2$. If f is the pointwise limit of $\{f_n\}$ in T_1, and if G is open in T_1, there is a sequence $\{G_j\}$ of open sets in T_2, with union G, with $\bar{G}_j \subseteq G$ (all j), and with*

$$f^{-1}(G) = \bigcup_{j=1}^{\infty} \bigcup_{m=1}^{\infty} \bigcap_{n \geqslant m} f_n^{-1}(G_j)$$

Proof. The existence of $\{G_j\}$ uses ϱ_2 as in the proof of Theorem 18.1 (18.3). If $x \in f^{-1}(G)$, then for some j, m, and all $n \geqslant m$,

$$f(x) \in G, \quad f(x) \in G_j, \quad f_n(x) \in G_j, \quad x \in f_n^{-1}(G_j)$$

and x lies in the right side. Conversely, if x lies in the right side, then for some j, m, and all $n \geqslant m$,

$$x \in f_n^{-1}(G_j), \quad f_n(x) \in G_j, \quad f(x) \in \bar{G}_j \subseteq G, \quad x \in f^{-1}(G)$$

In a useful and precise sense each $f \in \mathcal{BF}(T_1)$ is almost continuous when T_1, T_2 satisfy reasonable conditions.

THEOREM 19.4. *If $(T_1, \mathcal{G}_1)$ is a Baire space, (T_2, ϱ_2) a pseudometric space, and $f \in \mathcal{BF}(T_1)$, there is a $Z \subseteq T_1$ of the first $\mathcal{G}_1$-category such that f is continuous in $\backslash Z$.*

Proof. For f continuous we take Z empty. Further, if $\{f_n\}$ is pointwise convergent to some f as $n \to \infty$, and if f_n is continuous in $\backslash Z_n$, where Z_n is of the first $\mathcal{G}_1$-category $(n = 1, 2, \ldots)$ then for each n, f_n is continuous in $\backslash Z_0$, where Z_0 is the union of the Z_j $(j = 1, 2, \ldots)$, so that Z_0 is of the first $\mathcal{G}_1$-category.

For each $\varepsilon > 0$, let $X_{mn}(\varepsilon)$ be the set of $x \in T_1$ with $\varrho_2(f_m, f_n) \le \varepsilon$. This set is $\mathcal{G}_1$-closed in $\backslash Z_0$ as f_m and f_n are continuous there. Hence

$$X_m(\varepsilon) \equiv \bigcap_{n>m} X_{mn}(\varepsilon) = \{x : \varrho_2(f_m, f_n) \le \varepsilon \ (all \ n > m)\}$$

is also $\mathcal{G}_1$-closed in $\backslash Z_0$. As $\{f_n\}$ is pointwise convergent in T_1, then T_1 is the union of $X_m(\varepsilon)$ for $m = 1, 2, \ldots$ T_1 being a Baire space, given an arbitrary non-empty $G \in \mathcal{G}_1$, there is an integer m such that $X_m(\varepsilon)$ is $\mathcal{G}_1$-dense in a portion G_1 of G. Then $G_1 \backslash Z_0 \subseteq X_m(\varepsilon)$ since $X_m(\varepsilon)$ is $\mathcal{G}_1$-closed in $\backslash Z_0$. Further, we have $\varrho_2(f_m, f) \le \varepsilon$ in $X_m(\varepsilon)$ on letting $n \to \infty$. As f_m is continuous in $\backslash Z_0$, there is a neighbourhood $G(x) \subseteq G_1$, of each $x \in G_1 \backslash Z_0$, such that the oscillation of f on $G(x) \backslash Z_0$ is less than 3ε. The complement of the union of all such G_1, is a nowhere $\mathcal{G}_1$-dense set $Z(\varepsilon)$, since there is a G_1 in each $G \in \mathcal{G}_1$. Taking $\varepsilon = j^{-1}$ $(j = 1, 2, \ldots)$, we have f continuous in $\backslash Z$, where Z is the union of Z_0 and the $Z(j^{-1})$, of the first $\mathcal{G}_1$-category. Thus the property of the theorem holds for the pointwise limit of every pointwise convergent sequence of functions having the property. Hence the family of Baire functions is contained in the family of functions with the property of the theorem.

Corollary. The continuity in $\backslash Z$ can be taken relative to $\backslash Z_0$, since the oscillation on $G(x) \backslash Z_0$ is small.

As in the case of second category spaces, the use of uniform spaces does not result in a greater generality, since the imposed conditions lead to the pseudometrizability of the uniform space.

Let $f: T_1 \to T_2$. If $\mathcal{X}$ is a family of sets $X \subseteq T_1$, we denote by $(\mathcal{X})$ the family of $f(X)$, for all $X \in \mathcal{X}$. If $\mathcal{X}$ is a family of sets $X \subseteq T_2$, we denote by $f^{-1}(\mathcal{X})$ the family of $f^{-1}(X)$ for all $X \in \mathcal{X}$.

THEOREM 19.5. (19.10) *If* $f : T_1 \to T_2$, *and if* $\mathcal{X}$ *is a family of* $X \subseteq T_2$, *then*

$$f^{-1}(\mathcal{B}(\mathcal{X})) = \mathcal{B}(f^{-1}(\mathcal{X})), \quad f^{-1}(\mathcal{A}(\mathcal{X})) = \mathcal{A}(f^{-1}(\mathcal{X}))$$

(19.11)   Let $(T_j, \mathcal{G}_j)$ be a topological space with the family $\mathcal{F}_j$, of $\mathcal{G}_j$-closed sets in T_j, for $j = 1, 2$. If $f : T_1 \to T_2$ is continuous,

$$f^{-1}(\mathcal{B}(\mathcal{G}_2)) \subseteq \mathcal{B}(\mathcal{G}_1), \quad f^{-1}(\mathcal{A}(\mathcal{G}_2)) \subseteq \mathcal{A}(\mathcal{G}_1),$$
$$f^{-1}(\mathcal{B}(\mathcal{F}_2)) \subseteq \mathcal{B}(\mathcal{F}_1), \quad f^{-1}(\mathcal{A}(\mathcal{F}_2)) \subseteq \mathcal{A}(\mathcal{F}_1)$$

(19.12)   If in (19.11) f is a Baire function while $\mathcal{G}_2$ is given by a pseudometric ϱ_2, then the conclusions of (19.11) still hold.

Part of (19.12) is given by Banach (1932), p. 17, Théorème 6.

Proof. For (19.10) use *Ex. 3.24.* For (19.11) also use Theorem 9.1 (9.1; 9.3). For (19.12) use *Exs. 2.7, 3.24,* and Theorems 8.2, 18.1 (18.1), 18.3 with

(19.13) $f^{-1}(\mathcal{G}_2) \subseteq \mathcal{B}(\mathcal{G}_1)$

Thus we only have to prove this last result. Theorem 19.3 shows that if each member of a sequence $\{f_n\}$ has the property then the limit (if it exists) also has the property, and Theorem 9.1 (9.1) shows that every continuous function has the property.

Images of analytic, Borel, and even $\mathcal{G}_{1\delta}$-sets, are more difficult to study. If f is a bijection, Theorem 19.5 can be applied to f^{-1} since $f = (f^{-1})^{-1}$. If f is not a bijection all such images are analytic sets. But even if f is continuous and X a $\mathcal{G}_{1\delta}$-set, $f(X)$ can be an arbitrary set from $\mathcal{A}(\mathcal{G}_2)$. For we can apply Theorem 18.7 (18.23). To prove that images of analytic sets are analytic, we begin with continuous functions and a preliminary result.

THEOREM 19.6. *Let (T_1, ϱ_1) be a pseudometric space, T_2 a Hausdorff space. Let $X_n \subseteq T_1$ with diameter tending to 0 as $n \to \infty$, and let X_1, $X_2, \ldots$ intersect in one point, x. If $f : T_1 \to T_2$ is continuous, and if $x \in A \subseteq T_1$, then the intersection of $\mathcal{G}_2 f(AX_1)$, $\mathcal{G}_2 f(AX_2)$, $\ldots$ contains $y = f(x)$ and no other point.*

Proof. As $x \in AX_n$, then $y = f(x) \in f(AX_n)$, and y is in the final intersection. If z is in the intersection and $z \neq y$, there are disjoint $\mathcal{G}_2$-neighbourhoods G, G_1 of y, z, respectively. For each n, $z \in \mathcal{G}_2 f(AX_n)$, so that G_1 contains a point y_n of $f(AX_n)$, and an $x_n \in AX_n$ satisfies $f(x_n) = y_n$. Since $x, x_n \in X_n$, $\varrho_1(x, x_n)$ is at most the diameter of X_n, and $x_n \to x$ as $n \to \infty$. Since f is continuous, $y_n \to y$, and there is an integer N with $y_n \in G(n \geqslant N)$. This contradicts $y_n \in G_1$ since G, G_1 are disjoint. Hence the result.

By a similar method, if (17.16) is true in Theorem 17.3, the sequence $\{\bar{G}_{2n}\}$ can have at most one point of intersection.

THEOREM 19.7. *Let (T_1, ϱ_1) be a locally complete metric space, the topology $\mathcal{Q}_1$ having a countable base, and let T_2 be a Hausdorff space. If $f : T_1 \to T_2$ is continuous and $A \subseteq T_1$ an analytic set, then $f(A)$ is analytic.*

Proof. For each $x \in T_1$ there is a $\mathcal{Q}_1$-neighbourhood, fundamental sequences within which are convergent. By Theorem 18.4 (18.8) we can suppose that A is the nucleus of a determining system of sets $X(\mathbf{n}, j)$, each being the closure of an open set of the base and lying in one of these neighbourhoods. Further, we can suppose that in (18.4) the $\mathcal{Q}_1$-neighbourhood of x has diameter less than $1/j$, obtaining new $\mathcal{H}_1$ that we can denote by $\mathcal{H}_{1j}$, and we still have $\mathcal{Q}_1 \subseteq \mathcal{H}_{1j\sigma}$. It follows that each $X(\mathbf{n}, j)$ is the union of an at most countable number of sets of $\mathcal{H}_1$ of diameter less than $1/j$. By Theorem 18.3 we can assume that the diameter of $X(\mathbf{n}, j)$ itself is less than $1/j$. As usual, we can also assume that $X(\mathbf{n}, j)$ is monotone decreasing in j.

If, for given $\mathbf{n} \in \mathcal{J}$, no $X(\mathbf{n}, j)$ is empty, then as T_1 is locally complete, the intersection of the $X(\mathbf{n}, j)$ is not empty. It can have only one point, x, as ϱ_1 is a metric. By Theorem 19.6 $f(x)$ is the only common point of sets $\mathcal{Q}_2 f(X(\mathbf{n}, j))$. Hence if the latter intersection is empty, so is the former, and $X(\mathbf{n}, j)$ is empty for some value of j onwards. Hence by *Ex. 3.19*.

$$f(A) = f\left(\bigcup_{\mathbf{n} \in \mathcal{J}} \bigcap_{j=1}^{\infty} X(\mathbf{n}, j)\right) = \bigcup_{\mathbf{n} \in \mathcal{J}} f\left(\bigcap_{j=1}^{\infty} (X(\mathbf{n}, j)\right)$$

$$= \bigcup_{\mathbf{n} \in \mathcal{J}} \bigcap_{j=1}^{\infty} \mathcal{Q}_2 f(X(\mathbf{n}, j))$$

and $f(A)$ is an analytic set in T_2 from a determining system of closed sets.

The family $\mathcal{J}$ of sequences of positive integers has the metric

$$\varrho_0(\mathbf{m}, \mathbf{n}) = \begin{cases} j(\mathbf{m}, \mathbf{n})^{-1} & (\mathbf{m} \neq \mathbf{n}) \\ 0 & (\mathbf{m} = \mathbf{n}) \end{cases}$$

where $j(\mathbf{m}, \mathbf{n})$ is the integer j such that $m_k = n_k$ for all $k < j$, but $m_j \neq n_j$. Then $(\mathcal{J}, \varrho_0)$ is called the *Baire null space*.

THEOREM 19.8. *Let* (T, ϱ) *be a locally complete metric space with a countable base. If A is an analytic set in T, and if $(\mathcal{J}, \varrho_0)$ is the Baire null space, there is a continuous function $f: \mathcal{J} \to T$ with $f(\mathcal{J}) = A$.*

Proof. As in Theorem 19.7, A is the nucleus of a determining system $X(\mathbf{n}, j)$,

$$X(\mathbf{n}, j) \subseteq X(\mathbf{n}, j+1) \quad (j \geqslant 1), \quad diam \ X(\mathbf{n}, j) \to 0 (j \to \infty) \quad (all \ \mathbf{n} \in \mathcal{J}),$$

$$X(\mathbf{n}) \equiv \bigcap_{j=1}^{\infty} X(\mathbf{n}, j)$$

and either $X(\mathbf{n}) = \text{sing}(x)$ for some $x \in A$, or $X(\mathbf{n}, j)$ is empty for some j onwards. In the first case we put $f(\mathbf{n}) = x$, so that $f(\mathcal{J}) \supseteq A$. To ensure equality we first choose fixed points

$$x_0 \in A, \quad x(\mathbf{n}, j) \in A \cap X(\mathbf{n}, j)$$

for all j such that the last intersection does not vanish. If $X(\mathbf{n})$ is empty, $X(\mathbf{n}, k)$ is empty for k large enough. If $A \cap X(\mathbf{n}, 1)$ is empty we put $f(\mathbf{n}) = x_0$, while if $A \cap X(\mathbf{n}, j)$ is the last non-empty set of the sequence for increasing j, we put $f(\mathbf{n}) = x(\mathbf{n}, j)$. Then $f(\mathcal{J}) = A$, and we only have to prove f continuous. Let $\mathbf{m} \to \mathbf{n}$, $y = f(\mathbf{m})$, $x = f(\mathbf{n})$, and let k be an integer. Then for $\mathbf{m}$ near enough to $\mathbf{n}$, $m_l = n_l$ $(l \leqslant k)$. If $X(\mathbf{n})$ is not empty then x, y belong to the same $X(\mathbf{n}, k)$, with diameter tending to 0 as $k \to \infty$, so that $\varrho(y, x) \to 0$. If $X(\mathbf{n})$ is empty, then $y = x$ as soon as $k > h$, or even for all $k > 0$, depending on whether $A \cap X(\mathbf{n}, h)$ is the last non-empty set, or $A \cap X(\mathbf{n}, 1)$ is empty. Hence the result.

THEOREM 19.9. *Let f be a Baire function $f: T_1 \to T_2$, where T_1, T_2 are locally complete metric spaces with countable bases. If A is an analytic set of T_1, then $f(A)$ is an analytic set of T_2.*

Proof. If the metric in T_j is ϱ_j $(j = 1, 2)$, a suitable metric on $T_1 \times T_2$ is

$$\varrho((x, y), (x', y')) = \{\varrho_1(x, x')^2 + \varrho_2(y, y')^2\}^{1/2}$$

The Cartesian product of the countable bases for T_1, T_2, is a countable base for $T_1 \times T_2$; while $T_1 \times T_2$ is a locally complete space. For if $\{(x_n, y_n)\}$ is a fundamental sequence in $T_1 \times T_2$, then $\{x_n\}$ and $\{y_n\}$ are fundamental sequences in T_1, T_2, respectively. If, further, $\{(x_n, y_n)\}$ lies in some $G_1(x) \times G_2(y)$, where $G_1(x)$, $G_2(y)$ are the neighbourhoods of $x \in T_1$, $y \in T_2$, respectively, that occur in the definition of local completeness, then $x_n \in G_1(x)$, $y_n \in G_2(y)$ (all n), and the sequences are convergent. Hence so is the sequence $\{(x_n, y_n)\}$. Further, we consider the set in $T_1 \times T_2$,

$$X(f; \varepsilon) \equiv \{(x, y) : \varrho_2(f(x), y) < \varepsilon\}$$

If f is continuous this is open. By Theorem 19.2, $X(f; \varepsilon)$ is a Borel set when f is a Baire function. (Naturally we take $\delta = 1/j$ for integers j that are large enough.) Since ϱ_2 is a metric,

$$X(f) \equiv \{(x, y) : f(x) = y\} = \bigcap_{j=1}^{\infty} X(f; 1/j)$$

is a Borel set. Its intersection with the analytic set $A \times T_2$ is the analytic set

$$\{(x, y) : x \in A, \ y = f(x)\}$$

and the projection of this set on to T_2, is the set $f(A)$. This is analytic by Theorem 19.7, since the projection function is continuous.

THEOREM 19.10. (Banach (1932), p. 18, Théorème 8). *If ϱ_2 is a pseudometric in T_2 and if $f_j : T_1 \to T_2 (j = 1, 2)$ are Baire functions, then $\varrho_2(f_1(.), f_2(.)) : T_1 \to R$ is a Baire function, where R is the real line.*

Proof. If f_1, f_2 are continuous, so is $\varrho_2 (f_1, f_2)$. Also by (11.5),

$$\varrho_2(x, y) = \varrho_2(y, x)$$

is continuous in y, so that

$$\varrho_2 \left(\lim_{m \to \infty} f_m, \lim_{n \to \infty} g_n \right) = \lim_{m \to \infty} \lim_{n \to \infty} \varrho_2(f_m, g_n)$$

Hence the result.

THEOREM 19.11. (Banach (1932), p. 18, Théorème 9). *Let ϱ_2 be a pseudometric in T_2, and let $f_n : T_1 \to T_2$ be Baire functions for $n = 1$,*

$2, \ldots$ *Then the set X of points where the sequence is fundamental, is a Borel set.*

Proof. As in Theorem 19.2, if f is the pointwise limit of $\{f_n\}$, where the values of each f_n are real and non-negative, then

$$\{x : f(x) < \varepsilon\} = \bigcup_{\delta > 0} \bigcup_{m=1}^{\infty} \bigcap_{n=m}^{\infty} \{x : f_n(x) < \varepsilon - \delta\}$$

It follows that if f is a non-negative Baire function, the set of points where $f < \varepsilon$, is a Borel set. Hence by Theorem 19.10,

$$X_{jkl} \equiv \{x : \varrho_2(f_j(x), f_k(x)) < l^{-1}\} \qquad (j, k, l = 1, 2, \ldots)$$

is a Borel set. Hence the result, since

$$X = \bigcap_{l=1}^{\infty} \bigcup_{j=1}^{\infty} \bigcap_{k=j}^{\infty} X_{jkl}$$

THEOREM 19.12. (Banach (1932), p. 18, Théorème 10). *If $\{f_n\}$ and $\{g_n\}$ are sequences of Baire functions, and if, for each $x \in T_1$,*

$$h(x) \equiv \lim_{n \to \infty} \sup \varrho_2(f_n(x), g_n(x)) < \infty$$

then h is a Baire function.

Proof. For integers j, k we put

$$h_{jk}(x) \equiv \sup_{j < n < j+k} \varrho_2(f_n(x), g_n(x)), \qquad h(x) = \lim_{j \to \infty} \lim_{k \to \infty} h_{jk}(x)$$

Thus we need only show that each h_{jk} is a Baire function. By Theorem 19.10, $h_{j1}(x)$ is a Baire function. Further,

$$h_{j, k+1}(x) = \tfrac{1}{2}\{h_{jk}(x) + h_{j+k, 1}(x) + |h_{jk}(x) - h_{j+k, 1}(x)|\}$$

so that by using induction, and ϱ_2 as the modulus in Theorem 19.10, we prove the result.

THEOREM 19.13. *Let $(T_1, \mathcal{G}_1)$ be a Baire space, and (T_2, ϱ_2) a complete metric space, and $f_n : T_1 \to T_2$ $(n = 1, 2, \ldots)$ Baire functions. If $\{f_n\}$ is convergent in a set X of the second $\mathcal{G}_1$-category, and divergent outside X, then $\{f_n\}$ is equicontinuous relative to Y in a set Y of the second $\mathcal{G}_1$-category, with $X \backslash Y$ of the first $\mathcal{G}_1$-category. If the f_n are continuous in T_1, the equicontinuity is relative to T_1.*

This is a generalization of Alexiewicz (1950), Theorem 1, p. 5, the proof there being suggested by S. Mazur.

Proof. By Theorem 19.11, and since T_2 is complete, X is a Borel set. By Theorems 18.3, 18.5, X is a Baire set, so that there is a non-empty $G \in \mathcal{G}_1$ with $X \backslash G$ and $G \backslash X$ of the first $\mathcal{G}_1$-category. By Theorem 19.4, each f_n is continuous in $G \backslash Z$ for some Z independent of n and of the first $\mathcal{G}_1$-category. By including $G \backslash X$ in Z we have the following result.

(19.14) Each f_n ($n = 1, 2, \ldots$) is continuous in $G \backslash Z$, and $\{f_n\}$ is pointwise convergent in $G \backslash Z$, where $G \in \mathcal{G}_1$ is not empty, with Z of the first $\mathcal{G}_1$-category.

Following S. Mazur, we use the space c of convergent sequences $\mathbf{y} = \{y_n\}$ of elements of T_2, but using the simpler metric

$$\varrho(\mathbf{y}_1, \mathbf{y}_2) = \sup_{n > 1} \varrho_2(y_{1n}, y_{2n})$$

The sequence $\{f_n\}$ may now be considered as a function $\mathbf{f} : T_1 \to c$, and the continuity of $\mathbf{f}$ at $x_0 \in T_1$, is clearly equivalent to the equicontinuity of the f_n at x_0, where both continuity and equicontinuity are taken relative to $G \backslash Z$. However, if in (19.14) each f_n is continuous in T_1, and not just in $G \backslash Z$, the continuity of $\mathbf{f}$ and equicontinuity of the f_n are taken relative to T_1. For each fixed j we now put

$$f_{jn}(x) = \begin{cases} f_n(x) & (n \leqslant j) \\ f_j(x) & (n > j) \end{cases} \qquad \mathbf{f}_j(x) = \{f_{jn}(x)\}$$

By finite intersection of open sets, each $\mathbf{f}_j$ is continuous in $G \backslash Z$ (or in T_1). Applying Theorem 19.4 again, as in the last statement of the proof of the theorem, we see that $\mathbf{f} = \lim_{j \to \infty} \mathbf{f}_j$ is continuous relative to $G \backslash Z$ (or T_1) in a set $Y \subseteq G$ with $G \backslash Y$ of the first $\mathcal{G}_1$-category. As $X \backslash Y$ is also then of the first $\mathcal{G}_1$-category, we have proved the result.

The characteristic function $ch(X; x)$ of a set $X \subseteq T$ has been defined in *Ex.* 4.14 as the function that takes the value 1 in X and 0 in $\backslash X$.

THEOREM 19.14. *If T is a pseudometric space, the characteristic function of each Borel set is a Baire function.*

Proof. From Theorem 11.5 (11.13), a pseudometric space is normal. From Theorem 10.4 (Urysohn), if F_1, F_2 are disjoint closed sets, there is a continuous function f on T to [0, 1], with $f = 0$ on F_1, $f = 1$ on F_2. From Theorem 18.1 (18.3), every open set in T is the union of a countable number of closed sets. If G is the open set and $\{F_n\}$ the sequence of closed sets, we can assume the sequence monotone increasing. Then $\backslash G$ and F_n are disjoint closed sets, so that there is a continuous function f_n with value 0 on $\backslash G$ and 1 on F_n. Thus the characteristic function of G is $\lim_{n \to \infty} f_n(x)$, a Baire function. By construction of the Borel sets, it follows that the characteristic function of each Borel set is a Baire function.

Ex. 19.1. If T_1 is locally compact with a countable base, and if A is an analytic set of T_1, show that A can be given by a determining system of sets whose closures are compact. If f is continuous and X compact, show that $f(X)$ is closed. If also f is a bijection, show that

$$f(\mathcal{A}(\mathcal{G})) = \mathcal{A}(f(\mathcal{G})) = f(\mathcal{A}(\mathcal{F})) = \mathcal{A}(f(\mathcal{F})) \subseteq \mathcal{A}(\mathcal{F}) = \mathcal{A}(\mathcal{G})$$

Ex. 19.2. Extend *Ex. 19.1.* to Baire bijections f.

Ex. 19.3. Show that in Theorem 19.9, instead of $f : T_1 \to T_2$ being a Baire function, we need only assume that

$$\{(x, y) : f(x) = y\}$$

is analytic.

Ex. 19.4. Define f to be an $(\mathcal{A})$ function, when for each $\varepsilon > 0$,

$$\{(x, y) : \varrho_2(f(x), y) < \varepsilon\}$$

is analytic, where ϱ_2 is a metric in T_2. Show that every pointwise limit of a pointwise convergent sequence of $(\mathcal{A})$ functions is an $(\mathcal{A})$ function, so that every Baire function is an $(\mathcal{A})$ function. Show also that every $(\mathcal{A})$ function satisfies the condition of *Ex. 19.3.*

Ex. 19.5. Let T_1, T_2 be locally complete metric spaces with countable bases. If f is an $(\mathcal{A})$ function or, more generally, a function satisfying *Ex. 19.3*, show that the relations between families given in the last line of *Ex. 19.1* still holds.

5

THE PRINCIPLES OF UPPER
BOUNDEDNESS AND UNIFORM
CONVERGENCE

20. Upper Boundedness and Upper Limits in a Topological Space

WE continue the study of the upper boundedness theorem, bringing in the topology $\mathcal{G}$ of T, and assuming throughout the notation of Chapter 2. In particular, θ is the function in $T \times T$ to T. Sometimes we have:

(20.1) Every non-empty open set G is a θ-base for T.

But in any case $Th(G)$ is usually a substantial part of T. Let $\mathcal{G}_0$ be the family of all *pinned* $G \in \mathcal{G}$, i.e. $G \in \mathcal{G}$ is not empty, and $x \in \theta(x, G)$ $(x \in G)$. Then an $X \subseteq T$ is a Th_n-$\mathcal{G}$-set, if $Th_n(X) \supseteq G$ for some $G \in \mathcal{G}_0$; and $X \subseteq T$ is a *Th-$\mathcal{G}$-set*, if X is a Th_n-$\mathcal{G}$-set for some integer n. By Theorem 6.1 (6.2), a *Th-$\mathcal{G}$*-set X has $Th(X) = T$, if (20.1) is true, and this explains the usefulness of the definition.

Let $L(\lambda)$ be the function of section 5, i.e. it is finite, real, and monotone increasing in $\lambda \geqslant 0$, with a conventional $L(+\infty) = +\infty$, and

(20.2) $\quad L(\lambda) \geqslant L_0(\lambda) \equiv \lambda, \quad L_{n+1}(\lambda) \equiv L(L_n(\lambda)) \geqslant L_n(\lambda) \geqslant 0 \quad (n \geqslant 0)$

A function N on T to the extended real line (i.e. $-\infty$ and $+\infty$ are allowed) is a *θ-L convex function* if

(20.3) $\qquad N(\theta(x, y)) \leqslant L\left(\sup\{N(x); N(y); 0\}\right) \qquad (x, y \in T)$

(20.4) e.g. $\qquad N(\theta(x, y)) \leqslant N(x) + N(y), \quad L(\lambda) = 2\lambda$

Theorem 5.1 on upper boundedness now takes a more special form.

98

THEOREM 20.1. *If N is a θ-L convex function, and if, for some real $\lambda \geqslant 0$, the set $P(\lambda)$, of x where $N(x) \leqslant \lambda$, is a Th_n-$\mathcal{G}$-set, then a $G \in \mathcal{G}_0$ has*

(20.5) $$N(x) \leqslant M = L_n(\lambda) \qquad (x \in G)$$

(20.6) $$N(\theta(x, y)) \leqslant L\left(\sup\{M; N(y)\}\right) \qquad (x \in G)$$

(20.7) $$N(x) < +\infty \quad \text{in} \quad P(\lambda) \cup Th(P(\lambda))$$

(20.8) *If (20.1) is true, or, more generally, if $P(\lambda)$ is a θ-base for T, then $N(x) < +\infty$ (all $x \in T$).*

(20.9) *If X is the set where $N(x) < +\infty$, then $X \supseteq Th(X)$.*

(20.10) *If $L(0) = 0$, and if $N(x) \leqslant 0$ in X, then $N(x) \leqslant 0$ in $Th(X)$.*

The proofs are straightforward.

A modification deals with uniform upper limits. If (20.3) is not necessarily true, but is true for all $x, y \in P(\varepsilon)$, for some $\varepsilon > 0$, we can say that N is a *restricted θ-L convex function*.

THEOREM 20.2. *Let N be a restricted θ-L convex function, and let n (e.g. $n = 1$) be independent of λ in $0 < \lambda \leqslant \varepsilon$, such that, for all these λ, $P(\lambda)$ is a Th_n-$\mathcal{G}$-set. If $L(0+) = 0$, then for each $\lambda > 0$, $N \leqslant \lambda$ in some $G \in \mathcal{G}_0$. In some sense this implies that $\lim \sup N(x) \leqslant 0$. If each $G \in \mathcal{G}_0$ contains a point u independent of G, and if each neighbourhood of u is in $\mathcal{G}_0$, then the 'lim sup' occurs as $x \to u$ in the topology $\mathcal{G}$. If $N \geqslant 0$ in T, then 'lim sup' can be replaced by 'lim'.*

The proof uses (20.5) since $L_1(0+) = 0$, $L_2(0+) = 0,\ldots$

We can now add a few results to Theorem 5.3.

THEOREM 20.3. *If in Theorem 5.3, $P_a(\lambda)$ is closed for each $a \in A$, then $P^\circ(\lambda)$ is closed. If A is countable, and $P_a(\lambda)$ a Borel or analytic set, then $P^\circ(\lambda)$ is a Borel or analytic set, respectively. In the three cases $P^1(\lambda)$ is an $F_{\sigma\delta}$-set, a Borel set, and an analytic set, respectively. Here, $P_a(\lambda)$, $P^\circ(\lambda)$, $P^1(\lambda)$ are the respective sets where*

$$N(a, x) \leqslant \lambda, \quad \sup_{a \in A} N(a, x) \leqslant \lambda, \quad \lim_{a \to \infty} \sup N(a, x) \leqslant \lambda \quad (a \geqslant 0 \text{ in } A)$$

The results follow from (5.21).

When $N(a, x)$ is monotone increasing in a for each fixed x, then (5.15; 5.16; 5.17) coincide. But otherwise (5.16) need not give a closed set even when each $P_a(\lambda)$ is closed. (See *Ex. 20.1*.)

Theorems 20.1, 20.2 can be generalized to cover mappings from one topological space to another, but results in this direction are omitted.

Historical Notes. The $Th_n\text{-}\mathcal{G}$-sets and $Th\text{-}\mathcal{G}$-sets generalize the H_n-sets and H-sets of Henstock (1963a), p. 307. The case $n = 1$ of Theorem 20.2 generalizes Pettis (1950), p. 296, Theorem 1, Corollary 1.2, and p. 305, concluding remark (2).

Alexiewicz (1950a, b; 1951a, b) gives a general theory based on a rather different plan from that adopted here. First, Alexiewicz defines the equicontinuity of the functions f of a family $\mathcal{D}$ at a point $x \in T_1$, as at the beginning of section 19. Note that as in Mazur's proof of part of Theorem 19.13, we can put

$$N(x, y) \equiv \sup_{f \in \mathcal{D}} \varrho_2(f(x), f(y))$$

Then $N(x, y)$ is continuous in x at $x = y$ if and only if $\mathcal{D}$ is equicontinuous at y, for $N(y, y) = 0$. Theorem 20.2 gives results in connection with this.

The essential plan of Alexiewicz is that he omits any connection, such as are supplied by $\theta(x, y)$ and $Th_n(X)$, between certain subsets of T_1 and larger subsets such as T_1 itself, and he postulates what is required. The postulates, for sequences of functions, have been altered by errata facing Alexiewicz (1950), p. 1, and are as follows:

(r_1) Equicontinuity in a residual implies equicontinuity,
(r_2) Equicontinuity in a second category set implies equicontinuity,
(r_3) Equicontinuity in a second category set implies uniform equicontinuity,
(c) Convergence in a sphere implies convergence everywhere.

We can still use (r_1, r_2, c) if we replace the pseudometric space (T_1, ϱ_1) of Alexiewicz by a Baire space $(T_1, \mathcal{G}_1)$. But, as shown in Chapter 2, the arguments used in proceeding from a subset X to a larger subset possibly equal to T_1, are independent of the topology, although topological properties give the strongest results found so far. If we drop topology from the postulates of Alexiewicz it would be difficult to decide what to put in its place. For that reason I have kept to my original plan of using θ and Th_n-sets, specializing the results of Alexiewicz in one direction in order to generalize in another direction by making the topology unnecessary but very useful.

Ex. 20.1. Let T be the space of reals, with $\theta(x, y) = x - y$, and put

$$N(j, x) = \begin{cases} 1 & (x \leqslant -j^{-1}) \\ jx+2 & (-j^{-1} \leqslant x \leqslant 0) \\ 2 & (x \geqslant 0) \end{cases}$$

Show that each $N(j, x)$ satisfies (20.4), and that, for each fixed x, $N(j, x)$ is monotone decreasing as $j \to \infty$. Find $\lim_{j \to \infty} N(j, x)$ and show that the set where the limit is not greater than 1, is not closed in the modulus topology.

21. The Thickness of a Set in a Topological Space

The results of section 6 can in turn be made richer on supposing that the space T has a topology $\mathcal{G}$. For simplicity we assume that for each fixed y, $\theta(x, y)$ is an injection. Then there is a single point in the inverse image $\theta^{-1}(v, y)$ for each $v \in \theta(T, y)$, so that we can define an inverse *function*, and we can use the same notation $\theta^{-1}(v, y)$. The family $\mathcal{O}$ of Theorem 6.2 is taken to be the family $\mathcal{G}_0$ of pinned open sets, and we can sometimes weaken (20.1) to the requirement (21.1) each $G \in \mathcal{G}_0$ is a θ-base for T.

A set $X \subseteq T$ is now a strong θ-base for T, if there is a $G \in \mathcal{G}_0$ with

$$Th(X^v) = T(v \in G), \quad X^v \equiv X \cap \theta^{-1}(v, X)$$

Let $Z \subseteq T \times T$. A function $f(x, y)$ in Z to T is *continuous in x to the identity* if, given a non-empty $G \in \mathcal{G}$, there are a $y \in G$ and a $G_1 \in \mathcal{G}_0$, such that (v, y) is in Z and $f(v, y)$ in G, for each $v \in G_1$. If this occurs for all $y \in G$, we say that f is *strongly continuous in x to the identity*. Also $f(x, y)$ is *open in y* for each fixed $x \in T$, if $f(x, G) \in \mathcal{G}$ for each

$G \in \mathcal{G}$. If $f(x, y)$ is continuous in x to the identity, and open in y for each fixed $x \in T$, we say that f is *stable*.

If $x \in \theta(x, X)$ for some $X \subseteq T$ and each $x \in T$, and not just each $x \in X$, we say that X is *strongly pinned*.

T is *connected* if no closed non-empty $X \subset T$ can be open.

THEOREM 21.1. *(21.2) If $\theta^{-1}(x, y)$ is continuous in x for each fixed $y \in T$, then $\theta(G, G) \in \mathcal{G}$, $Th(G) \in \mathcal{G}$ $(G \in \mathcal{G})$.*

(21.3) If each non-empty $G \in \mathcal{G}$ is a Th_n-$\mathcal{G}$-set, (21.1) implies (20.1).

(21.4) $\theta^{-1}(x, y)$ is continuous in x to the identity if and only if, for each non-empty $G \in \mathcal{G}$, there are $y \in G$ and $G_1 \in \mathcal{G}_0$ with $G_1 \subseteq \theta(G, y)$, and then $G_1 \subseteq \theta(G, G)$.

(21.5) Let each $G_1 \in \mathcal{G}_0$ be strongly pinned, and let $\theta^{-1}(x, y)$ be continuous in x for each $y \in T$, and stable. If $G \in \mathcal{G}$ then $Th(G)$ is open and closed. If also T is connected, then either G is empty or $Th(G) = T$.

(21.6) If θ^{-1} is stable, and $G \in \mathcal{G}$ not empty, there is a $G_1 \in \mathcal{G}_0$ such that the non-empty $G^v \in \mathcal{G}$ $(v \in G_1)$.

(21.7) In (21.6), (21.1) implies that each non-empty open set is a strong θ-base for T.
A set $X \subseteq T$ is a Th_1-$\mathcal{G}$-set if $\theta^{-1}(x, y)$ is continuous in x to the identity, and if any one of the following hold:

(21.8) X contains a non-empty $G \in \mathcal{G}$,

(21.9) $G \backslash X$ is nowhere dense in T, for some non-empty $G \in \mathcal{G}$,

(21.10) X is closed, and is either dense in some non-empty $G \in \mathcal{G}$, or is of the second category.

Proof. For (21.2) we use Theorem 9.1 (9.1). If

$$G \in \mathcal{G}, \quad \theta(G, y) \in \mathcal{G},$$

$$\theta(G, G) = \bigcup_{y \in G} \theta(G, y) \in \mathcal{G}. \quad Th(G) = \bigcup_{n=1}^{\infty} Th_n(G) \in \mathcal{G}$$

102

For (21.3) we use (21.1) and Theorem 6.1 (6.2). If $G \in \mathcal{G}$ is not empty,

$$Th_n(G) \supseteq G_1 \in \mathcal{G}_0, \quad Th(G) \supseteq Th(Th_n(G)) \supseteq Th(G_1) = T,$$
$$Th(G) = T$$

For (21.4) let the non-empty $G \in \mathcal{G}$, with θ^{-1} continuous in x to the identity. Then there are $y \in G$ and $G_1 \in \mathcal{G}_0$ such that, for each $v \in G_1$, $v \in \theta(T, y)$, $x \equiv \theta^{-1}(v, y) \in G$. Then $v = \theta\,(x, y) \in \theta\,(G, y) \subseteq \theta(G, G)$. Conversely, if there are $y \in G$ and $G_1 \in \mathcal{G}_0$ such that $G_1 \subseteq \theta(G, y)$, then

$$v = \theta(x, y) \quad (v \in G_1, \quad some \quad x \in G), \quad x = \theta^{-1}(v, y)$$

and θ^{-1} is continuous in x to the identity.

For (21.5) let $G \in \mathcal{G}$ be non-empty. From (21.2), $Th(G) \in \mathcal{G}$, and from (21.4), $G_1 \subseteq \theta(G, G)$ for some $G_1 \in \mathcal{G}_0$. Let $x \in Th(G)'$. Then $x \in \theta^{-1}(x, G_1)$ since G_1 is strongly pinned. Also $G_1 \in \mathcal{G}$ and θ^{-1} is open in y, so that $\theta^{-1}(x, G_1) \in \mathcal{G}$. Hence there are y, g satisfying

$$y \in Th(G) \cap \theta^{-1}(x, G_1), \quad g \in G_1 \subseteq \theta(G, G), \quad y = \theta^{-1}(x, g),$$
$$x = \theta(y, g)$$

As $y \in Th(G)$, there is an integer m with $y \in Th_m(G)$. As G_1 is pinned, $\{Th_n(G_1)\}$ is monotone increasing. Also $Th_{m-1}(G_1) \subseteq Th_m(G)$. Hence $g \in G_1 \subseteq Th_{m-1}(G_1)$; $g, y \in Th_m(G)$; $x \in Th_{m+1}(G) \subseteq Th(G)$, and $Th(G)$ is closed. Thus if $G \in \mathcal{G}$, $Th(G)$ is open and closed. If T is also connected and G not empty, $Th(G)$ is not empty since $\theta(x, y)$ is defined in $T \times T$, and $Th(G) = T$. (By *Ex. 21.3* it is not enough to have G_1 pinned.)

For (21.6), $\theta^{-1}(v, G)$ contains $\theta^{-1}(v, y) \in G$, for some $y \in G$ and all $v \in G_1$, and G^v is not empty. As θ^{-1} is open in y for each fixed x, $\theta^{-1}(v, G) \in \mathcal{G}$, $G^v \in \mathcal{G}$. For (21.7) we use (21.3; 21.4; 21.6). For (21.8) we use (21.4). In (21.9) we use Theorem 12.1 (12.1). Each non-empty $G \in \mathcal{G}$ contains a non-empty $G_2 \in \mathcal{G}$ free from points of the closure of $G \backslash X$, $G \cap X$ contains G_2, and we use (21.8). In (21.10) a set of the second category is dense in some non-empty open set, and in both cases since X is closed, X contains a non-empty open set and we use (21.8).

Using $\mathcal{G}$ with section 6, we examine properties of sets in more detail, $\mathcal{P}$ denoting the family of sets $X \subseteq T$ with property p. If p is p_j we put $\mathcal{P}_j$ for $\mathcal{P}$. We also note definitions (6.9; ...; 6.17) and add the following:

(21.11) We call T a $\bar{p}$-$\mathcal{G}$-space if each $G \in \mathcal{G} \cap \mathcal{P}$ is empty, i.e. if each non-empty open set is 'thick'.

(21.12) A set $X \subseteq T$ is a p-$\mathcal{G}$-Baire set if $G \backslash X \in \mathcal{P}$ for some non-empty $G \in \mathcal{G}$. In (6.11; 6.12) we also substitute $\mathcal{G}_0$ for $\mathcal{O}$.

THEOREM 21.2 (21.13) *If p is shrinkable and finitely additive, if T is a $\bar{p}$-$\mathcal{G}$-space, and if $X \subseteq T$ is a p-$\mathcal{G}$-Baire set, then $X \notin \mathcal{P}$.* (21.14) *If θ^{-1} is stable, and T a $\bar{p}$-$\mathcal{G}$-space, then each non-empty $G \in \mathcal{G}$ is strongly-$\bar{p}$, and each p-$\mathcal{G}$-Baire set X is a p-Baire set.* (21.15) *If in (21.14) p is shrinkable, θ^{-1}-invariant and finitely additive, then X is a Th_1-$\mathcal{G}$-set.*

Proof. If in (21.13), $G \in \mathcal{G}$ is non-empty and $G \backslash X \in \mathcal{P}$, then $G \cap X \in \mathcal{P}$ implies that $G \in \mathcal{P}$, which is false. Hence $G \cap X \notin \mathcal{P}$, $X \notin \mathcal{P}$. (21.14) follows from (21.6), and (21.15) from (21.14) and Theorem 6.3, as $\mathcal{O} = \mathcal{G}_0$ here.

In the case of (21.14) we restrict our study of p-Baire sets to the p-$\mathcal{G}$-Baire sets.

By using the topology $\mathcal{G}$ we can define the property p_3 of being nowhere dense. We use continuity of θ^{-1} and three other properties that are sufficient to ensure that p_3 is θ^{-1}-invariant.

(21.16) For each fixed $x \in T$, θ^{-1} is open in y, using $T_1 = T$, $T_2 = \theta^{-1}(x, T)$, $\mathcal{G}_1 = \mathcal{G}$, and $\mathcal{G}_2$ the relative topology of T_2 from $\mathcal{G}$.

(21.17) For each fixed $x \in T$, θ^{-1} is an injection in y.

(21.18) For each fixed $x \in T$, $\theta^{-1}(x, T)$ is closed.

(21.17; 21.16) give the existence and continuity of an inverse function of $\theta^{-1}(x, y)$ relative to y.

THEOREM 21.3. (21.19) *If θ^{-1} satisfies (21.16; ...; 21.18), then for* $X \subseteq T$, $x \in T$,

$$\theta^{-1}(x, \bar{X}) \supseteq \mathcal{G}\theta^{-1}(x, X)$$

(21.20) *If $\theta^{-1}(x, y)$ is continuous in y, then*

$$\theta^{-1}(x, \bar{X}) \subseteq \mathcal{G}\theta^{-1}(x, X)$$

(21.21) *If (21.19; 21.20) hold, and if X is nowhere dense (or of the first category) in X_1, then $\theta^{-1}(x, X)$ is nowhere dense (or of the first category) in $\theta^{-1}(x, X_1)$.*

Proof. For (21.19) we use Theorem 8.2 and (21.16; ...; 21.18). Then

$$\backslash \bar{X} \in \mathcal{G}, \quad \theta^{-1}(x, \backslash \bar{X}) = G \cap \theta^{-1}(x, T) \text{ (some } G \in \mathcal{G}),$$

$$\theta^{-1}(x, X) \subseteq \theta^{-1}(x, \bar{X}) = \theta^{-1}(x, T) \backslash \theta^{-1}(x, \backslash \bar{X}) = \theta^{-1}(x, T)\backslash G,$$

an intersection of closed sets, and so closed. Hence the result.

Theorem 9.1 (9.2) gives (21.20). If (21.19; 21.20) are true, then

$$(21.22) \qquad \qquad \theta^{-1}(x, \bar{X}) = \mathcal{G}\theta^{-1}(x, X)$$

Thus in (21.21), if $\theta^{-1}(x, X)$ is not nowhere dense in $\theta^{-1}(x, X_1)$, then $\theta^{-1}(x, \bar{X})$ contains the non-empty $G \cap \theta^{-1}(x, X_1)$, for some $G \in \mathcal{G}$, and for a $y \in \bar{X}$, $\theta^{-1}(x, y) \in G \cap \theta^{-1}(x, X_1)$, $y \in X_1$. By continuity, openness, and (21.17), there are $G_j \in \mathcal{G}$ ($j = 1, 2$) with

$$y \in G_1, \quad \theta^{-1}(x, G_1) \subseteq G, \quad \theta^{-1}(x, G_1) = G_2 \cap \theta^{-1}(x, T), \quad G_2 \subseteq G$$

or else we can replace G_2 by $G_2 \cap G$. Hence

$$\theta^{-1}(x, \bar{X}) \supseteq G \cap \theta^{-1}(x, X_1) \supseteq G_2 \cap \theta^{-1}(x, X_1) = \theta^{-1}(x, G_1) \cap \theta^{-1}(x, X_1)$$

$$= \theta^{-1}(x, G_1 \cap X_1), \quad \bar{X} \supseteq G_1 \cap X_1$$

and X is dense in $G_1 \cap X_1$. This set contains y and so is not empty, giving a contradiction. Hence the first result, and so the second. They show that p_3 and the property p_4 of being of the first category, are θ^{-1}-invariant if θ^{-1} is continuous in y and satisfies (21.16; ...; 21.18).

A p_3-$\mathcal{G}$-Baire set X is trivial as $G\backslash X$ is nowhere dense for some non-empty $G \in \mathcal{G}$, giving (21.9). But p_4 is important. A $\bar{p}_4$-$\mathcal{G}$-space is a Baire space, so that a p_4-$\mathcal{G}$-Baire set in such a space is a set containing a Baire set of the second category in a Baire space. Most applications of the Hahn–Banach–Steinhaus theorem use this.

THEOREM 21.4 (21.23) p_3 and p_4 are finitely additive and shrinkable. (21.24) If θ^{-1} is stable, and a continuous injection in y, with $\theta^{-1}(x, T)$ closed, and if $E \subseteq T$ contains a Baire set of the second category in the Baire space T, then $Th_1(E) \supseteq G$ for some $G \in \mathcal{G}_0$, so that $G \in \mathcal{G}$ is non-empty.

Proof. Theorem 12.1 (12.2) and *Ex. 12.9* give (21.23). For (21.24) we use the previous remarks with Theorem 21.2 (21.14), and E is a p_4-Baire set. As θ^{-1} is open in y with $T_j = T$, $\mathcal{G}_j = \mathcal{G}(j = 1, 2)$, $\theta^{-1}(x, T)$ is open and (21.16) is true. Thus (21.19; 21.20) hold and p_4 is θ^{-1}-invariant by (21.21). Using (21.23), E satisfies the conditions of Theorem 6.3, $E \in \mathcal{E}$, and $Th_1(E) \supseteq G$ for some $G \in \mathcal{G}_0$, since $\mathcal{O} = \mathcal{G}_0$ here. Hence (21.24).

It may happen that some non-empty open sets are of the first category, and then Theorem 21.4 (21.24) is useless, so that we consider definitions (6.15; ...; 6.17). Neither p_3 nor p_4 is hereditary in general, for see *Ex. 21.5*. But $p_5 = h(p_3)$ and $p_6 = h(p_4)$ are hereditary; and so are $p_7 = th(p_3)$, $p_8 = th(p_4)$, if each θ-sequence of sets is monotone increasing, for Theorem 6.1 (6.4) follows. Here we omit (p_3) from the terms $\alpha(p_3)$-set, $\beta(p_3)$-set so that a set satisfying p_5 is called an α-set, other sets of T being β-sets. As $\mathcal{P}_5 \subseteq \mathcal{P}_3$, a p_5-$\mathcal{G}$-Baire set is a p_3-$\mathcal{G}$-Baire set and so is trivial. But from Theorem 6.4 (6.19) we obtain two results.

THEOREM 21.5 (21.25). If $Th(X) = T$, a β-set, then for some n, $Th_n(X)$ is dense in some non-empty $G \in \mathcal{G}$.
(21.26) If $Th(X) = T$, of the second category, $Th_n(X)$ is of the second category for some n, and in particular it is dense in some non-empty $G \in \mathcal{G}$. If $Th_n(X)$ is closed it contains a non-empty $G \in \mathcal{G}$, in (21.25) or (21.26).

If X is an α-set, $Th(X)$ is called an α-*sub-union*. All other θ-sub-unions can be called β-*sub-unions*. If X is an α-set and $Th(X) = T$, we can call T an α-*union*. If T is a θ-union but not an α-union for any X, we can say that T is a β-*union*. Note that T is a θ-union if and only if $Th(T) = T$, and that an α-sub-union is a β-set if it is dense in some non-empty open set.

A p_7-$\mathcal{Q}$-Baire set X is called an α-*Baire set,* and there is a non-empty $G \in \mathcal{Q}$ with $G \backslash X$ contained in an α-sub-union of T.

THEOREM 21.6. *Let $\theta(x, y)$ be continuous in x for each fixed y, with θ^{-1} strongly continuous in x to the identity, and let each pair of sets from $\mathcal{Q}_0$ have a point in common. In order that $T_1 \equiv Th(X)$ is a β-sub-union it is necessary and sufficient that T_1 is a β-union under the relative topology $\mathcal{Q}_1$ of T_1 from $\mathcal{Q}$, that is $\mathcal{Q}$-dense in a set of $\mathcal{Q}_0$.*

Proof. If T_1 is a β-sub-union of T, then for some $n \geqslant 1$, $Th_n(X)$ is dense in some non-empty $G \in \mathcal{Q}$. If $y \in G \cap Th_n(X)$, using Theorem 9.1 (9.2) we have

$$\theta(Th_n(X), y) \subseteq \theta(Th_n(X), Th_n(X)) = Th_{n+1}(X),$$

$$\theta(G, y) \subseteq \theta(\mathcal{Q}Th_n(X), y) \subseteq \mathcal{Q}\theta(Th_n(X), y) \subseteq \mathcal{Q}Th_{n+1}(X)$$

By Theorem 21.1 (21.4), as θ^{-1} is continuous in x to the identity, $\theta(G, y)$ contains a $G_1 \in \mathcal{Q}_0$. Hence $Th(X)$ is $\mathcal{Q}$-dense in G_1, while $Th_{n+1}(X)$ is the same, and so is $\mathcal{Q}$-dense in $Th(X) \cap G_1$, and $\mathcal{Q}_1$-dense in $T_1 \cap G_1 \in \mathcal{Q}_1$. For fixed T_1 the X in $Th(X) = T_1$ is otherwise arbitrary, so that T_1 is a β-union for $\mathcal{Q}_1$.

Conversely, if $T_1 = Th(X)$ is a β-union for $\mathcal{Q}_1$ that is $\mathcal{Q}$-dense in $G_2 \in \mathcal{Q}_0$, then for some integer n and some $G_3 \in \mathcal{Q}$, with points in common with T_1, $Th_n(X)$ is $\mathcal{Q}_1$-dense in $T_1 \cap G_3$. Hence by Theorem 9.1 (9.2) applied to $(T_1, \mathcal{Q}_1)$, and by a similar argument to that in the first part, there is a $G_4 \in \mathcal{Q}_0$ with $Th_{n+1}(X)\mathcal{Q}_1$-dense in $T_1 \cap G_4$. Hence $Th_{n+1}(X)$ is $\mathcal{Q}_1$-dense in $T_1 \cap G_2 \cap G_4$, while T_1 is $\mathcal{Q}$-dense in G_2. Hence $Th_{n+1}(X)$ is $\mathcal{Q}$-dense in $G_2 \cap G_4$, which is in $\mathcal{Q}$, and is not empty by hypothesis. As X is arbitrary, apart from $Th(X) = T_1$, T_1 is a β-sub-union in T.

THEOREM 21.7.

(21.27) *Let $\theta^{-1}(x, y)$ be continuous in x to the identity. If X is a β-set, and if a sequence $\{F_n\}$ of closed sets is such that $F_n \supseteq Th_n(X)$, then for some integer n, F_n is a Th_1-$\mathcal{Q}$-set.*

Let $\theta(x, y)$ be continuous in (x, y). Then the following hold:

(21.28) $$Th_1(\bar{X}) \subseteq \mathcal{Q}Th_1(X)$$

(21.29) *if $\{Th_n\}$ is a θ-sequence, so is $\{\mathcal{Q}Th_n\}$,*

(21.30) *the property of being sequentially closed, is hereditary.*

(21.31) *If θ^{-1} is continuous in x to the identity, if θ is continuous in (x, y), and if $\mathcal{Q}$ is Hausdorffian with a countable base, then every set containing a sequentially closed β-set X is a Th-$\mathcal{Q}$-set.*

Proof. In (21.27), X is a β-set, so that there is an integer n such that $Th_n(X)$, and so F_n, are dense in a non-empty $\mathcal{Q}$-set. Then Theorem 21.1 (21.10) completes the result. (21.28) follows from the two-dimensional case of Theorem 9.1 (9.2). Hence also (21.29). For (21.30) we need the definition in section 15 of a sequentially closed set. An arbitrary sequence $\{z(n)\}$ in $Th_1(X)$ has

$$z(n) = \theta\big(x(n), y(n)\big) \, (x(n), y(n) \in X)$$

so that for a subsequence $\{n_j\}$ of integers, $\{x(n_j)\}$ converges to an $x \in X$. In turn, $\{y(n_j)\}$ contains a subsequence $\{y(m_j)\}$ convergent to a $y \in X$. As $\theta(x, y)$ is continuous in (x, y), we obtain

$$z(m_j) = \theta\big(x(m_j), y(m_j)\big) \to \theta(x, y) \in Th_1(X)$$

proving (21.30). Note that Ex. 21.9 shows that we cannot replace 'sequentially closed' by 'closed' in this result. Now for (21.31) we use (21.30) to show that $Th_n(X)$ is sequentially closed, for each integer n. Then Theorem 15.3 (15.17) shows that $Th_n(X)$ is closed, so that it can be put as the F_n of (21.27).

Properties p_6, p_7, p_8 seem to need a simple θ such as can be obtained from a group operation.

If in a topological space an outer measure is defined, it can sometimes be used to distinguish between 'thick' and 'thin' sets. First, a real-valued set function μ on sets of T, is *sub-additive*, if

$$\mu(X \cup Y) \leqslant \mu(X) + \mu(Y) \qquad (\text{all } X, Y \subseteq T)$$

Also μ is *monotone increasing*, if $\mu(X) \leqslant \mu(Y)$ when $X \subseteq Y$. An *outer measure* is a non-negative sub-additive and monotone increasing set function. Further, μ is θ^{-1}-invariant, if

$$\mu(\theta^{-1}(x, X)) = \mu(X) \, (x \in T, X \subseteq T)$$

Often the variation of Chapter 10 is such a set function.

108

THEOREM 21.8. *Let μ be a θ^{-1}-invariant outer measure, let $\mu(X\backslash E) = 0$, and let $\mu(X^v) \neq 0$, for some $G \in \mathcal{G}_0$, and all $v \in G$. Then $Th_1(E) \supseteq G$.*

Proof. For, by the hypotheses,

$$\mu(X_v) \leqslant \mu(X\backslash E) + \mu(\theta^{-1}(v, X\backslash E)) = 2\mu(X\backslash E) = 0, \quad X^v \nsubseteq X_v$$

The result now follows from Theorem 6.2.

Usually we suppose that $\mu(G) > 0$ for each non-empty $G \in \mathcal{G}$, and then Theorem 21.1 (21.6) is relevant if θ^{-1} is stable, so that we can take $X = G$. Thus omitting a set of outer measure zero from a non-empty open set, leaves us with a Th_1-$\mathcal{G}$-set, if θ^{-1} is stable. However, this is usually rather trivial.

We can go further by defining $p_9(\delta)$, relative to a set X with $\mu(X)$ finite, and to δ in $(0, 1)$, to be the property of E such that $\mu(E) < \delta \cdot \mu(X)$. Then $p_9(\delta)$ is shrinkable, and finitely additive except that δ is replaced by $n\delta$ when there is a union of n sets E. The θ^{-1}-invariance of $p_9(\delta)$ is replaced by the θ^{-1}-invariance of μ. To obtain non-trivial results we need X to be *strongly-$\bar{p}_9(\delta)$ relative to itself*, i.e. there is a $G(\delta) \in \mathcal{G}_0$ such that

(21.32) $\quad \mu(X^v) \equiv \mu(X \cap \theta^{-1}(v, X)) \geqslant \delta \cdot \mu(X) \qquad (v \in G(\delta))$

THEOREM 21.9. *Let μ be a θ^{-1}-invariant outer measure of sets of T. If a set E is such that for some η in $(0, \frac{1}{2})$ we can find a strongly-$\bar{p}_9(2\eta)$ set X relative to itself, with*

(21.33) $\qquad\qquad \mu(X\backslash E) < \eta \cdot \mu(X)$

then E is a Th_1-$\mathcal{G}$-set.

Proof. From (21.33) we have

$$\mu(X_v) = \mu[(X\backslash E) \cup \theta^{-1}(v, X\backslash E)] \leqslant \mu(X\backslash E) + \mu(\theta^{-1}(v, X\backslash E))$$
$$= 2\mu(X\backslash E) < 2\eta \cdot \mu(X)$$

By (21.32) with $\delta = 2\eta$, and then Theorem 6.2,

$$\mu(X^v) > \mu(X_v), \quad X^v \nsubseteq X_v, \quad Th_1(E) \supseteq G(2\eta)$$

Usually the non-empty sets of $\mathcal{G}$ are strongly-$\bar{p}_9(\delta)$, relative to themselves, when we apply Theorem 21.9. But in the case of the infinite-dimensional cube of section 61, no open set has this property and there seems to be no way of using a theorem of Hahn–Banach–Steinhaus type. We have to prove the results another way. One could conjecture that if T is not a finite-dimensional space, T is not strongly-$\bar{p}_9(\delta)$ relative to itself, or relative to a non-empty member of $\mathcal{G}$, unless T has infinite measure. But this is an unsolved problem.

An $E \subseteq T$ is μ-*measurable* in the sense of Carathéodory, if, for each $X \subseteq T$,

$$\mu(X \cap E) + \mu(X \backslash E) = \mu(X)$$

For such E the metric density theorem can sometimes be proved, that

$$\mu(G \backslash E)/\mu(G) \to 0$$

as the neighbourhood G of the point x shrinks in some sense about x, for all $x \in E$, except for a set $X_1 \subseteq E$ of x with $\mu(X_1) = 0$. In this case (21.32) is satisfied with $X = G$, for all μ-measurable sets E of T with $\mu(E) > 0$, since we can use any point x of E that is not in the exceptional set X_1.

For example, T can be the Euclidean n-dimensional space with the usual metric topology, with Lebesgue n-dimensional measure μ, and with $\theta^{-1}(x, y)$ denoting vector addition. Then the metric density theorem holds, while each non-empty open set is strongly-$\bar{p}_9(\delta)$, relative to itself, and μ is θ^{-1}-invariant. It follows that:

THEOREM 21.10. *The set of vector differences between points of a set of positive measure in Euclidean n-dimensional space includes a sphere with centre the origin.*

Historical Notes. In Bourbaki (1958), Livre 3, Chapitre 9, p. 109, (EB″), a $\bar{p}_4$-$\mathcal{G}$-space is called a Baire space. Theorems 21.1 (21.5) and 21.4 (21.24) together form a generalization of Banach (1932), pp. 21–22, Théorèmes 1, 2. The α-sets and β-sets are found in Sargent (1950), (1953), pp. 439–440, and Henstock (1963a), p. 314. The α-Baire sets are in Henstock (1963a), p. 316. Theorem 21.6 generalizes Sargent (1953), pp. 440–1, Lemma 2, while in Theorem 21.7, (21.28; 21.29) generalize Sargent (1953), p. 440, Lemma 1, and (21.27; 21.30; 21.31) generalize Henstock (1963a), p. 315, (58; 56; 57).

Steinhaus (1919), p. 99, Theorem 8, states that the set of distances between points of a set of positive Lebesgue measure on the real axis contains an interval $[0, a]$, for some $a > 0$. This is generalized in Henstock (1963a), p. 318, (67), and in Theorems 21.9, 21.10 here. If we replace $\theta(x, y) = x - y$ by $\theta(x, y) = \frac{1}{2}(x+y)$, vector addition, we have part of a theorem of Ostrowski (1929) on convex functions. For this result see section 32 and Theorem 32.10. $\theta(x, y) = x/y$ gives Ray (1962–65), Theorem 3.

Ex. 21.1. Each set containing a $Th_n\text{-}\mathcal{G}$-set, is also a $Th_n\text{-}\mathcal{G}$-set.

Ex. 21.2. If no $\mathcal{G}$-set is countable, and if X is countable, prove that X cannot be a $Th\text{-}\mathcal{G}$-set (Henstock (1963a), p. 312, (42)).

Ex. 21.3. In Theorem 21.1 (21.5) it is not enough to have G_1 pinned but not strongly pinned. For let T be the real line with the modulus topology, and take $\theta(x, y) = \frac{1}{2}(x+y)$. Then $\theta^{-1}(x, y) = 2x - y$, continuous in x for each $y \in T$, and stable, with $\mathcal{G}_0 = \mathcal{G}$, so that all conditions are satisfied except that each $G \in \mathcal{G}_0$ is pinned but not strongly pinned. Prove these results. Also show that if $X = (0, 1)$ then $X = \theta(X, X) = Th(X)$, which is not closed.

Ex. 21.4. If θ^{-1} is stable, and if $E \subseteq T$, a non-empty $G \in \mathcal{G}$, and $G_1 \in \mathcal{G}_0$, are such that

$$E^v = (G\backslash E) \cup \theta^{-1}(v, G\backslash E)$$

does not contain the whole of any non-empty $\mathcal{G}$-set, for each $v \in G_1$, prove that $Th(E) \supseteq Th(G_1)$. The case $\theta^{-1}(x, y) = x \cdot y$ is given in Henstock (1963a), p. 312, Theorem 10.

Ex. 21.5. If θ^{-1} is vector addition in the Euclidean plane T with the metric topology, show that the union X of two non-parallel lines l_1, l_2, is nowhere dense, but $Th_1(X) = T$, of the second category (see Henstock (1963a), p. 316, (59)).

Ex. 21.6. If $X \in \mathcal{P}_6$, show that $Th(X) \in \mathcal{P}_4$, and conversely.

Ex. 21.7. If θ satisfies $X \subseteq \theta(X, X)$ (*all* $X \subseteq T$), prove that $p_8 = p_6$. (If $X \in \mathcal{P}_8$ then $X \subseteq Th(Y)$, where $Th_n(Y) \in \mathcal{P}_4$ ($n \geq 1$), so that $Th(Y) \in \mathcal{P}_4$. By Theorem 6.1 (6.4),

$$Th_n(X) \subseteq Th_n(Th(Y)) = Th(Y), \quad Th_n(X) \in \mathcal{P}_4 \quad (n \geq 1), \quad X \in \mathcal{P}_6$$

Conversely, if

$$X \in \mathcal{P}_6, \quad \text{then} \quad Th_n(X) \in \mathcal{P}_4, \quad Th_n(Th(X)) = Th(X) \in \mathcal{P}_4,$$
$$X \subseteq Th(X) \quad \text{i.e.} \quad X \in \mathcal{P}_8)$$

Ex. 21.8. Each α-sub-union is of the first category in T, and each set of the second category in T is a β-set that cannot be contained in an α-sub-union.

Ex. 21.9. Let T be the set of reals with the modulus topology, and with $\theta^{-1}(x, y) = x+y$. If X is the closed set of points $n+n^{-1}$ $(n = 1,2,\ldots)$, show that 1 is a limit-point, but not a point, of $Th_1(X)$, so that $Th_1(X)$ is not closed.

Ex. 21.10. Let $X \subseteq Y \subseteq T$. If Y is an α-set, so is X. If X is a β-set, so is Y.

22. Category, β-sets, and Measure in Upper Boundedness Theorems

By using section 21 we can now clothe the skeletal schemes of Chapter 2 and section 20 with topological flesh. There are many combinations of details, but the following are typical.

THEOREM 22.1.

(22.1) *Let T be a Baire space, let θ^{-1} be stable, and a continuous injection in y, with $\theta^{-1}(x, T)$ closed, let N be a $\theta - L$ convex function, and let $N(x)$ be bounded in a Baire set of the second category. Then N is bounded in a set of $\mathcal{G}_0$.*

(22.2) *If in (22.1) every set of $\mathcal{G}_0$ is a θ-base for T, then $N < \infty$ in T.*

(22.3) *If in (22.1), θ^{-1} is continuous in x, T is connected, and each set of $\mathcal{G}_0$ is strongly pinned, then $N < \infty$ in T.*

Proof. Use Theorems 20.1 (20.5), 21.1 (21.5), 21.4 (21.24).

THEOREM 22.2. *Let T, θ^{-1}, $\mathcal{G}_0$ satisfy the conditions of (22.1; 22.2) or (22.1; 22.3). Let $N(n, x)$ be a $\theta - L$ convex function for an L independent of n, and for each $\lambda > 0$, let the set of points where $N(n, x) \leq \lambda$*

be a Baire set, for $n = 1, 2, \ldots$ *If, for a sequence* $\{x_n\}$ *of points of* T,

(22.4) $$N(n, x_n) = +\infty \qquad (n = 1, 2, \ldots)$$

then the set of points x *where*

(22.5) $$N(n, x) = +\infty \qquad (n = 1, 2, \ldots)$$

is of the second category, with its complement of the first category.

Proof. Use Theorems 5.2, 22.1.

THEOREM 22.3. *Let* T, θ^{-1}, $\mathcal{G}_0$ *satisfy the conditions of* (22.1; 22.2) *or* (22.1; 22.3). *Let* $N(n, x)$ *be a* $\theta - L$ *convex function for an* L *independent of* n, *and continuous on the right. If, for a Baire set* X *of the second category,*

(22.6) $$\lim_{n \to \infty} \sup N(n, x) < \infty \qquad (x \in X)$$

then (22.6) *is true in all* T.

Proof. Use Theorems 5.4, 21.1 (21.5), 21.4 (21.24).

THEOREM 22.4. *Let* T, θ^{-1} *satisfy the conditions of* (22.1), *let* N *be a restricted* $\theta - L$ *convex function, and for each* $\lambda > 0$, *let* $N \leqslant \lambda$ *in a Baire set of the second category. If* $L(0+) = 0$, *then to each* $\lambda > 0$ *there is a* $G \in \mathcal{G}_0$ *with* $N \leqslant \lambda$ *in* G.

Proof. Use Theorems 20.2, 21.4 (21.24).

THEOREM 22.5. *Let* $\theta^{-1}(x, y)$ *be continuous in* x *to the identity, and let* N *be a* $\theta - L$ *convex function.*

(22.7) *If the set of points where* $N \leqslant \lambda$, *is closed for each* $\lambda > 0$, *and if it is a* β-*set for some* $\lambda > 0$, *then* N *is bounded in a set of* $\mathcal{G}_0$.

(22.8) *Alternatively, if* θ *is continuous in* (x, y), *if* $\mathcal{G}$ *is Hausdorffian with a countable base, and if there is a sequentially closed* β-*set in which* N *is bounded, then* N *is again bounded in a set of* $\mathcal{G}_0$.

(22.9) *If also each set of* $\mathcal{G}_0$ *is a* θ-*base for* T, *or if* T *is connected, if each* $G \in \mathcal{G}_0$ *is strongly pinned, and if* θ^{-1} *is continuous in* x *and stable, then in either case,* $N < \infty$ *in* T.

Proof. Use Theorems 20.1 (20.5), 21.1 (21.5), 21.7 (21.27; 21.31).

113

THEOREM 22.6. *Let $\theta^{-1}(x, y)$ be continuous in x to the identity, let N be a $\theta - L$ convex function for an L independent of n and continuous on the right, and let $P^1(\lambda)$ be the set where*

$$(22.10) \qquad \limsup_{n \to \infty} N(n, x) \leqslant \lambda$$

(22.11) *If $P^1(\lambda)$ is closed for each $\lambda > 0$, and is a β-set for some $\lambda > 0$, then (22.6) holds in a set of $\mathcal{G}_0$.*

(22.12) *If, for some $\lambda > 0$, $P^1(\lambda)$ contains a sequentially closed β-set, if θ is continuous in (x, y), and if $\mathcal{G}$ is Hausdorffian with a countable base, then again (22.6) holds in a set of $\mathcal{G}_0$.*

(22.13) *If the conditions in (22.9) are also true, then (22.6) holds in T.*

Proof. Use Theorems 5.1, 5.3, 21.1 (21.5), 21.7 (21.27; 21.31).

THEOREM 22.7. *Let μ be a θ^{-1}-invariant outer measure of sets of T, and let every non-empty $G \in \mathcal{G}$ be strongly-$\bar{p}_9(\delta)$ relative to itself, for each $\delta \in (0, 1)$. If $N(x)$ is a $\theta - L$ convex function bounded in a set E for which there are an $\eta \in (0, \frac{1}{2})$ and a non-empty $G \in \mathcal{G}$, with*

$$(22.14) \qquad \mu(G \backslash E) < \eta \cdot \mu(G)$$

then N is bounded in a set of $\mathcal{G}_0$. If also one set of conditions in (22.9) holds, then $N < \infty$ in T.

Proof. Use Theorems 20.1 (20.5), 21.1 (21.5), 21.9.

We can say that a function N is *almost continuous* if, for each $\lambda > 0$, the condition on E involving (22.14), is true for $E = P(\lambda)$, or else $\mu(P(\lambda)) = 0$. Also μ is *countably sub-additive*, if, for every sequence $\{X_n\}$ of sets,

$$\mu \left(\bigcup_{n=1}^{\infty} X_n \right) \leqslant \sum_{n=1}^{\infty} \mu(X_n)$$

THEOREM 22.8. *Let μ be a countably sub-additive θ^{-1}-invariant outer measure of sets of T, for which every non-empty $G \in \mathcal{G}$ is strongly-$\bar{p}_9(\delta)$ relative to itself, for each $\delta \in (0, 1)$. Let one set of the conditions in (22.9) hold. Let $N(n, x)$ be an almost continuous $\theta - L$ convex function for an L independent of n, for $n = 1, 2, \ldots$ If (22.4) is true for a* *sequence* $\{x_n\}$ *of points of T, then the set of points x where* (22.5) *is false, has outer measure zero.*

Proof. Use Theorems 5.2, 22.7, and the definitions.

THEOREM 22.9. *Let* μ, $\mathcal{G}$ *satisfy the conditions in* Theorem 22.7, *with one set of conditions from* (22.9). *Let* $N(n, x)$ *be a* $\theta - L$ *convex function for an L independent of n, and continuous on the right, for* $n = 1, 2, \ldots$ *If* (22.6) *is true in a set E that satisfies the conditions in* Theorem 22.7 *involving* (22.14) *(which usually occurs if* $\mu(E) > 0$, *and if each* $N(n, x)$ *is almost continuous), then* (22.6) *is true in all T.*

THEOREM 22.10. *Let* μ, $\mathcal{G}$ *satisfy the conditions in* Theorem 22.7, *let N be an almost continuous restricted* $\theta - L$ *convex function, let* $L(0+) = 0$, *and for each* $\lambda > 0$, *let* $N \leq \lambda$ *in a set E with* $\mu(E) > 0$. *Then for each* $\lambda > 0$ *there is a* $G \in \mathcal{G}_0$ *with* $N \leq \lambda$ *in G.*

Proof. Use Theorems 20.2, 21.9.

Next we have a theorem that does not involve θ, so that we cannot use Theorem 20.1.

THEOREM 22.11. *Let* $(T_1, \mathcal{G}_1)$ *be a Baire space and* (T_2, ϱ_2) *a pseudometric space. If* $f_n : T_1 \to T_2$ *is a Baire function, for* $n = 1, 2, \ldots$, *and if*

$$(22.15) \qquad \limsup_{n \to \infty} \varrho_2(f_n(x), 0) < \infty$$

for each x in a set X of the second $\mathcal{G}_1$*-category, there are a non-empty* $G \in \mathcal{G}_1$, *a set* $Z \subseteq T_1$ *of the first* $\mathcal{G}_1$*-category, and an integer N, with*

$$(22.16) \qquad \varrho_2(f_n(x), 0) \leq N \qquad (x \in G \backslash Z, \ n = 1, 2, \ldots)$$

If all the f_n *are continuous, Z is empty.*

Proof. Let X_{jn} be the set of points x with $\varrho_2(f_n(x), 0) \leq j$, and let X_j be the intersection of $X_{j1}, X_{j2}, \ldots$ From (22.15), the union of the X_j contains X, while by Theorem 19.4 there is a set Z of the first category with each f_n continuous in $\backslash Z$. Clearly Z can be empty if the f_n are already continuous. As $X \backslash Z$ is of the second $\mathcal{G}_1$-category, there are a non-empty $G \in \mathcal{G}_1$ and some integer N, for which X_N

is dense in $G \backslash Z$. Now X_{Nn} is closed in $\backslash Z$ since f_n is continuous in $\backslash Z$. Hence X_N is closed in $\backslash Z$, and $G \backslash Z \subseteq X_N$, proving the result.

THEOREM 22.12. *Let* $(T_1, \mathcal{G}_1)$ *be a Baire space,* (T_2, ϱ_2) *a pseudometric space. Let* θ^{-1} *be a continuous injection in y, and stable, with* $\theta^{-1}(x, T_1)$ *closed. Let* $\{f_n\}$ *be a sequence of Baire functions such that for an L with* $L(0) = 0$,

$$(22.17) \qquad N(x) \equiv \lim_{n \to \infty} \sup_{j > k \geqslant n} \varrho_2(f_j(x), f_k(x))$$

is a $\theta - L$ *convex function. Then the set X of points where* $\{f_n(x)\}$ *is a fundamental sequence, is either of the first category, or contains a nonempty* $\mathcal{G}_1$-*set. In the latter case we can proceed to* T_1 *as usual.*

Proof. By Theorem 20.1 (20.10), X contains $Th(X)$. By Theorem 19.11, X is a Borel set, and so a Baire set by Theorem 18.5. If X is of the second $\mathcal{G}_1$-category, we use Theorem 21.4 (21.24).

A particular case is when T_2 is an additive group with pseudonorm $\| \cdot \|$ and with

$$f_n(\theta(x, y)) = f_n(x) + f_n(y)$$

In this case we have

$$\|f_j(\theta(x, y)) - f_k(\theta(x, y))\| = \|f_j(x) + f_j(y) - f_k(x) - f_k(y)\|$$
$$\leqslant \|f_j(x) - f_k(x)\| + \|f_j(y) - f_k(y)\|$$
$$N(\theta(x, y)) \leqslant N(x) + N(y)$$

THEOREM 22.13. *Let* $(T_1, \mathcal{G}_1)$ *be a Baire space,* (T_2, ϱ_2) *a pseudometric space, and let* θ^{-1} *be stable, and a continuous injection in y, with* $\theta^{-1}(x, T_1)$ *closed, and with* $Th(G) = T_1$ *for each non-empty* $G \in \mathcal{G}_1$. *Let* $\{f_{mn}(x)\}$ *be a double sequence of Baire functions such that*

$$(22.18) \qquad N(m, x) = \lim_{n \to \infty} \sup_{j > k \geqslant n} \varrho_2(f_{mj}(x), f_{mk}(x))$$

is a $\theta - L$ *convex function. If, for a sequence* $\{x_m\}$ *of points of* T_1, *the sequence* $\{f_{mn}(x_m)\}$ $(n = 1, 2, \ldots)$ *is not fundamental for any* $m = 1, 2, \ldots$, *then the set X of points x for which the sequence* $\{f_{mn}(x)\}$ $(n = 1, 2, \ldots)$ *is not fundamental for each* $m = 1, 2, \ldots$, *is of the second category, and* $\backslash X$ *is of the first category.*

116

Proof. Let X_m be the set of points where $\{f_{mn}(x)\}$ $(n = 1, 2, \ldots)$ is a fundamental sequence. By Theorem 22.12, and the existence of $x_m \in T_1$, X_m must be of the first category. Hence the result since T_1 is a Baire space.

Historical Notes. Theorems 22.11, 22.12 generalize Banach (1932), p. 19, Théorème 11, and p. 24, Théorème 5. Theorem 22.13 generalizes the famous theorem on the condensation of singularities, Banach (1932), p. 24, Théorème 6. We have already had similar theorems.

6

GROUP STRUCTURE

23. Basic Definitions

IN order to define some useful special operators $\theta(x, y)$ we now suppose that the space T of Chapter 2 has an algebraic structure. T is a *semigroup*, if there is a mapping $m: T \times T \to T$, called *multiplication*, and usually written $m(x, y) = x \cdot y$, the *product* of x and y, such that

$$(23.1) \qquad x \cdot (y \cdot z) = (x \cdot y) \cdot z \qquad (all\ x, y, z \in T)$$

T is a *group*, if it is a semigroup with product satisfying:
(23.2) there is an element $u \in T$, called the *identity(unit)* of T, such that

$$x \cdot u = u \cdot x = x \qquad (all\ x \in T)$$

(23.3) to each $x \in T$ there is an element $x^{-1} \in T$, called the *inverse* of x, with

$$x \cdot x^{-1} = x^{-1} \cdot x = u$$

T is a *commutative (Abelian) group*, if it is a group with product obeying

$$(23.4) \qquad x \cdot y = y \cdot x \qquad (all\ x, y \in T)$$

The product $m(x, y)$ in a group is written $x+y$ only if the group is commutative, and then $x+y$ is the *sum* of x and y, and $m(x, y)$ is the operation of *addition*, and we say that T is an *additive group*. The unit is called the *zero*, the inverse of x is written $-x$, and we write $x-y$ for $x+(-y)$.

THEOREM 23.1

(23.5) *The unit u and inverse x^{-1} in a group are uniquely defined.*

(23.6)
$$(x \cdot y)^{-1} = y^{-1} \cdot x^{-1}$$

(23.7)
$$(x^{-1})^{-1} = x$$

Proof. If $x, v \in T$ satisfy $x = x \cdot v$, then by (23.1; 23.2; 23.3),

$$u = x^{-1} \cdot x = x^{-1} \cdot (x \cdot v) = (x^{-1} \cdot x) \cdot v = u \cdot v = v$$

Similarly, if $x, v \in T$ satisfy $x = v \cdot x$, then $v = u$, and u is unique.
Further, if $x \cdot y = u$, then by the group axioms,

$$x^{-1} = x^{-1} \cdot u = x^{-1} \cdot (x \cdot y) = (x^{-1} \cdot x) \cdot y = u \cdot y = y$$

Similarly, if $y \cdot x = u$, then $y = x^{-1}$. Hence (23.5). For (23.6),

$$(y^{-1} \cdot x^{-1}) \cdot (x \cdot y) = y^{-1} \cdot \{x^{-1} \cdot (x \cdot y)\} = y^{-1} \cdot \{(x^{-1} \cdot x) \cdot y\}$$
$$= y^{-1} \cdot (u \cdot y) = y^{-1} \cdot y = u$$

Hence (23.5) gives (23.6). For (23.7), if $y = (x^{-1})^{-1}$ then

$$y \cdot x^{-1} = u, \quad x = u \cdot x = (y \cdot x^{-1}) \cdot x = y \cdot (x^{-1} \cdot x) = y \cdot u = y$$

Let $x, y \in T$ and $X, Y \subseteq T$. As usual for functions, we then write

$$X^{-1} = \{z^{-1} : z \in X\}, \quad x \cdot X = \{x \cdot z : z \in X\}, \quad X \cdot y = \{z \cdot y : z \in X\}$$
$$x \cdot X \cdot y = \{x \cdot z \cdot y : z \in X\}, \quad X \cdot Y = \{v \cdot w : v \in X, w \in Y\}$$

For additive groups we use the corresponding notation

$$-X, \quad x+X, \quad X+y, \quad x+X+y, \quad X+Y$$

By induction we can define $x^0 = u$, and $x^{n+1} = x^n \cdot x$ $(n = 0, 1, 2, \ldots)$

Sometimes we suppose that there is a root function $r : T \to T$ that satisfies

(23.8)
$$r(x) \cdot r(x) = x$$

and that is uniquely defined.

THEOREM 23.2. *If the root function r can be defined in the group T,*

9   119

then

(23.9) $r(u) = u$

(23.10) $r(x^{-1}) = r(x)^{-1}$

(23.11) *If T is also a commutative group, then*

$$r(x \cdot y) = r(x) \cdot r(y)$$

Proof. For (23.9), $u^2 = u$. For (23.10), by (23.6),

$$r(x)^{-1} \cdot r(x)^{-1} = \{r(x) \cdot r(x)\}^{-1} = x^{-1}$$

For (23.11) we have

$$\{r(x) \cdot r(y)\} \cdot \{r(x) \cdot r(y)\} = r^2(x) \cdot r^2(y) = x \cdot y$$

We define $r_k(x)$ by the recurrence relation

$$r_1(x) = r(x), \quad r_{n+1}(x) = r(r_n(x)) \qquad (n \geqslant 1)$$

In all groups we can say that a set X is *symmetric*, if $x^{-1} \in X$ when $x \in X$.

Using the group structure we give three examples of the θ of Chapter 2. First, in section 24 we consider $\theta(x, y) = x \cdot y^{-1}$, $\theta^{-1}(v, y) = v \cdot y$. Secondly we consider $\theta(x, y) = x \cdot y$, $\theta^{-1}(v, y) = v \cdot y^{-1}$ in section 32. Thirdly, in section 32 we need the root function, and we consider $\theta(x, y) = r(x \cdot y)$, $\theta^{-1}(v, y) = v^2 \cdot y^{-1}$, in connection with ordinary convex functions.

24. Difference Sets in a Group

A *subgroup* T_0 of a group T, is a subset of T that is itself a group with the group operation of T. If $T_0 \subset T$, then T_0 is called a *proper subgroup*. We consider a subgroup $Th(X)$ constructed from a set $X \subseteq T$ by using a special θ.

Throughout this section we assume that

$$\theta(x, y) = x \cdot y^{-1}, \quad \theta^{-1}(v, y) = v \cdot y$$

Given $X \subseteq T$, the sets $D_n \subseteq T$ form a *difference sequence*, if

(24.1) $D_{n+1} \supseteq D_n \cdot D_n^{-1} \quad (n \geqslant 0), \quad D_0 = X$

This is precisely a θ-sequence for the given θ. The name 'difference sequence' is given because of the form in which it occurs in an additive group, since then

$$\theta(D_n, D_n) = D_n - D_n$$

We write D for the union of the $D_n (n \geqslant 1)$. If equality in (24.1), then $\{D_n\}$ is a *minimal difference sequence*, and we write $D_n(X)$, $D(X)$, for D_n, D, respectively.

THEOREM 24.1. *If $\{D_n\}$ is a difference sequence in T with X not empty, then*

(24.2) $u \in D_n$, *and if* $x \in D_n$, *then* $x \in D_{n+1}$, $x^{-1} \in D_{n+1}$ $(n \geqslant 1)$, *so that $\{D_n\}$ is monotone increasing;*

(24.3) *D is a subgroup of T.*

(24.4) *If $\{D_n\}$ is a minimal difference sequence in T, then the D_n $(n \geqslant 1)$ are symmetric.*

(24.5) *$D(X)$ is the smallest subgroup of T containing $D_1(X)$.*

(24.6) *Each subgroup of T is the union of a difference sequence.*

Proof. For (24.2), let $x \in X$. Then by induction,

$$u = x \cdot x^{-1} \in D_1, \quad u = u \cdot u^{-1} \in D_n \quad (n > 1)$$

so that if $y \in D_n$ for some $n \geqslant 1$, then

$$y = y \cdot u^{-1} \in D_{n+1}, \quad y^{-1} = u \cdot y^{-1} \in D_{n+1}$$

For (24.3), $u \in D$. If $x, y \in D$, there are integers m, n, with

$$x \in D_m, \quad y \in D_n, \quad y^{-1} \in D_{n+1}, \quad y^{-1} \in D$$

using (24.2). Also, if $r = \max(m, n+1)$,

$$x, y^{-1} \in D_r, \quad x \cdot y = x \cdot (y^{-1})^{-1} \in D_{r+1} \subseteq D$$

Thus (24.3) is true. For (24.4), with $n \geqslant 1$, if

$$x \in D_n \quad \text{then} \quad x = y \cdot z^{-1} (y, z \in D_{n-1}), \quad x^{-1} = z \cdot y^{-1} \in D_n$$

If T_1 is a subgroup of T containing $D_1(X)$, then by induction, each $D_n(X)$, and so $D(X)$, are in T_1, so that a subgroup of T that contains $D_1(X)$, must, at least, be as great as $D(X)$. Then (24.3) completes the proof of (24.5). (24.6) is trivial but interesting, since we can take

T_1 as the subgroup, and

$$X = T_1, \quad D_n(X) = T_1, \quad D(X) = T_1$$

From *Ex. 24.1*, X need not lie in $D(X)$, and $X \cup D(X)$ need not be a group, and X need not be symmetric. This is the anomalous behaviour of X mentioned in section 5. Further, we have no need of the notation $\{X\}$ for the smallest subgroup containing X, for such a subgroup contains X and the unit u, and so

$$X_1 \equiv X \cup \text{sing}(u); \quad \text{and is} \quad D(X_1) \quad \text{as} \quad D_1(X_1) \supseteq X$$

A set $X \subseteq T$ is a *generating system in T*, if no proper subgroup of T contains X, and this is true if, and only if, X is not empty and $D(X_1) = T$, i.e. X_1 is a θ-base for T. It should be an important algebraic problem to give suitable conditions on X in order that $D(X_1) = T$, or even that $D(X) = T$. If T has a finite number of generators, we can consider each generator in turn, to find whether it is in the subgroup. But if T has an infinity of generators the problem is more difficult and seems to be almost untouched. For example, there seems to be nothing in Fuchs (1958). However, the $Th(P(\lambda))$ of Theorem 5.1 is here written $D(P(\lambda))$, a subgroup of T, and conditions on $P(\lambda)$ that make it a θ-base for T, throw light on the question of when is a subgroup a proper subgroup, and when is it the whole group? The given conditions usually involve a topology, so that one possible way of tackling the problem when a topology is not given in a group, is to construct a topology from the group elements. See, for example, Kaloujnine (1947). In this connection the Cauchy sequences of Fuchs (1958), p. 114 seem to have a definition that does not agree with any reasonable extension of the definition of a fundamental sequence, since $g_n - g_{n+1}$ is involved, and not $g_n - g_m$. But this may be taken care of in the algebraic theory.

In connection with the property $th(p)$ we need the following result.

THEOREM 24.2. *If T is a commutative group, then*

$$D_n(X \cup (x \cdot X)) = \bigcup_{m=-j}^{j} x^m D_n(X) \qquad (j = 2^{n-1}, n \geqslant 1)$$

Proof. We use induction and the commutativity. First,

$$D_1(X \cup (x \cdot X)) = \{y \cdot z^{-1} : y, z \in X, \text{ or } y \in X, z \in x \cdot X \text{ or } y \in x \cdot X, z \in X\}$$
$$= D_1(X) \cup [x^{-1} \cdot D_1(X)] \cup [x \cdot D_1(X)]$$

By commutativity the fourth case, when $y, z \in x \cdot X$, reduces to the first case. Thus the theorem is true for $n = 1$. If true for n, then

$$D_{n+1}(X \cup (x \cdot X)) = \{y \cdot z^{-1} : y \in x^r \cdot D_n(X), \quad z \in x^s \cdot D_n(X);$$
$$r, s = 0, \pm 1, \ldots, \pm j\}$$

For fixed r, s we use the commutativity to obtain

$$y = x^r \cdot y_0, \quad z = x^s \cdot z_0 (y_0, z_0 \in D_n(X)),$$
$$y \cdot z^{-1} = x^{r-s} \cdot y_0 \cdot z_0^{-1} \in x^{r-s} \cdot D_{n+1}(X)$$

and each point in the last set can be obtained in this way. As

$$r - s = 0, \pm 1, \ldots, \pm 2^n$$

the theorem is true for $n+1$. Hence the result.

Here, a set X is pinned, if $x \in \theta(x, X)$ (*all* $x \in X$), so that for some $v \in X$,

$$x = x \cdot v^{-1}, \quad v = u$$

from Theorem 23.1 (23.5). Thus $u \in X$. Conversely, if $u \in X$, then X is pinned, and in fact X is strongly pinned. Also θ^{-1}-invariance can be called *left-translation-invariance*, and we can put Theorems 6.2, 6.3, 6.4 into the present language. In connection with definition (6.16) we can also say that $D(X)$ is an $\alpha(p)$-*group*, if $D_n(X) \in \mathcal{P}(n \geq 0)$. All other subgroups of T can be called β (*p*)-*groups*. Note that we need not have $D(X) \in \mathcal{P}$.

A theorem using $th(p)$ depends heavily on results like Theorem 24.2, so that we only give the theorem in the forms of Theorems 24.3, 29.7, 32.3. The difficulty is that $th(p)$ need not be finitely additive, even if p is. See *Ex. 21.5*.

THEOREM 24.3. (24.7) *If T is a commutative group, if p is finitely additive and left-translation-invariant, if $p_2 = th(p)$, and if $X \in \mathcal{P}_2$, then*

$$X \cup (x \cdot X) \in \mathcal{P}_2$$

(24.8) *If in (24.7), E is a p_2-Baire set, then $E \in \mathcal{E}$.*

Proof. As p is left-translation-invariant and finitely additive, and as there is a set $Y \in \mathcal{P}_1$, where $p_1 = h(p)$, such that $X \subseteq D(Y)$, Theorem 24.2 gives

$$D_n(Y \cup (x \cdot Y)) = \bigcup_{m=-j}^{j} x^m \cdot D_n(Y) \in \mathcal{P},$$

$$X \cup (x \cdot X) \subseteq D(Y) \cup (x \cdot D(Y)) \subseteq D(Y \cup (x \cdot Y))$$

and (24.7). For (24.8), a strongly-$\bar{p}_2$ set X exists with $X \backslash E \in \mathcal{P}_2$, so that there is a set $Y \subseteq T$ with

$$X \backslash E \subseteq D(Y), \quad D_n(Y) \in \mathcal{P} \quad (n \geq 0)$$

By (24.7), $X_v \in \mathcal{P}_2$, so that $X_v \cap X^v \in \mathcal{P}_2$ since $th(p)$ is shrinkable. But, for some $V \in \mathcal{U}$, $X^v \notin \mathcal{P}_2 (v \in V)$, $X^v \nsubseteq X_v$. Theorem 6.2 completes the proof.

There is a simple result for functions satisfying (5.7) for this θ.

THEOREM 24.4. *Let N be a function on a group T to the extended real line, that satisfies*

(24.9) $N(x \cdot y^{-1}) \leq N(x) + N(y) \qquad (x, y \in T)$

If N is finite for a point of T, then

(24.10) $0 \leq N(u) < +\infty, \quad \frac{1}{2}N(u) \leq N(x) \leq +\infty \qquad (x \in T)$

Proof. Let $y \in T$, $N(y)$ finite. By (24.9), for all $x \in T$,

$$N(y) = N((y \cdot u) \cdot u^{-1}) \leq N(y \cdot u) + N(u) = N(y) + N(u), \quad N(u) \geq 0$$

$$N(u) = N(x \cdot x^{-1}) \leq 2N(x)$$

For $x = y$, $N(u)$ is finite and non-negative, and (24.10) follows. In particular, $N \geq 0$. We can have $N(u) > 0$, since $N(x) + C$ satisfies (24.9) if N does, and if $C \geq 0$, constant. Then $N(u) + C \geq C$.

Historical Note: The $\{D_n\}$ were effectively in Sargent (1953) and as $\{H_n\}$ in Henstock (1963a).

Ex. 24.1. If X contains a single element $x \neq u$, then $D_1(X)$ contains u alone.

Ex. 24.2. Let T be the set of real numbers, with addition, and let X be the set of $+1$, -1. Find $D_n(X)$, $D(X)$.

124

25. The Hahn–Banach Theorem for Additive Groups

Let R, C be the respective spaces of real and complex numbers. A *functional* f in a group T, is a function f in $Y \subseteq T$ to R or C. A functional f is *multiplicative*, if

$$(25.1) \qquad x \cdot y^{-1} \in Y, \quad f(x \cdot y^{-1}) = f(x) - f(y) \qquad (x, y \in Y)$$

If the values of such an f are known on a set $X \subseteq T$, then by using (25.1), the values of f can be found on $D(X)$, a subgroup of T that is sometimes T itself. For example, if X contains a point y, we put $x = y$ in (25.1) to show that $f(u)$ exists with value 0. Putting $x = u$, then $f(y^{-1}) = -f(y)$, and we obtain

$$(25.2) \quad f(x \cdot y) = f(x) + f(y), \quad f(u) = 0, \quad f(x^{-1}) = -f(x)$$

A *real* functional f is *submultiplicative*, if

$$(25.3) \qquad x \cdot y \in Y, \quad f(x \cdot y) \leqslant f(x) + f(y) \qquad (x, y \in Y)$$

If $f(u)$ exists, $x = u = y$ gives $f(u) \geqslant 0$.

When the group T is additive, we replace 'multiplicative' and 'submultiplicative' by 'additive' and 'subadditive', respectively. Then we say that a functional f is *homogeneous for positive integers*, if $f(tx) = tf(x)$ for each positive integer t, where $tx \in Y$ when $x \in Y$. Here, as for the power notation,

$$0x = u, \quad 1x = x, \quad 2x = x + x, \quad 3x = x + x + x,$$
$$4x = x + x + x + x, \ldots$$

Naturally an additive functional is homogeneous for positive integers.

THEOREM 25.1. *Let g be a subadditive functional, homogeneous for positive integers, on the additive group T, and let f be a real additive functional defined on $D(X) \neq T$, with $f(x) \leqslant g(x)$ on $D(X)$. Then there is a real additive functional h on T, with $h(x) \leqslant g(x)$ on T, and $h(x) = f(x)$ on $D(X)$.*

Proof. Let $z \in \backslash D(X)$, $Y = X \cup \text{sing } (z)$. Then we extend the definition of f to $D(Y)$.

125

Let t, v be positive integers, and $x, y \in D(X)$. Then

$$\begin{aligned} tf(y)-vf(x) &= f(ty)-f(vx) = f(ty-vx) \leqslant g(ty-vx) \\ &= g((ty+tvz)-(vx+tvz)) \leqslant g(ty+tvz)+g(-vx-tvz) \\ &= tg(y+vz)+vg(-x-tz) \end{aligned}$$

Hence $\qquad -vg(-x-tz)-vf(x) \leqslant tg(y+vz)-tf(y)$

Thus if the sup and inf are for all $x \in D(X)$ and all positive integers t,

$$m \equiv \sup\,[-t^{-1}\{g(-x-tz)+f(x)\}] \leqslant \inf\,[t^{-1}\{g(x+tz)-f(x)\}] \equiv M$$

where m, M are finite. Let r be any number in $m \leqslant r \leqslant M$. Then for all $x \in D(X)$ and all positive integers t,

$$(25.4) \qquad -g(-x-tz)-f(x) \leqslant tr \leqslant g(x+tz)-f(x)$$

If $y \in D(Y)$, then $y = x+tz$, where $x \in D(X)$ and t is a real integer, and we can define $h(y)$ to be $f(x)+tr$. Then h is real and additive on $D(Y)$, with $h(x) = f(x)$ when $x \in D(X)$. If t is positive, $h(y) \leqslant g(y)$ from the second inequality in (25.4). If t is negative, we use the first inequality in (25.4), with $-x$ for x, obtaining

$$h(y) = f(x)-|t|r \leqslant f(x)+g(x-|t|z)+f(-x) = g(x+tz) = g(y)$$

Hence we can extend the definition of f from $D(X)$ to $D(X \cup \text{sing}\,(z))$, for each $z \in \backslash D(X)$.

To conclude the proof we assume that $\backslash D(X)$ is well ordered, by Axiom 9.1 if necessary. Then we can define a subset Z of $\backslash D(X)$, such that $z \in Z$, if and only if z does not lie in $D(Z(z))$, where $Z(z)$ is the set of X and all $w \in \backslash D(X)$ with $w < z$ in the well ordering. Then Z is well ordered, and by transfinite induction the process can be extended to all Z, and so to all T.

Note that if at any stage we have $m < M$, then h cannot be uniquely defined.

THEOREM 25.2. *Let g be a subadditive functional, homogeneous for positive integers, on the additive group T. Then there is a real additive functional f that satisfies $g(x) \geqslant f(x)$ for all $x \in T$.*

Proof. Taking an arbitrary $z \in T$, we define $f(tz) = tg(z)$ for each integer t. Then f is defined on the group T_1 of all such tz with the

126

fixed z. If $t > 0$, $f(tz) = g(tz)$, since g is homogeneous for positive integers. Also

$$f(0) = 0 \leqslant g(0), \quad g(z) + g(-z) \geqslant g(0) \geqslant 0, \quad g(z) \geqslant -g(-z)$$

where 0 is the zero in T. Hence for $t < 0$,

$$f(tz) = tg(z) \leqslant -tg(-z) = g(tz)$$

so that $f(x) \leqslant g(x)$ in T_1. Applying Theorem 25.1 we obtain the result.

Note that if T, U are groups and $f: T \to U$, we can say that f is *multiplicative*, if

(25.5) $$f(x \cdot y^{-1}) = f(x) \cdot f(y)^{-1}$$

If necessary, we could restrict the domain of definition of f to be a subset of T.

Historical Note. Theorem 25.1 was proved for linear vector spaces by Banach (1929a, b), and is the algebraic half of the Hahn–Banach theorem. See also Banach (1932), pp. 27–9.

26. Bimultiplicative Functionals and an Inequality

A *two-variable functional* f in T, is a function f in $Z \subseteq T \times T$ to R or C. A *bimultiplicative functional* f in T, is a two-variable functional in T that is multiplicative in each variable separately. If T is an additive group we replace 'bimultiplicative' by 'biadditive'. A two-variable functional f in T, is *non-negative definite*, if $f(x, x) \geqslant 0$ for all $x \in T$ for which it is defined. f is *positive definite*, if $f(x, x) > 0$ for all $x \in T$, $x \neq u$, for which it is defined.

THEOREM 26.1. *Let f be bimultiplicative and non-negative definite in T, such that $f(x, x), f(x, y), f(y, x), f(y, y)$ are defined, for certain $x, y \in T$. Then*

(26.1) $$f(x, y) + f(y, x) \quad \text{is real,}$$

(26.2) $$\{f(x, y) + f(y, x)\}^2 \leqslant 4f(x, x)\, f(y, y),$$

(26.3) $$f^{1/2}(x \cdot y, x \cdot y) \leqslant f^{1/2}(x, x) + f^{1/2}(y, y).$$

127

When $f(x, y) = f(y, x)$, (26.2) can be called the Cauchy–Schwarz–Buniakowsky inequality, for functionals on a group. This can be traced back to Cauchy (1821), for a finite sum, to Buniakowsky (1859), for integrals, and to Schwartz (1885). Theorem 26.1 is an extension from linear spaces to groups. Also (26.3) shows that $f^{1/2}(x, x)$ can sometimes be used as a norm to construct a metric, called a *quadratic metric*, in at least part of T. The norm is then called a *Hilbert norm*, and the subset of T is called a *Hilbert space*.

Proof. By existence, bimultiplicativity, and non-negative definiteness,

$$f(x, x) + f(x, y) + f(y,x) + f(y, y) = f(x \cdot y, x \cdot y) \geqslant 0$$

which gives (26.1), and also

$$f(x, x) + f(y, y) \geqslant -f(x, y) - f(y, x)$$

Substituting x^{-1} for x, does not alter the left side, but changes the sign of the right side. Hence

$$f(x, x) + f(y, y) \geqslant |f(x, y) + f(y, x)|$$

Replacing x by x^m, y by y^n, for positive integers m, n, we have

$$m^2 f(x, x) + n^2 f(y, y) = f(x^m, x^m) + f(y^n, y^n) \geqslant |f(x^m, y^n) + f(y^n, x^m)|$$
$$= mn|f(x, y) + f(y, x)|$$

If $f(x, x) = 0$, then for $n = 1$, $m \to \infty$,

$$|f(x, y) + f(y, x)| \leqslant f(y, y)/m \to 0, \quad f(x, y) + f(y, x) = 0$$

and (26.2) is true in this case. If $f(x, x) > 0$, we complete the square.

$$\{mf(x, x) - \tfrac{1}{2}n|f(x, y) + f(y, x)|\}^2 + n^2\{f(x, x)f(y, y)$$
$$- \tfrac{1}{4}|f(x, y) + f(y, x)|^2\} \geqslant 0$$

We have (26.2) on dividing by n^2 and letting

$$m/n \to \tfrac{1}{2}|f(x, y) + f(y, x)|/f(x, x)$$

For (26.3),

$$f(x \cdot y, x \cdot y) = f(x, x) + f(y, y) + f(x, y) + f(y, x)$$
$$\leqslant f(x, x) + f(y, y) + 2\{f(x, x)f(y, y)\}^{1/2} = \{f(x, x)^{1/2} + f(y, y)^{1/2}\}^2$$

128

7

GROUP AND TOPOLOGICAL STRUCTURES

27. The Displacement of Neighbourhoods in a Group with a Topology

WHEN the group T of Chapter 6 has a topology $\mathcal{G}$ we can specialize the results of Chapter 5. We link the algebraic and topological structures by considering continuity properties of $\theta^{-1}(x, y) = x \cdot y$, using section 9. Here, $x \cdot y$ is continuous in x at x_0, for a fixed $y \in T$, if, given $G \in \mathcal{G}$ with $x_0 \cdot y \in G$, there is a $G_1 \in \mathcal{G}$ with $x_0 \in G_1$, such that for each point $v \in G_1$, $v \cdot y \in G$. Since $x \cdot y$ is the group multiplication, which always exists as a single value, we could have written the condition as $G_1 \cdot y \subseteq G$. If true for all $x_0 \in T$, we omit the phrase, 'at x_0'. A similar definition holds for the continuity in y at y_0, of $x \cdot y$ for a fixed $x \in T$.

THEOREM 27.1. *Let $x \cdot y$ be continuous in x for a fixed $y \in T$.*

(27.1) $\qquad\qquad$ *If $G \in \mathcal{G}$, then $\quad G \cdot y^{-1} \in \mathcal{G}$,*

(27.2) $\qquad\qquad\qquad (\mathcal{G}X) \cdot y \subseteq \mathcal{G}(X \cdot y)$,

(27.3) $\qquad\qquad$ *if F is closed, then so is $F \cdot y^{-1}$,*

(27.4) $\qquad\qquad\qquad (\mathcal{G}X) \cdot y^{-1} \supseteq \mathcal{G}(X \cdot y^{-1})$;

(27.5) $\qquad\qquad$ *If F is compact, so is $F \cdot y$.*

If $x \cdot y$ and $x \cdot y^{-1}$ are continuous in x for a fixed $y \in T$, then

(27.6) $\qquad\qquad\qquad (\mathcal{G}X) \cdot y = \mathcal{G}(X \cdot y)$,

(27.7) $\quad$ *if X is nowhere dense in X_1, then $X \cdot y$ is nowhere dense in $X_1 \cdot y$,*

(27.8) $\quad$ *if X is of the first category in X_1, then $X \cdot y$ is of the first category in $X_1 \cdot y$,*

129

(27.9) *if X is of the second category in X_1, then $X \cdot y$ is of the second category in $X_1 \cdot y$.*

Proof. (27.1; ... ; 27.4) follow directly from Theorem 9.1, since, for a fixed y, $x \cdot y$ is a bijection from T to T. For (27.5) let $F \cdot y$ have a cover consisting of open sets G. Then F has a cover consisting of sets $G \cdot y^{-1}$ that are open by (27.1), so that a finite number cover F. Thus the corresponding finite number of G cover $F \cdot y$, which is therefore compact. (27.6) follows from (27.2; 27.4), and (27.7) from Theorem 12.1 (12.1) and (27.1; 27.6). Then (27.8; 27.9) are easy deductions. Note that (27.7) cannot be proved if $x \cdot y$ is continuous in x, but not $x \cdot y^{-1}$. For if

$$X_1 \cap G \subseteq \mathcal{Q}(X \cdot y^{-1}), \quad \text{then} \quad (X_1 \cap G) \cdot y \subseteq \overline{X}$$

by (27.2), but $G \cdot y$ need not be in $\mathcal{Q}$ unless $x \cdot y^{-1}$ is continuous. See *Ex. 27.1.*

THEOREM 27.2. *Let $x \cdot y$ be continuous in y for a fixed $x \in T$.*

(27.10) $\qquad\qquad$ *If $\quad G \in \mathcal{Q}, \quad$ then $\quad x^{-1} \cdot G \in \mathcal{Q}$,*

(27.11) $\qquad\qquad\qquad x \cdot \mathcal{Q}X \subseteq \mathcal{Q}(x \cdot X)$,

(27.12) $\qquad\qquad$ *if F is closed, then so is $x^{-1} \cdot F$,*

(27.13) $\qquad\qquad\qquad x^{-1} \cdot \mathcal{Q}X \supseteq \mathcal{Q}(x^{-1} \cdot X)$,

(27.14) $\qquad\qquad$ *if F is compact, so is $x \cdot F$.*

Let $x \cdot y$ and $x^{-1} \cdot y$ be continuous in y for a fixed $x \in T$. Then

(27.15) $\qquad\qquad\qquad x \cdot \mathcal{Q}X = \mathcal{Q}(x \cdot X)$,

(27.16) *if X is nowhere dense in X_1, then $x \cdot X$ is nowhere dense in $x \cdot X_1$,*

(27.17) *if X is of the first category in X_1, then $x \cdot X$ is of the first category in $x \cdot X_1$,*

(27.18) *if X is of the second category in X_1, then $x \cdot X$ is of the second category in $x \cdot X_1$.*

Ex. 27.1. Let T be the real line with topology consisting of T, the empty set, and unions of open intervals $\left(-n-\frac{1}{2}, -n+\frac{1}{2}\right)$, for

$n = 0, 1, 2, \ldots$ Show that $x + 1$ is continuous in x, and that the closure of $\text{sing}\,(1-1) = \text{sing}\,(0)$ contains $\left(-\frac{1}{2}, \frac{1}{2}\right)$, but $\left(\frac{1}{2}, \frac{3}{2}\right)$ is not an open set, though it is in the closure of $\text{sing}\,(1)$. Further, if $X = \text{sing}\,(1)$, $X_1 = \text{sing}\,(0)$, then X is nowhere dense in X_1. But $X + 1$ is dense in $X_1 + 1$.

Ex. 27.2. Show that $\theta^{-1}(x, y) = x \cdot y$ satisfies $(21.16; 21.17; 21.18)$, if $x \cdot y$ is continuous in y for each fixed $x \in T$. Thus give another proof of $(27.16; 27.17)$, under slightly stronger conditions.

Ex. 27.3. If $x \cdot y$ is continuous in x for each $y \in T$, or in y for each $x \in T$, and if $G_1, G_2 \in \mathcal{G}$, prove that $G_1 \cdot G_2 \in \mathcal{G}$. If $x \cdot y$ is continuous in x for each $y \in T$, then $G_1 \cdot X \in \mathcal{G}(G_1 \in \mathcal{G}, X \subseteq T)$.
(For the first, $G_1 \cdot G_2 = \bigcup G_1 \cdot y \in \mathcal{G} \, (y \in G_2)$.)

Ex. 27.4. If $x \cdot y$ is continuous in x for each $y \in T$, and if some $G \in \mathcal{G}$ is of the second category in T, then $G \cdot y$ is of the second category for all $y \in T$. By using Theorem 12.4 (12.12), show that as T is of the second category, then $\text{II}(T)$ is not empty. Hence prove that every non-empty open set in T is of the second category, and T is a Baire space. (Compare Mehdi (1964), p. 324, Lemma 1).

28. Two-variable Continuity of the Ratio $x \cdot y^{-1}$

By definition of the product topology in $T \times T$, the function $x \cdot y^{-1}$ is continuous in (x, y) at (x_0, y_0) if, given $G \in \mathcal{G}$ with $x_0 \cdot y_0^{-1} \in G$, there are $G_1, G_2 \in \mathcal{G}$ with $x_0 \in G_1$, $y_0 \in G_2$, and $G_1 \cdot G_2^{-1} \subseteq G$. If this is true for all (x_0, y_0) and if T is a $\mathcal{C}_2$-space, T is called a *topological group*.

THEOREM 28.1. (28.1) $x \cdot y^{-1}$ *is continuous in* (x, y) *at all* (x_0, y_0) *(i.e. continuous in* $T \times T$*) if, and only if,* $x \cdot y$ *is continuous in x for fixed* y*, and in y for fixed x, with* $x \cdot y^{-1}$ *continuous at a point* (x_0, y_0)*.*

(28.2) *If $x \cdot y^{-1}$ is continuous in* $T \times T$*, then T is a regular space.*

(28.3) *Let* $p \in T$*(e.g.* $p = u$*) be such that, for each* $z \neq p$*, there is either a neighbourhood of p excluding z, or a neighbourhood of z*

excluding p. If $x \cdot y^{-1}$ is continuous in $T \times T$ then T is a topological group.

Proof. For (28.1) we need only prove the 'if' part. Let G be a neighbourhood of a point $x_1 \cdot y_1^{-1}$. Since $x \cdot y$ is continuous in x, y separately, (27.1; 27.10) give

$$G_1 = x_0 \cdot x_1^{-1} \cdot G \cdot y_1 \cdot y_0^{-1} \in \mathcal{G}, \quad x_1 \cdot y_1^{-1} \in G, \quad x_0 \cdot y_0^{-1} \in G_1$$

Thus there are neighbourhoods G_2 of x_0, G_3 of y_0, such that

$$G_2 \cdot G_3^{-1} \subseteq G_1, \quad x_1 \in x_1 \cdot x_0^{-1} \cdot G_2 \in \mathcal{G}, \quad y_1 \in y_1 \cdot y_0^{-1} \cdot G_3 \in \mathcal{G}$$

If x_2, y_2 lie in the respective neighbourhoods of x_1, y_1, then

$$x_2 \cdot y_2^{-1} \in x_1 \cdot x_0^{-1} G_2 \cdot G_3^{-1} \cdot y_0 \cdot y_1^{-1} \subseteq x_1 \cdot x_0^{-1} \cdot G_1 \cdot y_0 \cdot y_1^{-1} = G$$

proving the continuity at (x_1, y_1).

For (28.2) we prove that $\mathcal{G}$ satisfies the condition in Theorem 10.3 when $x = u$. Other points are similar. Let G_4 be a neighbourhood of u. As $u \cdot u^{-1} = u$, and as an intersection of two $\mathcal{G}$-sets is a $\mathcal{G}$-set, there is a neighbourhood G_5 of u with $G_5 \cdot G_5^{-1} \subseteq G_4$. Let $x \in \bar{G}_5$. Then by (27.10), $x \cdot G_5$ is a $\mathcal{G}$-set containing x, so that $x \cdot G_5$ contains a point $y \in G_5$, since $x \in \bar{G}_5$. Thus

$$z = x \cdot y \in G_5, \quad x = z \cdot y^{-1} \in G_5 \cdot G_5^{-1} \subseteq G_4, \quad \bar{G}_5 \subseteq G_4$$

For (28.3) let $x \neq y$, and put $z = x \cdot y^{-1}$. $p \neq p$. If a neighbourhood G_6 of z excludes p, then by continuity of $x \cdot y^{-1}$ there are neighbourhoods G_7 of x and G_8 of $(y^{-1} \cdot p)^{-1} = p^{-1} \cdot y$ with $G_7 \cdot G_8^{-1} \subseteq G_6$. Hence G_7 is disjoint from $p \cdot G_8$, which is a $\mathcal{G}$-set by Theorem 27.2 (27.10). For $x \cdot y = x \cdot (u \cdot y^{-1})^{-1}$ is continuous in (x, y) and so in y. Thus $p \cdot G_8$ is a neighbourhood of y disjoint from the neighbourhood G_7 of x. If, on the other hand, a neighbourhood G_9 of p excluded z, then by the continuity of $x \cdot y^{-1}$ at (p, u) there are neighbourhoods G_{10} of p and G_{11} of u with $G_{10} \cdot G_{11}^{-1} \subseteq G_9$. Then G_{10} and $z \cdot G_{11}$ are disjoint, so that $G_{10} \cdot p^{-1} \cdot y$ and $z \cdot G_{11} \cdot p^{-1} \cdot y$ are disjoint. The former contains y, the latter x, and the two sets are in $\mathcal{G}$ by the continuity of $x \cdot y$ in x, y separately, and by Theorems 27.1 (27.1), 27.2 (27.10). Hence (28.3).

In Banach (1932), p. 21, an additive group that is a complete metric space, is called a space of type (G) if it satisfies the axioms

(28.4) $\qquad \lim_{n \to \infty} x_n = x \quad implies \quad \lim_{n \to \infty} (-x_n) = -x$

(28.5)

$$\lim_{n \to \infty} x_n = x \quad and \quad \lim_{n \to \infty} y_n = y \quad imply \quad \lim_{n \to \infty} (x_n + y_n) = x + y$$

THEOREM 28.2. *A space of type (G) is a topological group.*

Proof. By Theorem 11.3 (11.9) a metric space has a countable local base, so that by Theorem 15.1 (15.7), to each $x \in X'$ there corresponds a sequence of points of X converging to x. Hence by (28.4; 28.5),

$$\lim_{n \to \infty} x_n = x \quad and \quad \lim_{n \to \infty} y_n = y \quad imply \quad \lim_{n \to \infty} (x_n - y_n) = x - y$$

$$x \in X', \quad y \in Y', \quad imply \quad x - y \in (X - Y)'$$

$$x \in \bar{X}, \quad y \in \bar{Y}, \quad imply \quad x - y \in \mathcal{G}(X - Y), \quad \bar{X} - \bar{Y} \subseteq \mathcal{G}(X - Y)$$

and Theorem 9.1(9.2) is true for $f(x, y) = x - y$. As $f : T \times T \to T$, we have the continuity of $x - y$ in $T \times T$. A metric space is Hausdorffian, completing the proof. Thus we can include many results of Banach (1932).

Ellis (1957) has given the following theorem.

Let $x \cdot y$ be continuous in $T \times T$, and let T be a locally compact T_2-space. Then T is a topological group.

The proof has been deleted through lack of space.

Ex. 28.1. If $x \cdot y^{-1}$ is continuous in $T \times T$, and $G \in \mathcal{G}$, $X \subseteq T$, then $G \cdot X = G \cdot \bar{X}$.

(If $y \in G \cdot \bar{X}$ then $y = g \cdot z (g \in G, z \in \bar{X})$, $u \in g^{-1} \cdot G \in \mathcal{G}$.
Thus there are a neighbourhood G_1 of u, and a point x, with

$$G_1^{-1} \subseteq g^{-1} \cdot G, \quad x \in X \cap (G_1 \cdot z), \quad y = h \cdot x,$$

$$h = y \cdot x^{-1} = g \cdot z \cdot x^{-1} \in g \cdot G_1^{-1} \subseteq G, \quad y = h \cdot x \in G \cdot X)$$

29. Difference Sets and D-$\mathcal{G}$-sets

Throughout this section we assume that $\theta^{-1}(x, y) = x \cdot y$, and we consider the difference sets of section 24, specializing results in section 21. Here, a pinned set is strongly pinned, and is precisely a set containing the unit u, while $\mathcal{G}_0$ is the family of neighbourhoods of u. With the special θ, $\mathcal{G}_0$, (20.1; 21.1) become,

(29.1)   Each non-empty $G \in \mathcal{G}$ is a θ-base for T

(29.2)   each neighbourhood of u is a θ-base for T.

THEOREM 29. (29.3) θ^{-1} *is strongly continuous in x to the identity, if, and only if, $x \cdot y$ is continuous in x at u, for each fixed $y \in T$.*

(29.4) *Let $T_j = T$, $\mathcal{G}_j = \mathcal{G}$ ($j = 1,2$). Then θ^{-1} is open in y for each fixed $x \in T$, if, and only if, $x \cdot y$ is continuous in y for each fixed x.*

(29.5) θ^{-1} *is stable, if $x \cdot y$ it is continuous in x at u, for an everywhere dense set of y, and continuous in y for each x.*

(29.6) $\theta^{-1}(x, T) = T$, *closed, while θ^{-1} is an injection in y; and* (21.16) *is true, if, and only if, $x \cdot y$ is continuous in y for each fixed x.*

Thus the hypotheses in section 21 reduce considerably in this case. For proofs we need only examine the definitions.

A set $X \subseteq T$ is a *strong θ-base for T*, if, for some $G \in \mathcal{G}_0$, $D(X^v) = = T(v \in G)$. A set $X \subseteq T$ is a $D_n - \mathcal{G}$-set, if $D_n(X) \supseteq G$ for some $G \in \mathcal{G}_0$, while X is a $D - \mathcal{G}$-set, if it is a $D_n - \mathcal{G}$-set for some integer n.

THEOREM 29.2. (29.7) *If $x \cdot y$ is continuous in x for each fixed $y \in T$, then $D_1(G) \in \mathcal{G}_0$, $D(G) \in \mathcal{G}_0$, for each non-empty $G \in \mathcal{G}$, and* (29.2) *implies* (29.1). (29.8) *If $x \cdot y$ is continuous in x and y separately, then $D(G)$ is open and closed, for each $G \in \mathcal{G}$. If also G is not empty, there is a $G_1 \in \mathcal{G}_0$ such that the non-empty $G^v \in \mathcal{G}$, for each $v \in G_1$. If also* (29.2) *holds, then each non-empty $G \in \mathcal{G}$ is a strong θ-base for T.*

A set $X \subseteq T$ is a $D_1 - \mathcal{G}$-set, if $x \cdot y$ is continuous in x at u, for each fixed $y \in T$, and if one of the following holds:

(29.9) X contains a non-empty $G \in \mathcal{G}$;

134

GROUP AND TOPOLOGICAL STRUCTURES

(29.10) $G\backslash X$ *is nowhere dense in* T, *for some non-empty* $G \in \mathcal{G}$;

(29.11) X *is closed, and is either dense in some non-empty* $G \in \mathcal{G}$, *or is of the second category.*

Proof. Use Theorems 21.1, 29.1.

THEOREM 29.3. *If* $x \cdot y$ *is continuous in* x, y *separately, and if* T *is a* $\bar{p} - \mathcal{G}$-*space then each non-empty* $G \in \mathcal{G}$ *is strongly-*$\bar{p}$, *and each* $p - \mathcal{G}$-*Baire set* X *is a p-Baire set. If also p is shrinkable, left-translation-invariant, and finitely additive, then* X *is a* $D_1 - \mathcal{G}$-*set.*

Proof. Use Theorems 21.2, 29.1.

THEOREM 29.4. *If* $x \cdot y$ *is continuous in* x, y *separately, and if* $E \subseteq T$ *contains a Baire set of the second category, then* E *is a* $D_1 - \mathcal{G}$-*set.*

Proof. First, T contains an open set of the second category, so that by *Ex. 27.4*, T is a Baire space. We now use Theorems 21.4, 29.1.

When some, and so all, non-empty open sets are of the first category, we need deeper theorems. We use the same notation as in section 21, except that by Theorem 24.1 the $D(X)$ are subgroups. Thus if X is an α-set, $D(X)$ is called an α-*subgroup*, while if the subgroup T_1 is not an α-subgroup we call it a β-*subgroup*. If $T = T_1$, then 'sub' is dropped, so that if X is an α-set and $D(X) = T$, then T is an α-*group*, all other groups T being β-*groups*.

THEOREM 29.5. *Let* $x \cdot y$ *be continuous in* x *for each fixed* y. *Then in order that a subgroup* D *should be a* β-*subgroup of* T, *it is necessary and sufficient that* D *be a* β-*group, under the relative topology* $\mathcal{G}_1$ *of* D *from* $\mathcal{G}$, *that is* $\mathcal{G}$-*dense in a* $\mathcal{G}$-*neighbourhood of* u.

Proof. We use Theorems 21.6, 29.1.

THEOREM 29.6.

(29.12) *Let* $x \cdot y$ *be continuous in* x *for each fixed* y. *If* X *is a* β-*set, and if a sequence* $\{F_n\}$ *of closed sets is such that* $F_n \supseteq D_n(X)$, *then there is an integer n such that* F_n *is a* $D_1 - \mathcal{G}$-*set.*

Let $x \cdot y^{-1}$ *be continuous in* $T \times T$. *Then the following hold:*

(29.13) $D_1(\bar{X}) \subseteq \mathcal{G}D_1(X)$,

(29.14) *if* $\{D_n\}$ *is a difference sequence, so is* $\{\bar{D}_n\}$,

(29.15) *the property of being sequentially closed, is hereditary.*

(29.16) *If T is a topological group, $\mathcal{G}$ having a countable base, then every set containing a sequentially closed β-set X is a $D - \mathcal{G}$-set.*

Proof. Use Theorems 21.7, 29.1.

A set X is an α-*Baire set*, if there is a non-empty $G \in \mathcal{G}$ such that $G \backslash X$ is contained in an α-subgroup of T. An α-Baire set is a $p_7 - \mathcal{G}$-Baire set, where $p_7 = th(p_3)$, and where p_3 is the property that a set is nowhere dense.

Ex. 21.5 shows that the union of two α-sets can be a θ-base for T. This causes some difficulty, but we can at least have Theorem 29.7.

THEOREM 29.7.

(29.17) *If T is a commutative group, if x·y is continuous in y, for each fixed x, and if X is contained in an α-subgroup, then so is*

$$X \cup (x \cdot X)$$

(29.18) *If in (29.17) no non-empty $\mathcal{G}$-set can be contained in an x-subgroup, and if X is an α-Baire set, then X is a $D_1 - \mathcal{G}$-set.*

Proof. By Theorem 27.2 (27.16), the continuity of $x \cdot y$ in y for each fixed x, implies that the property p_3, of being nowhere dense, is left-translation-invariant. It is finitely additive, by Theorem 12.1 (12.2), so that all the conditions of Theorem 24.3 are satisfied, with $\mathcal{V} = \mathcal{G}_0$, giving the result.

As an α-subgroup of T is of the first category, (29.18) is included in Thorem 29.4, unless all $\mathcal{G}$-sets are of the first category. Similarly, for some integer n, the F_n of Theorem 29.6 (29.12) contains a $\mathcal{G}$-set, and so is of the second category if every $\mathcal{G}$-set has this property. There is an advance on Theorem 29.4, in that $D_n(X)$, and not $D_1(X)$, is involed. But (29.12; 29.16; 29.18) form a significant advance when all $\mathcal{G}$-sets are of the first category, since Theorem 29.4 is then void.

However, *Ex. 21.5* shows that we cannot take even finite unions of x-sets except in special circumstances. It also shows that we cannot replace G in *Ex. 21.4* by a general $D_1 - \mathcal{G}$-set, since $l_1 \cup l_2$ is a $D_1 - \mathcal{G}$-set, l_1 is an α-set, and $(l_1 \cup l_2) \backslash l_1$ is an α-set contained in l_2, and so cannot be a $D_1 - \mathcal{G}$-set. Thus it seems unlikely that (29.12;

29.16; 29.18) could be combined into one result, so that we look for other criteria that give $D_1 - \mathcal{Q}$-sets.

One criterion can be furnished by the cardinal number, *card* (X), of $X \subseteq T$. As $f(y) = x \cdot y$ is a bijection,

$$(29.19) \qquad \text{card } (x \cdot X) = \text{card } (X)$$

By cardinal multiplication, and $x \cdot y^{-1}$ for fixed $y \in X$,

$$\text{card } (X) \leqslant \text{card } (D_1(X)) \leqslant \text{card } (X)^2$$

Assuming card (X) infinite, the multiplicative axiom shows that the two extreme terms are equal, so that

$$(29.20) \qquad \text{card } (D(X)) = \text{card } (D_1(X)) = \text{card } (X)$$

By addition of cardinal numbers,

$$(29.21) \quad \max \left(\text{card } (X), \text{ card } (Y)\right) \leqslant \text{card } (X \cup Y) \leqslant \text{card } (X)$$
$$+ \text{card } (Y)$$

Let card $(T) > \aleph_0$. Then the property p_{10}, that card $(X) < \text{card } (T)$, is shrinkable, left-translation-invariant by (29.19), hereditary by (29.20), and finitely additive by (29.21), while $p_{10} = p_{10}^\sigma = h(p_{10})$ $th(p_{10})$. Thus by (29.20) and Theorem 6.4,

$$(29.22) \qquad \text{if} \quad \text{card } (T) > \aleph_0, \quad \text{card } (X) < \text{card } (T),$$

$$D(Y) = T, \quad \text{then} \quad D(X) \neq T, \text{card } (Y) = \text{card } (T)$$

(29.23) If T has a topology $\mathcal{Q}$ with a countable base, and if card $(T) > \aleph_0$ then T is a $\bar{p}_{10} - \mathcal{Q}$-space, assuming that $x \cdot y$ is continuous in y for each $x \in T$, and that T is a $\mathcal{O}_a$-space. We use an argument similar to that of *Ex. 27.4*. Since T is the union of the countable number of sets of the base $\mathcal{B}$, then one set G_1 at least of $\mathcal{B}$ does not lie in $\mathcal{P}_{10}$. There is a sequence $\{G_j^*\} \subseteq \mathcal{B}$ of neighbourhoods of u, with intersection containing only u, since T is a $\mathcal{O}_2$-space. We can choose a point x in each set $G \in \mathcal{B}$, and then by left-translation we can move x to u, and so G to $G(x)$, a neighbourhood of u. Let us now discard from $\mathcal{B}$ all G for which $G(x) \nsubseteq$ $G_1(x_1) \cap G_1^*$, where $G_1(x_1)$ is the corresponding displacement of G_1. Then the family $\mathcal{B}_1$ of all remaining $G \in \mathcal{B}$ is also a base for $\mathcal{Q}$, and by the same argument there is a $G_2 \in \mathcal{B}_1 \backslash \mathcal{P}_{10}$, and we can define $\mathscr{B}_2$, and so on. By (29.19) we see that a monotone decreasing sequence of neighbourhoods of u, with intersection containing only u, is not in $\mathcal{P}_{10}$. Hence every neighbourhood of u, and so every non-empty $G \in \mathcal{G}$, is not in $\mathcal{P}_{10}$.

A strongly-$\bar{p}_{10}$ set X is such that, for some $G \in \mathcal{G}_0$,

$$(29.24) \qquad \text{card } (X \cap (v \cdot X)) = \text{card } (T) \, (v \in G)$$

Thus card $(X) = $ card (T), but (29.24) implies more than this, and depends on the positions of points of X. The situation is easier if we take $X \in \mathcal{G}$. When the conditions of (29.23) hold, or when (29.1) holds with card $(T) > \aleph_0$ so that we can apply (29.22), then T is a $\bar{p}_{10} - \mathcal{G}$-space. Then we can apply Theorem 29.2 (29.8) to show that if the non-empty $G \in \mathcal{G}$, there is a $G_1 \in \mathcal{G}_0$ such that the non-empty $G^v \in \mathcal{G}(v \in G_1)$, provided that $x \cdot y$ is continuous in x and y separately, i.e. each non-empty $G \in \mathcal{G}$ is strongly-$\bar{p}_{10}$. Each $p_{10} - \mathcal{G}$-Baire set is now a p_{10}-Baire set, and Theorem 6.3 shows that it is a $D_1 - \mathcal{G}$-set. A $p_{10} - \mathcal{G}$-Baire set is such that there is a non-empty $G \in \mathcal{G}$ with the property that $G \backslash X$ is contained in the given set, where card $(X) < $ card (T). Thus we can put together the foregoing results to obtain:

THEOREM 29.8. *Let $(T, \mathcal{G})$ be a group and a topological space, in which $x \cdot y$ is continuous in x, y separately. If* card $(T) > \aleph_0$, *if a set E and a non-empty $G \in \mathcal{G}$ are such that* card $(G \backslash E) < $ card (T), *and if either T is a $\mathcal{U}_2$-space and $\mathcal{G}$ has a countable base, or each non-empty $G \in \mathcal{G}_0$ is a θ-base for T, then E is a $D_1 - \mathcal{G}$-set.*

We could now proceed to consider outer measure and the property $p_9(\delta)$. But after section 21 and Theorems 21.8, 21.9, we need only add here that for $\theta^{-1}(x, y) = x \cdot y$, a θ^{-1}-invariant outer measure, for which $\mu(x \cdot X) = \mu(X)$, is called a *(left-invariant) Haar outer measure*. In section 49 it will be shown that for certain topological groups a Haar measure always exists.

Historical Notes. Theorem 29.4 and the first result in (29.8) contain Banach (1932), p. 21, Théorème 21. Theorem 29.5 is a generalization to groups of Sargent (1953), pp. 440–1, Lemma 2. Also see Henstock (1963a).

Ex. 29.1. A $D_n - \mathcal{G}$-set is a $D_m - \mathcal{G}$-set, for each integer $m > n$.

Ex. 29.2. There is a closed set in $[0, 1]$ that is nowhere dense in $[0,1]$, and that has measure zero, and yet that is a $D_1 - \mathcal{G}$-set, so that neither Theorem 29.4 nor Theorem 21.9 for $\theta^{-1}(x, y) = x+y$, nor both together, are sufficient to give all $D_1 - \mathcal{G}$-sets even for the real line.

(The Cantor ternary set F of *Ex. 12.6* is closed and nowhere dense, while in its construction, removing the inner thirds of the intervals at the nth stage reduces the measure to $(2/3)^n$, where n tends to infinity. Thus the measure is 0. T_0 show that $D_1(F) \supseteq [0, 1]$ we take $0 \leqslant k \leqslant 1$. If $k \in F$ we take $y = k$ and $x = 0 \in F$. Then $y - x = k \in D_1(F)$. If $k \in \backslash F$ we use an argument similar to that of Bary (1964), p. 296, considering $F \times F$ in the compact space $C = [0, 1] \times [0, 1]$. Let F_n be the closed set obtained on removing the middle thirds of intervals to the nth stage, so that F is the intersection of all F_n. Let $F_{1n} = F_n \times F_n$. By considering the open rectangles of $C \backslash F_{1n}$, show that the line $y = x+k$ meets F_{1n} in at least one point, and so in a non-empty closed set F_{2n}. Show that for $n = 1, 2, \ldots$, the F_{2n} have a non-empty intersection, and so find $x, y \in F$ with $y - x = k$. Thus prove that $D_1(F) = [-1, 1]$. Also look for an alternative proof based on the expression of k as a ternary decimal $0 \cdot k_1 k_2 \ldots k_n \ldots$ Is there a rule that gives the nth decimal places of x, y in terms of k_n?)

30. Group-invariant Pseudometric

A group T can be a pseudometric space with pseudometric ϱ. We say that ϱ is *group-invariant*, if

$$(30.1) \qquad \varrho(x, y) = \varrho(x \cdot y^{-1}, u)$$

where u is the unit of T. Then $\varrho(x, u)$ is called the *pseudonorm* $\| x \|$ of x, and the axioms for a pseudometric space, $(11.1; 11.2)$, become the following:

(30.2) $$\|x\| = 0 \quad \text{if} \quad x = u$$

(30.3) $$\|x\| = \|x^{-1}\| \geqslant 0, \quad \text{for all} \quad x \in T$$

(30.4) $$\|x \cdot y\| \leqslant \|x\| + \|y\| \quad \text{for all} \quad x, y \in T$$

Conversely, if $\|x\|$ is given satisfying (30.2; 30.3; 30.4), then

(30.5) $$\varrho(x, y) = \|x \cdot y^{-1}\|$$

is a group-invariant pseudometric for T.

THEOREM 30.1. *If the pseudometric ϱ is group-invariant, then $x \cdot y$ is continuous in x for each fixed y.*

Proof. $\varrho(x \cdot y, x_0 \cdot y) = \|x \cdot y \cdot y^{-1} \cdot x_0^{-1}\| = \|x \cdot x_0^{-1}\| = \varrho(x, x_0)$

In general, $x \cdot y$ need not be continuous in y for each fixed x, since

$$\|x \cdot y \cdot y_0^{-1} \cdot x^{-1}\|, \quad \|y \cdot y_0^{-1}\|$$

need bear no relation to each other.

THEOREM 30.2. (30.6) *If ϱ is a group-invariant pseudometric for a commutative group T, then $x \cdot y^{-1}$ is continuous in (x, y).*
(30.7) *If in (30.6), ϱ is a metric, T is a topological group.*

Proof. $\varrho(x \cdot y^{-1}, x_0 \cdot y_0^{-1}) = \|x \cdot y^{-1} \cdot y_0 \cdot x_0^{-1}\| = \|x \cdot x_0^{-1} \cdot y_0 \cdot y^{-1}\|$

$$\leqslant \|x \cdot x_0^{-1}\| + \|y \cdot y_0^{-1}\| = \varrho(x, x) + \varrho(y, y)$$

giving (30.6). Then (30.7) follows since a metric space is Hausdorffian.

In some problems a conventional pseudonorm $\|x\|$ is defined that satisfies (30.2; 30.3; 30.4), but that can sometimes take the value $+\infty$. Then if X is a known set on which $\|x\|$ is finite, we can use

$$\|x \cdot y^{-1}\| \leqslant \|x\| + \|y\|$$

to show that $\|x\|$ is finite at all points of $D(X)$, by Theorem 5.1, so that sections 24, 29 are relevant here, giving various conditions for which $D(X) = T$, when we prove that the pseudonorm is finite in T. Such a pseudonorm can be constructed as in section 26 from a bimultiplicative non-negative definite functional f, and cases are considered in Chapter 9.

We define a *norm* to be a pseudonorm $\|\cdot\|$ that has $\|x\| = 0$ only if $x = u$. This corresponds to a group-invariant metric.

THEOREM 30.3. *Let T be an additive group with a pseudonorm $\|\cdot\|$, under which T is a Baire space, and let the $r(x) = \frac{1}{2}x$ of section 23 exist for each $x \in T$, with*

$$(30.8) \qquad \tfrac{1}{2}x \to 0 \quad as \quad x \to 0,$$

where 0 is the zero of T. Let X be a space, R^+ the set of non-negative reals, and $f: X \to R^+$. If, for each $a \in A$, the function $V_a : T \to X$ satisfies

$$(30.9) \quad f(V_a(x+y)) \leqslant f(V_a(x)) + f(V_a(y)) \qquad (all\ x,\ y \in T),$$

(30.10) *for each $\varepsilon > 0$, the set of x where $f(V_a(x)) \leqslant \varepsilon$, is closed,*

(30.11) *there is an integer k_0, depending on x, $\varepsilon > 0$, such that*

$$\sup_{a \in A} f(V_a(2^{-k}x)) \leqslant \varepsilon \qquad (all\ x \in T,\ all\ k \geqslant k_0),$$

where $2^{-k}x$ is the $r_k(x)$, then as $x \to 0$, $f(V_a(x)) \to 0$ uniformly for $a \in A$.

Proof. By (30.9), for

$$N_k(x) = \sup_{a \in A} \{ f(V_a(2^{-k}x)) + f(V_a(-2^{-k}x)) \}$$

$$f(V_a(x-y)) + f(V_a(y-x)) \leqslant f(V_a(x)) + f(V_a(-x)) + f(V_a(y))$$
$$+ f(V_a(-y)), N_k(x-y) \leqslant N_k(x) + N_k(y)$$

Further, given $\varepsilon > 0$, by (30.11) there is an integer k_1 depending on x, ε, such that

$$(30.12) \qquad N_k(x) \leqslant \varepsilon \qquad (all\ k \geqslant k_1)$$

Thus T is the union for $k = 1, 2, \ldots$, of sets $P_k(\varepsilon)$ of those x satisfying (30.12), so that since T is of the second category, there is an integer k, depending on ε, such that $P_k(\varepsilon)$ is dense in some sphere S.

By Theorem 30.2 (30.6), $x - y$ is continuous in (x, y), so that if $x \to x_0$ then $x - x_0 \to 0$. Thus using Theorem 23.2 $(23.10; 23.11)$

141

with (30.8),

$$r(x) - r(x_0) = r(x - x_0) \to 0, \quad r(x) \to r(x_0), \quad \tfrac{1}{2}x \to \tfrac{1}{2}x_0,$$
$$2^{-k}x \to 2^{-k}x_0$$

Hence by (30.10), and then by arbitrary intersections, the sets where

$$f(V_a(2^{-k}x)) \leqslant \varepsilon, \quad \sup_{a \in A} f(V_a(2^{-k}x)) \leqslant \varepsilon$$

are closed; and we have a similar result with $-x$ for x. Hence if the sets involving the two suprema, for x and $-x$, are F, F^*, we have

$$\bar{P}_k(\varepsilon) \subseteq F \cap F^* \subseteq P_k(2\varepsilon)$$

and $P_k(2\varepsilon)$ contains the sphere S. Hence by Theorems 5.1 (5.8) and 29.2 (29.7), there is a $\delta > 0$ such that if $x \in T$, $\|x\| < \delta$,

$$N_k(x) \leqslant L_1(2\varepsilon) = 4\varepsilon$$

Putting $y = 2^{-k}x$, then for $\|x\| < \delta$, where k, δ depend on ε, but not on $a \in A$,

$$(30.13) \qquad f(V_a(y)) + f(V_a(-y)) < 4\varepsilon \qquad (a \in A)$$

Now let y be an arbitrary point of T in $\|y\| < \delta \cdot 2^{-k}$. Then if $x = 2^k y$, so that $2^{-k}x = y$, we have by (30.4) used repeatedly,

$$\|x\| = \|2^k y\| \leqslant 2^k \|y\| < \delta, \quad \|x\| < \delta$$

and (30.13) follows when $\|y\| < \delta \cdot 2^{-k}$. Hence the theorem.

For example, X could be a group with pseudonorm f, and for (30.10) we could assume each V_a continuous.

31. β-groups*

Sargent (1953), pp. 443–7 has constructed examples of normed vector β-spaces, some of which are of the first category, and so are $\bar{p}_7 - \mathcal{G}$-spaces that are not $\bar{p}_4 - \mathcal{G}$-spaces. She uses four axioms, the fourth of which can, in her notation, be replaced by the following, in which the

* This rather technical section may be omitted on a first reading.

I_m are intervals.

(31.1) If $x_m \in G(I_m)$, with $I_m \cap I_{m+1}$ a single point, and $I_m \cap I_{m+2}$ empty, for $m = 1, 2, \ldots$, and if $\{s(n)\}$ is a fundamental sequence, where $s(n) = \sum_{m=1}^{n} x_m$, then it is convergent.

Sargent's axiom 4 follows easily from (31.1). Conversely, if Sargent's axiom 4 is true, and if $\{s(n)\}$ is fundamental, then for a strictly increasing sequence $\{m(j)\}$ of positive integers,

$$\lim_{n \to \infty} \sup_{k \geqslant n} \|s(k) - s(n)\| = 0, \qquad \sup_{k \geqslant m(j)} \|s(k) - s(m(j))\| < 2^{-j}$$

$$\sum_{j=1}^{\infty} \|s(m(j+1)) - s(m(j))\| < 1$$

Since

$$s(m(j+1)) - s(m(j)) \in G(J_j), \qquad J_j = \bigcup_{n=m(j)+1}^{m(j+1)} I_n$$

where J_j is another interval and $\{J_j\}$ a sequence of intervals satisfying the conditions of Sargent's axiom 4, then $\{s(m(j))\}$ is convergent. Hence the fundamental $\{s(n)\}$ is also convergent, and (31.1) is true.

Thus the way is opened for us to generalize Sargent's construction. The intervals and their division can be replaced by intervals and continued bisection, and so by a repeated choice of 0 (for the left half) or 1 (for the right half). Similarly, divisions of an n-dimensional rectangle with sides parallel to the coordinate axes, can be replaced by 2^n-section, and so by a bisection relative to each coordinate in turn. For a rectangle with a countable infinity of dimensions and with sides parallel to the coordinate axes, suitable bisections can be put in sequence by Cantor's diagonal process. It follows that the use of 0, 1 sequences covers many cases.

We can also generalize from a normed vector space to a commutative topological group, with a pseudometric such that all spheres are open sets. It is likely that the theory may be generalized further, to more general θ, but for simplicity I have limited the generality.

Let T be an additive topological group, with a subgroup T_1 dense in T. Let Δ be the set of all finite ordered sets $d^n = (d_1, \ldots, d_n)$ of

143

0's and 1's, including the empty set, i.e. let $\varDelta$ be the set of all finite 0, 1 sequences. We put

$$d^n j = (d_1, \ldots, d_n, j) \qquad (j = 0, 1)$$

If also $c^m \in \varDelta$, then $d^n \subseteq c^m$ is to denote that $n \leqslant m$ and that

$$c^m = (d_1, \ldots, d_n, c_{n+1}, \ldots, c_m).$$

AXIOM 31.1 *If $x \in T$, $d^n \in \varDelta$, then there is an $x(d^n) \in T$.*

AXIOM 31.2 *If $x \in T_1$, then $x(d^n) \in T_1$, $x(d^n) - x(c^m) \in T_1$ ($d^n \subseteq c^m$; d^n, $c^m \in \varDelta$).*

AXIOM 31.3. $(x+y)(d^n) = x(d^n) + y(d^n)$.

AXIOM 31.4. $[x(c^m)](d^n) = x(c^m)$ ($d^n \subseteq c^m$; d^n, $c^m \in \varDelta$).

AXIOM 31.5. $[x(d^n j)](d^n(1-j)) = 0$ ($j = 0, 1$).

AXIOM 31.6. $x(d^n 0) + x(d^n 1) = x(d^n)$.

AXIOM 31.7. *Given $G \in \mathcal{G}_0$, $d^n \in \varDelta$, there is a $G_1 \in \mathcal{G}_0$ such that if $x \in T$, $c^m \in \varDelta$, $d^n \subseteq c^m$, $x(d^n) \in G_1$, then $x(c^m) \in G$.*

This corresponds to Sargent's axiom 2.

AXIOM 31.8. *If $x \in T$, and if $\{d_m\}$ is an arbitrary infinite 0, 1 sequence, then*

$$\lim_{n \to \infty} - x(d^n) = 0$$

AXIOM 31.9. *There is a pseudometric ϱ in T such that, for each $\varepsilon > 0$, each $x \in T$, the sphere $S(x, \varepsilon) \in \mathcal{G}$.*

If $X \subseteq T$, $d^n \subseteq c^m$, and d^n, $c^m \in \varDelta$, let $X(d^n)$, $X(d^n, c^m)$ be the sets of all $x \in X$ with $x = x(d^n)$ and $x = x(d^n) - x(c^m)$, respectively.

AXIOM 31.10. *There is a neighbourhood $G(x)$ of each $x \in T$ with the following property. For each infinite 0, 1 sequence $\{d_m\}$, with $d_j(m)$ denoting $d^{m-1}j$, each strictly increasing sequence $\{m_{jk}\}$ of integers m for which $d_m = j$, and each fundamental sequence $\{x_k\}$ in $G(x)$, using ϱ, that satisfies*

$$(31.2) \qquad x_0 = 0, \quad x_k - x_{k-1} \in T_1(d_j(m_{j, k-1}), d_j(m_{j, k}))$$

144

*for either $j = 0$ or $j = 1$, independent of k, the closure of the set of x_k
$(k = 1, 2, \ldots)$ is semi-compact.*

This corresponds to Sargent's axiom 4, with the change from spaces that are like complete spaces, to spaces that are like locally semi-complete spaces. The proliferation of axioms here is necessary to ensure that Sargent's methods carry through. We prove that T is a β-group, in easy stages.

LEMMA 31.1. $0(d^n) = 0$, $(-x)(d^n) = -(x(d^n))$, and $T(d^n)$, $T_1(d^n)$, $T(d^n, c^m)$, $T_1(d^n, c^m)$ are groups with $T_1(d^n) \subseteq T(d^n) \subseteq T$, $T_1(d^n, c^m) \subseteq T(d^n, c^m) \subseteq T$, where $d^n \subseteq c^m$ and d^n, $c^m \in \Delta$.

Proof. By axioms 31.1, 31.3, if $x \in T$ then

$$0(d^n), \quad x(d^n) \in T, \quad x = x+0, \quad x(d^n) = x(d^n)+0(d^n), \quad 0(d^n) = 0$$

$$x(d^n)+(-x)(d^n) = (x-x)(d^n) = 0(d^n) = 0$$

Using axiom 31.2, the rest now follow.

LEMMA 31.2. *If $X \subseteq T$, and d^n, $c^m \in \Delta$, $d^n \subseteq c^m$, then $X(d^n)' \subseteq X'(d^n)$, $X(d^n, c^m)' \subseteq X'(d^n, c^m)$, so that if X is closed, so are $X(d^n)$, $X(d^n, c^m)$.*

Proof. If $y \in X(d^n)'$, $G \in \mathcal{G}_0$, there is an x such that

$$x = x(d^n) \in X(d^n) \subseteq X, \quad x \in y+G$$

so that $y \in X'$. To show that $y = y(d^n)$ we first find a $G_2 \in \mathcal{G}_0$ such that $G_2 - G_2 \subseteq G$, and then let G_3 be the G_1 of axiom 31.7 for G_2 replacing G, for d^n empty, and for c^m replaced by d^n. Then in the previous result we can replace G by $G_2 \cap G_3$, assuming that

$$x-y \in G_2 \cap G_3 \subseteq G_2; \quad x-y(d^n) = x(d^n)-y(d^n)$$

$$= (x-y)(d^n) \in G_2$$

$$y-y(d^n) = (x-y(d^n))-(x-y) \in G_2-G_2 \subseteq G,$$

$$y = y(d^n) \in X'(d^n)$$

We have used axiom 31.3, Lemma 31.1, $\mathcal{G}$ being Hausdorffian, and $G \in \mathcal{G}_0$ arbitrary. Similarly for $X'(d^n, c^m)$. Then if X is closed.

$$X' \subseteq X, \quad X(d^n)' \subseteq X'(d^n) \subseteq X(d^n),$$

$$X(d^n, c^m)' \subseteq X'(d^n, c^m) \subseteq X(d^n, c^m),$$

and $X(d^n)$, $X(d^n, c^m)$ are closed.

LEMMA 31.3. $T_1(d^n)$, $T_1(d^n, c^m)$ *are dense in* $T(d^n)$, $T(d^n, c^m)$, *respectively.*

Let $y \in T(d^n)$, so that $y = y(d^n)$. As T_1 is dense in T, given $G \in \mathcal{G}_0$, there is an $x \in T_1 \cap (y + G_1)$, where G_1 is as in axiom 31.7 with d^n empty and c^m replaced by d^n. By Lemma 31.1 and axioms 31.2–4, 31.7,

$$x(d^n) \in T_1, \quad x(d^n) = x(d^n)(d^n) \in T_1(d^n), \quad x(d^n) - y = x(d^n) - y(d^n)$$

$$= (x - y)(d^n) \in G, \quad x(d^n) \in y + G$$

As $G \in \mathcal{G}_0$ is arbitrary, $y \in T_1(d^n)'$, and the result is proved for $T_1(d^n)$. Similarly for $T_1(d^n, c^m)$, also using axioms 31.5, 31.6.

LEMMA 31.4. *If* $\{F_k\}$ *is a difference sequence of closed sets, so are*

$$\{F_k(d^n)\}, \quad \{F_k(d^n, c^m)\}, \quad for \quad d^n, \quad c^m \in \Delta, \quad d^n \subseteq c^m.$$

Proof. These follow from axioms 31.1, 31.3, and Lemmas 31.1, 31.2.

LEMMA 31.5. *If* $\{F_k\}$ *is a difference sequence of closed sets, with* $F_k(d^n)$ *nowhere dense in* $T(d^n)$ $(k \geqslant 1)$, *then* $F_k(d^n j)$ *is nowhere dense in* $T(d^n j)(k \geqslant 1)$, *either for* $j = 0$ *or for* $j = 1$, *independent of* k.

Proof. By Lemma 31.4, $\{F_k(d^n)\}$ is monotone increasing in k. If the result is false there are an integer k and $G_j \in \mathcal{G}$, such that if

$$x_j \in G_j(d^n j), \quad x_j = x_j(d^n j) \in G_j, \quad \text{then} \quad x_j \in F_k(d^n j) \qquad (j = 0, 1)$$

since the latter set is closed. As $x + y$ is continuous in y for each $x \in T$, there are $G_{j+2} \in \mathcal{G}_0$ with $x_j + G_{j+2} \subseteq G_j$ $(j = 0, 1)$. By axiom 31.7 there is a $G_4 \in \mathcal{G}_0$ such that if $x(d^n) \in G_4$, then $x(d^n j) \in G_2 \cap G_3$. By axioms 31.3–7, if

$$x = x_0 + x_1, \quad \text{then} \quad x(d^n j) = x_0(d^n j) + x_1(d^n j) = x_j(d^n j) = x_j,$$

$$x(d^n) = x(d^n 0) + x(d^n 1) = x_0 + x_1 = x. \quad \text{If} \quad y \in x + G_4(d^n),$$

$$\text{then} \quad y = y(d^n), \quad y - x \in G_4(d^n), \quad (y - x)(d^n j) \in G_{j+2},$$

$$y(d^n j) \in x_j + G_{j+2}(d^n j) \subseteq F_k(d^n j) \subseteq F_k(d^n), \quad y = y(d^n) = y(d^n 0)$$

$$+ y(d^n 1) \in F_k(d^n) + F_k(d^n) \subseteq F_{k+1}(d^n) - F_{k+1}(d^n) \subseteq F_{k+2}(d^n).$$

Hence $F_{k+2}(d^n)$ contains $x + G_4(d^n)$, a portion of $T(d^n)$, contrary to hypothesis. Hence the lemma.

THEOREM 31.1. *If T is an additive topological group, with a subgroup T_1 dense in T, and obeying axioms 31.1 to 31.10, then T is a β-group.*

Proof. If false, then by Theorem 29.6 (29.14), T is the union of a difference sequence $\{F_k\}$ of closed sets each of which is nowhere dense in T. By Lemmas 31.4, 31.5, there is an infinite 0, 1 sequence $\{d_m\}$ such that, for each fixed n, $\{F_k(d^m)\}$ is a difference sequence of closed sets each nowhere dense in $T(d^m)$. In axiom 31.10, $\{m_{0,k}\}$ is an arbitrary strictly increasing sequence. Hence if $d_m = 0$ for an infinity of m, we can assume, without loss of generality, that $d_m = 0$ for all m. (A similar proof holds when $d_m = 1$ for all but a finite number of m.) Then we can simplify the symbols, replacing d^n, $d_0(m_{0,k})$ by n, m_k, so that, for example, we write $X(n)$ for $X(d^n)$.

By Lemma 31.2, $F_1(1)$ is closed, and it is nowhere dense in $T(1)$, so that there are y_1 and $G_1 \in \mathcal{Q}$, such that

$$y_1 \in T(1), \quad y_1 \in G_1, \quad \bar{G}_1 \cap F_1(1) \text{ empty}, \quad G_1 \subseteq G(y_1)$$

the $G(y_1)$ being the set of axiom 31.10. By axiom 31.8 there is an integer m_1 with

$$-y_1(m_1) \in -y_1 + G_1 (\in \mathcal{Q}_0), \quad y_1 - y_1(m_1) \in G_1$$

By Lemma 31.3, $T_1(1, m_1)$ is dense in $T(1, m_1)$. Hence there is an

$$x_1 \in T_1(1, m_1) \cap G_1, \quad \text{so that} \quad x_1 \notin F_1(1), \quad x_1 \notin F_1$$

This begins an inductive process. Suppose that

$$x_0 = 0, x_1, \ldots, x_n; \quad m_0 = 1, m_1, \ldots, m_n; \quad G_1, \ldots, G_n$$

respectively points of T, positive integers, and sets of $\mathcal{Q}$, have been defined with the following properties. For $j = 1, 2, \ldots, n$.

(31.3) $\qquad x_j \in (x_{j-1} + G_j) \backslash F_j$, the sets $x_{j-1} + G_j$

$\qquad\qquad\qquad$ being monotone decreasing

(31.4) $\qquad\qquad\qquad x_j - x_{j-1} \in T_1(m_{j-1}, m_j)$

(31.5) $\qquad\qquad\qquad \varrho(x_j, x_k) < 1/j \qquad (j < k \leqslant n)$

(31.6) $\quad \bar{G}_j \cap F_k(m_{j-1})$ is empty, for some $k \geqslant j+1$, while

$$x_{j-1} \in F_{k-1} \qquad (j > 1)$$

By (31.5) with $k = n$, and axiom 31.9, there is a non-empty

$$(31.7) \qquad G^1 = \{z : \varrho(z + x_n, x_j) < 1/j \, (1 \leqslant j \leqslant n)\}$$

$$= \bigcap_{j=1}^{n} S(x_j, 1/j) - x_n \in \mathcal{G}_0$$

Since $\{F_j\}$ is monotone increasing with union T, there is a $k \geqslant n+2$, with $x_n \in F_{k-1}$. Since $F_k(m_n)$ is nowhere dense in $T(m_n)$, there is a

$$(31.8) \qquad y_{n+1} \in G^1 \cap (x_{n-1} - x_n + G_n) \cap T(m_n) \backslash F_k(m_n)$$

for by (31.3; 31.7)

$$G^1 \in \mathcal{G}_0, \qquad x_{n-1} - x_n + G_n \in \mathcal{G}_0$$

But $F_k(m_n)$ is closed, and $\mathcal{G}$ is regular, by Theorem 28.1 (28.2), so that there is a $G_{n+1} \in \mathcal{G}$ with

$$(31.9) \qquad y_{n+1} \in G_{n+1} \subseteq G^1 \cap (x_{n-1} - x_n + G_n),$$

$$\bar{G}_{n+1} \cap F_k(m_n) \quad \text{empty}, \qquad x_n + G_{n+1} \subseteq x_{n-1} + G_n$$

and (31.6) and the second part of (31.3) are true for $j = n+1$. By axiom 31.8 there is an m_{n+1} such that

$$-y_{n+1}(m_{n+1}) \in -y_{n+1} + G_{n+1}(\in \mathcal{G}_0), \qquad y_{n+1} - y_{n+1}(m_{n+1}) \in G_{n+1}$$

Hence by (31.8; 31.9),

$$y_{n+1} - y_{n+1}(m_{n+1}) \in G_{n+1} \cap T(m_n, m_{n+1}) \backslash F_k(m_n)$$

As $T_1(m_n, m_{n+1})$ is dense in $T(m_n, m_{n+1})$, there is an

$$(31.10) \qquad x_{n+1} = x_n + z \quad \text{with} \quad z \in T_1(m_n, m_{n+1}) \cap G_{n+1} \backslash F_k(m_n) \subseteq G^1$$

so that (31.4) is true for $j = n+1$. Also, by (31.7), (31.5) is true with $n+1$ for n. By (31.10), as $\{F_j\}$ is a monotone increasing difference sequence,

$$x_n \in F_{k-1}, \qquad x_{n+1} - x_n \notin F_k, \qquad \text{hence} \qquad x_{n+1} \notin F_{k-1}, \qquad x_{n+1} \notin F_{n+1}$$

and (31.3) follows. Thus we have continued the induction.

By (31.5), $\{x_j\}$ is a fundamental sequence, which by (31.3) lies in

$$x_0 + G_1 = G_1 \subseteq G(y_1)$$

Also (31.4) shows that (31.2) is satisfied. Hence we can apply axiom 31.10 and find a $w \in T$ that satisfies

$$w \in \bar{L}_{n+1}(\{x_n\}) \subseteq x_n + \bar{G}_{n+1}, \quad w - x_n \notin F_k(m_n), \quad x_n \in F_{k-1},$$
$$w \notin F_{k-1}, \quad w \notin F_n \quad \text{(some } k \geqslant n+2\text{)}$$

The other steps follow from (31.3; 31.6 $(j = n+1)$). As w is independent of n, it follows that w is not in the union T of the F_n, contrary to hypothesis. Hence the theorem.

Ex. 31.1. Let T_2 be the space of functions

$$x(t) = \int_a^t y(\cdot)\, dm \qquad (a \leqslant t \leqslant b)$$

where $0 < b - a < \infty$, $m(u, v) = v - u$, and where the integration is the generalized Riemann integration of Chapter 10, which is equivalent to Denjoy integration. As $x(t)$ is continuous we can define a norm on T_2 by

$$\|x\|_\infty = \sup_{a < t < b} |x(t)|$$

Then T_2 is a β-group.

(Take $T = T_1 = T_2$, and for each closed interval I and each d^n write

$$E = I \cup [a, b] \cap (-\infty, t], \quad x(I; t) = \int_E y(\cdot)\, dm,$$
$$x(d^n; t) = x([c, c+2^{-n}]; t),$$
$$c = a + (b-a) \sum_{j=1}^n 2^{-j} d_j$$

Axioms 31.1–6, 31.8–9 are easily proved. For axiom 31.7 show that all non-zero $x(c^m; t)$ are differences of $x(d^n; u)$ relative to u, so that

$$\|x(c^m; \cdot)\| = \sup_{a < t < b} |x(c^m; t)| \leqslant 2 \cdot \sup_{a < t < b} |x(d^n; t)| = 2\|x(d^n; \cdot)\|$$

Axiom 31.10 follows by Henstock (1963c), p. 113, Theorem 46.1 for the ordinary Riemann-complete integral, and a similar result for the integrals resulting from *Ex. 43.9, 43.11*, that include Burkill's approximate Perron integral and Denjoy's general integral. The results can also be extended to infinite intervals.) *Ex. 31.1* includes the first and third examples of Sargent (1953), the latter being the space of functions f that are *ACG* on [a, b], with the same norm. For every such f is approximately derivable almost everywhere in [a, b], and $f + con$-*stant* is the general Denjoy integral of the approximate derivative of f. (Saks (1937), p. 115, Theorem (5.4), p. 222, Theorems (4.2), (4.3), the bottom of p. 223, and p. 241, the definition of the general Denjoy integral.) By Tolstov (1939) the general Denjoy integral is equivalent to a Perron integral using perfect sets as in *Ex. 43.9*, and by a standard method such a Perron integral can be proved equivalent to the generalized Riemann integral of *Ex. 43.9*. Thus general Denjoy theory comes under that of our integral.

Ex. 31.2 Let T_3 be the space of functions f integrable in the Cauchy–Lebesgue sense in [a, b], $0 < b - a < \infty$. In the notation of generalized Riemann integration, f is integrable relative to $m(v, u) = v - u$, using *Ex. 43.3* with $n = 1$. Also there is a finite number of points $x_1, \ldots, x_s$ round which we can fit open intervals as small as we please, of union G, and $|f|$ is integrable relative to m on [a, b]/G. Then T_3 is a β-group with the same norm.
(A limit of a general sequence of members of T_3 would involve an infinity of points over which $|f|$ is not integrable relative to m. To avoid this, Sargent takes $T = T_3$, and T_1 the subgroup of step functions in T_3. Show that T_1 is dense in T_3, and prove all axioms.)

Ex. 31.3 With the same norm let T_4 be the space of functions f continuous on [a, b], with finite derivatives of all orders except at a countable set in (a, b). Taking $T = T_1 = T_4$, show that T_4 is a β-group.

Ex. 31.2, 31.3 are not so important for our purpose.

Ex. 31.4 Let T_5 be the space of functions f absolutely continuous on [a, b] with the same norm. Show that T_5 is an α-group, and an α-subgroup of the space C of all continuous functions on [a, b].
The indirect proof of Sargent (1953), pp. 448–9, may be found in this book, Theorem 63.4.

32. Sum Sets and Averaging Sets

In sections 24, 29 we dealt with

$$\theta(x, y) = x \cdot y^{-1}, \quad \theta^{-1}(v, y) = v \cdot y$$

Here we deal with two more pairs of functions. Throughout this section we use θ_j, θ_j^{-1} ($j = 1, 2$) to denote

$$\theta_1(x, y) = x \cdot y, \qquad \theta_1^{-1}(v, y) = v \cdot y^{-1},$$
$$\theta_2(x, y) = r(x \cdot y), \qquad \theta_2^{-1}(v, y) = v^2 \cdot y^{-1}$$

where for the latter pair we suppose that the root function $r(\cdot)$ exists in T. When T is an additive group these formulae become

$$\theta_1(x, y) = x + y, \qquad \theta_1^{-1}(v, y) = v - y,$$
$$\theta_2(x, y) = \tfrac{1}{2}(x + y), \quad \theta_2^{-1}(v, y) = 2v - y$$

A real function N of a real variable x, is *convex* if

(32.1) $$N(\tfrac{1}{2}(x + y)) \leqslant \tfrac{1}{2}\{N(x) + N(y)\}$$

in the domain of definition of N. We can generalize this idea by using $N : T \to R_e$, where R_e is the set of all real numbers, together with the conventional $+\infty$, $-\infty$. Then we say that N is *convex*, if

(32.2) $$N(\theta_2(x, y)) \leqslant \tfrac{1}{2}\{N(x) + N(y)\}$$

This immediately implies the inequality

(32.3) $$N(\theta_2(x, y)) \leqslant \sup \{N(x); N(y); 0\}$$

and (5.6) is a generalization of this inequality, which explains the name, *θ-L-convex function*.

We use the following descriptive notation. Given $X \subseteq T$, a sequence $\{S_n\}$ of sets of T is a *sum sequence*, if

(32.4) $$S_{n+1} \supseteq S_n \cdot S_n \quad (n \geqslant 0), \quad S_0 = X$$

A sequence $\{A_n\}$ of sets of T is an *averaging sequence*, if

(32.5) $$A_{n+1} \supseteq r(A_n, A_n) \quad (n \geqslant 0), \quad A_0 = X$$

These are precisely θ_j-sequences ($j = 1, 2$). The further definitions of $S_n(X)$, $S(X)$, $A_n(X)$, $A(X)$, are as usual.

A set X is pinned, and strongly pinned, using θ_1, if, and only if, $u \in X$. $(x \in \theta_1(x, X)$, $x \in x \cdot X$, $u \in X$.) A set X is *pinned*, using θ_2, if and only if X is not empty, since

$$x = r(x \cdot x) \in r(x \cdot X) = \theta_2(x, X) \qquad (x \in X)$$

But X is strongly pinned, using θ_2, if, and only if, $X = T$.

THEOREM 32.1. (32.6) *If* $\{S_n\}$ *is a sum sequence in* T, *and if* $x \in S_n$, *then* $x^2 \in S_{n+1}$.

(32.7) *If* $S_1(X)$ *is symmetric, i.e.* $x \in S_1(X)$ *implies* $x^{-1} \in S_1(X)$, *then* $\{S_n(X)\}$ *is a difference sequence, and the results of sections* 24, 29 *apply.*

(32.8) *Every averaging sequence is monotone increasing.*

Proof. (32.6; 32.8) are obvious, while for (32.7), if x, $y \in S_1(X)$ then

$$x^{-1}, \quad y^{-1} \in S_1(X), \quad x \cdot y^{-1} \in S_2(X), \quad (x \cdot y^{-1})^{-1} = y \cdot x^{-1} \in S_2(X)$$

and the result follows by induction.

THEOREM 32.2. *If* T *is a commutative group, then*

$$(32.9) \qquad S_n(X \cup (x \cdot X)) = \bigcup_{j=0}^{N} x^j \cdot S_n(X) \qquad (N = 2^n)$$

$$(32.10) \qquad A_n(X \cup (x \cdot X)) = \bigcup_{j=0}^{N} r(x^j) \cdot A_n(X) \qquad (N = 2^n)$$

Easy proofs follow by induction.

We could now proceed to specializations of the theorems of Chapter 2 that involve a property p. But instead we shall be content to consider a theorem involving $th(p)$ analogous to Theorem 24.3, in the proof of which we use Theorem 32.2.

THEOREM 32.3. *If* T *is a commutative group, and if* E *is a* p_2-*Baire set, where* $p_2 = th(p)$, *using* θ_j, *with finitely additive and* θ_j^{-1}-*invariant* p, *then* $E \in \mathcal{E}$. $(j = 1, 2)$.

The proof follows that of Theorem 24.3.

We now suppose that T has a topology $\mathcal{G}$, proceeding as in section 29. Then the family $\mathcal{G}_0$ of pinned sets of $\mathcal{G}$ is the family of neighbourhoods of u, when we use θ_1, and is $\mathcal{G}$, less the empty set, when we use θ_2. Thus in the second case the conditions that correspond to (29.1; 29.2) are the same.

THEOREM 32.4 (32.11) *If θ_1^{-1} is continuous in x to the identity then each non-empty $G \in \mathcal{G}$ contains a point y and also y^{-1}.*

(32.12) θ_2^{-1} *is continuous in x to the identity, if, and only if, in each non-empty $G \in \mathcal{G}$ there is a point y for which $r(G \cdot y)$ contains an interior point. In particular, θ_2^{-1} is continuous in x to the identity if $x \cdot y$ is continuous in (x, y).*

(32.13) θ_j^{-1} *is open in y, for each fixed x, if, and only if, y^{-1} and $x^j \cdot y$ are continuous in y for each fixed x ($j = 1, 2$).*

(32.14) θ_2^{-1} *is stable, if $x \cdot y^{-1}$ is continuous in (x, y).*

(32.15) $\theta_j^{-1}(x, T) = T$, *closed; θ_j^{-1} is an injection in y; while for (21.16) we use (32.13) ($j = 1, 2$).*

Proof. If θ_1^{-1} is continuous in x to the identity, and if the non-empty $G \in \mathcal{G}$, then there are a $y \in G$ and a $G_1 \in \mathcal{G}_0$, such that

$$\theta_1^{-1}(G_1, y) \subseteq G, \quad G_1 \cdot y^{-1} \subseteq G, \quad y^{-1} = u \cdot y^{-1} \in G_1 \cdot y^{-1}$$

since the sets of $\mathcal{G}_0$ here are the neighbourhoods of u. Hence the result, (32.11). It shows that either θ_1^{-1} is not continuous in x to the identity, or the topology is specialized. For (32.12), θ_2^{-1} is continuous in x to the identity, if, and only if, given a non-empty $G \in \mathcal{G}$. there are a $y \in G$ and a non-empty $G_1 \in \mathcal{G}$, such that $\theta_2^{-1}(G_1, y) \subseteq G$. Hence $G_1 \subseteq r(G \cdot y)$, and the first result. For the second, if $x \cdot y$ is continuous in (x, y), then $G \cdot y$ is a neighbourhood of y^2. Thus there is a neighbourhood G_2 of y for which

$$G_2^2 \subseteq G_2 \cdot G_2 \subseteq G \cdot y, \quad G_2 \subseteq r(G \cdot y)$$

giving the second result. Note that X^2 is the set of x^2 for $x \in X$, whereas $X \cdot X$ is the set of $x \cdot y$ for $x, y \in X$. For (32.13), θ_j^{-1} is open in y, for each fixed x, if, and only if

$$\theta_j^{-1}(x, G) \in \mathcal{G}, \quad x^j \cdot G^{-1} \in \mathcal{G} \quad (x \in T, \quad G \in \mathcal{G}, \quad j = 1, 2)$$

In particular, taking $x = u$, and since $y = x^{-1}$ implies $x = y^{-1}$, we have the continuity of y^{-1} by Theorem 9.1 (9.1), and similarly, taking arbitrary $x \in T$ we have the continuity of $x^j \cdot y$ in y. The converse now follows easily. From (32.12; 32.13), θ_2^{-1} is stable if $x \cdot y$ is continuous in (x, y) and y^{-1} is continuous in y, which is equivalent to the continuity of $x \cdot y^{-1}$ in (x, y), giving (32.14). (32.15) is trivial.

Thus again the hypotheses in section 21 can be simplified.

A set $X \subseteq T$ is a *strong θ_1-base for T*, if, for some neighbourhood G of u,

$$S(X^v) \equiv S(X \cap \theta_1^{-1}(v, X)) = T \qquad (v \in G)$$

A set $X \subseteq T$ is a *strong θ_2-base for T*, if, for some non-empty $G \in \mathcal{G}$,

$$A(X^v) \equiv A(X \cap \theta_2^{-1}(v, X)) = T \qquad (v \in G)$$

Note that of course the set X^v changes since its definition uses the particular θ^{-1} in question.

A set $X \subseteq T$ is an $S_1 - \mathcal{G}$-*set*, if $S_1(X) \supseteq G$ for some neighbourhood G of u. A set $X \subseteq T$ is an $A_1 - \mathcal{G}$-*set*, if $A_1(X) \supseteq G$ for some non-empty $G \in \mathcal{G}$. The $S - \mathcal{G}$-*sets* and $A - \mathcal{G}$-*sets* follow as usual.

THEOREM 32.5 (32.16) *If $x^j \cdot y$ is continuous in x for each $y \in T$, then for each non-empty $G \in \mathcal{G}$,*

$(j = 1)$ $S_1(G) \in \mathcal{G}_0$, $S(G) \in \mathcal{G}_0$ $(j = 2)$ $A_1(G) \in \mathcal{G}$, $A(G) \in \mathcal{G}$

(32.17) *If y^{-1} and $x \cdot y$ are continuous in y for each fixed x, and if $x \cdot y$ is continuous in x for each fixed y, then to each $G \in \mathcal{G}$ that contains a point w, and w^{-1}, there is a neighbourhood G_1 of u, such that (using θ_1^{-1}) $G^v \in \mathcal{G}$ is non-empty for each $v \in G_1$.*

(32.18) *If $x \cdot y^{-1}$ is continuous in (x, y), and if $G \in \mathcal{G}$ is not empty, there is a non-empty $G_2 \in \mathcal{G}$ such that (using θ_2^{-1}) $G^v \in \mathcal{G}$ is non-empty for each $v \in G_2$.*

X is an $S_1 - \mathcal{G}$-set, if one of the following holds:

(32.19) *X contains w^{-1} and a neighbourhood of w, with $x \cdot w$ continuous in x;*

(32.20) *$x \cdot y$ and x^{-1} are continuous in x for each fixed y, with $G \backslash X$ nowhere dense in T, for some non-empty symmetric $G \in \mathcal{G}$,*

(32.21) *$x \cdot y$ and x^{-1} are continuous in x for each fixed y, and X is clos-*

ed, and either dense in some non-empty symmetric $G \in \mathcal{G}$, or is of the second category.

X is an $A_1 - \mathcal{G}$-set, if either of the following holds:

(32.22) *$G \backslash X$ is nowhere dense in T, for some non-empty $G \in \mathcal{G}$,*

(32.23) *X is closed, and is either dense in some non-empty $G \in \mathcal{G}$, or is of the second category.*

Proof. For (32.20), $G \cap X$ contains a non-empty $G_3 \in \mathcal{G}$, and by continuity of x^{-1}, $G_3^{-1} \in \mathcal{G}$. By symmetry of G, $G_3^{-1} \subseteq G$, and since $G \backslash X$ is nowhere dense, there is a non-empty $G_4 \in \mathcal{G}$ with $G_4 \subseteq G_3^{-1} \cap X$. Taking $w \in G$ and using (32.19) we have the result. Similarly for (32.21). For proofs of any remaining non-trivial results, use proofs similar to those for Theorem 21.1, with Theorem 32.4 where necessary. By use of this theorem we can often find θ_j-bases and strong θ_j-bases for T.

THEOREM 32.6. (32.24) *If y^{-1} and $x \cdot y$ are continuous in y for each fixed x, and $x \cdot y$ continuous in x for each fixed y, and if T is a $\bar{p} - \mathcal{G}$-space, then each $G \in \mathcal{G}$ that contains a point w, and w^{-1}, is strongly-$\bar{p}$, using θ_1^{-1}, and each $p - \mathcal{G}$-Baire set, relative to such a G, is a p-Baire set. If also p is shrinkable, θ_1^{-1}-invariant, and finitely additive, each $p - \mathcal{G}$-Baire set, relative to such a G, is an $S_1 - \mathcal{G}$-set.*

(32.25) *If $x \cdot y^{-1}$ is continuous in (x, y), and if T is a $\bar{p} - \mathcal{G}$-space, then each non-empty $G \in \mathcal{G}$ is strongly-$\bar{p}$, using θ_2^{-1}, and each $p - \mathcal{G}$-Baire set is a p-Baire set. If also p is shrinkable, θ_2^{-1}-invariant, and finitely additive, each $p - \mathcal{G}$-Baire set is an $A_1 - \mathcal{G}$-set.*

Proof. Use Theorems 21.2, 32.5, or similar proofs.

THEOREM 32.7. (32.26) *If y^{-1} and $x \cdot y$ are continuous in y for each fixed x, and $x \cdot y$ continuous in x for each fixed y, and if a set E contains Baire set E_1 that has two points w, w^{-1} of the second category (i.e. $(w, w^{-1} \in II(E_1))$ then $S_1(E) \supseteq G$ for some neighbourhood G of u.*

(32.27) *If $x \cdot y^{-1}$ is continuous in (x, y), and if a set E contains a Baire set of the second category, then $A_1(E) \supseteq G_1$ for some non-empty $G_1 \in \mathcal{G}$.*

Proof. In either case, *Ex. 27.4* shows that T is a Baire space. For (32.27) we use Theorems 21.4, 32.4. For (32.26) we cannot use Theorem 21.4 since θ_1^{-1} is not normally stable. However, we are given extra properties to ensure that the G connected with the Baire set satisfies the condition in (32.24), and we can finish the proof using Theorem 32.4.

When every $\mathcal{Q}$-set is of the first category, we could proceed as in sections 21, 29, modifying the definitions to suit the θ_j. The following theorem should cause no difficulty.

THEOREM 32.8. (32.28) *Let $x \cdot y$ and x^{-1} be continuous in x for each fixed y, and let X be a symmetric β-set, using sum sequences. If a sequence $\{F_n\}$ of closed sets is such that $F_n \supseteq S_n(X)$, then there is an integer n such that F_n is an $S_1 - \mathcal{Q}$-set.*

(32.29) *If T is a topological group, and if $\mathcal{Q}$ has a countable base, then every set containing a sequentially closed symmetric β-set, using sum sequences, is an $S - \mathcal{Q}$-set.*

(32.30) *If X is a β-set, using averaging sequences, and if a sequence $\{F_n\}$ of closed sets is such that $F_n \supseteq A_n(X)$, then for some n, F_n contains a non-empty $\mathcal{Q}$-set.*

(32.31) *If $\mathcal{Q}$ is Hausdorffian, with a countable base, and if $r(x \cdot y)$ is continuous in (x, y), then every set containing a sequentially closed β-set, using averaging sequences, is an $A - \mathcal{Q}$-set.*

As at the ends of sections 21, 29, we could consider the effect of a Haar outer measure μ on questions concerning the thickness of sets. To ensure that μ, having the property that $\mu(x \cdot X) = \mu(X)$, is also θ_j^{-1}-invariant, for $j = 1, 2$, we need only assume that

(32.32) $$\mu(X^{-1}) = \mu(X)$$

The strong result is found by considering the property $p_9(\delta)$, as usual. We require a set X to be *strongly-$\bar{p}_9(\delta)$ relative to itself*, i.e. there is a $G(\delta) \in \mathcal{Q}_0$ such that

(32.33) $$\mu(X^v) \equiv \mu(X \cap \theta_j^{-1}(v, X)) \geqslant \delta \cdot \mu(X) \qquad (v \in G(\delta))$$

$(0 < \delta < 1)$

156

For θ_1^{-1}, $\mathcal{G}_0$ is the family of neighbourhoods of u, while for θ_2^{-1}, $\mathcal{G}_0$ is the family of all non-empty $\mathcal{G}$-sets.

THEOREM 32.9. *Let μ be a Haar outer measure on T that satisfies* (32.32). *If a set E is such that for some η in $0 < \eta < \frac{1}{2}$ we can find a strongly-$\bar{p}_9(2\eta)$ set X relative to itself, using θ_j^{-1}, with $\mu\,(X\backslash E) < \eta \cdot \mu(X)$, then E is an $S_1 - \mathcal{G}$-set $(j = 1)$, or an $A_1 - \mathcal{G}$-set $(j = 2)$.*

For proof see Theorem 21.9.

We can now examine the theory of Mehdi (1964), turning again to the inequality (32.2) that defines a convex function N on T. Since (32.2) is a special case of (32.3), and so of (5.6), we see at once that if N is bounded above on a set E then N is a bounded above on $A(E)$, while (32.2) shows by induction that the upper bound for $A(E)$ can be the same as for E. We look for criteria on E to ensure that $A(E)$ contains a $G \in \mathcal{G}_0$, i.e. a non-empty $G \in \mathcal{G}$, and to this end we need only examine the theorems of this section. It is worth while to collect together the results in the form of another theorem.

THEOREM 32.10 (32.34) *Let N be a real-valued convex function in the space T that is bounded above on a set E by a number r. Then N is bounded above by r in $A_1(E)$. Also, if T is a topological group, and if E contains a Baire set of the second category, then $A_1(E)$ contains a non-empty $G \in \mathcal{G}$.*

(32.35) *Let T be a topological group containing a second category set. If N is a real-valued convex function that is finite on a non-empty open set H, and if*

$$P(\lambda) = \{x : x \in H, \quad N(x) \leqslant \lambda\}$$

is a Baire set for a sequence $\{\lambda_n\}$ of values of λ tending to infinity (e.g. N is a convex real-valued Baire function) then there is some $P(\lambda)$ that contains a non-empty $G \in \mathcal{G}$.

(32.36) *Let T be the space R^n of vectors with n real components, and let h be the volume rectangle function in R^n (i.e. h is the product of the lengths of the n edges of a rectangle that meet at a vertex). If the set E contains an h-measurable set E_1 with positive h-measure, or, in the language of section 44, with positive $V(h; \mathcal{A}; R^n; E_1)$, for an $\mathcal{A}$ according to Ex. 43.3 then $A_1(E)$ contains a non-empty rectangle.*

(32.37) *Let T be an additive topological group for which $\frac{1}{2}x$ exists and is unique, for every $x \in T$. If N is a convex function bounded above in a non-empty $G \in \mathcal{G}$, then N is continuous in G.*

Theorem 32.7 (32.27) contains (32.34), which contains the first parts of Mehdi (1964), p. 323, Theorem 3, and p. 325, Theorem 4, while (32.35) contains Mehdi (1964), p. 326, Theorem 6, and (32.36) contains the first parts of results of Ostrowski (1929), Kestelman (1947), Kurepa (1956), quoted in Mehdi (1964), Theorem A, p. 321. (32.37) covers enough of the second parts for them to be easily completed for vector spaces, and in this sense includes Mehdi (1964), p. 324, Lemma 2.

Proof. T is a Baire space in (32.35), by *Ex. 27.4*, so that H is of the second category. It is the union of the $P(\lambda_n)$, since $\lambda_n \to \infty$, so that there is an integer n for which $P(\lambda_n)$ is a Baire set of the second category. By (32.34) $A_1(P(\lambda_n))$ contains the non-empty $G \in \mathcal{G}$, and as in Theorem 5.1,

$$A_1(P(\lambda_n)) \subseteq P(\tfrac{1}{2}(\lambda_n + \lambda_n)) = P(\lambda_n)$$

giving the result.

For (32.36), $V(h; \mathcal{A}; R^n; X)$ is the Haar outer measure in this case, the group using vector addition, and (32.32) is satisfied. Each non-empty rectangle X with sides parallel to the axes, is strongly-$\bar{p}_9(\delta)$ relative to itself, for each δ in $0 < \delta < 1$. For if $\mathbf{v}$, with components v_j, lies in the cube $|v_j| < \varepsilon\,(1 \le j \le n)$, then X^V has volume

$$> \prod_{j=1}^{n} (r_j - \varepsilon)$$

where r_j is the length of the edges of X parallel to the jth axis. Further, almost all points of E_1 are points of metric density, i.e. for $x \in \bar{X}, r_j \to 0\,(1 \le j \le n)$

$$\mu(E_1 \cap X)/\mu(X) = V(h; \mathcal{A}; R^n; E_1 \cap X)/V(h; \mathcal{A}; R^n; X) \to 1$$

A proof for $n = 1$ is given in Henstock (1963c), p. 80, Theorem 35.3, with p. 65, Theorem 32.1 (32.3). The proof for general n follows in a similar way on replacing the latter theorem involving a result like Sierpinski's lemma, by one corresponding to Vitali's theorem, for the generalized Riemann integrals involved. Corresponding

158

remarks can be given when μ is defined as a Lebesgue outer measure. Thus with the given θ_2^{-1}, Theorem 32.9 gives (32.36).

In each case we have reduced the problem to that of (32.37). We show that

(32.38) $\quad N(tx+(1-t)y) \leqslant tN(x)+(1-t)N(y) \quad (0 < t = q \cdot 2^{-s} < 1)$

where q is an odd integer, s a positive integer. Suppose true for all t with $0 < s < u$. Then if $0 < q < 2^{u-1}$,

$$N(q \cdot 2^{-u} \cdot x + (1-q \cdot 2^{-u})y) = N(\tfrac{1}{2}\{q \cdot 2^{1-u} \cdot x + (1-q \cdot 2^{1-u})y\} + \tfrac{1}{2}y)$$
$$\leqslant \tfrac{1}{2}N(q \cdot 2^{1-u} \cdot x + (1-q \cdot 2^{1-u})y) + \tfrac{1}{2}N(y) \leqslant q \cdot 2^{-u}N(x)$$
$$+ (\tfrac{1}{2} - q \cdot 2^{1-u})N(y) + \tfrac{1}{2}N(y)$$

If $2^{u-1} < q < 2^u$, we deal similarly with

$$N(\tfrac{1}{2}x + \tfrac{1}{2}\{(q \cdot 2^{1-u} - 1)x + (2-q \cdot 2^{1-u})y\})$$

so that by induction we prove (32.38).

For fixed y, n, we now consider the function $f(z) = x$, where

$$z = 2^{-n} \cdot x + (1-2^{-n})y, \quad f(z) = 2^n z - (2^n - 1)y$$

Then f is continuous since T is an additive topological group. Let $N \leqslant M$ in the non-empty $G \in \mathcal{G}$, let $y \in G$, let $\varepsilon > 0$, and let n be a positive integer such that $M \cdot 2^{-n} < \varepsilon$. Then there is a neighbourhood G_1 of y, depending on n and so on ε, with $f(G_1) \subseteq G$. By (32.38) for $t = 2^{-n}$,

(32.39) $\quad N(z) \leqslant 2^{-n}N(x) + (1-2^{-n})N(y) \leqslant N(y) + M \cdot 2^{-n}$
$$< N(y) + \varepsilon \quad (z \in G_1)$$

As T is an additive topological group, there is a neighbourhood G_2 of y such that if

$$x = y + (x-y) \in G_2, \quad \text{then} \quad 2y - x = y - (x-y) \in G_1$$
$$N(y) = N(\tfrac{1}{2}x + \tfrac{1}{2}(2y - x)) \leqslant \tfrac{1}{2}N(x) + \tfrac{1}{2}N(2y - x) < \tfrac{1}{2}N(x) + \tfrac{1}{2}N(y)$$
$$+ \tfrac{1}{2}\varepsilon, |N(y) - N(x)| < \varepsilon \quad (x \in G_1 \cap G_2)$$

Clearly $G_1 \cap G_2$ depends on y, ε alone, and we have proved the continuity of N in each open set in which N is bounded above.

To complete the proof of Mehdi's lemma for topological vector

159

LINEAR ANALYSIS

spaces one need only translate G suitably, the snag in our theory being that various points need not be definable, various functions need not be continuous, unless we allow multiplication by rational scalars, that are not $q \cdot 2^{-s}$.

Ex. 32.1 If A, B are of positive measure and are measurable on the real line, show that $A+B$ contains an interval.

(If a, b are points of metric density of A, B, respectively, then $A_1 \equiv A \cap (B+a-b)$ is of positive measure, and so apply (32.36) using $\frac{1}{2}(A+B) \supseteq \frac{1}{2}\{A_1+(A_1+b-a)\}$.)

Other results can be found in Henstock and Macbeath (1953).

33. Bounded Sets and Continuity, with the Hahn–Banach Theorem for Normed Groups

If T is a group and $X \subseteq T$, let $N = 2^n$ and

$$X^{(n)} \equiv \{x^N : x \in X\}$$

We can say that a set B in a group T with a topology $\mathcal{G}$, is *bounded*, if, given a neighbourhood G of the unit u of T, the family of these neighbourhoods being denoted by $\mathcal{G}_0$, there is a positive integer m for which

(33.1) $B \subseteq G^{(n)}$ $(n \geqslant m)$

We suppose that T has the root function $r(x)$, and we say that $X \subseteq T$ is *starlike*, if $r(x) \in X$ for all $x \in X$. Then

(33.2) $X \subseteq X^{(1)} \subseteq X^{(2)} \subseteq \ldots$

We can say that $\mathcal{G}$ is a *starlike topology*, if the starlike sets of $\mathcal{G}_0$ form a local base for $\mathcal{G}$ at u.

THEOREM 33.1 (33.3) *Let $\mathcal{G}$ be a starlike topology. Then every point in T forms a bounded set, if, and only if, for each $G \in \mathcal{G}_0$, T is the union of $G^{(n)}$ (for $n = 1, 2, \ldots$).*

(33.4) *Let $\mathcal{G}$ be a starlike topology. If every point in T forms a bounded set, and if $r(x)$ is continuous, then every compact set is bounded.*

The second result can be compared with Weston (1957b), p. 4.

160

Proof. For (33.3), if T is the union of the $G^{(n)}$, for each $G \in \mathcal{G}_0$, then we can take G starlike since $\mathcal{G}$ is a starlike topology. If $x \in T$, then there is an m for which $x \in G^{(m)}$, and then by (33.2), $x \in G^{(n)}$ ($n \geqslant m$), and x forms a bounded set. The converse is obvious. For (33.4), $f(x) = x^2$ is open, so that each $G^{(n)}$ is open, for each $G \in \mathcal{G}_0$. Given $x \in T$, there is an m for which $x \in G^{(n)}$ ($n \geqslant m$). Then a finite number of the $G^{(m)}$ cover the compact set, so that as we can take G to be starlike, we can take the greatest, say q, of the finite number of m, and the compact set lies in $G^{(q)}$, and so in $G^{(n)}$, for all $n \geqslant q$.

THEOREM 33.2. *Let T, U be groups with topologies, let $f : T \to U$ be a multiplicative function that is continuous at $u \in T$, and let $B \subseteq T$ be bounded. Then $f(B)$ is bounded.*

Proof. Let u, u_1 be the units in T, U. Then since f is multiplicative,

$$f(u) \cdot f(u) = f(u \cdot u) = f(u), \quad f(u) = u_1$$

Then by continuity, if H is a neighbourhood of u_1, there is a neighbourhood G of u with $f(G) \subseteq H$. There is a positive integer m for which $B \subseteq G^{(n)}$ ($n \geqslant m$), so that by multiplicativity, the result follows from

$$f(B) \subseteq f(G^{(n)}) = f(G)^{(n)} \subseteq H^{(n)} \qquad (n \geqslant m)$$

A function $f : T \to U$ is said to be *bounded*, if it sends bounded sets into bounded sets. Thus a continuous multiplicative function is bounded. The converse is true under stronger conditions.

THEOREM 33.3. *Let $(T, \mathcal{G})$, $(U, \mathcal{H})$ be groups with topologies, and with root functions, such that in each topology the neighbourhoods of the unit have a countable base of starlike sets. Let $x \cdot y$ be continuous in $T \times T$, each single point of T forming a bounded set there. Then each bounded multiplicative function $f : T \to U$ is continuous.*

Proof. As $x \cdot y$ is continuous in $T \times T$, if $G \in \mathcal{G}_0$, there is a $G_1 \in \mathcal{G}_0$ with $G_1 \cdot G_1 \subseteq G$. We can assume that G, G_1 are two of the starlike sets that form the countable base for $\mathcal{G}_0$, so that by induction we can assume that the countable base of starlike sets in T is a sequence $\{G_n\}$ that satisfies

(33.5) $\qquad G_{n+1}^{(1)} \subseteq G_{n+1} \cdot G_{n+1} \subseteq G_n \qquad (n = 1, 2, \ldots)$

It follows from (33.2) that also

(33.6) $$G_1 \supseteq G_2 \supseteq G_3 \supseteq \ldots$$

Let $x_j \to u$, $x_j \neq u$, as $j \to \infty$, and put

(33.7) $$k(j) = 2^n (x_j \in G_{2n} \backslash G_{2n+2})$$

Clearly we can assume that $x_j \in G_2$ *(all j)*. Then from (33.5; 33.6; 33.7),

$$x_j^{k(j)} \in G_{2n}^{(n)} \subseteq G_n \subseteq G_m \qquad (all\ n \geqslant m)$$

and, given a neighbourhood G of u, there are an m, and then a J depending on m, such that

$$x_j^{k(j)} \in G_m \subseteq G \qquad (all\ j > J)$$

As G_m is starlike, it satisfies (33.2). As each point of T is a bounded set, there is an integer $K \geqslant 1$ with

$$x_j^{k(j)} \in G_m^{(n)} \qquad (n \geqslant K)$$

for $j = 1, 2, \ldots, J$, and so for all j, and $\{x_j^{k(j)}\}$ is a bounded set. By multiplicativity, and since bounded sets are sent into bounded sets, there is a bounded set $C \subseteq U$ with

$$f(x_j)^{k(j)} = f(x_j^{k(j)}) \in C \qquad (j = 1, 2, \ldots)$$

Given a starlike neighbourhood H of u_1, then from this there is an integer m, independent of j, such that

$$f(x_j)^{k(j)} \in C \subseteq H^{(m)} \qquad (all\ j)$$

Using the root function m times in U, and since H is starlike,

$$f(x_j)^{l(j)} \in H, \quad f(x_j) \in H \qquad (all\ j\ with\ k(j) \geqslant 2^m)$$

where $l(j)$ is a power of 2, and thus $f(x_j)$ converges to u_1, since starlike H form a base for the neighbourhoods of u_1.

We have proved that a sequence in T and tending to u, is transformed into a sequence in U and tending to u_1. By the multiplicativity and Theorems 9.1, 15.1 (15.7), we have the result.

It is sometimes useful to have the following corollary.

(33.8) A multiplicative function $f : T \to U$ that sends sequences converging to zero into bounded sets, is continuous if T, U satisfy the hypotheses of Theorem 33.3.

One of the most useful tools in the study of the boundedness and continuity of multiplicative functions is that of the norm of a function. We first need a norm $||\cdot||_T$ on the group T (p.141). It is *homogeneous for positive integers*, if for each positive integer n, and for each $x \in T$,

(33.9) $$||x^n||_T = n||x||_T.$$

We also need a norm $||\cdot||_U$ on the group U, with the same property. Then the norm, norm (f), of a function $f: T \to U$, is defined by

$$\text{norm}(f) = \sup_{||x||_T < 1,\ x \neq u} ||f(x)||_U/||x||_T$$

THEOREM 33.4. (33.10) *Let the norms on the groups T, U be homogeneous for positive integers, and let $f: T \to U$ be a multiplicative function.*

(33.11) *In (33.10), if T has the root function and f is bounded, then* norm (f) *is finite.*

(33.12) *In (33.10), if $||f(x)||_U$ is lower semi-continuous on T, a β-group, then f is bounded.*

(33.13) *If T, U are normed with norms $||\cdot||_T$, $||\cdot||_U$, respectively, and if $f: T \to U$ is multiplicative, and is such that* norm $(f) < \infty$, *then* norm (f) *is unchanged if we replace T by a subset T_1 dense in T.*

Proof. In (33.11), if $x \in S(u; 1)$, the sphere in T with centre u and radius 1, then by homogeneity, $r_n(x) \in S(u; 2^{-n})$. Hence if G is a neighbourhood of u, there is an integer n such that, by homogeneity again,

$$S(u; 2^{-n}) \subseteq G, \quad S(u; 1) \subseteq S(u, 2^{-n})^{(m)} \subseteq G^{(m)} \quad (\text{all } m \geqslant n)$$

Hence $S(u; 1)$ is a bounded set. As f is a bounded operator, $f(S(u; 1))$ is a bounded set, and so is contained in $S^{(m)}$, for some integer m, where S is the sphere in U with centre u_1 and radius 1, so that S is an open set in U. This implies that $||f(x)||_U$ is bounded for $x \in S(u; 1)$. Also, given any number $A < \text{norm}(f)$, this being finite or infinite, there is a $y \in S(u; 1)$, $y \neq u$, with

$$||f(y)||_U/||y||_T > A; \quad ||f(y^2)||_U/||y^2||_T = ||f(y)||_U/||y||_T$$

163

by homogeneity of both norms. Hence by repeated application we can assume that

$$\tfrac{1}{2} \leqslant \|y\|_T < 1$$

Hence it follows that

(33.14) $\text{norm} (f) = \sup\limits_{\frac{1}{2} \leqslant \|x\|_T < 1} \|f(x)\|_U / \|x\|_T$

$\qquad\qquad\qquad \leqslant 2 \cdot \sup\limits_{\|x\|_T < 1} \|f(x)\|_U < \infty$

(33.15) $\|f(x)\|_U \leqslant \|x\|_T \cdot \text{norm} (f)$

i.e. f is continuous since it is multiplicative.

For (33.12), let X_N be the set of all $x \in T$ with $\|f(x)\|_U \leqslant 2^N$. Then $\{X_N\}$ is a difference sequence with union T, for

$$\|f(x \cdot y^{-1})\|_U = \|f(x) \cdot f(y)^{-1}\|_U \leqslant \|f(x)\|_U + \|f(y)\|_U \leqslant 2^{N+1}$$

$$(x, y \in X_N)$$

Since T is a β-group, X_M is dense in a sphere $S_1 \subseteq T$ for some integer M; while X_M is closed by the lower semi-continuity of $\|f(x)\|_U$. Hence since f is multiplicative, there is a sphere S_2 with centre u, such that $\|f(x)\|_U \leqslant 2^{M+1}$ in S_2. Since the norms are homogeneous for positive integers, and by multiplicativity of f, there is an $M_1 > 0$ such that $\|f(x)\|_U \leqslant M_1$ in $S(u; 1)$. (33.14) then follows by homogeneity of the norms for positive integers, and f is bounded, by (33.15).

For (33.13) we see that (33.15) gives the continuity of f. Note that if f is given as continuous, we can drop the requirement that norm $(f) < \infty$. Designing the proof to fit in with this, let $M < \text{norm} (f)$. Then in T there is an $x \neq u$ with

$$\|f(x)\|_U > M\|x\|_T, \quad \tfrac{1}{2} \leqslant \|x\|_T < 1$$

Since T_1 is dense in T, and since f is continuous, then given $\varepsilon > 0$, there is a $y \in T_1$ with

$$\|y \cdot x^{-1}\|_T < \varepsilon, \quad \|f(y) \cdot f(x)^{-1}\|_U < \varepsilon$$

164

so that if $N(f)$ denotes the norm for f, using T_1,

$$N(f) \geqslant \|f(y)\|_U / \|y\|_T > (\|f(x)\|_U - \varepsilon)/(\|x\|_T + \varepsilon)$$
$$> (M\|x\|_T - \varepsilon)/(\|x\|_T + \varepsilon)$$

Being true for all $\varepsilon > 0$, we have

$$N(f) \geqslant M, \quad N(f) \geqslant \operatorname{norm}(f)$$

This is sufficient if the last is infinite, while if it is finite, the opposite inequality comes from (33.15).

THEOREM 33.5. *Let T be an additive group with the operation $x \to \frac{1}{2}x$, and with a norm homogeneous for positive integers. Let f be a real bounded additive functional defined on $D(X) \neq T$. Then there is a real continuous additive functional h defined on T, with $h(x) = f(x)$ $(x \in D(X))$, and with norm $(h) = $ norm (f).*

Proof. From Theorem 33.4 (33.11), norm (f) is finite, for the space $D(X)$. Thus we can put $g(x) = \operatorname{norm}(f) \cdot \|x\|_T$ in Theorem 25.1. Then

$$g(x+y) = \operatorname{norm}(f) \cdot \|x+y\|_T \leqslant \operatorname{norm}(f) \left(\|x\|_T + \|y\|_T \right)$$

and g is subadditive. Also g is homogeneous for positive integers since $\| \cdot \|_T$ is. Hence from Theorem 25.1 there is a real additive functional h on T, with $h(x) = f(x) (x \in D(X))$, and with $h(x) \leqslant g(x)$ on all T. Replacing x by $-x$, we have

$$h(x) = -h(-x) \geqslant -g(-x) = -\operatorname{norm}(f) \cdot \| -x \|_T$$
$$= -\operatorname{norm}(f) \cdot \|x\|_T, \quad |h(x)| \leqslant \operatorname{norm}(f) \cdot \|x\|_T$$

and h is continuous everywhere in T, with

$$\operatorname{norm}(h) \leqslant \operatorname{norm}(f)$$

The opposite inequality is true since $f = h$ on $D(X)$.

THEOREM 33.6. *Let T be an additive group with the operation $x \to \frac{1}{2}x$, and with a norm homogeneous for positive integers. Let $D(X) \subset T$, and let $x \in T$ have*

(33.16) $\inf \{m^{-1}\|y - mx\|_T : y \in D(X), m = 1, 2, \ldots\} = d > 0.$

Then there is a real continuous additive functional h defined on T, *with*

$$h(x) = 1, \quad \text{norm}\,(h) = 1/d, \quad h(y) = 0\,(y \in D(X))$$

Proof. We put $Z = D(X \cup \text{sing}\,(x))$. Since $x \notin D(X)$ from (33.16), each $z \in Z$ has a unique representation $z = y + mx$, for $y \in D(X)$ and m an integer. Hence we can define $f(z) = m$, a real additive functional on Z, with $f(x) = 1$, and $f(y) = 0$ $(y \in D(X))$. By Theorem 33.5, to complete the proof we need only show that norm $(f) = 1/d$. If $m \neq 0$, since $y, -y \in D(X)$,

$$\|z\|_T = \|y + mx\|_T = \|-y - mx\|_T \geqslant |m|\,d = |f(z)|\,d,$$

$$|f(z)| \leqslant \|z\|_T/d, \quad \text{norm}\,(f) \leqslant 1/d.$$

Now given $\varepsilon > 0$, let m, y be such that

$$\|y - mx\|_T < md + \varepsilon, \quad m > 0. \quad \text{Then} \quad m = f(mx - y)$$

$$|\leqslant \text{norm}\,(f)\|mx - y\|_T < \text{norm}\,(f)\,(md + \varepsilon),$$

$$\text{norm}\,(f) > m/(md + \varepsilon), \quad \text{norm}\,(f) = 1/d$$

THEOREM 33.7. *Let T be a group with a topology $\mathcal{G}$, let $X \subset T$, $y \in \mathcal{G}D(X)$, and let $f: T \to R$ be real, multiplicative, and continuous. If $f = 0$ on X then $f(y) = 0$. On the other hand let T be an additive group that has the operation $x \to x/m$ of division by positive integers m, and with a norm homogeneous for positive integers. If $X \subset T$ and $y \in T$ are such that $X/m \subseteq X \subseteq D(X)$, and for all real, continuous, and additive $f: T \to R$ that are zero on X, we have $f(y) = 0$, then $y \in \mathcal{G}D(X)$, where $\mathcal{G}$ is the norm topology.*

Proof. The first part follows from Theorem 9.1 (9.2), since $f(D(X)) = \text{sing}\,(0)$. For the second, if $y \notin \mathcal{G}D(X)$, then by Theorem 11.5 (11.10),

$$\inf\{\|y - x\|_T : x \in D(X)\} = d > 0$$

Since $\|\cdot\|_T$ is homogeneous for positive integers, and since division by $m > 0$ is allowable, with $X/m \subseteq X$, then $D(X)/m \subseteq D(X)$, and

$$d \leqslant \inf\{\|x/m - y\|_T : x \in D(X)\} = \inf\{m^{-1}\|x - my\|_T : x \in D(X)\}$$

so that (33.16) is satisfied. Hence by Theorem 33.6 we have the result.

Historical Notes: Sargent (1953), p. 443, Theorem 4, gives (33.12) when T, U are normed vector spaces. Theorem 33.5 is the topological half of the Hahn–Banach Theorem, and is due to Hahn (1927), p. 216, Banach (1929a, b), pp. 212, 226, for normed linear spaces. Banach (1932) pp. 57–8, § 3, Lemme, gives a special case of Theorem 33.6, Theorem 33.7.

This is in Banach (1932), p. 58, Théorème 6, for linear normed spaces. We could generalize the definitions given below Théorème 6 in the following way.

A set X in a group T with a topology $\mathcal{G}$, is *fundamental*, if $D(X)$ is dense in T. X is *total*, if every continuous multiplicative functional defined on the whole of T, that is zero on X, is also zero everywhere in T. We could if necessary rewrite the above theorem using this notation.

Ex. 33.1. Let Γ be the space of integral (entire) functions

$$a \equiv a(z) \equiv \sum_{n=0}^{\infty} a_n z^n,$$

convergent for all complex z, in which we define a group norm

$$\|a\| = \sup \left(|a_0|, |a_n^{1/n}| \right) \qquad (n \geqslant 1)$$

With this, show that Γ is a complete linear metric space, convergence in Γ being uniform convergence in any finite circle. Iyer (1948, 1950) shows that no group norm can be linear, and so possibly it cannot be homogeneous for positive integers, but, nevertheless Iyer proves Theorem 33.5 for Γ.

34. Sequences of Bounded Multiplicative Functions

Much of the theory in the previous parts of the book had its origin in the necessity of unifying proofs from theories of summability and convergence factors. The original Hahn–Banach–Steinhaus theorem dealt with sequences of continuous linear functions $f_n : T \to U$, where the T and U are complete normed vector spaces (i.e. *Banach* spaces), and was discovered independently by Hahn (1922), Theorem 1, and Banach (1922), p. 157. The proof was simplified by Saks and extended in Banach and Steinhaus (1927), pp. 53–4. Since then many generalizations have been given, and one generalization,

Theorem 5.1, has formed the core of this book. Sargent (1953), p. 441, Theorem 1, supposes that T, U are normed vector spaces with T a β-space, and this is included in Theorem 34.1.

THEOREM 34.1. *Let $\{f_n\}$ be a sequence of bounded multiplicative operators from a normed group T with the root operation, to a normed group U, both norms being homogeneous for positive integers, and let*

$$(34.1) \qquad \lim_{n \to \infty} \sup \|f_n(x)\|_U < \infty \qquad (x \in T)$$

If T is a Baire space, or a β-group, then

$$(34.2) \qquad \text{norm } (f_n) < \infty \qquad (n = 1, 2, \ldots)$$

$$(34.3) \qquad \lim_{n \to \infty} \sup \text{ norm } (f_n) < \infty$$

Proof. By Theorem 33.4 (33.11; 33.15), each norm (f_n) is finite and f_n is continuous. We could have replaced boundedness by continuity and used (33.12). Also, by (34.1), for each $x \in T$ the sequence $\{f_n(x)\}$ is bounded in U. Then if X_N is the set of $x \in T$ where

$$(34.4) \quad \|f_n(x)\|_U \leqslant 2^N \qquad (n = 1, 2, \ldots), \qquad T = \bigcup_{N=1}^{\infty} X_N$$

Since each f_n is continuous, the set where $\|f_n(x)\|_U \leqslant 2^N$, is closed for each n, and the intersection X_N of closed sets is closed. (34.5) $\{X_N\}$ is a difference sequence.

For if x, $y \in X_N$ then

$$\|f_n(x \cdot y^{-1})\|_U = \|f_n(x) \cdot f_n(y)^{-1}\|_U \leqslant \|f_n(x)\|_U + \|f_n(y)\|_U \leqslant 2^{N+1},$$

$$D_1(X_N) \subseteq X_{N+1}$$

Hence from (34.4) alone, if T is a Baire space, or from (34.4; 34.5), if T is a β-group, there is an integer M for which X_M is dense in some sphere $S(x; \varepsilon)$ of T. Since X_M is closed, $S(x; \varepsilon) \subseteq X_M$. The rest of the proof depends on the geometry, and can be followed through in detail as follows.

If $2^{-j} \leqslant \varepsilon,$ $y \in S(u; 2^{-j}),$ then $\|x \cdot (y^{-1} \cdot x)^{-1}\|_T$

$$= \|y\|_T < \varepsilon, \quad y^{-1} \cdot x \in S(x; \varepsilon)$$

$$\|f_n(y^{-1} \cdot x)\|_U \leqslant 2^M, \quad \|f_n(x)\|_U \leqslant 2^M,$$

$$\|f_n(y)\|_U = \|f_n(x) \cdot f_n(y^{-1} \cdot x)^{-1}\|_U \leqslant 2^{M+1},$$

$$\text{norm}\,(f_n) = \sup\,\{\|f_n(x)\|_U / \|x\|_T : 0 < \|x\|_T < 1\}$$

$$= \sup\,\{\|f_n(y)\|_U / \|y\|_T : 2^{-j-1} \leqslant \|y\|_T$$

$$< 2^{-j}\} \leqslant 2^{M+1} \cdot 2^{j+1}$$

independent of $n = 1, 2, \ldots$, by homogeneity of the norms for positive integers. Hence (34.3). Clearly we can replace the integer variable n by a continuous variable s.

THEOREM 34.2. *For each $s \geqslant 0$ let $f(s; x)$ be a multiplicative function from a normed group T to a normed group U, both norms being homogeneous for positive integers; in T let $x \cdot y$ be continuous in y, and let*

(34.6) $$\lim_{s \to \infty} \sup \|f(s; x)\|_U < \infty \qquad (x \in T)$$

If T is a Baire space, and $\|f(s; x)\|_U$ a Baire function, then

(34.7) $$\lim_{s \to \infty} \sup \text{norm}\,(f(s; \cdot)) < \infty$$

We have omitted the boundedness of the functions and changed n to s.

Proof. From (34.6) there is an $s_0(x) < \infty$ such that

$$\|f(s; x)\|_U < \infty \; (s \geqslant s_0(x))$$

We have first to prove $s_0(x)$ bounded. Let Y_N be the set where $s_0(x) \leqslant N$. Then $s_0(x) \leqslant N$ in $D_1(Y_N)$, and so in $D(Y_N)$, i.e. Y_N is a subgroup of T. Further, $\|f(s; x)\|_U$ is a Baire function for each fixed s, so that Y_N is a Borel set, and so a Baire set by Theorem 18.5. As T is a Baire space, and is the union of the Y_N, there is a Y_M of the second category in T. By Theorem 29.4, and the continuity in x of $x \cdot y$ from Theorem 30.1, $D_1(Y_M) = Y_M$ contains a sphere with centre u. By homogeneity of norms in T, U, $s_0(x) \leqslant M$ in T. We can now use the proof of Theorem 34.1, but with X_N a Baire set, not necessarily closed, and the result follows.

THEOREM 34.3. *Let $\{f_n\}$ be a sequence of bounded multiplicative functions from a normed group T with the root function, to a normed group U, both norms being homogeneous for positive integers, and let T be a Baire space or a β-group. If X is the set of all elements x of T with*

$$(34.8) \qquad \lim_{n \to \infty} \sup \| f_n(x) \|_U < \infty$$

then either $X = T$, or X is an α-subgroup of T.

This was proved by Sargent (1953), Theorem 2, for linear continuous f_n in normed vector spaces T, U, and is an extension of Banach (1932), p. 80, Théorème 4, and due to Banach and Steinhaus.

Proof. Clearly X is a subgroup of T. If a β-subgroup, then by Theorem 30.1, $x \cdot y$ is continuous in x for each $y \in T$, so that by Theorem 21.6, X is a β-group dense in T. By Theorem 34.1, there is an M independent of n, with

$$\| f_n(x) \|_U \leqslant M \| x \|_T \qquad (x \in X)$$

Since X is dense in T, and f_n continuous, by Theorem 33.4 (33.13) (or clearly)

$$\| f_n(x) \|_U \leqslant M \| x \|_T \qquad (x \in T)$$

and $X = T$. Hence if $X \neq T$, then X is an α-subgroup of T, and in particular, is of the first category in T.

THEOREM 34.4. *Let f and $f(s;.)$ $(s \geqslant 0)$ be bounded multiplicative functions from a normed group T to a normed group U, both norms being homogeneous for positive integers, and let T have the root function and be a Baire space or a β-group. In order that*

$$(34.9) \qquad \lim_{s \to \infty} \sup \| f(s; x) \cdot f(x)^{-1} \|_U = 0 \qquad (x \in T)$$

it is necessary and sufficient that

$$(34.10) \qquad \operatorname{norm} (f(s;.)) < \infty \qquad (\text{each } s \geqslant 0)$$

$$(34.11) \qquad \lim_{s \to \infty} \sup \operatorname{norm} (f(s;.)) < \infty$$

and that (34.9) should hold in a fundamental subset of T.

Hahn (1922), Theorems 1, 3, 4, gave the case with n for s, T a Banach space, and U the space of reals. The version with T, U Banach spaces was in Banach and Steinhaus (1927), pp. 53–54, and Sargent (1953) gave the case with T a normed vector β-space, U a complete normed vector space.

Proof. The necessity follows from Theorem 34.1. For sufficiency we go algebraically from X to $D(X)$, and then by uniform continuity to $\mathcal{Q}D(X) = T$.

LINEAR TOPOLOGICAL SPACES, F-SPACES, BANACH SPACES

35. Rings, Fields, Linear Spaces

MUCH of the theory that is usually based on linear spaces has been given for groups instead, so that we need only give the briefest mention to more complicated algebraic structures in T.

First, a *ring* is an additive group R with group operation $x+y$, together with a function $f: R \times R \to R$, written $f(a, b) = ab$, and called *multiplication*, for which R is a semigroup distributive on the left and right, i.e.

$$(ab)c = a(bc), \quad a(b+c) = ab+ac, \quad (b+c)a = ba+ca$$

Then $a+b$ is the *sum* of a, b, and ab their *product*, while aa is written a^2. A ring R is *commutative*, if, for all $a, b \in R$, $ab = ba$. The unit of R is called the *zero*, 0.

By the uniqueness of the zero 0,

$$aa = (a+0)a = aa+0a, \quad 0a = 0 \quad \text{(all } a \in R)$$

and similarly $a0 = 0$.

If the non-zero elements of a ring R are a commutative group under multiplication, then R is called a *field*. Then it is also a commutative ring. In a field, the unit of the commutative group under multiplication, is written 1, and is called the *unit*, while the inverse of $x \in R$ in the multiplication group keeps the same name in the field, and is written x^{-1}. Note that 0 has no inverse under multiplication since $a0 = 0a = 0$.

A *linear space (vector space, linear vector space) T* over a field R, is an additive group T with unit θ, inverse $-x$ of $x \in T$, together with a function $f: R \times T \to T$, written $f(a, x) = ax$, that is distributive in a and x,

$$a(x+y) = ax+ay, \quad (a+b)x = ax+bx, \quad a(bx) = (ab)x,$$
$$1x = x$$

where a, b, $1 \in R$ and x, $y \in T$. The elements of T are *vectors*, and those of the coefficient field R are called *scalars*. Normally R is the set of real numbers (when T is called a *real vector space*) or the set of complex numbers (when T is called a *complex vector space*). In the linear space,

$$1x+0x = (1+0)x = 1x, \quad 0x = \theta(0, 1 \in R; x, \theta \in T)$$
$$a\theta = a(0\theta) = (a0)\theta = 0\theta = \theta(a, 0 \in R; \theta \in T)$$

and if $ax = \theta$ then $a = 0$ or $x = \theta$. For if $a \neq 0$, then since R is a field, a is in the multiplicative group of non-zero elements of R, and has an inverse a^{-1}, so that

$$\theta = a^{-1}\theta = a^{-1}(ax) = (a^{-1}a)x = 1x = x, \quad x = \theta$$

If $a \in R$, $y \in T$ are fixed, the functions $f(x) = ax$, $g(x) = x+y$ are called *scalar multiplication by a*, and *translation by y*, respectively. If a, b, . . ., c are scalars, x, y, . . ., z vectors, the finite sum $ax+by+ \ldots +cz$ is called a *linear combination* of the vectors x, y, . . ., z. A *linear subspace (subspace, linear manifold)* in T, is a subset of T that contains all linear combinations of its vectors. The subspace *spanned (determined)* by an $X \subseteq T$, is the set $sp(X)$ of all linear combinations of elements of X. Clearly $sp(X)$ is the smallest linear subspace that contains X. $sp(X)$ corresponds in some sense to $D(X)$ for a group. A vector x is *linearly dependent* on vectors y, . . ., z, if x is a linear combination of y, . . ., z. Otherwise x is *linearly independent of y*, . . ., z. The set $X \subseteq T$ is *linearly independent* if each $x \in X$ is linearly independent of the other elements of X. A *Hamel base for T*, is a maximal linearly independent set $X \subseteq T$.

If X is linearly independent, there is a Hamel base $Y \supseteq X$, while any two Hamel bases for T have the same cardinal number. The second property needs the Schroeder–Bernstein theorem. Proofs can, for example, be found in Day (1962), pp. 2, 3, Theorems 1, 2. Then we can say that the *dimension* of T is the cardinal numer of each Hamel base for T.

A functional f on $Y \subseteq T$, is *linear*, if $x - y \in Y$, $f(x-y) = f(x) - f(y)$ and $ax \in Y$, $f(ax) = af(x)$ when $x, y \in Y$ and $a \in R$, which is here the space of real or complex numbers. A two-variable functional $f(x, y)$ is *bilinear*, if linear in x and in y, separately. A two-variable functional $f(x, y)$ is *Hermitian*, R being the set of complex numbers, if f is linear in x, additive in y, and with $f(x, ay) = \bar{a}f(x, y)$, where $\bar{a}$ is the complex conjugate of a. A two-variable functional f is *non-negative (positive) definite*, if $f(x, x) \geqslant 0$ (respectively, $f(x, x) > 0$ when $x \neq 0$) for all $x \in T$.

We can quickly obtain a Cauchy–Schwarz–Buniakowsky inequality from each bilinear non-negative definite functional with real values, and from each Hermitian non-negative definite functional with complex values, by distributing $f(ax + by, ax + by) \geqslant 0$. Compare section 26 and Theorem 26.1.

We can also generalize section 25, and the Hahn–Banach theorem for additive groups. Not every functional h defined in Theorem 25.1 need be linear, so that in place of the subadditive functional g that is homogeneous for positive integers, we use a *sublinear* functional g, i.e. g is subadditive with $g(ax) = ag(x)$ for all $a \geqslant 0$, all $x \in T$.

THEOREM 35.1. *Let g be a sublinear functional on the linear space T, and let f be a real linear functional defined on $X \subseteq T$, and so on $sp(X)$, with $f(x) \leqslant g(x)$ on $sp(X)$. Then there is a real linear functional h on T, with $h(x) \leqslant g(x)$ there, and with $h(x) = f(x)$ on $sp(X)$.*

Proof. We need only follow the proof of Theorem 25.1, with $t = 1 = v$, since g and T are homogeneous relative to all real $a \geqslant 0$.

The original proof is in Banach (1929), and it is extended to complex functionals independently by Bohnenblust and Sobczyk (1938), Soukhomlinoff (1938), the latter dealing with quaternion scalars as well.

A real or complex functional f is *symmetric*, if $f(ax) = f(x)$ for all a with $|a| = 1$, where R is the coefficient field of complex numbers.

THEOREM 35.2. *Let g be a symmetric sublinear functional on the linear space T with coefficient field that of the complex numbers. Let f*

be a complex linear functional defined on $sp(X)$, with $|f(x)| \leqslant g(x)$. Then there is a complex linear functional h on T with $|h(x)| \leqslant g(x)$, and $h = f$ on $sp(X)$.

Proof. Taking T as a real vector space, we set

$$f(x) = f_1(x) + if_2(x), \quad f_j(x) \qquad (j = 1, 2)$$

being real. By Theorem 35.1, since

$$f_1(x) \leqslant g(x) \qquad (x \in sp(X))$$

there is a real linear functional $h_1(x)$ on T with

(35.1) $\quad h_1(x) \leqslant g(x) \qquad (x \in T), \quad h_1(x) = f_1(x) \qquad (x \in sp(X))$

Now f is linear, so that for $x \in sp(X)$,

$$i\{f_1(x) + if_2(x)\} = if(x) = f(ix) = f_1(ix) + if_2(ix), \quad f_1(ix) = -f_2(x)$$

We therefore define $h(x) = h_1(x) - ih_1(ix)$, so that by (35.1), $h = f$ on $sp(X)$, and $h(ix) = ih(x)$ by linearity of h_1 for real scalars, so that h is linear for complex scalars. Thus we only have to prove that $|h| \leqslant g$. Let b be the argument of the complex number $h(x)$, for fixed $x \in T$, with, say, $\arg(0) = 0$. Then

$$|h(x)| = h(x) e^{-ib} = h(e^{-ib}x) = h_1(e^{-ib}x) \leqslant g(e^{-ib}x) = g(x)$$

THEOREM 35.3. *Let g, T be as in Theorem 35.2. Then for arbitrary $z \in T$ there is a complex linear functional f on T, satisfying $f(z) = g(z)$, with $|f| \leqslant g$ in T.*

Proof. The result follows from Theorem 35.2 as for Theorem 25.2, with complex variations.

36. Linear Topological Space

The definition of a topological group was given in section 28, and that of a group pseudonorm in section 30. We extend these ideas to rings and linear spaces. The term 'normed ring' has a special significance, so that we shall say that a ring R *has an attached pseudonorm* $\|.\|$, if it is a group pseudonorm on the additive group, with

$||a|| \cdot ||b|| \leqslant ||ab||$ for multiplication. We drop the 'pseudo' if $||.||$ is a group norm.

A linear space T is a *linear topological space (topological vector space)* if T is a topological group under addition, if the coefficient field R has an attached norm, and if the mapping $(a, x) \to ax$ of $R \times T \to T$ is continuous using the product topology of R and T, and the topology of T.

THEOREM 36.1. *The closure of a linear subspace of T, is a linear subspace.*

Proof. Let $X \subseteq T$ be the linear subspace. Let $x, y \in \overline{X}$, $a, b \in R$, and let G be a neighbourhood of $ax+by$. Then there are neighbourhoods G_1 of x, G_2 of y and points u, v, with

$$aG_1 + bG_2 \subseteq G, \quad u \in G_1 \cap X, \quad v \in G_2 \cap X,$$
$$au + bv \in G \cap X, \quad ax + by \in \overline{X}$$

The closure $\mathcal{C}sp(X)$ of the linear subspace spanned by a set $X \subseteq T$, is called the *closed linear subspace spanned by X*. It is a linear subspace by Theorem 36.1. If $\mathcal{C}sp(X) = T$, then X is sometimes called *fundamental* (cf. section 33).

A set X is *separable* if there exists a countable set dense in X.

THEOREM 36.2. *If X is countable and R separable, then $\mathcal{C}sp(X)$ is separable.*

Using the norm topology, let R_1 be a countable set dense in R, and let Y be the set of all points $ax+by+ \ldots +cz$ (finite sums) with $a, b, \ldots, c \in R_1$, $x, y, \ldots, z \in X$. Then Y is countable, and is dense in $sp(X)$ and so in $\mathcal{C}sp(X)$.

A set $B \subseteq T$ is *bounded* if, given a neighbourhood G of the zero $\theta \in T$, there is an $\varepsilon > 0$, depending on G, B, with $aB \subseteq G$ (all $a \in R$ with $||a|| < \varepsilon$).

THEOREM 36.3. (36.1) *This definition of bounded sets agrees with that in section 33, if $\frac{1}{2} \in R$.*

(36.2) *If a sequence $\{a_n\} \subseteq R$ tends to 0, then $a_n x \to \theta$ for each $x \in T$.*

(36.3) *A compact subset of T is bounded, if there is in R a non-zero sequence $\{a_n\}$ tending to 0.*

(36.4) *A convergent sequence in T is bounded, if* (36.3) *holds.*

(36.5) *A continuous linear mapping from T to another linear topological space U, sends bounded sets into bounded sets.*

Proof. For (36.1) let B be bounded according to section 33, and let G be a neighbourhood of θ. Then there are $\varepsilon > 0$, and a neighbourhood G_1 of θ, with

$$(36.6) \qquad aG_1 \subseteq G \quad (\|a\| < \varepsilon)$$

There is an integer n for which

$$(36.7) \qquad B \subseteq G_1^{(n)}$$

Using (36.6; 36.7), if

$$\|a\| < 2^{-n}\varepsilon, \quad \text{then} \quad \|2^n a\| = \|a+a+\ldots+a\| \leqslant 2^n\|a\| < \varepsilon$$

$$aB \subseteq aG_1^{(n)} = (2^n a)\, G_1 \subseteq G$$

and B is bounded as in this section. The converse only needs $a = 2^{-n} < \varepsilon$.

For (36.2) we use the continuity of ax in a. For (36.3) let C be compact in T, and let G be a neighbourhood of θ. Since ax is continuous in (a, x) there are $\varepsilon > 0$, and a neighbourhood G_1 of θ, with (36.6). By (36.2) and the compactness of C, and the existence of $\{a_n\} \subseteq R$, $a_n \neq 0$ (*all n*), $a_n \to 0$, there is an integer m with

$$(36.8) \qquad C \subseteq T = \bigcup_{n=1}^{\infty} a_n^{-1}G_1, \quad C \subseteq \bigcup_{n=1}^{m} a_n^{-1}G_1$$

By (36.6; 36.8), if

$$\|a\| < \delta = \min_{1 \leqslant n \leqslant m} \varepsilon \|a_n\| > 0, \quad \text{then}$$

$$\|a \cdot a_n^{-1}\| \cdot \|a_n\| \leqslant \|a\| < \|a_n\| \varepsilon, \quad \|a \cdot a_n^{-1}\| < \varepsilon \qquad (1 \leqslant n \leqslant m)$$

$$aC \subseteq \bigcup_{n=1}^{m} aa_n^{-1}G_1 \subseteq G$$

For (36.4), a convergent sequence and its limit form a compact set. For (36.5) we need only use (36.1) and Theorem 33.2.

37. F-spaces and Banach Spaces

An *F-space*, or *space of type F*, is a linear space T with a coefficient field R, with a norm $\|.\|_R$ attached to R, and with a group norm $\|.\|_T$ in T, for which T is complete, and the mapping $(a, x) \to ax$ of $R \times T \to T$ is continuous in a for each x, and continuous in x for each a.

We can sometimes show that an *F*-space is a linear topological space.

THEOREM 37.1. *Let A be the non-empty set of all $a \in R$ with $\|a\|_R < 1$, and let R have a unique solution $\frac{1}{2}$ of the equation $\frac{1}{2} + \frac{1}{2} = 1$ ($1 \in R$), with*

$$(37.1) \quad \|(\tfrac{1}{2})^k a\|_R \to 0 \quad as \quad k \to \infty, \quad uniformly \; for \quad a \in A$$

Then the F-space T is a linear topological space.

Proof. First, $r(x) = \frac{1}{2}x$ is the root function in the additive group T, since
$$r(x) + r(x) = \tfrac{1}{2}x + \tfrac{1}{2}x = \left(\tfrac{1}{2} + \tfrac{1}{2}\right)x = 1x = x$$

Then Theorem 30.3 (30.8) is satisfied by the continuity of $\frac{1}{2}x$ in x. Taking $X = T$, and f as the norm $\|.\|_T$ in T, we put $V_a(x) = ax$, by hypothesis continuous in x for each fixed $a \in A$. Then (30.9) follows from the additivity in x of ax, and from the property of the norm, while (30.10) follows from the continuity of ax in x. By (37.1) and the continuity in a of ax for each fixed x, we have (30.11). Thus by Theorem 30.3,

$$\|ax\|_T < \varepsilon \qquad (\|a\|_R < 1, \quad \|x\|_T < \delta)$$

where $\delta > 0$ depends on $\varepsilon > 0$, *but not on $a \in A$.* Hence ax is continuous in (a, x) at $(0, \theta)$, and so everywhere in $R \times T$. As a metric space is Hausdorffian, to complete the proof we need only show that addition is continuous, and this follows from Theorem 30.2.

A *normed linear space T* is a linear space with a coefficient field R, with a norm $\|.\|_R$ attached to R, and with a group norm $\|.\|_T$ in T,

178

such that

(37.2) $\quad \|ax\|_T = \|a\|_R \cdot \|x\|_T \quad$ (all $a \in R$, all $x \in T$)

(37.3) for each $\varepsilon > 0$, there is an $a \in R$ with $0 < \|a\|_R < \varepsilon$

The norm topology in T is called its *strong topology*. A normed linear space that is complete in its norm topology, is called a *complete normed linear space (space of type B, B-space, Banach space)*. Clearly it is an *F*-space, and also a linear topological space.

If T only contains θ, then R is not needed. If T contains $x \neq \theta$, then $\|x\|_T > 0$, and we can use (37.2) with a, $b \in R$,

$$\|ab\|_R \cdot \|x\|_T = \|(ab)x\|_T = \|a(bx)\|_T = \|a\|_R \|bx\|_T$$
$$= \|a\|_R \cdot \|b\|_R \cdot \|x\|_T$$

Hence we have the useful properties

(37.4) $\quad \|ab\|_R = \|a\|_R \cdot \|b\|_R; \quad 1^2 = 1, \quad \|1\|_R > 0, \quad \|1\|_R = 1$

Then if there is an $a \in R$ with $0 < \|a\|_R < 1$, we have

$$\|a^n\|_R = (\|a\|_R)^n \to 0$$

as $n \to \infty$, and (37.3) is true.

Normally the coefficient fields R for both *F*-spaces and Banach spaces are formed of either the real or the complex numbers.

THEOREM 37.2. *A non-empty set B in a normed linear space T is bounded, if, and only if,*

$$\sup\{\|x\|_T : x \in B\} < \infty$$

Proof. By Theorem 36.3 (36.1) either definition of bounded sets can be used. If B is bounded, then since $S(\theta; 1)$ is a neighbourhood of $\theta \in T$, we have

$$B \subseteq S(\theta; 1)^{(n)} \subseteq S(\theta, 2^n)$$

and the supremum is not greater than 2^n. Conversely, if the supremum is bounded, it is less than s, for some positive number s. Each neighbourhood G of the zero $\theta \in T$ contains a sphere $S(\theta; r)$. Then

179

from (37.2),

$$\|ax\|_T < r \quad \text{when} \quad \|a\|_R < r/s, \quad x \in B, \quad \|x\|_T < s; \quad aB \subseteq G$$

and B is bounded under the second definition. It is then bounded under the first definition, if $\frac{1}{2} \in R$.

THEOREM 37.3. *Let $\{f_n\}$ be a sequence of bounded linear functions from a Banach space T whose coefficient field R contains $\frac{1}{2}$, to a normed group U, its norm, and the norm of R, being homogeneous for positive integers, and let*

$$\lim_{n \to \infty} \sup \|f_n(x)\|_U < \infty \qquad (x \in T)$$

Then norm $(f_n) < \infty$ $(n = 1, 2, \ldots)$, $\lim_{n \to \infty} \sup$ norm $(f_n) < \infty$

Proof. This typical result follows from Theorem 34.1, since by Theorem 17.3, a complete metric space is a Baire space, and since $\|.\|_T$ is also homogeneous for positive integers,

$$\|nx\|_T = \|n\|_R \|x\|_T = n\|1\|_R \|x\|_T = n\|x\|_T$$

38. The Unsymmetrical Theory of Gál

By using some unsymmetrical relations, Gál (1951; 1953) gives another version of the theorem on the condensation of singularities. It does not seem possible to include this in our general theory.

Let T be a complete normed vector space, and U a normed vector space, with norms $\|.\|_T, \|.\|_U$, respectively, and let $f : T \to U$. Then f is *bounded* when norm $(f) < \infty$ and *norm-homogeneous* when $\|f(ax)\|_U = |a| \cdot \|f(x)\|_U$, for all real a. Then

(38.1) $$\|f(x)\|_U \leqslant \|x\|_T \cdot \text{norm } (f)$$

The sequence $\{f_n(x)\}$ $(n = 1, 2, \ldots)$ of bounded norm-homogeneous functions, is *asymptotically subadditive*, if, for some constant K independent of n, x, y, and for some function $c(n, x)$ independent of y and tending to 0 as $n \to \infty$, for each fixed x,

(38.2) $$\|f_n(y)\|_U - \|f_n(x)\|_U - c(n, x) \cdot \text{norm}(f_n) \leqslant \|f_n(x+y)\|_U \leqslant$$
$$\|f_n(x)\|_U + K \cdot \text{norm}(f_n) \cdot \|y\|_T \qquad (\|x\|_T \leqslant 1, \quad \|y\|_T \leqslant 1)$$

180

THEOREM 38.1 *Let $\{f_{mn}(x)\}$ be a double sequence of bounded norm-homogeneous functions $f_{mn} : T \to U$ $(m, n = 1, 2, \ldots)$, such that, for each fixed m, the single sequence is asymptotically subadditive as $n \to \infty$. If, for each $m \geqslant 1$, there is an $x_m \in T$ with*

(38.3)
$$\limsup_{n \to \infty} \|f_{mn}(x_m)\|_U = +\infty$$

then there is an $x \in T$, independent of m, with

(38.4)
$$\limsup_{n \to \infty} \|f_{mn}(x)\|_U = +\infty \qquad (m = 1, 2, \ldots)$$

T is fixed throughout, but U only appears through its norm, so that if necessary it can vary with m, n, the final result being the same. Gál proves the result by an intricate construction of suitable sequences; a slight modification is given here.

Proof. By (38.1) we see that (38.3) gives

$$\limsup_{n \to \infty} \operatorname{norm}(f_{mn}) = +\infty \qquad (m = 1, 2, \ldots).$$

For each m we can therefore choose a subsequence of n, and so assume that as $n \to \infty$

(38.5)
$$\operatorname{norm}(f_{mn}) \to \infty \qquad (m = 1, 2, \ldots)$$

With f, f_n, f_{mn} we associate a g, g_n, g_{mn}, respectively, such that

$$g(x) = \|f(x)\|_U \cdot \operatorname{norm}(f)^{-1}$$

and similarly for the others. In the rest of the proof we use the g's and do not mention $\|.\|_U$ so that we can write $\|.\|$ for $\|.\|_T$. Since f is bounded and norm-homogeneous,

(38.6)
$$0 \leqslant g(x) \leqslant \|x\|$$

(38.7)
there is an $x \in T$ with $g(x) \geqslant 8/9$, $\quad \|x\| = 1$

(38.8)
$$g(ax) = |a| \cdot g(x) \qquad (all\ real\ a)$$

The second inequality in (38.2) gives

(38.9)
$$g_n(x+y) \leqslant g_n(x) + K\|y\|$$

for $\|x\| \leqslant 1$, $\|y\| \leqslant 1$, and then for all $x, y \in T$ by (38.8). This is an unsymmetrical form of (5.6).

The first inequality in (38.2) gives

(38.10) $\quad g_n(y) - g_n(x) - c(n, x) \leqslant g_n(x+y) \qquad (\|x\| \leqslant 1, \quad \|y\| \leqslant 1)$

This cannot be extended significantly by homogeneity. By (38.7),

(38.11) $\quad$ there is an $x_{mn} \in T$ with $\|x_{mn}\| = 1$, $g_{mn}(x_{mn}) \geqslant 8/9$

We choose $z_{mn} \in T$ with $\|z_{mn}\| = 0$ or 1, and $a_{mn} \geqslant 0$ with

(38.12) $$0 < \sum_{m,\,n=1}^{\infty} a_{mn} < 1$$

Since T is complete, there is then a $z \in T$ with

(38.13) $$z = \sum_{m,\,n=1}^{\infty} a_{mn} z_{mn}, \quad \|z\| \leqslant \sum_{m,\,n=1}^{\infty} a_{mn}$$

To choose the z_{mn}, a_{mn}, we put the pairs (m, n) of integers in sequence, (m, n) being the $\{j(m, n) - 1\}$ th member, where

$$j(m,\ n) = \tfrac{1}{2}(m+n-1)(m+n) + m$$

We put $a_{11} = 1/9$, $z_{11} = x_{11}$. If a_{kl}, z_{kl} have been defined for all $(k,\ l)$ with $j(k,\ l) < j(m, n)$ we put

$$r_{kl} = \sum_{j(u,\,v) < j(k,\,l)} a_{uv} z_{uv}$$

(38.14) $$\|r_{kl}\| \leqslant \sum_{u,\,v=1}^{\infty} a_{uv} < 1$$

by (38.12). Then r_{kl} is defined for all $(k,\ l)$ with $j(k,\ l) \leqslant j(m, n)$. We put

$$h_{mn} = \lim_{j \to \infty} \sup g_{mj}(r_{mn}) \geqslant 0$$

By (38.6; 38.14),

(38.15) $$h_{mn} \leqslant \|r_{mn}\| < 1$$

If $h_{mn} > 0$, we choose $a_{mn} = 0$, $z_{mn} = \theta$, the zero in T. If $h_{mn} = 0$, then

(38.16) $$g_{mj}(r_{mn}) \to 0 \quad \text{as} \quad j \to \infty$$

We put H_{mn} as the least of those $h_{kl} > 0$ for which $j(k,\ l) < j(m, n)$. If all those h_{kl} are 0, we put $H_{mn} = 1$. By (38.15),

(38.17) $$H_{mn} \leqslant 1$$

182

By (38.9) we have

(38.18) $$g_{mj}(x+y) \leqslant g_{mj}(x) + K_m \|y\|$$

where $K_m > 0$ is independent of x, y, j. We define

(38.19) $\quad L_m = \min(1, 1/K_1, \ldots, 1/K_m), \quad a_{mn} = H_{mn}(L_m/3)^{j(m,\,n)}$

By (38.17),

$$0 \leqslant a_{mn} \leqslant 3^{-j(m,\,n)}, \quad a_{11} = 1/9,$$

$$0 < \sum_{m,\,n=1}^{\infty} a_{mn} \leqslant \sum_{m,\,n=}^{\infty} 3^{-j(m,\,n)} = \sum_{j=2}^{\infty} 3^{-j} = 6^{-1} < 1$$

so that (38.12) is satisfied.

We now construct z_{mn}. If $a_{mn} > 0$, then by definition, $h_{mn} = 0$ and (38.16) holds, so that for all sufficiently large j,

(38.20) $$g_{mj}(r_{mn}) \leqslant a_{mn}/9$$

As $a_{mn} > 0$ and r_{mn} are fixed, (38.10; 38.14) show that for some large j_0, independent of y, and for all $j \geqslant j_0$,

(38.21) $\quad g_{mj}(r_{mn}+y) \geqslant g_{mj}(y) - g_{mj}(r_{mn}) - a_{mn}/9 \quad\quad (\|y\| \leqslant 1)$

We select some $j = k(n) = k(m,n)$ that satisfies (38.20; 38.21), and we define $z_{mn} = x_{m,\,k(m,\,n)}$. Then from (38.11),

(38.22) $$\|z_{mn}\| = 1, \quad g_{m,\,k(m,\,n)}(z_{mn}) \geqslant 8/9$$

To show that z satisfies (38.4), suppose first that $a_{mn} = 0$. Then

(38.23) $$\lim_{j \to \infty} \sup\, g_{mj}(r_{mn}) = h_{mn} > 0$$

Further, by the ordering of the (m, n) and by definition of H_{uv}, L_u,

$$\|z - r_{mn}\| = \left\| \sum_{j(u,\,v)\,>\,j(m,\,n)} a_{uv} z_{uv} \right\| \leqslant \sum_{j(u,\,v)\,>\,j(m,\,n)} H_{uv}(L_u/3)^{j(u,\,v)}$$

$$\leqslant h_{mn}(L_m/3)^{j(m,\,n)}(1 - L_m/3)^{-1} < h_{mn}L_m^2/6 \leqslant h_{mn}/(6K_m)$$

(38.24) $$\|z - r_{mn}\| < h_{mn}/(6K_m)$$

Secondly, if $a_{mn} > 0$, there is a $j = k(n) = k(m,n) \to \infty$ as $n \to \infty$, such that by (38.20; 38.21; 38.22),

(38.25) $\quad g_{mj}(r_{mn}) \leqslant a_{mn}/9$

(38.26) $\quad g_{mj}(r_{mn} + a_{mn}z_{mn}) \geqslant g_{mj}(a_{mn}z_{mn}) - g_{mj}(r_{mn}) - a_{mn}/9$

(38.27) $\quad g_{mj}(a_{mn}z_{mn}) \geqslant 8a_{mn}/9$

Further, we have

$$\| z - r_{mn} - a_{mn}z_{mn} \| \leqslant \sum_{j(u, v) > j(m, n)} H_{uv}(L_u/3)^{j(u, v)}$$

$$\leqslant H_{mn}(L_m/3)^{j(m, n)+1}(1 - L_m/3)^{-1} = a_{mn}L_m/(3 - L_m)$$

$$\leqslant a_{mn}L_m/2 \leqslant a_{mn}/(2K_m)$$

(38.28) $$\| z - r_{mn} - a_{mn}z_{mn} \| \leqslant a_{mn}/(2K_m)$$

Given $m \geqslant 1$, suppose that $\{a_{mn}\}$ has at least one zero, term, say, $a_{mn} = 0$. By (38.23), for an infinity of $j \geqslant 1$,

$$g_{mj}(r_{mn}) \geqslant 2h_{mn}/3$$

By (38.9; 38.24), for an infinity of $j \geqslant 1$, and for the fixed n,

$$g_{mj}(z) \geqslant g_{mj}(r_{mn}) - K_m \| r_{mn} - z \| \geqslant 2h_{mn}/3 - h_{mn}/6 = h_{mn}/2$$

and (38.5) gives (38.4) for z in this case.

If, for the given m, and all j, $a_{mj} > 0$, then by (38.9), and (38.25) to (38.28),

$$g_{m, k(n)}(z) = g_{m, k(n)}\big((r_{mn}+a_{mn}z_{mn})+(z-r_{mn}-a_{mn}z_{mn})\big)$$

$$\geqslant g_{m, k(n)}(r_{mn}+a_{mn}z_{mn}) - K_m \| z-r_{mn}-a_{mn}z_{mn} \|$$

$$\geqslant g_{m, k(n)}(a_{mn}z_{mn}) - g_{m, k(n)}(r_{mn}) - a_{mn}/9 - a_{mn}/2$$

$$\geqslant a_{mn}(8/9 - 1/9 - 1/9 - 1/2) = a_{mn}/6$$

Here, of course, we have not proved that

$$\lim_{j \to \infty} \sup g_{mj}(z) > 0$$

since $a_{mn} \to 0$ as $n \to \infty$. But we can ensure that (38.4) occurs for $x = z$ and for this particular m, on choosing the $j = k(m, n)$ so that

$$\text{norm } (f_{mj}) \geqslant n/a_{mn}$$

which is possible by (38.5) since n/a_{mn} is independent of j. Thus (38.4) occurs in either case, and we have proved the theorem.

Ex. 38.1 Let R be the real line, let $f: R \to R$. If $X \subseteq (-\infty, \infty)$ define $m(X) = V(m; \mathcal{A}; (-\infty, \infty); X)$ where $m(u, v) = v - u$ and $\mathcal{A}$ is in *Ex. 43.3*, $mm(f; I) = \sup \{h : f(t) \geqslant h \text{ in } Y, m(Y \cap I) \geqslant \frac{1}{2}m(I)\}$. This is the metric-mean of Kantorovitch (1931); see also Rappoport (1949). If $\{\delta_n\}$ is a sequence of positive numbers strictly decreasing to 0, and if

$$f_n(f; t) = \sum_{k=0}^{n} \binom{h}{k} t^k (1-t)^{n-k} \, mm\left(f; \left[\frac{k}{n} - \delta_n, \frac{k}{n} + \delta_n\right]\right)$$

show that f_n is asymptotically subadditive in the space of all continuous functions $f(t)$ in $[0, 1]$.

Ex. 38.2. Let f be a continuous function on $[0, 1]$, and let $X(1) \ldots$, $X(n)$ be arbitrary disjoint measurable subsets of $[0, 1]$ with union $[0, 1]$, and with n fixed. If

$$f_n(f) = \sup \sum_{j=1}^{n} \inf_{t \in X(j)} f(t) \cdot m(X(j))$$

the sup being taken over all such $X(1), \ldots, X(n)$ with n fixed, show that $f_n(f)$ is a bounded homogeneous functional, with norm $\leqslant 1$, that is asymptotically additive. Note that

$$\lim_{n \to \infty} f_n(f) = \int_0^1 f(t) \, dt$$

Exs. 38.1, 38.2 are from Gál (1953).

9

RIEMANN AND RIEMANN-STIELTJES INTEGRATION

39. Definitions

IN order to proceed further with the theory, we need various results on integration. The Riemann integral has been in the main superseded by the Lebesgue integral, but Chapter 10 gives an integral that includes Lebesgue's and yet which is built up like Riemann's. For this reason, and for the need of various elementary results, I give a little of Riemann theory.

For the definite integral of the calculus we take an interval $a \leqslant x \leqslant b$, written $[a, b]$, where $a < b$ are real numbers, and we subdivide it into a finite number of smaller intervals, not necessarily equal in length, by using numbers $a = x_0 < x_1 < \ldots < x_n = b$, calling this a division $\mathcal{D}$ of $[a, b]$, the norm of which is the greatest value of $x_j - x_{j-1}$ $(1 \leqslant j \leqslant n)$. If $y = f(x)$ is a real valued function its values in $[x_{j-1}, x_j]$ lie between

$$m_j = \inf f(x), \quad M_j = \sup f(x) \quad (x_{j-1} \leqslant x \leqslant x_j)$$

The *lower* and *upper sums* for the division $\mathcal{D}$ are, respectively,

$$s(\mathcal{D}) = \sum_{j=1}^{n} m_j(x_j - x_{j-1}), \quad S(\mathcal{D}) = \sum_{j=1}^{n} M_j(x_j - x_{j-1})$$

When $f(x) > 0$ in $[a, b]$, $s(\mathcal{D})$ is the area of a finite number of non-overlapping rectangles that lie below the graph, while $S(\mathcal{D})$ is the area of another finite number of non-overlapping rectangles, with union containing the points of the graph. If the area under the graph has a reasonable meaning, then it must lie between $s(\mathcal{D})$ and $S(\mathcal{D})$, so that we have the following definition.

Let f have real values. If for all sequences of divisions $\mathcal{D}$ with norm tending to 0, the sequence of $s(\mathcal{D})$ tends to a number A, while the sequence of $S(\mathcal{D})$ tends to the same A, then A is the value of the *Riemann integral of $f(x)$ on* $[a, b]$, and we write

$$A = (R) \int_a^b f(x)\, dx$$

We can omit the (R) when understood. This is Darboux's definition of the Riemann integral. Since for some $\mathcal{D}$, $s(\mathcal{D})$ and $S(\mathcal{D})$ must be finite, so that the m_j, M_j must be finite, it follows that

(39.1) if f is Riemann integrable on $[a, b]$, f is bounded there
The converse is false, for if f is 1 at each rational and 0 at each irrational, then for every $\mathcal{D}$, $m_j = 0$, $s(\mathcal{D}) = 0$, while $M_j = 1$, $S(\mathcal{D}) = b-a$.

Riemann's original definition is as follows. Let $\mathcal{D}$ be a division of $[a, b]$ as before, and let ξ_j be a point in $[x_{j-1}, x_j]$ $(j = 1, 2, \ldots, n)$. If the sum

$$\sigma(D) = \sum_{j=1}^n f(\xi_j)\ (x_j - x_{j-1})$$

tends to a number A, for all sequences of divisions $\mathcal{D}$ with norm $\to 0$, and for all choices of ξ_j in $[x_{j-1}, x_j]$, then A is the value of the *Riemann integral of f on* $[a, b]$, written as before.

THEOREM 39.1. *The two definitions of the Riemann integral are equivalent.*

Proof. First suppose that A is defined by Darboux's method. Since

$$m_j \leqslant f(\xi_j) \leqslant M_j, \quad s(\mathcal{D}) \leqslant \sigma(\mathcal{D}) \leqslant S(\mathcal{D})$$

$\sigma(\mathcal{D}) \to A$ also, and A is given by Riemann's definition. Conversely, given $\varepsilon > 0$, there is a ξ_j in $[x_{j-1}, x_j]$, with

$$m_j \leqslant f(\xi_j) < m_j + \varepsilon \qquad (j = 1, 2, \ldots, n),$$
$$s(\mathcal{D}) \leqslant \sigma(\mathcal{D}) < s(\mathcal{D}) + \varepsilon(b-a)$$

As $\varepsilon > 0$ is arbitrary, if $\sigma(\mathcal{D}) \to A$, then $s(\mathcal{D}) \to A$, and similarly $S(\mathcal{D}) \to A$.

If $f(x)$ takes complex values, its Riemann integral (when it exists) can be defined directly by using $\sigma(\mathcal{D})$, while the use of $s(\mathcal{D})$, $S(\mathcal{D})$ methods would first need the splitting up of f into its real and imaginary parts.

More generally, if $f(x)$ and $g(x)$ are two functions defined on $[a, b]$, the *Riemann–Stieltjes integral of f relative to g*,

$$(RSt) \int_a^b f(x)\, dg(x)$$

is the limit (if it exists) of

$$\sigma^*(\mathcal{D}) = \sum_{j=1}^n f(\xi_j) \{g(x_j) - g(x_{j-1})\}$$

as the norm of $\mathcal{D}$ tends to 0, with all choices of ξ_j. This is a Moore–Smith convergence using generalized sequences, as in section 9, but no stress is laid on this in elementary texts.

If the real or complex function $g(x)$, defined on $[a, b]$, is such that

$$\sum_{j=1}^n |g(x_j) - g(x_{j-1})| \leqslant M$$

for every division $\mathcal{D}$ of $[a, b]$, where M is independent of $\mathcal{D}$, we say that g is of *bounded variation on* $[a, b]$, with *variation var (g; [a, b])* *of g on* $[a, b]$ the least such value of M. This variation is in this case the same as in Chapter 10.

THEOREM 39.2. *If f is continuous and g of bounded variation on* $[a, b]$, *then f is Riemann–Stieltjes integrable relative to g on* $[a, b]$.

Proof. By uniformity of continuity, given $\varepsilon > 0$, there is a $\delta > 0$, such that

(39.1) $|f(v) - f(u)| < \varepsilon$ $(a \leqslant u < v \leqslant b, v - u < 2\delta)$

Let $\mathcal{D}$, $\mathcal{D}'$ be divisions $a = x_0 < x_1 < \ldots < x_n = b$ and $a = u_0 < u_1 < \ldots < u_m = b$, respectively, with norm $(\mathcal{D}) < \delta$, norm $(\mathcal{D}') < \delta$, and take

$$x_{j-1} \leqslant \xi_j \leqslant x_j \ (j = 1, 2, \ldots, n), \ \sigma(D) = \sum_{j=1}^n f(\xi_j) \{g(x_j) - g(x_{j-1})\}$$

$$\sigma(D') = \sum_{k=1}^m f(u_k) \{g(u_k) - g(u_{k-1})\}$$

188

We consider the intersections of every pair of intervals from $\mathcal{D}$, $\mathcal{D}'$. If

$$[x_{j-1}, x_j] \cap [u_{k-1}, u_k] = [u, v], \quad \text{then} \quad |\xi_j - u_k| < 2\delta$$

$$|f(\xi_j)\{g(v) - g(u)\} - f(u_k)\{g(v) - g(u)\}| \leqslant |f(\xi_j) - f(u_k)| \, |g(v) - g(u)|$$

$$\leqslant \varepsilon |g(v) - g(u)|, \quad |\sigma(D) - \sigma(D')| \leqslant \varepsilon \sum |g(v) - g(u)| \leqslant \varepsilon M$$

where we have used (39.1). Further, we could take $\delta > 1/q$, and then for $\mathcal{D}'$ we could take the division $\mathcal{D}_q$ given by

$$m - 1 < q(b-a) \leqslant m, \quad u_k = a + k/q \quad (0 \leqslant k < m)$$

For $r > q$ we can take $\mathcal{D}$ as $\mathcal{D}_r$, showing that $\{\sigma(D_n)\}$ is a fundamental and so convergent sequence, and then taking $\mathcal{D}$ as any division with norm $< \delta$, we prove that $\sigma(D)$ tends to the same limit as $\delta \to 0$.

Let the complex-valued g be continuous, and of bounded variation, on $[a, b]$, with $g(a) = g(b)$, and such that if $a \leqslant u < v \leqslant b$, $g(u) = g(v)$, then $u = a$, $v = b$. Then the set of values of g on the complex plane is a *closed contour* C. If f is a continuous function of the complex variable z, the *integral of f round C* can be defined to be

$$\int_C f(z) \, dz = (RSt) \int_a^b f(g(x)) \, dg(x)$$

This exists by Theorem 39.2, since g is of bounded variation and continuous, and so $f(g(x))$ is continuous. For an alternative definition, if $g(x_j) = z_j$, and for η_j a point on C *between* z_{j-1} and z_j, i.e. $\eta_j = g(\xi_j)$, then

$$\sigma(D) = \sum_{j=1}^n f(g(\xi_j)) \, (g(x_j) - g(x_{j-1})) = \sum_{j=1}^n f(\eta_j) \, (z_j - z_{j-1}) \to \int_C f \, dz.$$

THEOREM 39.3. *If g is of bounded variation in $[a, b]$, then g has an at most countable number of discontinuities $\{a_j\}$ in $[a, b]$, each one of which can be approached from above (except if $a_j = b$) and below (except if $a_j = a$) by points where g is continuous. Further, there exist*

$$(39.2) \qquad g(x-) = \lim_{u \to x, \, u < x} g(u) \, (a < x \leqslant b),$$

$$g(x+) = \lim_{u \to x, \, u > x} g(u) \, (a \leqslant x < b),$$

$$(39.3) \quad \sum_{j=1}^{\infty} \{|g(a_j) - g(a_j-)| + |g(a_j+) - g(a_j)|\} \leqslant M = var\,(g; [a, b]),$$

(39.4) $g_1(x)$ is continuous in $[a, b]$, where $g_1(a) = g(a)$,

$$g_1(x) = g(x) - \sum_1 \{g(a_j) - g(a_j-)\} - \sum_2 \{g(a_j+) - g(a_j)\}$$

where $\sum_1$ is over all a_j in $a < a_j \leqslant x$, and $\sum_2$ over all a_j in $a \leqslant a_j < x$;

(39.5) If f is continuous, then, except for obvious changes when $a_j = a$ or b,

$$\int_a^b f \, dg = \int_a^b f \, dg_1 + \sum_{j=1}^{\infty} f(a_j) \{g(a_j+) - g(a_j-)\}$$

Proof. Denoting $a < x < b$ by (a, b), let $\{[u_j, v_j]\}$ be a sequence of non-overlapping intervals in $[a, b]$. Then, for each n,

$$[a, b] \Big\backslash \bigcup_{j=1}^{n} (u_j, v_j)$$

is a set of intervals, possibly together with a, or b, or both, so that

$$\sum_{j=1}^{n} |g(v_j) - g(u_j)| \leqslant M \qquad (n = 1, 2, \ldots)$$

(39.6) $$\sum_{j=1}^{\infty} |g(v_j) - g(u_j)| \leqslant M$$

First take $u_1 = a, u_j = v_{j-1} \, (j = 2, 3, \ldots), v_j \to c \leqslant b$, so that

$$\lim_{j \to \infty} g(v_j) = g(a) + \sum_{j=1}^{\infty} \{g(v_j) - g(v_{j-1})\}$$

exists as an absolutely convergent series. Also, taking different $\{u_j\}$, in (39.6), we still have $g(v_j) - g(u_j) \to 0$, which shows that $g(c-)$ exists. Similarly for $g(c+)$ in $a \leqslant c < b$. Taking n points x_j in (a, b) we use $2n$ non-overlapping intervals $[u_j, x_j]$, $[x_j, v_j]$ in (39.6), and then let $u_j, v_j \to x_j$, obtaining

$$\sum_{j=1}^{n} \{|g(x_j) - g(x_j-)| + |g(x_j+) - g(x_j)|\} \leqslant M$$

Thus there are at most nM points x_j with $|g(x_j) - g(x_j-)| > 1/n$, and at most nM points x_j with $|g(x_j+) - g(x_j)| > 1/n$, so that for $n = 1, 2, \ldots$, we have a countable number of discontinuities alto-

190

gether, say a sequence $\{a_j\}$. By including intervals $[a, v]$, $[u, b]$, and $a_1, \ldots, a_n$, letting $v \to a$, $u \to b$, we have (39.3) for the first n of the a_j, and then we can let $n \to \infty$. As the series in (39.4) then are absolutely convergent, (39.4) follows. For (39.5), after Theorem 39.2 we need only prove that if f is continuous in $[a, b]$, $\{y_k\}$ a sequence of points in (a, b), and $\sum\limits_{k=1}^{\infty} c_k$ an absolutely convergent series, then

$$(39.7) \quad \sum_{k=1}^{\infty} c_k f(y_k) = \int_a^b f(x)\, dh(x), \quad h(x) \equiv \sum \{c_k : a < y_k \leqslant x\}$$

and similarly for $a \leqslant y_k < x$ replacing $a < y_k \leqslant x$. For (39.7), if $\mathcal{D}$ is as in Theorem 39.2,

$$\left| \sum_{k=1}^{\infty} c_k f(y_k) - \sum_{j=1}^{n} f(\xi_j)\{h(x_j) - h(x_{j-1})\} \right|$$

$$= \left| \sum_{j=1}^{n} \sum \{c_k[f(y_k) - f(\xi_j)] : x_{j-1} < y_k \leqslant x_j\} \right| \leqslant \varepsilon \sum_{k=1}^{\infty} |c_k|$$

Hence the result from Theorem 39.2.

Finally, to show that the points of continuity are dense in $[a, b]$, we observe that the discontinuities are countable, while the points in each interval are not countable.

Let $\varphi(x)$ be a finite monotone increasing function in $[0, c]$, for some $c > 0$, so that φ is of bounded variation. For convenience we assume that

$$\varphi(x) = \varphi(x-) \quad (x > 0)$$

Let $\psi(x)$ be defined by

$$\psi(y) = \inf\{x : x \geqslant 0, \quad \varphi(x) \geqslant y\}$$

Then we say that ψ is the *inverse function of φ, in the sense of Young*.

THEOREM 39.4. *If ψ is the inverse function of φ, in the sense of Young, then ψ is finite and monotone increasing in*

$$[\varphi(0), \varphi(c)], \quad \psi(y) = \psi(y-) \quad (\varphi(0) < y \leqslant \varphi(c))$$

191

If also φ is continuous, then for

$$\varphi(0) < y < \varphi(c), \quad \varphi(\psi(y)) = y, \quad and \quad \psi(\varphi(x)) = \inf z$$
$$with \quad \varphi(x) = \varphi(z), \quad z \geqslant 0, \quad when \quad 0 \leqslant x \leqslant c.$$

Proof. The first results follow by monotonicity, while for those in which φ is continuous, let $x > \psi(y)$. Then $\varphi(x) \geqslant y$, $\varphi(\psi(y)+) \geqslant y$. If $x < \psi(y)$ then $\varphi(x) < y$, $\varphi(\psi(y)-) \leqslant y$. Thus $\varphi(\psi(y)) = y$. The last result follows from the continuity of φ and the definition of ψ.

THEOREM 39.5. *If* $0 \leqslant a < b \leqslant c$, *and if ψ is the inverse function of* φ, *then*

$$(39.8) \qquad \int_a^b \varphi \, dx + \int_{\varphi(a)}^{\varphi(b)} \psi \, dy = [x\varphi(x)]_a^b$$

$$(39.9) \qquad \int_a^b \varphi \, dx + \int_{\varphi(a)}^y \psi \, dy = by - a\varphi(a) \qquad (\varphi(b) \leqslant y \leqslant \varphi(b+))$$

Proof. First suppose that φ, ψ are continuous, so that neither has any interval in which it is constant. By Theorem 39.2 the Riemann integrals exist. Let $\mathcal{D}$ be a division as there. Since φ is strictly increasing, let D_1 be the corresponding division

$$\varphi(a) = \varphi(x_0) < \varphi(x_1) < \ldots < \varphi(x_n) = \varphi(b)$$

By continuity of φ, norm $(\mathcal{D}_1) \to 0$ as norm $(\mathcal{D}) \to 0$, and then the following sum of two sums tends to the left side of (39.8). Using Theorem 39.4,

$$\sum_{j=1}^n \varphi(x_j)(x_j - x_{j-1}) + \sum_{j=1}^n \psi(\varphi(x_{j-1})) \{\varphi(x_j) - \varphi(x_{j-1})\}$$
$$= \sum_{j=1}^n \varphi(x_j)(x_j - x_{j-1}) + \sum_{j=1}^n x_{j-1}\{\varphi(x_j) - \varphi(x_{j-1})\}$$
$$= \varphi(x_n)(x_n - x_{n-1}) + x_{n-1}\varphi(x_n) - x_0\varphi(x_0) = b\varphi(b) - a\varphi(a)$$

Hence (39.8) when both φ and ψ are continuous.

We now use induction, assuming (39.8) true and inserting an interval where φ is constant, i.e. for some points u, v in $0 \leqslant u < v \leqslant c$

192

we have new inverse functions

$$\varphi_1(x) = \begin{cases} \varphi(x) & (0 \leqslant x \leqslant u) \\ \varphi(u) & (u \leqslant x \leqslant v) \\ \varphi(x+u-v) & (x \geqslant v) \end{cases}$$

$$\psi_1(y) = \begin{cases} \psi(y) & (0 \leqslant y \leqslant \varphi(u)) \\ \psi(y)+v-u & (y > \varphi(u)) \end{cases}$$

For $[a, b] \subseteq [u, v]$, the second integral in (39.8) has zero range, and so is 0. The first integral is $\varphi(u)(b-a)$, which is now the right side of (39.8). For $[a, b]$ in $[0, u]$ or $[v, c]$, (39.8) is true by induction, and hence by union of intervals, (39.8) is true for all $[a, b] \subseteq [0, c]$. Hence we can insert n intervals over which φ is constant. Using Theorem 39.3 (39.3) we can let $n \to \infty$ to prove (39.8) when φ is alone continuous.

To drop the continuity of φ we insert jumps, treating each insertion separately. As before, it is enough to take $0 \leqslant u < c, v > 0$, and consider

$$\varphi_2(x) = \begin{cases} \varphi(x) & (0 \leqslant x \leqslant u), \\ \varphi(x)+v & (x > u), \end{cases}$$

$$\psi_2(y) = \begin{cases} \psi(y) & (0 \leqslant y \leqslant \varphi(u)) \\ u & (\varphi(u) < y \leqslant \varphi(u)+v) \\ \psi(y-v) & (y > \varphi(u)+v) \end{cases}$$

$$\int_{\varphi_2(u)}^{\varphi_2(y)+} \psi_2(y)\, dy = u\{(\varphi_2(u)+)-\varphi_2(u)\}.$$

The corresponding integral of φ is from u to u, and so is zero, and (39.8) is true in this case, and so is true always. The extra result needed for (39.9) comes in a similar way.

THEOREM 39.6. *Let f be of bounded variation in $[a, b]$. If $a = x_0 < < x_1 \ldots < x_n = b$ is a division of $[a, b]$, and if $x_{j-1} \leqslant \xi_j < x_j$, then*

$$\sum_{j=1}^{n} \int_{x_{j-1}}^{x_j} |f(\xi_j)-f(x)|\, dx \leqslant V \cdot \max (x_j-x_{j-1})$$

where V is the variation of f in $[a, b]$.

193

Proof. Each integral exists by Theorem 39.2 and *Ex. 39.4.* If V_j is the variation of f in $[x_{j-1}, x_j)$, the set where $x_{j-1} \leqslant x < x_j$, then for $x_{j-1} < x < x_j$

$$(39.10) \qquad \int_{x_{j-1}}^{x} |f(\xi_j) - f(x)| \, dx \leqslant V_j(x - x_{j-1})$$

By continuity of the integral we can let $x \to x_j-$, so that (39.10) is true for $x = x_j$. Summing over j, we have the result, since the right becomes

$$\sum_{j=1}^{n} V_j(x_j - x_{j-1}) \leqslant \max_{j} (x_j - x_{j-1}) \sum_{j=1}^{n} V_j.$$

THEOREM 39.7. *Let f be continuous and g, $g(u,.)$ have variation bounded by M independent of u, all for x in $[a, b]$. If*

$$(39.11) \qquad g(u, b) - g(u, a) \to g(b) - g(a) \quad as \quad u \to \infty$$

$$(39.12) \; and \quad \int_{a}^{b} |g(u, x) - g(x) - g(u, a) + g(a)| \, dx \to 0 \quad as \quad u \to \infty$$

$$(39.13) \; then \qquad \lim_{u \to \infty} \int_{a}^{b} f \, dg(u,.) = \int_{a}^{b} f \, dg$$

(39.14) *In particular, we can omit (39.12), if $g(u, x) \to g(x)$ almost everywhere.*

We need Chapter 10 (or Lebesgue theory) to explain the 'almost everywhere' in (39.14) and to prove (39.12) there. It is included to show that Theorem 39.7 includes a theorem of Helly (1921) and Bray (1919). See also Evans (1927), p. 15. This is a theorem on limits under the integral sign of a new type, and there is an extension to n dimensions using the $IR(f ; s)$ of section 63.

Proof. Given $\varepsilon > 0$, there is a $\delta > 0$ with (39.1) true. Let $\mathcal{D}$ be as in Theorem 39.2. If f^* has $f(x_j) = f^*(x_j)(j = 0, 1, 2, \ldots, n)$ with f^* linear in each $[x_{j-1}, x_j]$, then by Theorem 39.2,

$$\left| \int_{a}^{b} f \, dg - \int_{a}^{b} f^* \, dg \right| \leqslant \varepsilon M, \qquad \left| \int_{a}^{b} f \, dg(u,.) - \int_{a}^{b} f^* \, dg(u,.) \right| \leqslant \varepsilon M$$

Hence we need only assume $f = f^*$. We can also replace g by $g - g(a)$, and so assume that $g(a) = 0$, and similarly, that $g(u, a) = 0$.

Integrating by parts, using an extension of *Ex. 39.5*,

$$\left| \int_a^b f\,dg(u,.) - \int_a^b f\,dg \right|$$

$$= \left| f(b)\{g(u,b) - g(b)\} - \int_a^b \{g(u,x) - g(x)\}f'(x)\,dx \right|$$

$$\leqslant |f(b)|\,|g(u,b) - g(b)| + k\int_a^b |g(u,x) - g(x)|\,dx$$

where k is the maximum gradient of the finite number of lines forming the graph of f. Applying (39.11; 39.12) gives (39.13).

Note that f cannot even be 1 in $a \leqslant x \leqslant t$, and 0 in $t < x \leqslant b$, for some t in $a < t < b$, for then (39.13) becomes $g(u, t+) \to g(t+)$, which is not necessarily true.

We now turn to a result of Helly (1921).

THEOREM 39.8. *Let the family $g(u,.)(u \to \infty)$ of functions be such that their variation in $[a, b]$ is bounded by M independent of u. Then there are a sequence $u_j \to +\infty$, and a function g of bounded variation in $[a, b]$, with $\lim_{j \to \infty}\{g(u_j, x) - g(u_j, a)\} = g(x) - g(a)$ ($a < x \leqslant b$).*

Proof. Clearly we can assume that $g(u, a) = 0$. Taking real and imaginary parts, and then

$$\mathrm{var}\,(g(u,.);\,[a, x]) \pm g(u, x)$$

we can assume that $g(u, x)$ is monotone increasing in x. For if two families $g(u, x)$, $h(u, x)$ satisfy the same conditions, and also the conclusion, there is a sequence $\{u_j\}$ for which $g(u_j, x) \to g(x)$, and since the family of $h(u_j, x)$ is of the same kind, there is a subsequence $\{v_j\}$ of $\{u_j\}$ for which $h(v_j, x)$ tends to $h(x)$, and then

$$ag(v_j, x) + bh(v_j, x) \to ag(x) + bh(x)$$

Let $0 = g(u, a) \leqslant g(u, x) \leqslant M (a \leqslant x \leqslant b)$, where $g(u, x)$ is monotone increasing in x. Let $\{r_m\}$ be the sequence of rational numbers in $[a, b]$. Since $g(u, r_1)$ is bounded it has a limit-point, and there is a subsequence $\{u_j^1\}$ for which $g(u, r_2)$ tends to the limit-point, unless $g(u, r_1)$ takes only a finite number of values, when again we can choose a suitable subsequence. Next, in a similar way, we can find a subsequence $\{u_j^2\}$ of $\{u_j^1\}$, such that $g(u_j^2, r_2)$ tends to a limit, and so on. The diagonal sequence $\{u_j^j\}$ lies in $\{u_j^m\}$ for all $j \geqslant m$, so that $g(u_j^j, r_m)$ tends to the limit, say, $g(r_m)$, as $j \to \infty$, for each $m = 1, 2, 3, \ldots$

We now put

$$\liminf_{j \to \infty} g(u_j^j, x) = \underline{g}(x), \qquad \limsup_{j \to \infty} g(u_j^j, x) = \bar{g}(x)$$

and if equal, we write $g(x)$ as the common value, e.g.

$$(39.15) \qquad g(r_m) = \bar{g}(r_m) = \underline{g}(r_m)$$

Clearly $\underline{g}$ and $\bar{g}$ are monotone increasing in $[a, b]$, with $\underline{g}(a) = \bar{g}(a) = 0$, and with values bounded by M, so that they are of bounded variation, and so are continuous except for a countable number of discontinuities, their points of continuity being dense in $[a, b]$, by Theorem 39.3. If $\underline{g}$, $\bar{g}$ are continuous at $y \in (a, b)$, let $r_m < y < r_n$. By monotonicity, and then continuity,

$$g(u_j^j, r_m) \leqslant g(u_j^j, y) \leqslant g(u_j^j, r_n), \qquad g(r_m) \leqslant \underline{g}(y) \leqslant \bar{g}(y) \leqslant g(r_n),$$
$$\underline{g}(y) = \bar{g}(y)$$

Thus there remain b and the points of discontinuity of either or both of $\underline{g}$, $\bar{g}$. As the set of points is countable we can proceed as for the rationals and obtain a subsequence of $\{u_j^j\}$ to prove the result.

Ex. 39.1. Show that a constant function is Riemann–Stieltjes integrable relative to any function finite on $[a, b]$. Show that a finite sum of multiples of monotone increasing functions finite everywhere on $[a, b]$, is of bounded variation on $[a, b]$. Show that the function

$$(39.16) \qquad f(x) = x^2 \cdot \sin(x^{-2}) \qquad (x \neq 0), \quad f(0) = 0$$

is not of bounded variation in any interval including $x = 0$. Hence show that we cannot split up f into a finite number of monotone increasing functions g for which the integral of 1 relative to g can be defined by Darboux's method.

Ex. 39.2. Show that the derivative of (39.16) exists everywhere as

$$f'(0) = 0, \qquad f'(x) = 2x \cdot \sin(x^{-2}) - 2x^{-1} \cos(x^{-2}) \qquad (x \neq 0)$$
$$(39.17)$$

Ex. 39.3. If $g(x) = 0(x < \frac{1}{2}(a+b))$, 1 otherwise, then g is Riemann integrable in $[a, b]$ with value $\frac{1}{2}(b-a)$.

Ex. 39.4. If g is of bounded variation, prove that it is Riemann integrable. (Using var $(g) \pm g$ we can assume that g is monotone increasing. Or we can use Theorem 39.3, dealing with each singularity separately.)

Ex. 39.5. Prove that if g is of bounded variation,

$$\int_a^b x \, dg + \int_a^b g \, dx = bg(b) - ag(a)$$

(Use $a = x_0 < x_1 < \ldots < x_n = b$, with $x_{j-1} < \xi_j < x_j$, for one, and $a < \xi_1 < \xi_2 < \ldots < \xi_n < b$, with $\xi_j < x_j < \xi_{j+1}$, for the other.)

Ex. 39.6. If $\varphi = 1$ in $x > 0$, show that $\psi = 0$ in $0 \leq x \leq 1$, with (39.8).

Ex. 39.7. Find a φ that gives

$$\psi(y) = y + \sum \{2^{-m} : r_m < y\}$$

where $\{r_m\}$ is an arbitrary sequence of distinct numbers in $(0, 1)$. Show that the derivative of φ lies between 0 and 1. (Hence φ is absolutely continuous and is the Lebesgue integral of its derivative (see Henstock and Macbeath (1953), p. 187).

Ex. 39.8. If φ is the function of Ex. 12.7 for Cantor's ternary set, find the corresponding ψ.

Ex. 39.9. Let φ be finite and monotone *decreasing* in $[0, c]$, and let ψ be the inverse function of $-\varphi$. Then if $0 \leq a < b \leq c$,

$$\int_a^b \varphi \, dx - \int_{-\varphi(a)}^{-\varphi(b)} \psi \, dy = [x\varphi(x)]_a^b$$

Ex. 39.10. If $r > 1$, $x > 0$, and φ is finite and monotone increasing in $[0, \infty)$,

$$\Phi(x) \equiv \int_0^x \varphi(t) \, dt, \quad \Phi(rx) \geq \Phi(x) + (r-1) x\varphi(x) \geq r\Phi(x)$$

197

Ex. 39.11. If φ is monotone increasing in $[0, \infty)$ and is not identically 0, then, near to the origin,

$$\Psi(x) \equiv \int_0^x \psi(t)\, dt = O(x)$$

(There are numbers $a > 0$, $b > 0$, such that $\varphi(a) = b$, $a \geqslant \psi(b) \geqslant \psi(x)$ $(0 \leqslant x \leqslant b)$, $\Psi(x) \leqslant ax(0 \leqslant x \leqslant b)$.)

40. Young's, Hölder's, and Minkowski's Inequalities

In this section we study certain important inequalities that give special metrics, in order to define certain function spaces later. The inequalities come from a general inequality due to Young (1912) concerning inverse functions φ, ψ. Young assumes that φ, and so ψ, are continuous and strictly increasing, whereas Zaanen (1953), pp. 76–8 assumes only that φ, ψ are monotone increasing, and uses Lebesgue integration and Fubini's theorem. Henstock (1963c), pp. 131–2, assumes that φ is continuous and monotone increasing, and uses the variational integral. However, Theorem 39.5 enables us to assume the weak conditions of Zaanen and a simple proof that uses only Riemann integration.

THEOREM 40.1. *If* $0 \leqslant a \leqslant c$, $0 = \varphi(0) \leqslant b \leqslant \varphi(c)$, *then*

$$(40.1) \qquad \Phi(a) + \Psi(b) \geqslant ab, \quad \text{where} \quad \Phi(a) \equiv \int_0^a \varphi(x)\, dx,$$

$$\Psi(b) \equiv \int_0^b \psi(y)\, dy$$

Equality occurs in (40.1), *if, and only if,*

$$(40.2) \qquad \varphi(a) \leqslant b \leqslant \varphi(a+)$$

Proof. Since $\varphi(0) = 0$, ψ is defined in $[0, \varphi(c)]$; while the results are obvious if $a = 0$ or $b = 0$. Assuming $a > 0$, $b > 0$, if $y > \varphi(a+)$ then $\psi(y) > a$. Hence if $b > \varphi(a+)$, Theorem 39.5 (39.9) gives

$$\Phi(a) + \Psi(b) = \Phi(a) + \Psi(\varphi(a+)) + \int_{\varphi(a+)}^b \psi(y)\, dy$$

$$> a\varphi(a+) + a(b - \varphi(a+)) = ab$$

If $b < \varphi(a)$, there is a u in $0 \leqslant u < a$ with

$$\varphi(u) \leqslant b \leqslant \varphi(u+), \qquad \varphi(x) > b(u < x \leqslant a)$$

$$\Phi(a) + \Psi(b) = \Phi(u) + \Psi(b) + \int_u^a \varphi(x)\, dx > ub + b(a-u) = ab$$

by Theorem 39.5 (39.9) again. Hence if equality in (40.1) then (40.2) is true. Conversely, if (40.2) is true, Theorem 39.5 (39.9) gives equality.

For the first of two special cases, for fixed $p > 1$ let

$$y = \varphi(x) = x^{p-1}, \qquad x = \psi(y) = y^{1/(p-1)},$$

$$\Phi(x) = x^p/p, \qquad \Psi(y) = y^q/q$$

$$q = 1 + 1/(p-1) = p/(p-1), \qquad 1/p + 1/q = 1$$

(40.3) $\quad a^p/p + b^q/q \geqslant ab(a \geqslant 0,\ b \geqslant 0,\ p > 1,\ 1/p + 1/q = 1)$

(40.4) with equality if and only if $a^p = b^q$.

Secondly, let

$$\varphi(x) = 0(0 \leqslant x \leqslant e^{-1}), \qquad \log x + 1(x > e^{-1})$$

$$\psi(0) = 0, \qquad \psi(y) = e^{y-1}(y > 0), \qquad \psi(0+) = e^{-1}$$

$$\Phi(x) = 0(0 \leqslant x \leqslant e^{-1}), \qquad x \log x + e^{-1}(x > e^{-1});$$

$$\Psi(y) = e^{y-1} - e^{-1}$$

(40.5) $\qquad a \log a + e^{b-1} \geqslant ab(a \geqslant e^{-1},\ b \geqslant 0)$

with equality for $b = \log a + 1$. If $0 < a < e^{-1}$, $b \geqslant 0$, (40.1) gives

$$0 + e^{b-1} - e^{-1} \geqslant ab$$

As $a \log a$ has a minimum at $a = e^{-1}$ we have (40.5) again, with strict inequality. Hence (40.5) is true for $a > 0$, $b \geqslant 0$,

(40.6) with equality if and only if $a \geqslant e^{-1}$ and $b = \log a + 1$.

H. Kestelman has given me a simple proof of (40.5; 40.6) when $a \geqslant e^{-1}$. The graph of e^{y-1} lies above its tangents. In particular, at $y = 1 + \log a$,

$$e^{b-1} \geqslant ba - a \log a$$

with equality only at the point of contact, $b = 1 + \log a$.

Let X be a space, R^+ the space of non-negative real numbers, and $\mathscr{H}^+$ the space of all functions $f: X \to R^+$. In $\mathscr{H}^+$ we define, for each constant $c \geqslant 0$,

$$f \geqslant g, \quad h = f+g, \quad k = |f-g|, \quad l = cf, \quad f = 0$$

to occur, when, for all $x \in X$, respectively,

$$f(x) \geqslant g(x), \quad h(x) = f(x)+g(x), \quad k(x) = |f(x)-g(x)|,$$
$$l(x) = cf(x), \quad f(x) = 0$$

A functional L in $\mathscr{H}^+$ is *linear*, if, for each constant $c \geqslant 0$,

$$L(f+g) = L(f)+L(g); \quad L(f-g) = L(f)-L(g)\,(f \geqslant g);$$
$$L(cf) = cL(f)$$

in the sense that the left sides exist when the right sides exist. These conditions are all necessary, since $f \geqslant 0$ in $\mathscr{H}^+$. Also L is *non-negative*, if $L(f) \geqslant 0$ where it exists.

(40.7) If L is non-negative and linear, if $L(f)$, $L(g)$ exist, and if $f \geqslant g$, then $L(f) \geqslant L(g)$.

$$h = f-g \in \mathscr{H}^+, \quad L(f) = L(g)+L(h) \geqslant L(g)$$

A function $N \in \mathscr{H}^+$ is a *null function for* L, if $L(N)$ exists and is 0. A set $Y \subseteq X$ is a *null set for* L, if there is a null function N for L, with $N(x) > 0$ for all $x \in Y$.

We now suppose that L satisfies:

(40.8) if Y is a null set for L, and if $f \in \mathscr{H}^+$ with $f(x) = 0(x \notin Y)$, then f is a null function for L.

THEOREM 40.2. *Let L be linear and non-negative, and satisfy* (40.8).
(40.9) *If f, g are null functions for L, so are $f+g$, cf, for each constant $c \geqslant 0$.*

(40.10) *If Y is contained in a null set for L, then Y is a null set for L.*

(40.11) *The union of two null sets for L, is a null set for L.*

(40.12) *If f, g are null functions for L, and $h \in \mathscr{H}^+$, $p > 0$, then $|f-g|$, hf, f^p, and all $h \leqslant f$, $h \in \mathscr{H}^+$, are null functions for L.*

(40.13) *Let $h \in \mathscr{H}^+$ include in its formula a fixed finite number of null* *functions, and let $h_0 \in \mathscr{H}^+$ be the result of replacing each of these null functions by 0. Then $h - h_0$ is a difference of two null functions for L.*

(40.14) *If $L(h)$ exists, and if $h(x) = h_0(x)$, except in a null set for L, then $L(h_0)$ exists and is equal to $L(h)$.*

Proof. The linearity of L gives (40.9), while (40.10) follows from the definition of a null set. For (40.11), let Y_1, Y_2 be two null sets for L. There are null functions N_j for L, with $N_j(x) > 0(x \in Y_j)$, for $j = 1, 2$, while by (40.9), $N_1 + N_2$ is a null function for L, and it is positive in $Y_1 \cup Y_2$. To prove (40.12) we begin with $|f-g|$. If $|f(x) - -g(x)| > 0$, then either $f(x) > 0$, and x is in a null set Y_1 for L, or $g(x) > 0$, and x is in a null set Y_2 for L, or both. The result follows from (40.8; 40.10; 40.11). The other functions are 0 except in a null set, so that (40.8) gives the results. The more general (40.13) follows from (40.8; 40.11) and the use of

$$h_1(x) = \sup\,(h(x) - h_0(x), 0), \quad h_2(x) = \sup\,(h_0(x) - h(x), 0)$$

$$(all \ x \in X)$$

These can also be used for (40.14),

$$L(h) = L(h + h_2) = L(h + h_2 - h_1) = L(h_0)$$

THEOREM 40.3. *For each $t \in X$ let $\varphi(t; x)$ be finite and monotone increasing in $[0, c(t)]$, for some $c(t) > 0$, with $\varphi(t; 0) = 0$, and let $\psi(t; y)$, $\Phi(t; a)$, $\Psi(t; b)$ be the related functions. Let $f, g \in \mathscr{H}^+$, let $a > 0$, $b > 0$ be constants with $af(t) \leqslant c(t)$, $bg(t) \leqslant \varphi(t; c(t))$ $(t \in X)$. If L is a non-negative linear functional for which the three terms in (40.15) exist, then*

$$(40.15) \qquad L(\Phi(.\,; af)) + L(\Psi(.\,; bg)) \geqslant abL(fg)$$

If the left side of (40.15) is 1 for $a = a_0$, $b = b_0$, then

$$(40.16) \qquad L(fg) \leqslant a_0^{-1} b_0^{-1}$$

If equality in (40.15) or (40.16), then a null set Y for L satisfies

$$(40.17) \qquad \varphi(t; af(t)) \leqslant bg(t) \leqslant \varphi(t; af(t)+) \qquad (t \notin Y)$$

and conversely.

Proof. By Theorem 40.1 (40.1),

$$E(t) \equiv \Phi(t; af(t)) + \Psi(t; bg(t)) - abf(t)g(t) \geqslant 0, \quad E \in \mathcal{H}^+$$

Hence (40.15) follows by linearity and non-negativeness of L. If equality there, then $L(E) = 0$, and E is a null function for L, and the set Y where $E(t) > 0$, is a null set for L. Outside Y we use (40.2) to have (40.17). As (40.16) is a special case of (40.15) for $a = a_0$, $b = b_0$, equality in (40.16) implies equality in (40.15) for these values, and (40.17) again. For the converse we use (40.2; 40.8).

In the first special case, $p(t) > 1$ varies with t, and we have

(40.18) $\qquad L(a^{p(\cdot)} f^{p(\cdot)}/p(.)) + L(b^{q(\cdot)} g^{q(\cdot)}/q(.))$

$$\geqslant abL(fg) \quad (1/p(t) + 1/q(t) = 1)$$

with equality if, and only if, for a null set Y for L,

(40.19) $\qquad a^{p(t)} f^{p(t)}(t) = b^{q(t)} g^{q(t)}(t) \qquad (t \notin Y)$

Similarly for the second special case. Much work has been carried out with (40.18), for example, see Sobczyk (1941), Nakano (1951), Halperin and Nakano (1953), Kalman (1958). But for simplicity we only consider the case when $p(t)$ is a constant $p > 1$, in which case (40.18) becomes

(40.20) $\qquad a^p L(f^p)/p + b^q L(g^q)/q \geqslant abL(fg)$

If neither f^p nor g^q is a null function for L, we take

$$a^p = L(f^p)^{-1}, \quad b^q = L(g^q)^{-1}, \quad 1 = 1/p + 1/q \geqslant abL(fg)$$

(40.21) $\quad L(fg) \leqslant L(f^p)^{1/p} L(g^q)^{1/q} \qquad (p > 1, 1/p + 1/q = 1)$

Hölder's inequality. If f^p or g^q or both are null functions for L, then by (40.12), fg is a null function for L, and (40.21) is still true. If equality in (40.21), then (40.19), or the remarks on null functions, gives that

(40.22) $\qquad a^p f^p(x) = b^q g^q(x) \qquad (x \notin Y, a \geqslant 0, b \geqslant 0)$

where a, b are constants and Y is a null set.

THEOREM 40.4. *Let the non-negative linear functional L, and f,*

$g \in \mathcal{H}^+$, *have*

$$L(f^p), \quad L(g^p), \quad L((f+g)^{p-1}f), \quad L((f+g)^{p-1}g)$$

all existing. Then we have Minkowski's inequality

(40.23) $\qquad L((f+g)^p)^{1/p} \leqslant L(f^p)^{1/p} + L(g^p)^{1/p} \; (p \geqslant 1)$

(40.24) *Equality occurs in* (40.23) *when* $p = 1$; *and occurs when* $p > 1$, *if, and only if, there are constants* $a \geqslant 0$, $b \geqslant 0$, *and a null set* Y *for* L, *with*

$$af(x) = bg(x) \qquad (x \notin Y)$$

Proof. By linearity of L, (40.23) is true with equality when $p = 1$. Taking $p > 1$,

$$f \geqslant 0, \quad g \geqslant 0, \quad f+g \geqslant f, \quad f+g \geqslant g, \quad L((f+g)^p) \geqslant L(f^p),$$
$$L((f+g)^p) \geqslant L(g^p)$$
$$L((f+g)^p) = 0 \quad \text{implies} \quad L(f^p) = 0 = L(g^p)$$

and (40.23) is true with equality. Thus we take $L((f+g)^p) > 0$ and use Hölder's inequality, noting that $q(p-1) = p$,

$$L((f+g)^p) = L((f+g)^{p-1}f) + L((f+g)^{p-1}g)$$
$$\leqslant L((f+g)^p)^{1/q} L(f^p)^{1/p} + L((f+g)^p)^{1/q} L(g^p)^{1/p}$$

Dividing by the common factor, we have (40.23). In this case equality occurs in (40.23) if, and only if, both Hölder inequalities are equalities, so that (40.24) results from (40.22) twice, and Theorem 40.2 (40.11).

Historical Note. The original papers are Hölder (1889) and Minkowski (1896).

41. Spaces of Functions

Let X be a space, R the space of real (or complex) numbers, and $\mathcal{H}$ a linear space of some functions $f : X \to R$. We suppose that

(41.1) $\qquad$ if $\quad f \in \mathcal{H} \quad$ then $\quad |f| \in \mathcal{H}, \quad (1/\operatorname{sgn} f) \in \mathcal{H}$

where $\operatorname{sgn} z = z/|z| \; (z \neq 0)$, $\operatorname{sgn} 0 = 1$,

(41.2) if $f \in \mathcal{H}$, and if $p > 0$ is a constant, then $f^p \in \mathcal{H}$ where if f is complex, f^p denotes some particular choice of $f^p(x)$ (when many valued) for each $x \in X$.

By linearity and (41.2), if $f, g \in \mathcal{H}$ then

$$fg = \tfrac{1}{4}\{(f+g)^2 - f^2 - g^2\} \in \mathcal{H}$$

Let L be a non-negative linear functional in $\mathcal{H}^+$. We suppose that if $f \in \mathcal{H}$ then either $L(|f|)$ exists and is finite, or $L(|f|)$ has the conventional value $+\infty$, and we suppose that the linearity in $\mathcal{H}^+$ extends to values $+\infty$. Since $\mathcal{H}$ is also linear, if $f, g \in \mathcal{H}$,

(41.3) $$L(|f+g|) \leqslant L(|f|) + L(|g|)$$

Thus $L(|f|)$ can serve as a pseudonorm in L_1, the linear subspace of $\mathcal{H}$ in which $L(|f|)$ is finite.

More generally, let L_p be the space of $f \in \mathcal{H}$ for which $L(|f^p|) = L(|f|^p)$ is finite, for some fixed $p > 1$. If $f, g \in L_p$ then $f, g \in \mathcal{H}$, $f+g \in \mathcal{H}$, and by using (41.1; 41.2) and Minkowski's inequality, L_p is a linear space and $L(|f|^p)^{1/p}$ is a pseudonorm on L_p.

If 0 is the only null function, the pseudonorms are norms. Otherwise we assume that

(41.4) $h \in \mathcal{H}$, if $|h|$ is a null function for L

We change $L_p(p \geqslant 1)$ as in *Exs. 10.1, 11.1*, saying that f, g are *equivalent*, if $|f-g|$ is a null function for L. By (40.9; 40.12) and the conditions on $\mathcal{H}$, this is an equivalence relation, and we replace L_p by the space L_{pc} of cosets in L_p. If $g \in L_{pc}$, there is an $f \in L_p$, for which g is a set of functions $f+h$, where the $|h|$ are null functions for L. By (40.13; 40.14),

$$L(|f+h|^p)^{1/p} = L(|f|^p)^{1/p}$$

and every $f+h$ in the set g has the same pseudonorm, which can therefore be used as the pseudonorm of $g \in L_{pc}$. It is a norm, since $L(|f|^p) = 0$ implies that $|f|^p$, and so $|f|$, are null functions for L, and f lies in the same coset as 0. We write the norm, and the corresponding pseudonorm, as $\|\cdot\|_p$, and L_{pc} as L_p.

As $p \to 1$, with $1/p + 1/q = 1$, then $q \to \infty$, and Hölder's inequality does not hold in this case. However, we define

$$\text{ess sup}_{x \in X} |f(x)| = \inf_{h \in \mathcal{N}} \sup_{x \in X} |f(x) + h(x)|$$

where $\mathcal{N}$ is the family of $h \in \mathcal{H}$ with $L(|h|) = 0$. Let L_∞ be the space of $f \in \mathcal{H}$ with finite

$$\|f\|_\infty \equiv \text{ess sup}_{x \in X} f(x)$$

THEOREM 41.1. $\|f\|_\infty$ *is a pseudonorm in* L_∞, *a linear space.*
Proof. Given $f_j \in L_\infty$, $\varepsilon > 0$, we take $h_j \in \mathcal{N}$ with

$$\sup_{x \in X} |f_j(x) + h_j(x)| < \text{ess sup}_{x \in X} |f_j(x)| + \tfrac{1}{2}\varepsilon \qquad (j = 1, 2)$$

By Theorem 40.2 (40.13), $h_1 + h_2 \in \mathcal{N}$. Further,

$$\text{ess sup}_{x \in X} |f_1(x)| + \text{ess sup}_{x \in X} |f_2(x)| + \varepsilon > \sup_{x \in X} |f_1(x) + h_1(x)|$$

$$+ \sup_{x \in X} |f_2(x) + h_2(x)| \geqslant |f_1(x) + h_1(x)| + |f_2(x) + h_2(x)|$$

$$\geqslant |\{f_1(x) + f_2(x)\} + \{h_1(x) + h_2(x)\}|$$

$$\text{ess sup}_{x \in X} |f_1(x)| + \text{ess sup}_{x \in X} |f_2(x)| + \varepsilon \geqslant \sup_{x \in X} |\{f_1(x) + f_2(x)\}$$

$$+ \{h_1(x) + h_2(x)\}| \geqslant \text{ess sup}_{x \in X} |f_1(x) + f_2(x)|$$

The results follow since $\varepsilon > 0$ is arbitrary.

THEOREM 41.2. *If* $f, g \in \mathcal{H}$ *then*

$$L(|fg|) \leqslant L(|f|) \, \|g\|_\infty$$

Proof. For each $h \in \mathcal{N}$, by (40.13; 40.14; 40.7),

$$L(|fg|) = L(|f| \cdot |g + h|) \leqslant L(|f| \cdot \sup_{x \in X} |g(x) + h(x)|)$$

$$= L(|f|) \cdot \sup_{x \in X} |g(x) + h(x)|.$$

By choice of h we have Theorem 41.2, a Hölder inequality for this case.

We say that L_p and L_q are *complementary spaces* when $1/p + 1/q = = 1$, where $1 < p < \infty$, or where $p = 1$, $q = \infty$. Thus L_2 is complementary to itself.

A finite or infinite sequence $\{f_n\}$ of functions of $\mathscr{H}$, is said to be *orthogonal*, if $L(f_j \bar{f}_k) = 0$ for all indices j, k with $j \neq k$, the bar denoting the complex conjugate here. In this connection $\{f_n\}$ is said to be *normal*, if

$$L(|f_j|^2) = L(f_j \bar{f}_j) = 1 \qquad (all \ j)$$

A sequence that is orthogonal and normal, is called *orthonormal*. In this connection we have the theorem of Riesz (1907) and Fischer (1907), originally proved for Lebesgue integrals L.

THEOREM 41.3. *Let $\{a_j\}$ be a sequence of complex constants satisfying*

(41.5) $$\sum_{j=1}^{\infty} |a_j|^2 < \infty,$$

and let $\{f_j\}$ be an (infinite) orthonormal sequence in $\mathscr{H}$. If L_2 is complete for the norm $\| \cdot \|_2$, there is an $f \in L_2$ to which the series

(41.6) $$\sum_{j=1}^{\infty} a_j f_j(x)$$

converges, in norm $\| \cdot \|_2$, while for each integer n,

(41.7) $$a_n = L(f \bar{f}_n)$$

If $\{b_j\}$ is a second sequence of complex constants satisfying (41.5), giving rise to a $g \in L_2$, then we have a Parseval relation

(41.8) $$\sum_{j=1}^{\infty} a_j \bar{b}_j = L(f \bar{g})$$

(41.9) $$\sum_{j=1}^{\infty} |a_j|^2 = L(|f|^2)$$

Proof. Putting

$$k_n(x) = \sum_{j=1}^{n} a_j f_j(x)$$

and using orthonormality, and the convergence of (41.5), for $m > n$,

$$
\begin{aligned}
L(|k_m - k_n|^2) &= L((k_m - k_n)(\bar{k}_m - \bar{k}_n)) \\
&= L\left(\left(\sum_{j=n+1}^{m} a_j f_j(x)\right)\left(\sum_{j=n+1}^{m} \bar{a}_j \overline{f_j(x)}\right)\right) \\
&= \sum_{j=n+1}^{m}\sum_{r=n+1}^{m} a_j \bar{a}_r L(f_j \bar{f}_r) \\
&= \sum_{j=n+1}^{m} |a_j|^2 \to 0
\end{aligned}
$$

as $m, n \to \infty$. Hence $\{k_n(x)\}$ is a fundamental sequence in norm $\| \cdot \|_2$, and by completeness of L_2, there is an $f \in L_2$ to which k_n tends. Further, for $m > n$,

$$
\begin{aligned}
|a_n - L(f\bar{f}_n)| = |L(k_m \bar{f}_n) - L(f\bar{f}_n)| &= |L((k_m - f)\bar{f}_n)| \\
&\leqslant \|k_m - f\|_2 \cdot \|\bar{f}_n\|_2 = \|k_m - f\|_2 \to 0
\end{aligned}
$$

as $m \to \infty$. Finally, if, for each integer n,

$$
l_n(x) = \sum_{j=1}^{n} b_j f_j(x)
$$

where the b_j satisfy (41.5), then l_n tends to $g \in L_2$ in norm $\| \cdot \|_2$, and

$$
L(k_n l_n) = \sum_{j=1}^{n}\sum_{r=1}^{n} a_j \bar{b}_r L(f_j \bar{f}_r) = \sum_{j=1}^{n} a_j \bar{b}_j
$$

$$
k_n l_n - f\bar{g} = (k_n - f)\bar{g} + f(\bar{l}_n - \bar{g}) + (k_n - f)(\bar{l}_n - \bar{g})
$$

$$
\left|\sum_{j=1}^{n} a_j \bar{b}_j - L(f\bar{g})\right| \leqslant \|k_n - f\|_2 \|\bar{g}\|_2 + \|f\|_2 \|\bar{l}_n - \bar{g}\|_2
$$

$$
+ \|k_n - f\|_2 \|\bar{l}_n - \bar{g}\|_2 \to 0
$$

as $n \to \infty$, giving (41.8), and then (41.9) on taking $b_j = a_j$.

Proceeding further, we can define the *Orlicz spaces*, using the Young inverse functions $\varphi(t; x)$, $\psi(t; y)$, with integrals $\Phi(t; a)$, $\Psi(t; b)$, all depending on the extra variable t. We assume that if $f \in \mathcal{H}$ then

$\Phi(t; |f(t)|) \in \mathcal{H}$, and $\Psi(t; |f(t)|) \in \mathcal{H}$. Then L_Φ^* denotes the subspace of $\mathcal{H}$ for which

$$\|f\|_\Phi^* \equiv L\big(\Phi(t; |f(t)|)\big) < \infty$$

and similarly for Ψ. These spaces are not always linear so that (in the case when φ is independent of t) Orlicz defines linear spaces L_Φ, L_Ψ. Here we use $\varphi(t; \cdot)$. We put

$$\|f\|_\Phi = \sup L(|fg|), \quad \text{for all } g \text{ with} \quad \|g\|_\Psi^* \leqslant 1$$

$$\|g\|_\Psi = \sup L(|fg|), \quad \text{for all } f \text{ with} \quad \|f\|_\Phi^* \leqslant 1$$

The Orlicz spaces L_Φ, L_Ψ are the subspaces of $\mathcal{H}$ in which $\|f\|_\Phi$, $\|f\|_\Psi$ are finite, respectively.

THEOREM 41.4.

(41.10) L_Φ is linear and contains L_Φ^*, while if $f \in L_\Phi^*$ then

$$\|f\|_\Phi \leqslant \|f\|_\Phi^* + 1.$$

(41.11) $\qquad$ If $f \in L_\Phi \quad$ then $\quad \|f\|_\Phi = \sup |L(fg)|,$

$$\text{for all } g \text{ with} \quad \|g\|_\Psi^* \leqslant 1.$$

(41.12) $\qquad\qquad \|f_1 + f_2\|_\Phi \leqslant \|f_1\|_\Phi + \|f_2\|_\Phi.$

(41.13) $\qquad\qquad |L(fg)| \leqslant \|f\|_\Phi \cdot \max(1, \|g\|_\Psi^*).$

Proof. The linearity of L_Φ follows from the linearity of L, while if $f \in L_\Phi^*$, $\|g\|_\Psi^* \leqslant 1$, then by (40.15)

$$L(|fg|) \leqslant L(\Phi(., |f|)) + L(\Psi(., |g|)) \leqslant \|f\|_\Phi^* + 1$$

$$\|f\|_\Phi \leqslant \|f\|_\Phi^* + 1 < \infty, \quad f \in L_\Phi$$

For (41.11), for $g_1(x) = |g(x)|/\operatorname{sgn} f(x)$, we have

$$f(x) g_1(x) = |f(x) g(x)|,$$

$$\|g_1\|_\Phi^* = L(\Phi(., |g_1|)) = L(\Phi(., |g|)) = \|g\|_\Phi^*$$

The proof of (41.12) is straightforward.

For (41.13), using Ex. 39.10, we can assume that

$$1 < \|g\|_\Psi^* < \infty, \quad \Psi(t; |g(t)|/\|g\|_\Psi^*) \leqslant \Psi(t; |g(t)|)/\|g\|_\Psi^*,$$

$$\|g/\|g\|_\Psi^*\|_\Psi^* \leqslant 1, \quad |L(fg)| = \|g\|_\Psi^* |L(fg/\|g\|_\Psi^*)| \leqslant \|g\|_\Psi^* \|f\|_\Phi$$

Ex. 41.1. Show that $L_p = L_\Phi$ when $\varphi(x) = x^{p-1}$ $(p > 1)$; and for $p = 1$

$$\varphi(0) = 0, \quad \varphi(x) = 1(x > 0), \quad \psi(x) = 0(0 \leqslant x \leqslant 1),$$
$$\psi(x) = +\infty \quad (x > 1)$$
$$\Phi(x) = x(x \geqslant 0), \quad \Psi(x) = 0(0 \leqslant x \leqslant 1), \quad +\infty \ (x > 1)$$

Show that if $g \in L_\Psi^*$ then $|g(x)| \leqslant 1$ except in a null set; if we make the convention that f is a null function when zero outside a null set, even if infinite in a null set, then all $g \in \mathcal{H}$, $|g(x)| \leqslant 1$ except in a null set, have $g \in L_\Psi^*$. Show that $\|g\|_\Psi \leqslant$ ess sup $|g(x)|$, by using Theorem
$$ x \in X$$
41.2. Then prove the equality.

Ex. 41.2. If φ is independent of t, and if $\|f\|_\Phi = 0$, then f is a null function.

(From (41.13) with $|f|$, $|g|$ for f, g, we have $L(|fg|) = 0$ for all $g \in L_\Psi^*$. If g is constant at a value a in $0 < a < \varphi(c)$, and if I denotes the function identically equal to 1, then

$$\|g\|_\Psi^* = L(\Psi(a)) = \Psi(a) L(I) < \infty, \quad aL(|f|) = L(|fg|) = 0)$$

This requires the finiteness of $L(I)$.

10

THE GENERALIZED RIEMANN AND VARIATIONAL INTEGRALS

42. Introduction

IT IS well known that the limit of a convergent sequence of Riemann integrable functions need not be Riemann integrable. For example, the rationals can be put in a distinct sequence $\{r_n\}$. If $f_n(r_m)$ = 1($m \leqslant n$), and otherwise $f_n(x)$ is 0, then f_n is Riemann integrable while the limit function is not Riemann integrable (see after (39.1)). This limitation resulted in the development of Lebesgue integration, and there is no lack of textbooks on that theory. Here we give another approach; we use under another name the newer theory of Riemann-complete integration, and also of variational integration, referring the reader to Henstock (1963c) for details of two special cases that cover simple one-dimensional and two-dimensional integration.

Our integral is a modification of the definite and indefinite integrals of the calculus. It does not need a measure theory *ab initio*, and yet it includes all Lebesgue and Radon integrals, and all special Denjoy integrals. We gain the advantages of Lebesgue integration while retaining much of the simplicity of Riemann integration. For example, the property that, for bounded convergent sequences of functions,

$$\lim_{n \to \infty} \int_0^1 f_n(x)\, dx = \int_0^1 \lim_{n \to \infty} f_n(x)\, dx$$

holds in Lebesgue but not in Riemann integration. Since Lebesgue, it has been assumed that this is true since Lebesgue measure is completely additive, while Riemann (*i.e.* Jordan) measure is only finitely additive. *This view is completely false*, our integration has this property whatever the initial interval measure that is used. The precise property that gives the limit result will in the sequel be called *decomposability*.

The theory of Henstock (1963c) can be developed to deal with integrals of functions of points in spaces from which the usual measure spaces are developed and, in general, when a Lebesgue type integral can be defined, then also an integral of our type can be defined to include it. The list of examples at the end of this section includes, for example, one to cover the case of the Haar integral in locally compact groups.

As an introduction we begin as in Chapter 9. Let f be a function in $[a, b]$, and let $\mathcal{D}$ be a division $a = x_0 < x_1 < \ldots < x_n = b$. For ξ_j in $[x_{j-1}, x_j]$ we write

$$\sigma(\mathcal{D}) \equiv \sum_{j=1}^{n} f(\xi_j) (x_j - x_{j-1})$$

We can obtain each such value even if we restrict the ξ_j to lie at the ends of the intervals. For if $x_{j-1} < \xi_j < x_j$ then

$$f(\xi_j) (x_j - x_{j-1}) = f(\xi_j) (\xi_j - x_{j-1}) + f(\xi_j) (x_j - \xi_j)$$

Repeating for all such ξ_j we have a new division $\mathcal{D}'$ in which all ξ are at the ends of their intervals, and also $\sigma(\mathcal{D}) = \sigma(\mathcal{D}')$

Given a constant $\delta > 0$, with each point x in $[a, b]$ we associate all intervals $[t, x]$, $[x, t]$ that lie in $[a, b]$, with length $< \delta$, x being their *associated point*. A division $\mathcal{D}$ that uses such intervals and takes the ξ at the associated point x, is said to be *compatible with δ*, with *sum*

$$\sigma(\mathcal{D}) = \sum f(x) |x - t|.$$

Then the remarks on Riemann integration may be summed up as follows:

THEOREM *42.1. A number I is the Riemann integral of a function $f(x)$ in $a \leqslant x \leqslant b$, if, and only if, to each $\varepsilon > 0$ there corresponds a $\delta > 0$ such that every division $\mathcal{D}$ of $[a, b]$ that is compatible with δ, has sum $\sigma(\mathcal{D})$ satisfying*

$$|\sigma(\mathcal{D}) - I| < \varepsilon.$$

In order to obtain the corresponding Riemann-complete integral of Henstock (1963c), Chapter 2, we need only replace the constant $\delta > 0$ by a function $\delta(x) > 0$ in the definition of compatibility and in Theorem 42.1. Then the property described in the theorem defines the integral.

The indefinite integral or anti-derivative of the calculus is also a Riemann-complete integral (Henstock (1963c), p. 7, section 4). For example, the function (39.17) of *Ex. 39.2* can be integrated by the Calculus, and so by the Riemann-complete integral, to give the function (39.16). But (39.17) is not Lebesgue integrable, because of the second term in $f'(x)$. The special Denjoy integral was designed to cover the deficiencies of the Lebesgue integral in this respect, but we need no longer go to such lengths.

In the next sections we generalize the theory of the Riemann-complete integral as in Henstock (1961b). But instead of using numbered axioms, it now seems best to develop a collection of names like that in the theory of measure spaces. Everything is based on the idea of a *division*, so that now we omit the word 'complete', reserving it for use with fundamental sequences. In consequence we can no longer call the integral 'Riemann-complete'. Instead we call it the *generalized Riemann integral*.

43. The Space of Definition

For the integration theory of this book we need a general space R of definition, the space K of real or complex values, and a function of certain sets of points in R with values in K. Those interested in a more general K can find details in Henstock (1963c), Chapter 9, pp. 140–3. Conflation of these with the present theory will give what is required.

We use certain non-empty sets $I \subseteq R$, calling them *(generalized) intervals,* and we denote their family by $\mathscr{S}$. It is convenient to exclude the empty set from $\mathscr{S}$, so that we can say that two intervals are *non-overlapping,* if no $I \in \mathscr{S}$ lies in both. A set $E \subseteq R$ is an *elementary set,* if E is an interval or a finite union of non-overlapping intervals. Two elementary sets are *non-overlapping*, if no $I \in \mathcal{S}$ lies in both. Then the union of two non-overlapping elementary sets is also an elementary set.

A *division* $\mathcal{D} \equiv \mathcal{D}(I)$ of E is either a single interval $I = E$, or a finite number of non-overlapping intervals I with union E. Thus E is an elementary set. A subfamily $\mathcal{S}_1 \subseteq \mathcal{S}$ is a *division collection for* E, if there is a division of E formed from some or all of the intervals of $\mathcal{S}_1$, so that E is again an elementary set.

In the integration we use a non-negative function $\mu(I)$ of the (generalized) interval I, multiplying $\mu(I)$ by the value $f(x)$ of a function f at a point x associated in some way with I. Abstracting this idea, we need an index set Γ, and a function $x(\gamma; I)$ of $\gamma \in \Gamma$, $I \in \mathcal{S}$, with values the points of R. Then we call $x(\gamma; I)$ the *associated point of* I, *relative to* γ, evaluating f at this point. Often, for some particular topology, I has closure $\bar{I}$, with $x(\gamma; I) \in \bar{I}$. If, for each $\gamma \in \Gamma$ there is some $\mathcal{S}_\gamma \subseteq \mathcal{S}$, we can write $\mathbf{S}$ for the vector with components $\mathcal{S}_\gamma$. Then, to carry over the idea of a division collection into this situation, we say that $\mathbf{S}$ *divides* E, if

$$\mathcal{S}. \equiv \bigcup_{\gamma \in T} \mathcal{S}_\gamma$$

is a division collection for E. If $\mathcal{D}$ is a division obtained from $\mathcal{S}.$, we can associate with $\mathcal{D}$ a specification giving the $\gamma \in \Gamma$ corresponding to each $I \in \mathcal{D}$, so that $I \in \mathcal{S}_\gamma$, and we denote the division and specification by the general symbol $\mathcal{D}_\Gamma$, saying that $\mathcal{D}_\Gamma$ *comes from* $\mathbf{S}$. Sometimes an $I \in \mathcal{D}$ is in more than one $\mathcal{S}_\gamma$, and then, for fixed $I \in \mathcal{D}$, we can still vary $\mathcal{D}_\Gamma$ by varying the choice of γ.

Restrictions on $\mathcal{S}$ cannot always describe completely those $\mathbf{S}$ to be used in the theory, so that we proceed by supposing that the $\mathbf{S}$ we use lie in a family $\mathcal{A}$ of $\mathbf{S}$. The family $\mathcal{A}$ is said to *divide all elementary sets*, if, given an arbitrary elementary set $E \subseteq R$, there is an $\mathbf{S} \in \mathcal{A}$ that divides E. This is a basic requirement for our integration.

We say that $\mathcal{A}$ *is partially ordered in the sense of divisions*, if, given $\mathbf{S}_1$ and $\mathbf{S}_2$ in $\mathcal{A}$ that both divide E, there is a vector $\mathbf{S}_3 \in \mathcal{A}$ that divides E and is such that

$$\mathcal{S}_{3\gamma} \subseteq \mathcal{S}_{1\gamma} \cap \mathcal{S}_{2\gamma} \qquad (\gamma \in \Gamma).$$

If $\gamma \in \Gamma$ and S divides E, we define $X(\gamma; E; S)$ to be the set of associated points $x(\gamma; I)$, for all $I \subseteq E$ with $I \in \mathcal{S}_\gamma$. Then we say that the associated points are *stable relative to $\mathcal{A}$*, if, for each elementary set E and each $\gamma \in \Gamma$, $X(\gamma; E; S)$ depends only on γ and E, being independent of the $S \in \mathcal{A}$ that divide E. We can then omit S from the symbol, writing $X(\gamma; E)$.

We can define the *sum* $S_1 + S_2$ of S_1 and S_2 as the vector with components

$$\mathcal{S}_{1\gamma} \cup \mathcal{S}_{2\gamma} \qquad (\gamma \in \Gamma).$$

THEOREM 43.1. *If S_1, S_2 divide the non-overlapping E_1, E_2, respectively, then $S_1 + S_2$ divides $E_1 \cup E_2$.*

Proof. If $\mathcal{D}^k(I^k)$ is a division of E_k from S_k ($k = 1, 2$,) then no I^1, I^2 overlap as E_1, E_2 do not. Hence the combined set of I^1, I^2, with the given associated points, forms a division of $E_1 \cup E_2$ with specification, and comes from $S_1 + S_2$.

We can say that $\mathcal{A}$ is *additive*, if we have $S_1 + \ldots + S_k \in \mathcal{A}$ when there are non-overlapping sets $E_1, \ldots, E_k$, such that $S_j \in \mathcal{A}$ and divides E_j, and $\mathcal{S}_{j\gamma}$ consists only of intervals contained in E_j, for $j = 1, \ldots, k$, and all $\gamma \in \Gamma$.

If S divides $E_1 \cup E_2$, where E_1, E_2 are non-overlapping elementary sets, then the *restriction of S to E_j* is the vector with components

$$\{I : I \in \mathcal{S}_\gamma, \quad I \subseteq E_j\} \qquad (\gamma \in \Gamma, \quad j = 1,2).$$

If, for each non-overlapping elementary sets E_1, E_2, and each $S \in \mathcal{A}$ that divides $E_1 \cup E_2$, the restriction of S to E_j is in $\mathcal{A}$ and divides E_j ($j = 1, 2$), we can say that $\mathcal{A}$ *has the restriction property*.

A triple $(R, \mathcal{S}, \mathcal{A})$ can be called a *division space*, if $\mathcal{A}$ divides all elementary sets, is partially ordered in the sense of divisions, is additive, and has the restriction property, the associated points being stable relative to $\mathcal{A}$. On a division space we can set up an integral with properties like those of the Riemann integral, except for properties connected with Fubini's theorem.

Before imposing more properties on the space, we prove a collection of simple results. First, if E_1, E are elementary sets with $E_1 \subset E$, there might not always be an elementary set E_2 non-overlapping with E_1, such that the union of E_1, E_2, is E. However, the partial sets that we shall now define, have this property.

A *partial division* Q of an elementary set E, is a collection of none, some, or all I from a division $\mathcal{D}(I)$ of E that comes from some $\mathbf{S} \in \mathcal{A}$ that divides E. If with the intervals of Q we associate a specification for γ that is obtained from $\mathcal{D}_\Gamma$, we write Q_Γ. A *partial set E_1 of E*, is the union of the I from a partial division of E. Then the set E_2 is the union of the rest of the intervals of $\mathcal{D}(I)$. For convenience we can write $E - E_1$ for E_2.

Let $\mathcal{D}$, $\mathcal{D}'$ be two divisions of an elementary set E. We say that $\mathcal{D}' \leqslant \mathcal{D}$, if each $I \in \mathcal{D}$ is a finite union of some I of $\mathcal{D}'$.

THEOREM 43.2. *Let $(R, \mathcal{S}, \mathcal{A})$ be a division space.*

(43.1) *If E_1 is a partial set of E, and if $\mathbf{S} \in \mathcal{A}$ divides E, then $\mathbf{S}$ divides E_1.*

(43.2) *If $\mathcal{D}$ is a division of E from an $\mathbf{S} \in \mathcal{A}$ that divides E, there is an $\mathbf{S}^* \in \mathcal{A}$ that divides E, such that $\mathcal{D}' \leqslant \mathcal{D}$ for each division $\mathcal{D}'$ of E from $\mathbf{S}^*$.*

(43.3) *Let non-overlapping E_1, E_2 each be partial sets of E. Then $E_1 \cup E_2$ is also a partial set of E.*

(43.4) *Let E_1 be a partial set of E, and Q a partial division of E formed of intervals with union non-overlapping with E_1, such that their union with E_1 is E. If Q is from $\mathbf{S} \in \mathcal{A}$ that divides E, and if $\mathbf{S}_1 \in \mathcal{A}$ divides E_1, then there is a division $\mathcal{D}$ of E_1 from $\mathbf{S}_1$ such that $Q \cup \mathcal{D}$ is a division of E from $\mathbf{S}$.*

Proof. For (43.1) let E_1 come from a division $\mathcal{D}_1$ of E. Then we can use $E_2 = E - E_1$, so that as $\mathcal{A}$ has the restriction property, the restriction of $\mathbf{S}$ to E_1, and so $\mathbf{S}$ itself, divide E_1.

For (43.2), since $\mathcal{A}$ has the restriction property, there is an $\mathbf{S}(I) \in \mathcal{A}$ that divides I, for each $I \in \mathcal{D}$. By Theorem 43.1, since $\mathcal{A}$ is additive, the sum $\mathbf{S}^*$ of the $\mathbf{S}(I)$ divides E and lies in $\mathcal{A}$, and by construction, $\mathcal{D}' \leqslant \mathcal{D}$ for each division $\mathcal{D}'$ of E from $\mathbf{S}^*$.

For (43.3) let E_j be formed from a partial division from $\mathcal{D}_j$, which in turn is from $\mathbf{S}_j \in \mathcal{A}$ that divides E. Let $E_{j+2} = E - E_j$.

Then the intervals of the partial divisions forming E_j, E_{j+2} do not overlap. Let $\mathbf{S}_{j+2}$, $\mathbf{S}_{j+4}$ be the restrictions of $\mathbf{S}_j$ to the intervals of E_j, E_{j+2}, all for $j = 1, 2$. Then there is an $\mathbf{S}_7 \in \mathcal{A}$ that divides E and satisfies

$$\mathcal{S}_{7\gamma} \subseteq (\mathcal{S}_{3\gamma} \cup \mathcal{S}_{5\gamma}) \cap (\mathcal{S}_{4\gamma} \cup \mathcal{S}_{6\gamma}) \qquad (\gamma \in \Gamma)$$

We have used Theorem 43.1 and that $(R, \mathcal{S}, \mathcal{A})$ is a division space. The $\mathcal{S}_{7\gamma}$ are families of intervals that lie either in E_1 or in E_2 or in $E_3 \cap E_4$. Hence $E_1 \cup E_2$ is also a partial set.

For (43.4) let $\mathbf{S}_2$, $\mathbf{S}_3$ be the restrictions of $\mathbf{S}$ to E_1, and to the union E_2 of the intervals of Q. Since $(R, \mathcal{S}, \mathcal{A})$ is a division space, $\mathbf{S}_{j+1} \in \mathcal{A}$ and divides E_j, for $j = 1, 2$, and there is an $\mathbf{S}_4 \in \mathcal{A}$ that divides E_1, with

$$\mathcal{S}_{4\gamma} \subseteq \mathcal{S}_{1\gamma} \cap \mathcal{S}_{2\gamma}$$

If $\mathcal{D}$ is a division of E_1 from $\mathbf{S}_4$, then $\mathcal{D}$ is from $\mathbf{S}_1$, and $Q \cup \mathcal{D}$ is a division of E from $\mathbf{S}$, as required.

It will appear subsequently that in order to obtain good theorems on the limit of a sequence of integrals we have to proceed further. First,

$$\mathcal{S}_\gamma(X) \equiv \{I : I \in \mathcal{S}_\gamma, \quad x(\gamma; I) \in X\}, \quad for \quad \gamma \in \Gamma, \quad \mathbf{S} \in \mathcal{A}, \quad X \subseteq R.$$

This takes out of $\mathcal{S}_\gamma$ all intervals with associated point in X. Now let $\{\mathbf{S}_j\}$ be a finite or infinite sequence of members of $\mathcal{A}$, each dividing a fixed set E, and for the same j let $\{X_j\}$ be a sequence of mutually disjoint subsets of R. The union of the X_j need not be R nor E. If, for all such $\{\mathbf{S}_j\}$, $\{X_j\}$, E, there is an $\mathbf{S}^* \in \mathcal{A}$ that divides E, with

$$\mathcal{S}_\gamma^*(X_j) \subseteq \mathcal{S}_{j\gamma}(X_j) \qquad (\gamma \in \Gamma, \quad j = 1, 2, \ldots),$$

we say that $\mathcal{A}$ has decomposable vectors.

A similar and stronger condition is as follows. We say that $\mathcal{A}$ has fully decomposable vectors, if, for each elementary set E, and each family of vectors $\mathbf{S}(x, \gamma) \in \mathcal{A}$ that divide E and depend on $x \in R$, $\gamma \in \Gamma$, one vector to each pair (x, γ), there is an $\mathbf{S}^* \in \mathcal{A}$ that divides E, with

$$\mathcal{S}_\gamma^* (sing(x)) \subseteq \mathcal{S}_\gamma(x, \gamma)(sing(x)) \qquad (x \in R, \quad \gamma \in \Gamma)$$

This pointwise decomposition has affinities with Cantor's diagonal process.

We can now say that a division space $(R, \mathcal{S}, \mathcal{A})$ is *decomposable (fully decomposable)*, if $\mathcal{A}$ has decomposable (respectively, fully decomposable) vectors. Integration on a decomposable division space has all properties of the Lebesgue integral save those connected with Fubini's theorem.

For the latter we consider product spaces. Let R_x, R_y be spaces of points, and put

$$R_z = R_x \times R_y$$

For $t = x, y, z$ we add the extra suffix t to objects connected with R_t, this suffix being placed before every other suffix.

For $t = x, y$ let Γ_t be the index set for R_t, and let $\mathcal{S}_t$ be a family of some non-empty subsets I_t of R_t, called *(generalized) t-intervals*, and with *associated points* $t(\gamma_t; I_t)$ $(\gamma_t = \gamma(t) \in \Gamma_t)$. Then the index set for R_z is taken to be

$$\Gamma_z = \Gamma_x \times \Gamma_y, \quad \text{with} \quad \gamma_z = \gamma(z) = (\gamma_x, \gamma_y)$$

Also the family $\mathcal{S}_z$, of some non-empty $I_z \subseteq R_z$, is taken to be the family of all product sets

$$I_z = I_x \times I_y \quad (I_t \in \mathcal{S}_t, \quad t = x, y),$$

the I_z having *associated point*

$$z(\gamma_z; I_z) = (x(\gamma_x; I_x), y(\gamma_y; I_y))$$

We can then give the various definitions for $R_t(t = x, y, z)$ as for R. In particular, we have families $\mathcal{A}_t$ $(t = x, y, z)$ of vectors, and we suppose that the associated points are stable relative to $\mathcal{A}_t$ $(t = x, y)$. Then we can say that $\mathcal{A}_x$, $\mathcal{A}_y$, $\mathcal{A}_z$ *have the Fubini property in common*, if the following property holds.

Let E_x, E_y be arbitrary elementary sets, and let $\mathbf{S}_z$ be an arbitrary vector of $\mathcal{A}_z$ that divides $E_z = E_x \times E_y$. Then to each pair (x, γ_x) with $\gamma_x \in \Gamma_x$, $x \in X(\gamma_x; E_x)$, there corresponds an $\mathbf{S}_y(x; \gamma_x) \in \mathcal{A}_y$ that divides E_y. Further, to each collection of divisions $\mathcal{D}_y(x; \gamma_x)$ of E_y from $\mathbf{S}_y(x; \gamma_x)$, one division for each $(x; \gamma_x)$ $x \in X(\gamma_x; E_x)$, there corresponds an $\mathbf{S}_x \in \mathcal{A}_x$ that divides E_x, such that if

$$I_x \in \mathcal{S}_{x,\gamma(x)}, \quad x = x(\gamma_x; I_x), \quad I_y \in \mathcal{D}_y(x; \gamma_x), \quad y = y(\gamma_y; I_y)$$

then

$$I_z \equiv I_x \times I_y \in \mathcal{S}_{z,\gamma(z)}, \quad \gamma_z = (\gamma_x, \gamma_y), \quad z(\gamma_z; I_z) = (x, y).$$

This of course is unsymmetrical in x, y, so that we require also the corresponding property with x, y interchanged. If also $(R_t, \mathcal{S}_t, \mathcal{A}_t)$ $(t = x, y, z)$ are division spaces, we call $(R_z, \mathcal{S}_z, \mathcal{A}_z)$ a *product division space*.

As the Fubini property is an abstraction of the property in Henstock (1963c), p. 102, Theorem 41.2, we shall be able to use a generalization of the proof of Henstock (1963c), pp. 106–109, Theorem 44.1, to give Fubini's theorem, when the integral has been defined.

The Fubini property is rather complicated, so that the following definition and theorem are sometimes useful. Given

$$E_t, \gamma_t \quad (t = x, y), \quad \mathbf{S}_z, \quad x \in X(\gamma_x; E_x),$$

let $S_{y,\gamma(y)}$ denote the family of $I_y \subseteq E_y$ such that for $\gamma_z = (\gamma_x, \gamma_y)$ and some $I_x \subseteq E_x$ with $x = x(\gamma_x; I_x)$, we have $I_x \times I_y \in \mathcal{S}_{z,\gamma(z)}$. Then, for the fixed x, γ_x, the vector $\mathbf{S}_y$ is called the *section by* (x, γ_x) *of* $\mathbf{S}_z$.

THEOREM 43.3. *Let* $(R_t, \mathcal{S}_t, \mathcal{A}_t)$ *be fully decomposable division spaces, for* $t = x, y$. *Let* E_x, E_y, *be arbitrary elementary sets, with* $E_z = E_x \times E_y$. *Given* $\mathbf{S}_z \in \mathcal{A}_z$ *that divides* E_z, *let the section* $\mathbf{S}_y$ *by* (x, γ_x) *of* $\mathbf{S}_z$ *be in* $\mathcal{A}_y$, *dividing* E_y, *for each* $\gamma_x \in \Gamma_x$ *and each* $x \in X(\gamma_x; E_x)$. *Further, for each fixed* x, γ_x, I_y, *let there be an* $\mathbf{S}_x \in \mathcal{A}_x$ *that divides* E_x, *such that the set of* I_x *given in the definition of* $\mathbf{S}_y$, *is* $\mathcal{S}_{x,\gamma(x)}$ *(sing(x))*. *Let the similar property with* x, y *interchanged, also hold. Then* $(R_z, \mathcal{S}_z, \mathcal{A}_z)$ *is a product division space.*

Proof. In the definition of the Fubini property let $\mathbf{S}_y(x, \gamma_x)$ be the section by (x, γ_x) of $\mathbf{S}_z$, and let $\mathcal{D}_y(x, \gamma_x)$ be a division of E_y from $\mathbf{S}_y(x, \gamma_x)$. Then to each $I_y \in \mathcal{D}_y(x, \gamma_x)$ there is an $\mathbf{S}_x$ of the theorem, depending on x, γ_x, and I_y. Taking the finite product for all $I_y \in \mathcal{D}_y(x, \gamma_x)$, we have $\mathbf{S}_{x1}(x, \gamma_x)$ in $\mathcal{A}_x$. By the property of full decomposability, the separate $\mathbf{S}_{x1}(x, \gamma_x)$ link up to form an $\mathbf{S}_{x2}$, usable as the S_x of the Fubini property. A similar proof can be used when x, y are interchanged.

Ex. 43.1 For intervals take closed n-dimensional rectangles

$$I = \bigtimes_{j=1}^{n} [a_j, b_j], \qquad (a_j < b_j, \quad j = 1, 2, \ldots, n)$$

These sets are used in Burkill integration of rectangle functions, no associated points being needed. In Riemann and Riemann–Stieltjes integration the associated points lie anywhere in I, while if f, g are functions of $\mathbf{x} \equiv (x_1, \ldots, x_n)$, the rectangle functions are

$$f(\mathbf{x}) \Delta_1 \ldots \Delta_n g \qquad (\mathbf{x} \in I),$$

$$\Delta_j g \equiv g(x_1, \ldots, x_{j-1}, b_j, x_{j+1}, \ldots, x_n) - g(x_1, \ldots, x_{j-1}, a_j, x_{j+1}, \ldots, x_n)$$

$$(j = 1, 2, \ldots, n)$$

Show first that we can restrict each $\mathbf{x}$ to lie at a corner of I without altering the sum over a division. Further, take either

$$N_1 = \max_{1 < j < n} (b_j - a_j) \quad \text{or} \quad N_2 = \left\{ \sum_{j=1}^{n} (b_j - a_j)^2 \right\}^{1/2}$$

to be the norm of I, norm (I), the same function for each I, and for each elementary set E define norm $(E) = \max$ norm (I) $(I \subseteq E)$. (As $N_1 \leqslant N_2 \leqslant n^{1/2}N_1$, either has the same effect.) Then for Riemann, Riemann–Stieltjes, and Hellinger–Burkill integration (Hellinger (1907), Burkill (1924)) we include in $\mathcal{A}$ those S, and only those, for which S, some $\varepsilon > 0$, and some elementary set E, are such that each $\mathcal{S}_y$ includes no $I \nsubseteq E$, and includes at least all $I \subseteq E$ with norm $(I) < \varepsilon$. The largest such $\varepsilon \leqslant$ norm (E) is denoted by $\mathcal{M}(S; E)$. Show that $\mathcal{A}$ is a product division space, but that it does not have decomposable vectors.

(For example, $n = 1$, $E = [0, 1]$, $S_j \in \mathcal{A}$ with $\mathcal{M}(S_j; [0, 1]) < j^{-2}$ $(j = 1, 2, \ldots)$,

$$X_1 = \text{sing}\,(0), \quad X_j = (j^{-1}, (j-1)^{-1}] \qquad (j = 2, 3, \ldots)$$

Let S^* be the vector in the definition of decomposability, and let $S^* \in \mathcal{A}$. Then there is an integer $j > 1$ with $(2j)^{-1} < \mathcal{M}(S; [0, 1])$, so that if

$$I_j = [(2j)^{-1}, j^{-1}], \quad \text{norm}(I_j) = (2j)^{-1}, \quad I_j \in \mathcal{S}_\gamma \quad (\text{each } \gamma \in \Gamma). \quad \text{But}$$
$$(2j)^{-1} > (j+1)^{-2} > (2j+1)^{-2}, \quad (2j)^{-1} \in X_{2j+1}, \quad j^{-1} \in X_{j+1}, \quad I_j \notin \mathcal{S}_\gamma.)$$

Ex. 43.2. Let $\mathcal{D}$, $\mathcal{D}'$ be two divisions of an elementary set E in a general abstract set R of points. We define $\mathcal{D}' \preccurlyeq \mathcal{D}$ as in Theorem 43.2. If in $\mathcal{A}$ we include those $\mathbf{S}$, and only those, for which there is a division $\mathcal{D}$ of an elementary set E such that all $\mathcal{D}'$ over E with $\mathcal{D}' \preccurlyeq \mathcal{D}$, come from $\mathbf{S}$, we obtain Moore–Pollard integration. (This is called Pollard–Getchell integration in Henstock (1963c), pp. 8–9, section 5. But Professor T. H. Hildebrandt (1964) points out that he taught Getchell this type of integral, and himself obtained it from E. H. Moore as a special case of the general limit of Moore (1915).) We assume that:

(43.5) if $I \in \mathcal{S}$, there are $\mathbf{S} \in \mathcal{A}$, $\gamma \in \Gamma$, such that $I \in \mathcal{S}_\gamma$;

(43.6) if the overlapping $I_1, I_2 \in \mathcal{S}$, then $I_1 \cap I_2 \in \mathcal{S}$.

Assuming where necessary that the associated points are stable relative to $\mathcal{A}$, prove that $(R, \mathcal{S}, \mathcal{A})$ is a product division space. For $R = [0, 1]$ and the usual intervals, show that $\mathcal{A}$ does not have decomposable vectors.

Ex. 43.3. As in *Ex. 43.1* take rectangles with associated corner points, but with a new $\mathcal{A}$ that has the property of full decomposability. To each $\mathbf{S} \in \mathcal{A}$ there corresponds an elementary set E with the following property. To each $\mathbf{x} \in E$ there corresponds a *defining rectangle*

$$J(\mathbf{x}) = \underset{j=1}{\overset{n}{\times}} (a_j, b_j) \qquad (a_j < x_j < b_j, j = 1, 2, \ldots, n)$$

such that if $I \subseteq J(\mathbf{x}) \cap E$, $\mathbf{x}(\gamma; I) = \mathbf{x}$, then $I \in \mathcal{S}_\gamma$. Alternatively we can use a function $\delta(\mathbf{x}) > 0$, and replace $J(\mathbf{x})$ by the sphere $S(\mathbf{x}; \delta(\mathbf{x}))$. This $\mathcal{A}$ is used in the Riemann-complete and variational integration of Henstock (1963c), for $n = 1, 2$, and also the corresponding Perron and Ward integration. Show that $(R, \mathcal{S}, \mathcal{A})$ is a fully decomposable product division space.

THE GENERALIZED RIEMANN AND VARIATIONAL INTEGRALS

(To prove that $\mathcal{A}$ divides all elementary sets, see Henstock (1963c), p. 22, Theorem 16.1 ($n = 1$), and p. 101, Theorem 41.1 ($n = 2$). The case $n = 1$ has a curious history. Lebesgue (1909), pp. 30–3, shows that his integral is a limit of Riemann sums, but gives no explicit details. Lusin (1912) uses the idea for trigonometric series, and W. H. and G. C. Young (1915) state the result. The first incomplete proofs are in Kurzweil (1957), p. 423, Lemma 1,1,1, and independently in Henstock (1961a) pp. 129–30, Theorem 16. For the references to Lebesgue, Lusin, and the Youngs, I am indebted to Professors Hildebrandt and Verblunsky, and for the reference to Kurzweil I am indebted to Dr. K. Karták. The first proper developments of a Lebesgue-type theory are given in Henstock (1960c; 1961a, b; 1963c). The defect in my proof for $n = 1$ was pointed out by M. McCrudden. When the defining interval at x is $(x - \delta_1(x),\ x + \delta_2(x))$, the proof breaks down for the case when, for some j,

$$x_{j-1} < x_{j+1} - \delta_1(x_{j+1}) < x_{j-1} + \delta_2(x_{j-1}) < x_j - \delta_1(x_j)$$
$$< x_j < x_{j+1} < x_{j+1} + \delta_2(x_{j+1}) < x_{j+2} - \delta_1(x_{j+2})$$
$$< x_j + \delta_2(x_j) < x_{j+2}$$

These intervals are so interlocked that the removal of one uncovers part of the main interval. However, we may assume $\delta_1(x) = \delta_2(x)$, as here, and then the proof is sound.)

Ex. 43.4. To the space of *Exs. 43.1, 43.3* we can add conventional vectors $\mathbf{x}$ with $x_j = -\infty$ or $x_j = +\infty$, for one or more j. The $J(\mathbf{x})$ for these new $\mathbf{x}$ can be Cartesian products of (a_j, b_j), when x_j is finite, and of $(-\infty, b_j)$ $(x_j = -\infty)$, and $(a_j, +\infty)$ $(x_j = +\infty)$. Coupled with the Riemann system of *Ex. 43.1*, we can then deal directly with Cauchy–Riemann and allied integrals. But the infinite integral in complex variable theory is of a different type, consisting more or less of the limit of the line segment part of a semicircular contour, or two line parts of a circular wedge, so that the two ends of the lines do not tend to infinity independently.

Coupling *Exs. 43.3, 43.4*, enables us to deal directly with Cauchy–Lebesgue integrals, and special Denjoy integrals over infinite intervals, avoiding the extra limit process. For $n = 1$ see Henstock (1963c), pp. 115–18, section 47.

Ex. 43.5. As in Vitali's covering theorem, take fixed λ, μ in $0 < \lambda \leqslant \mu$, and assume that the ratios of edges of the rectangles of $\mathcal{S}$ in *Ex. 43.3* lie between λ and μ, with associated points at the corners. It is unknown whether this system divides all elementary sets.

Ex. 43.6. Let the rectangles of *Ex. 43.3* have associated points at their centres instead of their corners. Show that $\mathcal{A}$ divides all elementary sets. We could also take $m_j > 0(j = 1, 2, \ldots, n)$ and identify $\mathbf{x}$ with $\mathbf{y}$, if $x_j = y_j (\bmod m_j)(j = 1, \ldots, n)$. McGrotty (1962) proves the result when $n = 1$. Then $n > 1$ is straightforward.

Ex. 43.7. In *Ex. 43.6* add the restriction of *Ex. 43.5*. In particular take cubes (the case $\lambda = \mu$). The case of $n = 2$ and squares with associated points at their centres in $-\pi \leqslant x_j < \pi$ $(j = 1, 2)$, with $m_1 = 2\pi = m_2$, is useful in dealing with trigonometric series. See Henstock (1961a), pp. 109, 110. It is unknown whether $\mathcal{A}$ divides all elementary sets, and *Exs. 43.5, 43.6* were considered in order to throw light on this case.

Ex. 43.8. We need curved rectangles to include results like those of Whitney (1957).

Ex.43.9. Let the real interval $[a, b]$ be the union of a sequence $\{P_j\}$ of perfect sets. For $\mathcal{S}_l$ and each x there is a $\delta(x) > 0$, such that $\mathcal{S}_l$ includes those intervals I, and only those, with

$$I = [u, x]; \quad x - u < \delta(x); \quad x, u \in P_j \quad (j = 1, 2, \ldots)$$

Similarly we define $\mathcal{S}_r$. As each P_j is perfect, if $x \in P_j$, there is a sequence of distinct points of P_j tending to x, and each point of $[a, b]$ has either left-hand or right-hand intervals, or both. This gives the integration of Tolstov (1939) that is equivalent to the general Denjoy integral. Prove that $\mathcal{A}$ divides all elementary sets.

(Say that an elementary set $E \subseteq [a, b]$ is *admissible*, if $\mathbf{S} \equiv (\mathcal{S}_l, \mathcal{S}_r)$ is complete in each subinterval. If two admissible elementary sets abut or overlap, their union is admissible. If H is the union of interiors of all admissible elementary sets, and if the closed interval $I \subseteq H$, then by Borel's covering theorem, I is covered by a finite number of such interiors, and so is admissible. If $P = [a, b] \setminus H$ then P is closed. Disregarding a, b, then P contains no isolated point, and so is perfect. It is a $\mathcal{G}_\delta$-set by Theorem 18.1 (18.3). If $P \cap (a, b)$ is not empty, then by Baire's density theorem (Theorem 17.3), P is of the second category since $[a, b]$ is complete. Hence there are a closed interval J and an integer j, such that $J^\circ \cap P$ is not empty, and that P_j is dense in $J \cap P$. Hence $J \cap P \subseteq P_j$, so that each $x \in J \cap P$ is the centre of an interval $K(x) = (x - \delta(x), x + \delta(x))$ such that every interval $[t, x]$, $[x, t]$ in $K(x)$, with $t \in P$, comes from $\mathcal{S}_l \cup \mathcal{S}_r$. By Young's covering theorem a finite number of $K(x)$, and so of $[t, x]$, $[x, t]$, cover $J \cap P$. The intervals of J outside the cover are admissible and finite in number, so that J is admissible and $J \cap P$ empty. Hence at most, $a, b \in P$. But there are suitable intervals from a, b to show that $[a, b]$ is admissible, completing the proof.)

Ex. 43.10. In *Ex. 43.9*, for some integer j, P_j contains an interval over which we have the arrangement of *Ex. 43.3* for $n = 1$. (Use category.)

Ex. 43.11. Let M be a continuous non-atomic measure on the Borel sets of $[a, b]$, with $M((x, y)) > 0$ for all $(x, y) \subseteq (a, b)$. Let $\mathcal{S}_l$ be the family of all $[u, x] \subseteq [a, b]$ with $a < x \leqslant b$, and with u in a set of left lower M-density $\geqslant d_l$ at x; this set of u varies with x. Similarly for $\mathcal{S}_r$, in which $[u, x]$, l, are replaced by $[x, u]$, r. If d_l, d_r are independent of x with $d_l + d_r > 1$, show that $\mathcal{A}$ divides all elementary sets. (See Henstock (1961a), pp. 130–2, and Theorem 17. The case $d_l = d_r = 1$, with M as Lebesgue measure, corresponds to Burkill's approximate Perron integral, Burkill (1932).)

Ex. 43.12. Let **x** be a real infinite sequence $\{x_j\}$, either with $|x_j| \leqslant \frac{1}{2}$ $(j = 1, 2, \dots)$ as in section 61, or we can identify **x** with **y** when $x_j \equiv y_j \pmod 1$ $(j = 1, 2, \dots)$, which is the infinite dimensional torus space. Either space is denoted by W. The intervals are a finite product of $[a_j, b_j] \subseteq [-\frac{1}{2}, \frac{1}{2}]$, together with an infinite product of $[-\frac{1}{2}, \frac{1}{2}]$ for the remaining j. To each **S** there corresponds a function $n = n(\mathbf{x}) \geqslant 1$ and a function $\delta(\mathbf{x}) > 0$, such that if $\gamma = \{\gamma_1, \ldots, \gamma_n\}$, $\gamma_j = l$ or r $(1 \leqslant j \leqslant n)$, then all

$$\left\{ \underset{j=1}{\overset{n}{\times}} I_j \right\} \times \left\{ \underset{j=n+1}{\overset{\infty}{\times}} [-\tfrac{1}{2}, \tfrac{1}{2}] \right\} \in \mathcal{S}_\gamma; \qquad I_j = [u_j, x_j],$$

$$x_j - u_j < \delta(x_j)(\gamma_j = l)$$

$$I_j = [x_j, v_j], \quad v_j - x_j < \delta(x_j)(\gamma_j = r) \qquad (j = 1, 2, \ldots, n)$$

Prove that $(R, \mathcal{S}, \mathcal{A})$ is a fully decomposable product division space. (Use Tychonoff's theorem.)

Ex. 43.13. Take the space $\mathcal{C}[a, b]$ of continuous functions on $[a, b]$. To construct 'intervals' take a division $\mathcal{D}(a = x_0 < x_1 < \ldots < x_n = b)$, and $u_j < v_j$ $(j = 0, 1, \ldots, n)$ where some u_j can be $-\infty$, and some v_j can be $+\infty$. Then the 'interval' is the set of all continuous functions f on $[a, b]$ with

$$u_j \leqslant f(x_j) \leqslant v_j \qquad (j = 0, 1, \ldots, n)$$

The system blends ideas from *Ex. 43.4*, *43.12*, and can be made to cover Wiener and Feynman integration. However, the theories of these integrals are so complicated that they warrant a separate and careful investigation that cannot be given here.

Ex. 43.14. Let R be a $\mathcal{T}_3$-space, and $\mathcal{H}$ the family of all non-empty closures of $G \in \mathcal{G}$. Let the intervals $I \in \mathcal{S}$ be the *compact* members of $\mathcal{H}$. Then each elementary set is also in $\mathcal{S}$. To each point $x \in I \in \mathcal{S}$ let there correspond a $J(x) \in \mathcal{H}$ with $x \in J(x)^\circ$, such that $\mathcal{S}_1$ is the set of all $J \in \mathcal{H}$, $J \subseteq J(x)$, with $x \in J^\circ$, for all $x \in I$. From these J show that we can construct a non-overlapping finite cover of I from $\mathcal{S}_1$. This proves that $\mathcal{A}$ divides all elementary sets. If R is a locally compact topological group a Haar measure on $\mathcal{S}$ is definable, and then our integration process includes the Haar integral over compact sets in that group. For non-compact sets we proceed as in *Ex. 43.4*.

(As I is compact we can select from $\mathcal{S}_1$ a finite subset $F_1, \ldots, F_n$, corresponding to distinct points $x_1, \ldots, x_n$ of I, such that I lies in the union of the F_j° $(j = 1, 2, \ldots, n)$. Since R is a $\mathcal{T}_3$-space, there are disjoint $G_j \in \mathcal{G}$ with $x_j \in G_j$, and with $\bar{G}_j \subseteq F_j^\circ$, the $\bar{G}_j$ being disjoint $(j = 1, 2, \ldots, n)$. Put

$$G_j^* = F_j^\circ \Big\backslash \bigcup_{k \neq j} \bar{G}_k; \qquad \bigcup_{j=1}^{n} G_j^* \supseteq I, \qquad \bar{G}_k \cap \bar{G}_j^* \quad \text{empty} \quad (k \neq j)$$

Thus we can assume that the $F_1, \ldots, F_n$ satisfy $\bar{G}_k \cap F_j$ empty $(k \neq j)$, for disjoint neighbourhoods G_j of x_j $(j = 1, 2, \ldots, n)$. We define a sequence of non-overlapping open sets

$$G_{11} = F_1^\circ, \quad G_{12} = F_2^\circ \backslash G_{11}, \quad G_{13} = F_3^\circ \backslash (\bar{G}_{11} \cup \bar{G}_{12}), \ldots,$$
$$G_{1n} = F_n^\circ \backslash (\bar{G}_{11} \cup \ldots \cup \bar{G}_{1n-1})$$

with $x_j \in G_{1j}$ $(j = 1, 2, \ldots, n)$, and we show that

$$I \subseteq \bigcup_{j=1}^{n} \bar{G}_{1j}$$

For if $x \in I$, $x \notin F_j^\circ \backslash F_1$ $(1 < j \leqslant n)$, then $x \in F_1 = \bar{G}_{11}$. If $x \in I$, $x \notin F_1$, there is a j with $x \in F_j^\circ \backslash F_1$ $(1 < j \leqslant n)$. If $x \notin F_j^\circ \backslash (\bar{G}_{11} \cup \bar{G}_{12})$ $(2 < j \leqslant n)$, then either $x \in F_2^\circ \backslash F_1 = G_{12}$, or $x \in \bar{G}_{11} \cup \bar{G}_{12}$, and so $x \in \bar{G}_{12}$. And so on.

Finally, $H_j = I \cap \bar{G}_{1j} \in \mathcal{S}_1$, since I is compact, and the $H_1, \ldots, H_n$ give the division of I.)

44. The Generalized Riemann and Variational Integrals

Let $(R, \mathcal{S}, \mathcal{A})$ be a division space. Then we integrate functions $f(x) \cdot \mu(I)$ of $I \in \mathcal{S}$ and $x = x(\gamma; I)$, $\gamma \in \Gamma$, with real or complex values, by considering sets $S(f\mu; \mathbf{S}; E)$ of sums

$$(\mathcal{D}_\Gamma) \sum f(x(\gamma; I)) \, \mu(I)$$

for all divisions $\mathcal{D}(I)$ of E from all $\mathbf{S} \in \mathcal{A}$ that divide E. Clearly $S(f\mu; \mathbf{S}; E)$ is not empty. As $\mathcal{A}$ is partially ordered in the sense of divisions, if $\mathbf{S}_1$ and $\mathbf{S}_2$ are in $\mathcal{A}$ and divide E, there is an $\mathbf{S}_3 \in \mathcal{A}$ that divides E, with

$$\mathcal{S}_{3\gamma} \subseteq \mathcal{S}_{1\gamma} \cap \mathcal{S}_{2\gamma} \qquad (\gamma \in \Gamma),$$

(44.1) $\qquad S(f\mu; \mathbf{S}_3; E) \subseteq S(f\mu; \mathbf{S}_1; E) \cap S(f\mu; \mathbf{S}_2; E).$

We say that $S(f\mu; \mathbf{S}; E)$ is *fundamental for the* $\mathbf{S} \in \mathcal{A}$ *that divide* E, or *fundamental* $(\mathcal{A}; E)$, if, given $\varepsilon > 0$, there is an $\mathbf{S} \in \mathcal{A}$ that divides E, with

(44.2) $S(f\mu; \mathbf{S}; E) - S(f\mu; \mathbf{S}; E) \subseteq S(0, \varepsilon),$

i.e. every pair of points of $S(f\mu; \mathbf{S}; E)$ is in distance less than ε apart.

Also $S(f\mu; \mathbf{S}; E)$ is *convergent for all* $\mathbf{S} \in \mathcal{A}$ *that divide* E, or *convergent* $(\mathcal{A}; E)$, with *limit* u, if, given $\varepsilon > 0$, there is an $\mathbf{S} \in A$ that divides E, such that

(44.3) $S(f\mu; \mathbf{S}; E) \subseteq S(u, \varepsilon),$

i.e. each point of $S(f\mu; \mathbf{S}; E)$ is within ε of u.

THEOREM 44.1. *If* $S(f\mu; \mathbf{S}; E)$ *is fundamental* $(\mathcal{A}; E)$ *it is convergent* $(\mathcal{A}; E)$ *and conversely.*

Proof. Let $\mathbf{S}_j$ be an $\mathbf{S}$ for which (44.2) is true for $\varepsilon = 1/j$. As in (44.1) we can also assume that

(44.4) $S(f\mu; \mathbf{S}_{j+1}; E) \subseteq S(f\mu; \mathbf{S}_j; E)$ $(j = 1, 2, \ldots).$

Taking one point u_j in $S(f\mu; \mathbf{S}_j; E)$, for each $j = 1, 2, \ldots$, (44.4) gives

$$u_k \in S(f\mu; \mathbf{S}_j; E) \qquad (\text{all } k \geqslant j, \; j = 1, 2, \ldots),$$

so that by (44.2), $\{u_j\}$ is a fundamental sequence. As the real line and complex plane are complete, $\{u_j\}$ has a limit u, and

$$S(f\mu; \mathbf{S}_j; E) - u = S(f\mu; \mathbf{S}_j; E) - u_j + (u_j - u) \subseteq S(0, 2/j).$$

Thus $S(f\mu; \mathbf{S}; E)$ is convergent $(\mathcal{A}; E)$.

Conversely, if (44.3) is true, then (44.2) is true with 2ε replacing ε.

The limit is another special case of a Moore–Smith limit. If it exists, then clearly it is unique, and it is called the *generalized Riemann integral of f with respect to* μ *in* E, *written*

$$\int_E f \, d\mu.$$

This agrees with the definitions in special cases given in Henstock (1963c), pp. 26, 104, 141.

THEOREM 44.2. *The integral is linear in f and μ.*

Proof. Let f, g be integrable with respect to μ in E. Then, given $\varepsilon > 0$, there are S_1, S_2 in $\mathcal{A}$ that divide E, such that if $\mathcal{D}_j$ is any division of E from S_j $(j = 1, 2)$,

$$\left| (\mathcal{D}_1) \sum f(x(\gamma; I)) \, \mu(I) - \int_E f \, d\mu \right| < \varepsilon,$$

$$\left| (\mathcal{D}_2) \sum g(x(\gamma; I)) \, \mu(I) - \int_E g \, d\mu \right| < \varepsilon.$$

As A is partially ordered in the sense of divisions, we can replace S_1, S_2 by an $S_3 \in \mathcal{A}$ that divides E, for which both conditions are true with $\mathcal{D} = \mathcal{D}_1 = \mathcal{D}_2$ from S_3. Then if a, b are constants we have

$$\left| (\mathcal{D}) \sum \big(af(x(\gamma; I)) + bg(x(\gamma; I)) \big) \, \mu(I) - a \int_E f \, d\mu - b \int_E g \, d\mu \right|$$

$$\leqslant (|a| + |b|) \varepsilon,$$

giving the result that $af + bg$ is integrable with respect to μ in E to

$$a \int_E f \, d\mu + b \int_E g \, d\mu.$$

Similarly we can prove linearity in μ.

THEOREM 44.3. *Let f, g, μ be real and let $f + ig$ be integrable with respect to μ in E, with integral $F + iG$, where F, G are real. Then f, g are integrable with respect to μ in E with integrals F, G respectively.*

Proof. If a, b are real then max $(|a|, |b|) \leqslant |a + ib|$. Thus

$$|(\mathcal{D}) \sum f(x(\gamma; I)) \, \mu(I) - F| \leqslant \left| (\mathcal{D}) \sum \big(f(x(\gamma; I)) \right.$$

$$\left. + ig(x(\gamma; I)) \big) \, \mu(I) - (F + iG) \right|$$

For suitable $S \in \mathcal{A}$ that divide E, and all divisions $\mathcal{D}$ from S and over E, the right side is as small as we please. Hence f is integrable to F, and similarly g to G.

THEOREM 44.4. *Let f, g be real and integrable with respect to $\mu \geqslant 0$ in E, with $f \geqslant g$.*

Then

$$\int_E f\, d\mu \geqslant \int_E g\, d\mu$$

Proof. We proceed as in Theorem 44.2, taking $\mathcal{D} = \mathcal{D}_1 = \mathcal{D}_2$ from $\mathbf{S}_3$. Then we obtain the result from

$$\int_E f\, d\mu + \varepsilon \geqslant \int_E g\, d\mu - \varepsilon \qquad (all\ \varepsilon > 0).$$

A function $H(I)$ of the intervals I is *finitely additive* on a subset $\mathcal{S}_1$ of $\mathcal{S}$ if, for each interval $J \in \mathcal{S}_1$ and each division $\mathcal{D}$ of J using the $I \in \mathcal{S}_1$, we have

$$(\mathcal{D})\sum H(I) = H(J).$$

Such an H can be defined unambiguously for those elementary sets that are finite unions of non-overlapping intervals of $\mathcal{S}_1$.

THEOREM 44.5. *If the generalized Riemann integral of f with respect to μ in E exists, then it is a finitely additive function of the partial sets of E. If the integral exists for non-overlapping elementary sets E, E_1, then the integral exists for $E \cup E_1$ as the sum of the other two integrals. Further, if for some $\mathbf{S} \in \mathcal{A}$ that divides E, and all sums $\mathbf{S}$ over E from $\mathbf{S}$,*

$$(44.5) \qquad \left| S - \int_E f\, d\mu \right| < \varepsilon,$$

then for each partial set P of E, and all sums S_1 over P from $\mathbf{S}$,

$$(44.6) \qquad \left| S_1 - \int_P f\, d\mu \right| \leqslant 2\varepsilon.$$

Proof. If P is a partial set of E, and if $\mathbf{S} \in \mathcal{A}$ divides E, then by Theorem 43.2 (43.1), $\mathbf{S}$ divides P and $E - P$. If S_1, S_2 are two sums over arbitrary divisions of P from $\mathbf{S}$, and if S_3 is a sum over a division of $E - P$ from $\mathbf{S}$, then $S_1 + S_3$, $S_2 + S_3$ are sums over two divisions of E from $\mathbf{S}$. Given $\varepsilon > 0$ we can choose an $\mathbf{S} \in \mathcal{A}$ that divides E, such that (44.5) is true. Then

$$|S_1 - S_2| = \left| \left(S_1 + S_3 - \int_E f\, d\mu\right) - \left(S_2 + S_3 - \int_E f\, d\mu\right) \right| < 2\varepsilon.$$

Thus (44.2) is true with 2ε for ε, and the existence of the integral over P follows by Theorem 44.1. Then (44.6) follows on taking S_2 arbitrarily near to the integral over P. Theorem 43.2 (43.3) shows that the union of two non-overlapping partial sets of E is another partial set of E, so that the integral exists over the union, and we do not need all the next part to prove the integral finitely additive.

Let the integral exist for non-overlapping elementary sets E, E_1. Then there are $\mathbf{S}$, $\mathbf{S}_1 \in \mathcal{A}$, respectively dividing E, E_1, such that all sums S over E from $\mathbf{S}$ satisfy (44.5), and all sums S_4 over E_1 from $\mathbf{S}_1$ satisfy

$$\left| S_4 - \int_{E_1} f \, d\mu \right| < \varepsilon. \qquad \text{Hence}$$

$$\left| S + S_4 - \int_{E} f \, d\mu - \int_{E_1} f \, d\mu \right| < 2\varepsilon,$$

$S + S_4$ being an arbitrary sum from $\mathbf{S} + \mathbf{S}_1$. This is in $\mathcal{A}$ since $\mathcal{A}$ is additive, so that the integral over $E \cup E_1$ exists as the sum of the integrals over E, E_1. This proves that the integral is finitely additive.

Let $h_\gamma(I)$ be a function of the $I \in \mathcal{S}$ and the $\gamma \in \Gamma$. We can then regard the function as the γ component of a vector function $\mathbf{h}(I)$. For example, we can have

$$h_\gamma(I) = f(x(\gamma; I)) \, \mu(I), \quad \text{or} \quad h_\gamma(I) = f(x(\gamma; I)) \, \mu(I) - \int_I f \, d\mu.$$

Then the *variation of* $\mathbf{h}$ *in* E is defined to be

$$V(\mathbf{h}; \mathcal{A}; E) = \inf V(\mathbf{h}; \mathbf{S}; E), \quad V(\mathbf{h}; \mathbf{S}; E) = \sup (\mathcal{D}_\Gamma) \sum |h_\gamma(I)|,$$

the inf being over all $\mathbf{S} \in \mathcal{A}$ that divide E, and the sup being over all divisions $\mathcal{D}$ of E from $\mathbf{S}$ with all possible specifications of the γ. The sup can sometimes be $+\infty$. Note that if $\mathbf{S}$, $\mathbf{S}_1 \in \mathcal{A}$ both divide E, with

(44.7) $\quad \mathcal{S}_\gamma \subseteq \mathcal{S}_{1\gamma}(\gamma \in \Gamma), \quad$ then $\quad V(\mathbf{h}; \mathbf{S}; E) \leqslant V(\mathbf{h}; \mathbf{S}_1; E).$

This is why it is appropriate to use the inf.

The *variation of* $\mathbf{h}$ *over a set* $X \subseteq R$, *relative to* E, *is*

$$V(\mathbf{h}; \mathcal{A}; E; X) = V(\mathbf{h}_1; \mathcal{A}; E),$$
$$h_{1\gamma}(I) = h_\gamma(I) \, ch(X; x(\gamma; I)) \qquad (\gamma \in \Gamma).$$

where $ch(X; .)$ is the characteristic function of the set X.

229

If the variation of **h** in E is 0, we say that **h** is *of variation zero in E*, while if the variation of **h** over X relative to E is 0, we say that **h** is *of variation zero in X, relative to E*.

If a function H of the partial sets of an elementary set E is finitely additive, and if $H-f\mu$ is of variation zero in E, i.e. **h** is of variation zero in E where

$$h_\gamma(I) = H(I)-f(x(\gamma; I))\,\mu(I) \qquad (\gamma \in \Gamma),$$

then we say that H is the *indefinite variational integral of f with respect to μ in E*.

THEOREM 44.6. *The indefinite variational integral H of f with respect to μ in E exists if, and only if, the generalized Riemann integral of f with respect to μ in E exists, and for all partial sets P of E,*

$$H(P) = \int_P f\, d\mu.$$

Thus H is uniquely defined.

Proof. If the generalized Riemann integral exists then by Theorem 44.5, (44.6) and the additivity of the integral, we have for all partial divisions Q of E from **S**,

$$\left| (Q_\Gamma) \sum \left(f(x(\gamma; I))\,\mu(I) - \int_I f\, d\mu \right) \right| \le 2\varepsilon.$$

Let $\mathcal{D}$ be a division of E from **S**. Then for sum over Q_Γ we use all $I \in \mathcal{D}$ for which the real parts of the terms of the sum are positive; then all $I \in \mathcal{D}$ for which the real parts of the terms are negative, obtaining

$$(\mathcal{D}_\Gamma) \sum \left| rl \left(f(x(\gamma; I))\,\mu(I) - \int_I f\, d\mu \right) \right| \le 4\varepsilon.$$

Similarly for the imaginary parts, so that finally

$$(\mathcal{D}_\Gamma) \sum \left| f(x(\gamma; I))\,\mu(I) - \int_I f\, d\mu \right| \le 8\varepsilon.$$

$$S\left(f\mu - \int_I f\, d\mu; \mathbf{S}; E \right) \le 8\varepsilon, \qquad S\left(f\mu - \int_I f\, d\mu; \mathcal{A}; E \right) = 0,$$

and the generalized Riemann integral is an indefinite variational integral. Conversely, if H is an indefinite variational integral then H is finitely additive for partial sets of E. Hence there is an $\mathbf{S} \in \mathcal{A}$ that divides E, such that all divisions $\mathcal{D}$ of E from $\mathbf{S}$ satisfy

$$\left|(\mathcal{D}) \sum f(x(\gamma; I)) \, \mu(I) - H(E)\right| < \varepsilon,$$
$$S(f\mu; \mathbf{S}; E) \subseteq \mathbf{S}(H(E), \varepsilon)$$

and f is integrable with respect to μ in E, to the value $H(E)$. A similar result holds for all partial sets of E.

THEOREM 44.7. *If E_1, E_2 are non-overlapping elementary sets, with $\mathbf{S}_j \in \mathcal{A}$, and dividing and being restricted to E_j ($j = 1, 2$), then*

(44.8) $\quad V(\mathbf{h}; \mathbf{S}_1; E_1) + V(\mathbf{h}; \mathbf{S}_2; E_2) = V(\mathbf{h}; \mathbf{S}_1 + \mathbf{S}_2; E_1 \cup E_2),$

(44.9) $\quad V(\mathbf{h}; \mathcal{A}; E_1) + V(\mathbf{h}; \mathcal{A}; E_2) = V(\mathbf{h}; \mathcal{A}; E_1 \cup E_2).$

The proofs are straightforward.

THEOREM 44.8. *If $V(\mathbf{h}; \mathcal{A}; E) < \infty$, $\varepsilon > 0$, and $\mathbf{S} \in \mathcal{A}$ dividing E, satisfy*

$$V(\mathbf{h}; \mathbf{S}; E) < V(\mathbf{h}; \mathcal{A}; E) + \varepsilon, \quad then \quad V(\mathbf{h}; \mathbf{S}; P) < V(\mathbf{h}; \mathcal{A}; P) + \varepsilon$$

for all partial sets P of E.

Proof. As $\mathbf{S}$ contains the sum of its restrictions to P and $E - P$, (44.7; ...; 44.9) imply

$$V(\mathbf{h}; \mathbf{S}; P) \leqslant V(\mathbf{h}; \mathbf{S}; E) - V(\mathbf{h}; \mathbf{S}; E - P) < V(\mathbf{h}; \mathcal{A}; E)$$
$$+ \varepsilon - V(\mathbf{h}; \mathcal{A}; E - P) = V(\mathbf{h}; \mathcal{A}; P) + \varepsilon.$$

In the rest of the section we have to assume that $(R, \mathcal{S}, \mathcal{A})$ is a decomposable division space.

THEOREM 44.9. *Let $(R, \mathcal{S}, \mathcal{A})$ be a decomposable division space, and let $\{X_j\}$ be a monotone increasing sequence of sets in R, with union X. Then*

$$\lim_{j \to \infty} V(\mathbf{h}; \mathcal{A}; E; X_j) = V(\mathbf{h}; \mathcal{A}; E; X)$$

231

Proof. As $X \supseteq X_j$, it follows that

(44.10) $$V(\mathbf{h}; \mathcal{A}; E; X) \geqslant V(\mathbf{h}; \mathcal{A}; E; X_j),$$

(44.11) $$V(\mathbf{h}; \mathcal{A}; E; X) \geqslant \lim_{j \to \infty} V(\mathbf{h}; \mathcal{A}; E; X_j).$$

Thus we can assume the limit finite. Let $\mathbf{S}_j \in \mathcal{A}$, dividing E, satisfy

(44.12) $\quad V(\mathbf{h}; \mathbf{S}_j; E; X_j) < V(\mathbf{h}; \mathcal{A}; E; X_j) + \varepsilon \cdot 2^{-j} \qquad (j \geqslant 1)$.

As $\mathcal{A}$ has decomposable vectors, there is an $\mathbf{S}^* \in \mathcal{A}$ that divides E, with

$$\mathcal{S}_\gamma^*(X_j \backslash X_{j-1}) \subseteq \mathcal{S}_{j\gamma}(X_j \backslash X_{j-1}) \qquad (\gamma \in \Gamma, \ X_0 \ empty, \ j = 1, 2, \ldots)$$

If $\mathcal{D}$ is a division of E from $\mathbf{S}^*$, and if Q, Q_j are the partial divisions of $\mathcal{D}$ with associated points in X and $X_j \backslash X_{j-1}$, respectively ($j \geqslant 1$), there is a greatest integer m (depending on $\mathcal{D}$) such that Q_m is not empty. Let E_j be the partial set from Q_j ($j = 1, 2, \ldots, m$). Then from Theorems 44.7, 44.8 and (44.10; 44.12),

$$(\mathcal{D}) \sum_m |h_\gamma(I)| \, ch(X; x(\gamma; I)) = (Q) \sum |h_\gamma(I)| = \sum_{j=1}^{m} (Q_j) \sum |h_\gamma(I)|$$

$$\leqslant \sum_{j=1}^{m} V(\mathbf{h}; \mathbf{S}_j; E_j; X_j) < \sum_{j=1}^{m} \{V(\mathbf{h}; \mathcal{A}; E_j; X_j) + \varepsilon \cdot 2^{-j}\}$$

$$< \sum_{j=1}^{m} V(\mathbf{h}; \mathcal{A}; E_j; X_m) + \varepsilon \leqslant V(\mathbf{h}; \mathcal{A}; E; X_m) + \varepsilon$$

$$\leqslant \lim_{j \to \infty} V(\mathbf{h}; \mathcal{A}; E; X_j) + \varepsilon,$$

$$V(\mathbf{h}; \mathcal{A}; E; X) \leqslant V(\mathbf{h}; \mathbf{S}^*; E; X) \leqslant \lim_{j \to \infty} V(\mathbf{h}; \mathcal{A}; E; X_j) + \varepsilon,$$

giving the opposite inequality to (44.11), and the result.

THEOREM 44.10. *Let $(R, \mathcal{S}, \mathcal{A})$ be a decomposable division space, and let $\{X_j\}$ be a sequence of subsets of R, with union X. Then*

$$V(\mathbf{h}; \mathcal{A}; E; X) \leqslant \sum_{j=1}^{\infty} V(\mathbf{h}; \mathcal{A}; E; X_j)$$

Proof. By (44.10) we can assume the X_j disjoint, and we can take the right side finite, and begin as in the proof of Theorem 44.9, obtaining

$$(\mathcal{D}) \sum |h_\gamma(I)| \, ch(X; x(\gamma; I)) \leqslant \sum_{j=1}^{m} V(\mathbf{h}; \mathbf{S}_j; E_j; X_j)$$

$$\leqslant \sum_{j=1}^{m} V(\mathbf{h}; \mathbf{S}_j; E; X_j) < \sum_{j=1}^{m} \{V(\mathbf{h}; \mathcal{A}; E; X_j) + \varepsilon \cdot 2^{-j}\},$$

$$V(\mathbf{h}; \mathcal{A}; E; X) \leqslant V(\mathbf{h}; \mathbf{S}^*; E; X) \leqslant \sum_{j=1}^{\infty} V(\mathbf{h}; \mathcal{A}; E; X_j) + \varepsilon.$$

THEOREM 44.11. *Let* $(R, \mathcal{S}, \mathcal{A})$ *be a decomposable division space.*

(44.13) *If* $V(\mu; \mathcal{A}; E; X) = 0$, *and if* f *is a point function, then* $V(f\mu; \mathcal{A}; E; X) = 0$. *Conversely, if* $V(f\mu; \mathcal{A}; E; X) = 0$, *and if* $f \neq 0$ *in* $X_1 \subseteq X$, *then* $V(\mu; \mathcal{A}; E; X_1) = 0$.

(44.14) *If* $V(\mu - \nu; \mathcal{A}; E) = 0$, *if* f *is a point function, and if* f *is integrable with respect to* μ *in* E, *then* f *is integrable with respect to* ν *in* E, *and the integrals are equal.*

Proof. Let X_j be the subset of X with $|f| \leqslant j$ $(j = 2, 3, \ldots)$. By Theorem 44.10 and (44.10),

$$V(f\mu; \mathcal{A}; E; X) \leqslant \sum_{j=2}^{\infty} V(f\mu; \mathcal{A}; E; X_j) \leqslant \sum_{j=2}^{\infty} j \cdot V(\mu; \mathcal{A}; E; X_j) = 0.$$

Hence the first part of (44.13). The second part follows on replacing X and f by X_1 and $1/f$ in the first part. Then (44.14) follows from (44.13) and Theorem 44.2, on noting from the definitions that since $f(\mu - \nu)$ has variation zero, the integral of f with respect to $\mu - \nu$ in E is 0.

Ex. 44.1. Show that Theorems 44.9, 44.10 are false for ordinary Riemann integration on the real line (*Ex. 43.1* with $n = 1$), by taking X_j as the set containing the first j rationals, with $E = [0, 1]$ and for $\mathbf{h}$ as $\mu([u, v]) = v - u$.

Ex. 44.2. Prove that integration by substitution holds, i.e. if

$$H(P) = \int_P f \, d\mu$$

exists for all partial sets P of E, and if either integral below exists, then both exist and are equal.

$$\int_E g \, dH = \int_E gf \, d\mu$$

Ex. 44.3. If **h, j** have variation zero, and $k_\gamma = h_\gamma + j_\gamma$ ($\gamma \in \Gamma$), then **k** has variation zero.

45. The Integrability of Functions of Functions

We now specialize some results of Henstock (1963c), pp. 43–46, section 25 and Henstock (1964), extending the results to general division spaces. We are concerned with a function $r(x_1, x_2)$ of two real variables that is homogeneous in the sense

(45.1) $$r(ax_1, ax_2) = ar(x_1, x_2),$$

so that if f, g are two point functions and μ a function of $I \in \mathcal{S}$,

(45.2) $$r(f\mu, g\mu) = r(f, g)\mu.$$

Limitation (45.1) is solely in order that our generalized Riemann integrals can be restricted to the types already defined. A more general theory can disregard this limitation.

We shall be concerned with two types of continuity condition on r. The first is that for constants $A, B > 0$,

(45.3) $$|r(y_1, y_2) - r(x_1, x_2)| \leqslant A|y_1 - x_1| + B|y_2 - x_2|.$$

E.g. this holds if the partial derivatives of r exist and are bounded. For the second condition we put, for each $\varepsilon > 0$ and fixed x_1, x_2,

$$r_1(x_1, x_2, \varepsilon) \equiv \sup |r(y_1, y_2) - r(x_1, x_2)| \, (|y_j - x_j| \leqslant \varepsilon, j = 1, 2).$$

Then the condition is that for arbitrarily large n, varying $\varepsilon_k > 0$ ($1 \leqslant k \leqslant n$)

(45.4) $$\sum_{k=1}^{n} x_{jk} \quad (j = 1, 2) \text{ fixed,}$$

(45.5) $$\sum_{k=1}^{n} r_1(x_{1k}, x_{2k}, \varepsilon_k) \to 0 \quad \text{as} \quad \sum_{k=1}^{n} \varepsilon_k \to 0.$$

Clearly (45.3) implies (45.5).

THEOREM 45.1. *Let R, Z, R^+ be the real line, the complex plane, and the line of non-negative numbers, respectively, and let T be $R \times R$ or $R^+ \times R^+$. Let $r(x_1, x_2) : T \to R(\text{or } Z)$ satisfy (45.1), and let $\mathbf{h}_j - \mathbf{k}_j$ have variation 0 in E ($j = 1, 2$). Then $\mathbf{a} - \mathbf{b} = r(\mathbf{h}_1, \mathbf{h}_2) - r(\mathbf{k}_1, \mathbf{k}_2)$ has variation 0 if either*

(45.6) *r satisfies (45.3) in T, or*

(45.7) *r satisfies (45.5) in T when the $\mathbf{h}_j = f_j \mu$ are integrable in $E (j = 1, 2)$*

Here we have written $\mathbf{a} - \mathbf{b}$, $r(\mathbf{h}_1, \mathbf{h}_2)$ for the vectors with components

$$a_\gamma - b_\gamma, \quad r(h_{1\gamma}, h_{2\gamma}) \qquad (\gamma \in \Gamma)$$

Proof. Given $\varepsilon > 0$, there are $\mathbf{S}_j \in \mathcal{A}$ that divide E, with

(45.8) $$V(\mathbf{h}_j - \mathbf{k}_j; \mathbf{S}_j; E) < \varepsilon \qquad (j = 1, 2)$$

As $\mathcal{A}$ is partially ordered in the sense of divisions we can replace the $\mathbf{S}_j$ by a single $\mathbf{S} \in \mathcal{A}$ that divides E, for which both results are true. If (45.3) holds, then for each division $\mathcal{D}$ of E from $\mathbf{S}$,

$$(\mathcal{D}) \sum |a_\gamma - b_\gamma| \leqslant A(\mathcal{D}) \sum |h_{1\gamma} - k_{1\gamma}| + B(\mathcal{D}) \sum |h_{2\gamma} - k_{2\gamma}| \leqslant (A + B)\varepsilon$$

and $\mathbf{a} - \mathbf{b}$ has variation zero. If (45.5) holds, with $\mathbf{h}_j = f_j \mu$ integrable to H_j, then by *Ex. 44.3*, $\mathbf{k}_j - H_j$ also has variation zero since $\mathbf{h}_j - \mathbf{k}_j$ has variation zero ($j = 1, 2$). Since

$$r(\mathbf{h}_1, \mathbf{h}_2) - r(\mathbf{k}_1, \mathbf{k}_2) = \{r(\mathbf{h}_1, \mathbf{h}_2) - r(H_1, H_2)\} + \{r(H_1, H_2) - r(\mathbf{k}_1, \mathbf{k}_2)\}$$

we therefore need only prove the first bracket of variation zero.

Let $\mathcal{D}$ be a division of E from $\mathbf{S}$, with intervals $I_1, \ldots, I_n$ and various γ. Then (45.4) is fixed at $H_j(E)$ ($j = 1, 2$) with

$$x_{jk} = H_j(I_k), \quad y_{jk} = h_{j\gamma}(I_k),$$

$$\sum_{k=1}^{n} \left| r(h_{1\gamma}(I_k), h_{2\gamma}(I_k)) - r(H_1(I_k), H_2(I_k)) \right| \leqslant \sum_{k=1}^{n} r_1(H_1(I_k), H_2(I_k), \varepsilon_k)$$

$$\varepsilon_k = V(\mathbf{h}_1 - H_1; \mathbf{S}; I_k) + V(\mathbf{h}_2 - H_2; \mathbf{S}; I_k)$$

By Theorem 44.7 and replacing $\mathbf{k}_j$ by H_j in (45.8), and by (45.5),

$$\sum_{n=1}^{n} \varepsilon_k \leqslant V(\mathbf{h}_1 - H_1;\, \mathbf{S};\, E) + V(\mathbf{h}_2 - H_2;\, \mathbf{S};\, E) < 2\varepsilon,$$

$$V(r(h_1,\, h_2) - r(H_1,\, H_2);\, \mathbf{S};\, E) \to 0$$

by choice of $\mathbf{S}$, completing the proof.

THEOREM 45.2. *In Theorem* 45.1 (45.7) *with* H_j *the integral of* $\mathbf{h}_j$, *let* r *have*

(45.9) $$r(x_1 + y_1,\, x_2 + y_2) \leqslant r(x_1,\, x_2) + r(y_1,\, y_2)$$

for all (x_1, x_2), (y_1, y_2), $(x_1 + y_1, x_2 + y_2)$ *in* T. *Then* $\mathbf{a}$ *is integrable if, and only if, for some* $\mathbf{S} \in \mathcal{A}$ *that divides* E,

(45.10) $$(\mathcal{D}) \sum r(h_{1\gamma},\, h_{2\gamma})$$

is bounded above, for all divisions $\mathcal{D}$ *over* E *from* $\mathbf{S}$.

Proof. We put $c(E) = r(H_1(E), H_2(E))$. It is finitely subadditive in an obvious sense since from (45.9), if $\mathcal{D}$ is a division of E,

$$(\mathcal{D}) \sum H_j(I) = H_j(E),$$

$$(\mathcal{D}) \sum r(H_1(I), H_2(I)) \geqslant r((\mathcal{D}) \sum H_1(I),\, (\mathcal{D}) \sum H_2(I)),$$

$$(\mathcal{D}) \sum c(I) \geqslant c(E).$$

If $\mathcal{D}$ is from an $\mathbf{S} \in \mathcal{A}$ that divides E, then Theorem 43.2 (43.2) shows that there is an $\mathbf{S}^* \in \mathcal{A}$ that divides E, such that $\mathcal{D}' \leqslant \mathcal{D}$ for all divisions $\mathcal{D}'$ of E from $\mathbf{S}^*$, and the finite subadditivity gives

$$(\mathcal{D}') \sum c(I) \geqslant (\mathcal{D}) \sum c(I).$$

If $S(c; \mathbf{S}; E)$ has a finite supremum s we can take the second sum greater than $s - \varepsilon$, so that the first sum lies between s and $s - \varepsilon$. If $S(c; \mathbf{S}; E)$ is unbounded above we can take the second sum as large as we please, and then the first sum has the same property. By Theorem 45.1 (45.7), $S(c; \mathbf{S}; E)$ is bounded or unbounded according as (45.10) is bounded or unbounded, and in the bounded case the integral of $\mathbf{a}$ is s, while in the unbounded case $S(\mathbf{a}; \mathbf{S}^*; E)$ lies in the set of $x \geqslant A$, for A arbitrarily large by choice of $\mathbf{S}^*$, so that $\mathbf{a}$ cannot be integrable.

Ex. 45.1. For $r(x_1, x_2) = x_1^t x_2^{1-t}(x_j \geqslant 0, j = 1, 2)$, where $0 < t < 1$, (45.1) is true. Prove that (45.5) is true, and (45.9) true for $-r$. (For (45.9) use Hölder's inequality. For (45.5) begin with $f' \geqslant 0$ where

$$f(x) \equiv x^t + z^t - (x+z)^t \geqslant 0 \qquad (x \geqslant 0, z \geqslant 0)$$

Then for $\qquad x_j \geqslant 0, \qquad x_j + z_j \geqslant 0,$

$$(x_1 + z_1)^t (x_2 + z_2)^{1-t} \leqslant (x_1^t + |z_1^t|)(x_2^{1-t} + |z_2^{1-t}|),$$

$$x_1^t x_2^{1-t} \leqslant (x_1 + z_1)^t (x_2 + z_2)^{1-t} + x_1^t |z_2^{1-t}| + |z_1^t| x_2^{1-t} + |z_1^t| |z_2^{1-t}|$$

For $y_j = x_j + z_j$ and by Hölder's inequality $(t = 1/p)$,

$$|r(y_1, y_2) - r(x_1, x_2)| \leqslant x_1^t |z_2^{1-t}| + |z_1^t| x_2^{1-t} + |z_1^t| |z_2^{1-t}|,$$

and (45.5) follows.)

Hence if f, g are non-negative and integrable with respect to $\mu \geqslant 0$ in E, it follows that $f^t g^{1-t}$ is integrable with respect to μ in E, for fixed t in $0 < t < 1$.

Ex. 45.2. Prove that $r(x_1, x_2) = \max(x_1, x_2)$ satisfies (45.3) with $A = 1 = B$, and (45.9), and that (45.10) is bounded above if either $S(\mathbf{a}; \mathbf{S}; E)$ lies in a compact set, for some $\mathbf{S} \in \mathcal{A}$ that divides E, or if $\mathbf{h}_j = f_j \mu$ where $\mu \geqslant 0, f_1 \leqslant f_3, f_2 \leqslant f_3$, and where f_j is integrable with respect to μ. Hence show that also $\max(f_1, f_2)$ is integrable with respect to μ.

Appling (1962a,b), (1963), and subsequent papers, gives many interesting integrability results for Hellinger–Burkill integration. The corresponding results for generalized Riemann integration can be obtained for the most part from Theorems 45.1, 45.2.

46. Limits of Integrals

When $\mu((u, v)) = v - u$, Lebesgue gave two sufficient conditions for

(46.1) $$\int_E f_j(x) \, d\mu \to \int_E f(x) \, d\mu \qquad (j \to \infty).$$

His are Lebesgue integrals on the real line, with extensions to more general spaces, and $f_j(x) \to f(x)$ as $j \to \infty$, for almost all $x \in E$. The first condition is that of *monotone convergence*, the f_j being monotone increasing in j with the left side of (46.1) bounded. The second condition is that of *majorized convergence*, with $|f_j| \le F$ for integrable F.

These results are proved for variational integrals on the real line in Henstock (1963c), p. 82, Theorem 36.1, and p. 85, Theorem 37.1, where the μ need not be completely additive, so that the reason for the failure of (46.1) in Riemann integration does not lie in the finite additivity of Jordan measure as contrasted with the complete additivity of Lebesgue measure. Here we see that the reason is that the division space for Riemann integration is not decomposable. We need a decomposable division space to prove (46.1) in Lebesgue's cases, but this is the only extra condition required. The y below can go through all positive integers or all real $y \ge 1$.

THEOREM 46.1. *Let* $(R, \mathcal{S}, \mathcal{A})$ *be a decomposable division space. Let* $\mu \ge 0$, *and for each* $x \in R$ *let* $f(x, y) \ge 0$ *be monotone increasing in* $y \ge 1$. *If for each* $y \ge 1$ $f(x, y)$ *is integrable with respect to* μ *in an elementary set* E, *with indefinite variational integral* $H(., y)$, *and if* $H(E, y)$ *is bounded above as* $y \to \infty$, *then*

(46.2) $$f(x) \equiv \lim_{y \to \infty} f(x, y)$$

exist (finite) for all x *save a set* X *with* $V(\mu; \mathcal{A}; E; X) = 0$. *Putting* $f(x) = 0$ *in* X, *then* f *is integrable with respect to* μ *in* E *with indefinite variational integral* $H(.) = \lim_{y \to \infty} H(., y)$.

Proof. We can restrict y to take integer values since

$$f(x, n) \le f(x, y) \le f(x, n+1) \qquad (n \le y \le n+1)$$

For fixed $j, k > 0$ let $X(j, k)$ be the set of x where $f(x, j) \ge k$, and let $X(k)$ be the set of x where

$$f(x) \equiv \lim_{j \to \infty} f(x, j) \ge k, \quad \text{or} \quad f(x, j) \to \infty \, (j \to \infty).$$

Given $\varepsilon > 0$, let $\mathbf{S}_j \in \mathcal{A}$ dividing E be such that for all divisions

238

$\mathcal{D}$ of E from S_j,

$$|(\mathcal{D}) \sum f(., j)\mu - H(E, j)| < \varepsilon \cdot 2^{-j}$$

If Q is the partial division from $\mathcal{D}$ with associated points in $X(j, k)$,

$$(Q) \sum k\mu \leqslant (\mathcal{D}) \sum f(., j)\mu \leqslant H(E, j) + \varepsilon \leqslant M + \varepsilon,$$

$$M \equiv \lim_{y \to \infty} H(E, y).$$

Hence as $\mu \geqslant 0$, and by definition of the variation over $X(j, k)$,

$$V(\mu; S_j; E; X(j, k)) \leqslant (M + \varepsilon)/k, \quad V(\mu; \mathcal{A}; E; X(j, k)) \leqslant M/k.$$

As $X(j, k)$ is monotone increasing in j and tends to $X(k)$ as $j \to \infty$, Theorem 44.9, which uses decomposable vectors, gives

$$V(\mu; \mathcal{A}; E; X(k)) \leqslant M/k, \quad X \subseteq X(k) \qquad (all\ k),$$

$$V(\mu; \mathcal{A}; E; X) = 0,$$

while $f(x)$ exists in $\backslash X$. By Theorem 44.11 we can now take $f(x, y) = 0$ for $x \in X$ without altering $H(., y)$ and then (46.2) is always true. We now take $k = 1/m$ for integers m, using Theorem 44.10. If

$$Y = \bigcup_{j, m=1}^{\infty} X(j, 1/m), \quad V(\mu; S_j; E; X(j, 1/m)) \leqslant m(M + \varepsilon),$$

$$V(\mu/(m \cdot 2^{j+m}); S_j; E; X(j, 1/m)) \leqslant (M + \varepsilon)/2^{j+m},$$

$$V(\mu/(m \cdot 2^{j+m}); S; E; Y) \leqslant M + \varepsilon.$$

Here, if $x \in Y$ we take the smallest j and then the smallest m, such that $x \in X(j, 1/m)$, so that Y is split up into disjoint sets, countable in number, and then S is the vector obtained by using these sets, the corresponding S_j, and the property of decomposability. Note that $\backslash Y$ is precisely the set where $f(x, y) = 0$ for all $y \geqslant 1$.

As (46.2) is now true for all x, let n be an integer, and let $q(x) \geqslant n$ be the smallest such integer (depending on x) for which

$$f(x) - f(x, q(x)) \leqslant \varepsilon/(m \cdot 2^{j+m}) \qquad (x \in Y)$$

As $\mathcal{A}$ is partially ordered in the sense of divisions there is an $S_j^* \in \mathcal{A}$ that divides E, that has the properties of both S_j and S. By using the disjoint sets X_q of points $x \in Y$ for which $q(x) = q$, with the corresponding S_q^*, the property of decomposability ensures the existence of an $\mathbf{S}^* \in \mathcal{A}$ that divides E, and that has the property of $\mathbf{S}^*_{q(x)}$ at each $x \in Y$. Let $\mathcal{D}$ be a division over E from $\mathbf{S}^*$, and Q the partial division from $\mathcal{D}$ for which the associated points lie in Y. Let

$$r = \max q(x(\gamma; I)) \qquad (I \in \mathcal{D}).$$

Then as $f(x)$ and $f(x, y)$ are zero outside Y,

$$(\mathcal{D}) \sum \{f(x) - f(x, q(x))\} \mu = (Q) \sum \{f(x) - f(x, q(x))\} \mu$$
$$\leqslant (Q) \sum \varepsilon \mu / (m \cdot 2^{j+m}) \leqslant \varepsilon(M + \varepsilon).$$

Further, Q can be split up into partial divisions $Q_n, \ldots, Q_r$ for which the associated points lie in $X_n, \ldots, X_r$, respectively, and we have

$$|(Q_q) \sum f(x, q) \mu - H(E_q, q)| < \varepsilon \cdot 2^{1-j}$$

by Theorem 44.5 (44.6), where $E_n, \ldots, E_r$ are the corresponding partial sets. As $H(E_q, q)$ lies between $H(E_q, n)$ and $H(E_q, r)$, these being finitely additive, we have

$$H(E, n) - 2\varepsilon \leqslant \sum_{q=n}^{r} H(E_q, q) - 2\varepsilon \leqslant \sum_{q=n}^{r} (Q_q) \sum f(x, q) \mu$$
$$= (\mathcal{D}) \sum f(x, q(x)) \mu \leqslant H(E, r) + 2\varepsilon,$$
$$H(E, n) - \varepsilon(M + 2 + \varepsilon) \leqslant (\mathcal{D}) \sum f(x) \mu \leqslant H(E, r) + \varepsilon(M + 2 + \varepsilon).$$

As we are given that $H(E, n)$ tends to M as $n \to \infty$, we can take n so that

$$|H(E, n) - M| < \varepsilon, \quad |(\mathcal{D}) \sum f(x) \mu - M| < \varepsilon(M + 3 + \varepsilon),$$

and f is integrable with respect to μ in E to the value $M \equiv \lim_{y \to \infty} H(E, y)$.

This completes the proof.

THEOREM 46.2 *Let* $(R, \mathcal{S}, \mathcal{A})$ *be a decomposable division space, let* $\mu \geqslant 0$, *and for each* $y \geqslant 1$ *let* $f(x, y)$ *be integrable with respect to* μ *in* E. *Let* $f(x, y) \geqslant f_1(x)$ *for all (possibly integer)* $y \geqslant 1$ *and some* f_1 *integrable with respect to* μ *in* E. *In the case when* y *takes all real values* $y \geqslant 1$, *also let*

(46.3) $$\inf_{Y \leqslant y \leqslant Z} f(x, y)$$

be integrable with respect to μ *in* E, *for each* Y, Z *in* $1 \leqslant Y < Z$.

Then

(46.4) $$\int_{E} \lim_{y \to \infty} \inf f(x, y)\, d\mu \leqslant \lim_{y \to \infty} \inf \int_{E} f(x, y)\, d\mu,$$

if the right side is finite.

Changing $f(x, y) \geqslant f_1(x)$ *to* $f(x, y) \leqslant f_2(x)$, *for all (possibly integer)* $y \geqslant 1$ *and for some* $f_2(x)$ *integrable with respect to* μ *in* E, *with*

(46.5) $$\sup_{Y < y < Z} f(x, y) \qquad (1 \leqslant Y < Z)$$

integrable with respect to μ *in* E, *when* y *takes all real values in* $y \geqslant 1$,

(46.6) $$\int_{E} \lim_{y \to \infty} \sup f(x, y)\, d\mu \geqslant \lim_{y \to \infty} \sup \int_{E} f(x, y)\, d\mu,$$

the left side possibly having the conventional value $+\infty$.

If in (46.4) *or* (46.6) $\lim_{y \to \infty} f(x, y)$ *exists except possibly in a set* X *with* $V(\mu; \mathcal{A}; E; X) = 0$, *then we do not need the corresponding* (46.3), (46.5).

If with the given X *and integrability conditions, for* $f(x) = 0$ *in* X, *and* $f_1(x) \leqslant f(x, y) \leqslant f_2(x)$, $f(x) = \lim_{y \to \infty} f(x, y)$ $(x \notin X)$, *then*

$$\int_{E} f\, d\mu = \lim_{y \to \infty} \int_{E} f(., y)\, d\mu.$$

Proof. In the first part, by considering $f(x, y) - f_1(x)$ we can assume $f(x, y) \geqslant 0$. First taking integer values, then

$$f(x, j) \leqslant \sum_{k=m}^{n} f(x, k) \qquad (m \leqslant j \leqslant n)$$

so that *Ex. 45.2* applied to $-f(x, j)$ $(m \leqslant j \leqslant n)$ gives the integrability of

$$\min_{m < j < n} f(x, j),$$

proving (46.3) integrable in this case. As it is monotone decreasing in Z, and is bounded below by 0, we can apply Theorem 46.1 to

$$f(x, Y) - \inf_{Y < y < Z} f(x, y) \geqslant 0 \qquad (Z \to \infty).$$

241

Thus $\inf\limits_{y > Y} f(x, y)$ is integrable with

$$\int_{E} \inf_{y > Y} f(.,y)\,d\mu = \lim_{Z \to \infty} \int_{E} \inf_{Y < y < Z} f(.,y)\,d\mu \leqslant \inf_{y > Y} \int_{E} f(.,y)\,d\mu.$$

Assuming the right side of (46.4) finite, we apply Theorem 46.1 as $Y \to \infty$ and we see that

$$\lim_{y \to \infty} \inf f(x, y) = \lim_{Y \to \infty} \left\{ \inf_{y > Y} f(x, y) \right\}$$

is finite except possibly in an X with $V(\mu; \mathcal{A}; E; X) = 0$, obtaining (46.4).

For the second part we apply the first part to $f_2(x) - f(x, y)$.

If $\lim\limits_{y \to \infty} f(x, y)$ ($x \notin X$) exists, we need only use a subsequence of y for which the integral of $f(x, y)$ tends to the right value in (46.4) to obtain it without using (46.3) (or tends to the right value in (46.6) to obtain it without (46.5)), as we have reduced to the sequence case.

The remaining results follow easily.

Extensions for Lebesgue integrals are given in Pratt (1960), while the corresponding results for the generalized Riemann integration are in Henstock (1963b). See also Henstock (1963c), pp. 88–9, *Ex. 37.1.*

THEOREM 46.3. *Let* $\mu \geqslant 0$, $p > 0$ *a real number, and* $\{f(x, j)\}$ *a sequence of point functions for the decomposable division space* $(R, \mathcal{S}, \mathcal{A})$ *such that, given* $\varepsilon > 0$, *there is an integer* $k(\varepsilon)$ *with*

$$(46.7) \qquad \|f(.,j) - f(.,k)\|_p^p \equiv \int_{E} |f(x, j) - f(x, k)|^p\,d\mu < \varepsilon$$

the integrals existing for each $j, k \geqslant k(\varepsilon)$, *then there are a point function* f, *a subsequence* $\{j_n\}$ *of integers, and a set* X *with*

$$(46.8) \quad f(x) = \lim_{n \to \infty} f(x, j_n) \qquad (x \notin X), \quad V(\mu; \mathcal{A}; E; X) = 0,$$

and for each integer $j \geqslant k(\varepsilon)$, *the integral exists in*

$$(46.9) \qquad \|f(.,j) - f\|_p^p = \int_{E} |f(.,j) - f|^p\,d\mu \leqslant \varepsilon$$

If g *satisfies the condition for* f *in* (46.9) *then* $f = g$ *except in a set* X.

If $\{f(x,j)\}$ satisfies the hypotheses of the theorem we say that $\{f(x,j)\}$ *converges in mean with index p*, while if $\{f(x,j)\}$ satisfies (46.9) we say that $\{f(x,j)\}$ *converges in mean to $f(x)$, with index p.*

Proof. We choose the sequence $\{j_n\}$ so that $j_n < j_{n+1}$ $(n = 1, 2, \ldots)$ and

$$\int_E |f(.,j) - f(.,k)|^p \, d\mu < 2^{-2np} \qquad (j \geqslant j_n, \quad k \geqslant j_n)$$

As at the beginning of Theorem 46.1, if X_n is the set where

$$|f(.,j_n) - f(.,j_{n+1})| \geqslant 2^{-n}, \quad \text{then} \quad V(\mu; \mathcal{A}; E; X_n) < 2^{-np}$$

If x is not in the union Y_N of $X_N, X_{N+1}, \ldots$, then

$$\sum_{n=N}^{\infty} |f(x,j_n) - f(x,j_{n+1})| \leqslant \sum_{n=N}^{\infty} 2^{-n} = 2^{-N+1}, \quad f(x) = \lim_{n \to \infty} f(x,j_n)$$

exists. Hence using Theorem 44.10,

$$X \subseteq Y_N, \quad V(\mu; \mathcal{A}; E; X) \leqslant V(\mu; \mathcal{A}; E; Y_N) \leqslant 2^{-Np}/(1 - 2^{-p}),$$
$$V(\mu; \mathcal{A}; E; X) = 0.$$

Taking $k = j_n$ in (46.7) and using (46.4) (Fatou's lemma) we have

$$\int_E |f(.,j) - f|^p \, d\mu \leqslant \liminf_{n \to \infty} \int_E |f(.,j) - f(.,j_n)|^p \, d\mu \leqslant \varepsilon$$
$$(j \geqslant k(\varepsilon))$$

giving (46.9), When for f we can substitute g, then by (46.4) again,

$$\int_E |f - g|^p \, d\mu \leqslant \liminf_{n \to \infty} \int_E |f(.,j_n) - g|^p \, d\mu \leqslant \varepsilon,$$

for each $\varepsilon > 0$. Theorem 44.11 completes the proof.

Ex. 46.1. A sequence can converge in mean without being pointwise convergent. (Put $f_n = 0$, apart from two sides of a triangle, the third side being on $y = 0$. Let the triangle move repeatedly from 0 to 1 with area tending to 0, but with height tending to infinity.)

Ex. 46.2. If a sequence is pointwise convergent, and convergent in mean, the limits are the same almost everywhere i.e. except in a set with variation 0.

47. μ-Measurability

In a decomposable division space $(R, \mathcal{S}, \mathcal{A})$ let E be an elementary set over which 1 is integrable with respect to a function μ of $I \in \mathcal{S}$. Let $\mathcal{A}$ also have the property that if $\mathbf{S} \in \mathcal{A}$ divides E, and if $\mathcal{D}\{I_1, \ldots, I_n\}$ is a division of E from $\mathbf{S}$, there are disjoint sets $J_j \subseteq I_j$ with union E, such that J_j contains the associated point of I_j ($j = 1, 2, \ldots, n$). Then we can define a *step function* f in E to be a function f that is constant at f_j on J_j, for $j = 1, 2, \ldots, n$, and some such division $\mathcal{D}$ of E.

A function f is *μ-measurable* if f is the limit almost everywhere of a sequence of step functions. Hence by Theorem 46.2 a bounded μ-measurable f is integrable if $\mu \geqslant 0$ and if every step function is integrable in E. More generally the μ-measurable f can lie between two functions each integrable in E, and then f is integrable in E.

If f is the limit almost everywhere of a sequence of μ-measurable functions then f is μ-measurable. For proof see Henstock (1963c), pp. 96–7; and p. 95 gives a partial converse that Lee (1965), Lemma 3, has improved. To replace this and Henstock (1963c), p. 94, Theorem 39.2, in part, we have:

THEOREM 47.1. *Let $\mu \geqslant 0$ be such that 1 is integrable with respect to μ in E. If f is integrable in E to H_1, then f is μ-measurable, provided that* (47.1) *there is a sequence $\{\mathbf{S}_j\} \subseteq \mathcal{A}$, each $\mathbf{S}_j$ dividing E, such that to each $x \in E$ there is an integer $j = j(x)$ with the property that if*

$$x \in I \in \mathcal{S}_{k\gamma}, \quad \gamma \in \Gamma, \quad k \geqslant j(x)$$

then x is the associated point of a finite number of non-overlapping intervals of the $\mathcal{S}_{k\gamma}$ with union I. We then say that x is an extra associated point of I.

Proof. In the integration we can replace μ by the integral H of 1 with respect to μ, and we can choose $\mathbf{S}_j^* \varepsilon \mathcal{A}$ dividing E, with

(47.2) $$|(\mathcal{D}_j) \sum fH - H_1| < 2^{-2j}$$

for all $\mathcal{D}_j$ from $\mathbf{S}_j^*$. As $\mathcal{A}$ is partially ordered in the sense of divisions we can suppose that $\{\mathbf{S}_j\}$ satisfies (47.1; 47.2). We choose a special sequence $\{\mathcal{D}_j\}$ satisfying (47.2),

(47.3) $$\mathcal{D}_1 \geqslant \mathcal{D}_2 \geqslant \mathcal{D}_3 \geqslant \ldots$$

For each integer j we put

$$f_j(t) = f_j(I) = f(x(\gamma, I)) \qquad (t \in J)$$

where J is the set associated with I in $\mathcal{D}_j$, so that f_j is a step function. By (47.1), we can have either $f_j(I)$ or $f(x)$ multiplying H in (47.2), where x is any extra associated point of I in $\mathcal{S}_{\gamma j}$. Denote either value by f. By Theorem 44.5 (44.6) and (47.2),

(47.4) $$(\mathcal{D}_j) \sum |fH(I) - H_1(I)| < 2^{3-2j}$$

Let E_j be the partial set from the partial division Q_j of $\mathcal{D}_j$, consisting of intervals I for which either

(47.5) $$|f_j(I) H(I) - H_1(I)| > 2^{-j} H(I)$$

or, for at least one extra associated point x of I,

(47.6) $$|f(x) H(I) - H_1(I)| > 2^{-j} H(I)$$

or both. From (47.4; 47.5; 47.6),

$$2^{-j} H(E_j) = 2^{-j}(Q_j) \sum H(I) < (Q_j) \sum |fH(I) - H_1(I)| < 2^{3-2j}$$

Removing from E_j all points that are associated points of intervals non-overlapping with E_j, we have a set K_j, and each interval I with associated point in K_j, that lies in an interval of $\mathcal{D}_j$, must lie in E_j. Hence as H is additive and non-negative,

(47.7) $$V\left(H; \mathcal{A}; E; \bigcup_{j=k}^{\infty} K_j\right) < \sum_{j=k}^{\infty} 2^{3-j} = 2^{4-k}$$

In the remaining intervals of $\mathcal{D}_j$, (47.5; 47.6) are false, so that

$$|f_j(I) - H_1(I)/H(I)| \leqslant 2^{-j}, \qquad |f(x) - H_1(I)/H(I)| \leqslant 2^{-j},$$

$$|f_j(I) - f(x)| \leqslant 2^{1-j} \left((j \geqslant k, j \geqslant j(x), x \in I \text{ in } D_j, x \notin \bigcup_{j=k}^{\infty} K) \right)$$

Thus by (47.1), $f_j(x) \to f(x)$ as $j \to \infty$, except for

$$x \in X = \bigcap_{k=1}^{\infty} \bigcup_{j=k}^{\infty} K_j, \quad V(H; \mathcal{A}; E; X) = 0$$

Note that by repeated bisection of E we can prove that the system of *Ex. 43.3* obeys (47.1).

THEOREM 47.2. *Let* $\mu \geqslant 0$ *be integrable and let* $f \in L_p$ *(i.e. let f be μ-measurable with $|f|^p$ integrable, for some $p \geqslant 1$.) Then there is a step function g, depending on $\varepsilon > 0$, such that*

$$\int_E |f-g|^p \, d\mu < \varepsilon$$

(Lee (1965), Lemma 4). *Proof.* We first assume that $|f| \leqslant M$, so that if $f_j(x)$ is the function of Theorem 47.1, with f replaced by f^p, we have, for some interval I depending on x, and $j \geqslant j(x)$,

$$|f_j(x)| \leqslant \frac{1}{H(I)} \left| \int_I f^p \, d\mu \right| + 2^{-j} \leqslant M^p + 2^{-j}, \quad |f_j(x)^{1/p}| \leqslant M$$

$$|f(x) - f_j(x)^{1/p}| \leqslant 2M, \quad \lim_{j \to \infty} f_j(x)^{1/p} = f(x)$$

almost everywhere. Hence by our form of Lebesgue's bounded convergence theorem, we can take $g = f_j(x)^{1/p}$ for large enough j.

If $f \in L_p$, f not bounded, we put $f^{(k)} = f$ if $|f| \leqslant k$, and otherwise $f^{(k)} = 0$. By Theorem 47.1, $f^{(k)}$ is bounded and μ-measurable, the limit almost everywhere of $f_j^{(k)}(x)$. Hence $f^{(k)} \in L_p$, $|f - f^{(k)}| \leqslant |f|$, and $f - f^{(k)} \to 0$ as $k \to \infty$. Hence by the majorized convergence theorem, we can choose k so large that

$$\int_E |f - f^{(k)}|^p \, d\mu < \tfrac{1}{2}\varepsilon$$

and the result is completed by the first part.

48. Integration in an Infinite Dimensional Space

We now expand *Ex. 43.12*. Let W be the space of all sequences $\mathbf{x} = \{x_j\}$ with $|x_j| \leqslant \tfrac{1}{2}$. We put $\mathbf{x}'_n$ as the sequence $x_1, x_2, \ldots, x_n$, $0, 0, \ldots$, and $\mathbf{x}''_n$ as the sequence $0, \ldots, 0, x_{n+1}, \ldots$, so that

$\mathbf{x} = \mathbf{x}'_n + \mathbf{x}''_n$. The *volume* of

$$I_n \equiv \bigtimes_{j=1}^{n} [a_j, b_j] \times \bigtimes_{j=n+1}^{\infty} [-\tfrac{1}{2}, \tfrac{1}{2}] = \bigtimes_{j=1}^{n} [a_j, b_j] \times W, \quad \text{is}$$

$$\mu(I_n) = \prod_{j=1}^{n} (b_j - a_j)$$

A functional f on W is called *cylindrical of order* n, if $f(\mathbf{x}) = f(\mathbf{x}''_n)$ for all $\mathbf{x}$. A set $X \subseteq W$ is called *cylindrical of order* n, if its characteristic function has this property, and then $X = W_n \times Y$, for some $Y \subseteq W$, where W_n is the set of $(x_1, \ldots, x_n)$ with $\mathbf{x}'_n \in W$.

THEOREM 48.1. *A μ-measurable functional f on W that is cylindrical of every finite order, is constant almost everywhere.*

Proof. Let X_m be the set where $|f| \leqslant m$. Then $f_m(x) = f(x)\, ch(X_m; x)$ is cylindrical of every finite order, bounded, and μ-measurable, and so is integrable relative to μ, say with integral F_m. Let $\mathcal{D}_{nr}$ be a division of W consisting of intervals I_n with $b_j - a_j = 1/r$ ($j = 1, 2, \ldots, n$). Since f_m is cylindrical of order n, $F_m(I_n)$ is the same for each I_n of $\mathcal{D}_{nr}$. Also $\mu(I_n)$ is the same, so that the ratio

$$d_{mnr} \equiv F_m(I_n)/\mu(I_n)$$

is the same for all I_n of $\mathcal{D}_{nr}$. Hence $d_m = d_{mnr}$ is independent of n, r, since

$$F_m(W) = (\mathcal{D}_{nr}) \sum F_m(I_n) = (\mathcal{D}_{nr}) \sum d_{mnr}\mu(I_n) = d_{mnr}\mu(W) = d_{mnr}$$

(48.1) Hence $F_m(I_n) = d_m\mu(I_n)$ $(I_n \in \mathcal{D}_{nr}; n, r = 1, 2, \ldots)$

Further, f_m is bounded by $\pm m$, so that $|F_m(I_n)| \leqslant m \cdot \mu(I_n)$ for all I_n, and not just those in $\mathcal{D}_{nr}$, and F_m is continuous, in the sense that if $\{I_{nj}\}$ is a strictly increasing sequence of I_n, with union between J_n° and J_n, this being another I_n, then $F_m(I_{nj}) \to F_m(J_n)$. By this continuity, finite additivity, and (48.1),

(48.2) $F_m(I_n) = d_m\mu(I_n)$ $(I_n \subseteq W, n = 1, 2, \ldots)$

and $F_m - d_m\mu(I_n)$ has variation 0. Hence $\{f(\mathbf{x})\, ch(X_m; \mathbf{x}) - d_m\}\, \mu(I_n)$ has variation 0, where $\mathbf{x}$ is the associated point of I_n, i.e. by Theorem 44.11,

(48.3) $f(\mathbf{x})\, ch(X_m;\mathbf{x}) = d_m$ almost everywhere

Since W is the union of the X_m it follows that for some m, X_m is of positive variation, and then $d_m = d_r$ for all $r > m$, since $X_m \subseteq X_r$. Hence letting $m \to \infty$ we prove the theorem.

THEOREM 48.2. (Jessen (1934), p. 273) *If $f \geqslant 0$ is integrable in W with respect to μ then for almost all $\mathbf{x} \in W$, the integral*

$$(48.4) \qquad f_m(\mathbf{x}) \equiv \int_{W_m} f(\mathbf{x}'_m + \mathbf{x}''_m)\, d\mu \qquad (m = 1, 2, \ldots)$$

exists, and we have

$$(48.5) \qquad \lim_{m \to \infty} f_m(\mathbf{x}) = \int_W f\, d\mu$$

Proof. We first use Fubini's theorem, an analogue of Henstock (1963c), p. 109, Theorem 44.2, obtained since we have a product division space. Then $f_m(\mathbf{x})$ exists almost everywhere since

$$(48.6) \quad M = \int_W f(\mathbf{x})\, d\mu = \int_W \left\{ \int_{W_m} f(\mathbf{x}'_m + \mathbf{x}''_m)\, d\mu \right\} d\mu = \int_W f_m(\mathbf{x})\, d\mu$$

Clearly $f_m(\mathbf{x})$ is cylindrical of order m, so that by Theorem 48.1 there are constants a, b, or a conventional $+\infty$, such that, almost everywhere in W

$$(48.7) \qquad \lim_{m \to \infty} \inf f_m(\mathbf{x}) = a, \qquad \lim_{m \to \infty} \sup f_m(\mathbf{x}) = b$$

Taking any number $c < b$, we write

$$(48.8) \quad X_m = \{\mathbf{x} : f_m(\mathbf{x}) \geqslant c\}, \quad Y_m = \bigcup_{j=1}^{m} X_j, \quad Y = \bigcup_{j=1}^{\infty} X_j$$

By (48.7), $Y \subseteq W$, $W \backslash Y$ is of variation zero. Since f_m is cylindrical of order m, so is X_m. We write Y_m as a union of disjoint μ-measurable sets

$$Z_m = X_m, \quad Z_{m-1} = X_{m-1} \backslash X_m, \quad Z_{m-2} = X_{m-2} \backslash (X_m \cup X_{m-1}), \ \ldots;$$

$$Z_j = W_j \times A_j (A_j \subseteq W)$$

248

since Z_j is cylindrical of order j. Thus

$$\int_{Z_j} f \, d\mu = \int_{A_j} \left\{ \int_{W_j} f(\mathbf{x}'_j + \mathbf{x}''_j) \, d\mu \right\} d\mu = \int_{A_j} f_j(\mathbf{x}) \, d\mu$$
$$\geqslant c \cdot V(\mu; \mathcal{A}; W; A_j)$$
$$= c \cdot V(\mu; \mathcal{A}; W; Z_j)$$

By (48.6), since the Z_j are μ-measurable,

$$M \geqslant \int_{Y_m} f(\mathbf{x}) \, d\mu = \sum_{j=1}^{m} \int_{Z_j} f(\mathbf{x}) \, d\mu \geqslant c \sum_{j=1}^{m} V(\mu; \mathcal{A}; W; Z_j)$$
$$= cV(\mu; \mathcal{A}; W; Y_m)$$

so that if $m \to \infty$ and $c \to b-$,

$$M \geqslant cV(\mu; \mathcal{A}; W; Y) = cV(\mu; \mathcal{A}; W) = c, \quad b \leqslant M$$

Similarly we can prove that $a \geqslant M$, so that by (48.6) the theorem is true.

THEOREM 48.3. *If f is bounded and μ-measurable, or if f and $|f|$ are integrable relative to μ, then (48.4) exists almost everywhere in W, with (48.5).*

Proof. If $|f| \leqslant M$, apply Theorem 48.2 to $f + M$ and M. Otherwise apply to $|f|$ and $|f| - f$.

49. Haar Measure on Locally Compact Groups

Haar (1933) has given a construction of a left invariant measure on locally compact groups, which has been proved unique by von Neumann (1936), followed by Weil (1940), who gives the existence of a left-invariant Lebesgue integral, and Cartan (1940), who proves the existence and uniqueness of the integral. This book at times needs the Haar measure, but not the Haar–Lebesgue integral as it is covered by *Ex. 43.14*. Thus we proceed as follows.

Let $\mathcal{C}$ be the family of compact closures of non-empty open sets. These open sets form a base for the topology since the group is locally compact. Let $G \in \mathcal{G}_0$, so that G is a neighbourhood of the group unit. Then each x is covered by $x \cdot G$. Let $C \in \mathcal{C}$. Then C is covered by a finite number of $x \cdot G$, so that we can define the integer $(C : G)$ to be the least number of $x \cdot G$ that form a cover of C.

LEMMA 49.1. *For each* $G \in \mathcal{G}_0$, *each* $C, C_1 \in \mathcal{C}$, *we have the following results:*

(49.1)
$$(C : G) \geqslant 1,$$

(49.2)
$$(x \cdot C : G) = (C : G) \qquad (all \ x \in T),$$

(49.3)
$$(C \cup C_1 : G) \leqslant (C : G) + (C_1 : G),$$

(49.4)
$$(C : G) \leqslant (C_1 : G), \quad if \quad C \subseteq C_1,$$

(49.5)
$$(C : G) \leqslant (C : C_1^{\circ})(C_1 : G).$$

Proof. The last is the only non-trivial result, and is true since each $x \cdot C_1^{\circ}$ that is in a cover of C, is covered in turn by $(x \cdot C_1 : G) = (C_1 : G)$ sets $y \cdot G$. Fixing $D \in \mathcal{C}$, we arrange that $\mu(D) = 1$ by using the ratio

$$\mu(C : G) = (C : G)/(D : G)$$

LEMMA 49.2. *For each* $G \in \mathcal{G}_0$, *each* $C, C_1 \in \mathcal{C}$, *we have the following results:*

(49.6)
$$0 < \mu(C : G) < \infty,$$

(49.7)
$$\mu(D : G) = 1,$$

(49.8)
$$\mu(xC : G) = \mu(C : G) \qquad (x \in T),$$

(49.9)
$$\mu(C \cup C_1 : G) \leqslant \mu(C : G) + \mu(C_1 : G),$$

(49.10)
$$\mu(C : G) \leqslant \mu(C_1 : G), \quad if \quad C \subseteq C_1,$$

(49.11)
$$(D : C^{\circ})^{-1} \leqslant \mu(C : G) \leqslant (C : D^{\circ}).$$

The last follows from (49.5),

$$(D : G) \leqslant (D : C^{\circ}) \cdot (C : G), \quad (C : G) \leqslant (C : D^{\circ}) \cdot (D : G).$$

LEMMA 49.3. *Let* $C, C_1 \in \mathcal{C}$ *be disjoint. Then there is a* $G_1 \in \mathcal{G}_0$ *such that for all* $G_2 \subseteq G_1$, $G_2 \in \mathcal{G}_0$, *we have*

$$\mu(C : G_2) + \mu(C_1 : G_2) = \mu(C \cup C_1 : G_2)$$

Proof. By Theorem 14.2 (14.3) there are two disjoint open sets G_3, G_4, such that

$$C \subseteq G_3, \ C_1 \subseteq G_4$$

Let us put

$$F = \backslash G_3, \quad X = \bigcup_{x \in C} x^{-1} \cdot F, \quad y \in X'$$

Then given $G \in \mathcal{G}_0$, there are z, x, with

$$z \in y \cdot G, \quad z \in \bigcup_{a \in C} a^{-1} \cdot F, \quad x \in C, \quad z \in x^{-1} \cdot F$$

Let $Y(G)$ be the set of $x \in C$ for which

$$(y \cdot G) \cap (x^{-1} \cdot F)$$

is not empty. Then $Y(G)$ has the finite intersection property. Also, since x^{-1} is continuous, if $x \in Y(G)'$, then

$$(y \cdot \bar{G}) \cap (x^{-1} \cdot F)$$

is not empty. Since T is regular, there is a $G_5 \in \mathcal{G}_0$ with $\bar{G}_5 \subseteq G$, so that $Y(G_5)' \subseteq Y(G)$. Hence there is a point $a \in \overline{Y(G)}$, and also $a \in Y(G)$, for all $G \in \mathcal{G}_0$. Hence, for all $G \in \mathcal{G}_0$,

$$(y \cdot G) \cap (a^{-1} \cdot F)$$

is not empty, y is in the closure of $a^{-1} \cdot F$, so that $y \in a^{-1} \cdot F$, and X is closed. As C and $F = \backslash G_3$ are disjoint, then $u \notin X$, $G_6 = \backslash X \in \mathcal{G}_0$, and by construction $x \cdot G_6$ and F are disjoint, for all $x \in C$. Similarly there is a $G_7 \in \mathcal{G}_0$ with $x \cdot G_7 \subseteq G_4$ for all $x \in C_1$. We take $G_1 = G_6 \cdot G_7 \in \mathcal{G}_0$, and then

$$x \cdot G_1 \subseteq G_3 \quad \textit{(all } x \in C\textit{)}, \quad x \cdot G_1 \subseteq G_4 \quad \textit{(all } x \in C_1\textit{)}$$

and the lemma follows easily. We have proved more than is strictly required.

THEOREM 49.1. *There is a finite function μ defined in $\mathcal{C}$, called the Haar measure, for which*

(49.12) $\mu(D) = 1,$

(49.13) $\mu(x \cdot C) = \mu(C) \, (C \in \mathcal{C}),$

(49.14) $\mu(C \cup C_1) \leqslant \mu(C) + \mu(C_1) \, (C, C_1 \in \mathcal{C}),$

(49.15) $(D : C^\circ)^{-1} \leqslant \mu(C) \leqslant (C : D^\circ),$

(49.16)   *if $C, C_1 \in \mathcal{C}$ and are disjoint, $\mu(C) + \mu(C_1) = \mu(C \cup C_1)$.*

For each $C \in \mathcal{C}$ the interval $[(D : C^\circ)^{-1}, (C : D^\circ)]$ is compact, so that by Tychonoff's theorem (Theorem 13.8), the Cartesian product of these intervals for $C \in \mathcal{C}$, is compact in the product topology. It follows that if $X(C, G)$, for $C \in \mathcal{C}, G \in \mathcal{G}_0$, is the collection of all $\mu(C : G_1)$, for $G_1 \in \mathcal{G}_0$, $G_1 \subseteq G$, then $X(C, G)$ has the finite intersection property, and there is a μ in the Cartesian product for which $\mu(C) \in X(C, G)'$, for each $G \in \mathcal{G}_0$. Further, if we assume the uniqueness of the Haar measure, given $C, C_1 \in \mathcal{C}$, there is a $G_1 \subseteq G$ for which $G_1 \in \mathcal{G}_0$ and

$$|\mu(C) - \mu(C : G_1)| < \tfrac{1}{2}\varepsilon, \quad |\mu(C_1) - \mu(C_1 : G_1)| < \tfrac{1}{2}\varepsilon$$

Hence as $\varepsilon > 0$ is arbitrary, we prove (49.13; 49.14; 49.16). The other two are obvious.

50. The Law of the Iterated Logarithm

Kolmogoroff (1929) gives a property of the sum of a sequence of independent random variables that really concerns the measure of a set of sequences. More complicated results are true, but Kolmogoroff's is sufficient for our purpose, and can be stated as follows.

THEOREM 50.1. *For each n let F_n be monotone increasing from 0 t $-\infty$, to 1 at $+\infty$. Let $\mathbf{z} \equiv \{z_k\}$ be a real infinite sequence, with*

$$\int_{-\infty}^{\infty} x \, dF_n = 0, \quad \int_{-\infty}^{\infty} x^2 \, dF_n = \sigma_n^2 < \infty,$$

$$s_n^2 = \sum_{k=1}^{n} \sigma_k^2, \quad S_n = \sum_{k=1}^{n} z_k$$

Let the interval function $h(I_n)$ for the Cartesian product I_n of $[a_j, b_j]$, for $1 \leqslant j \leqslant n$, and $(-\infty, \infty)$, for $j > n$, be

$$h(I_n) = \prod_{j=1}^{n} \{F_j(b_j) - F_j(a_j)\}$$

and denote the norm variation of h in a set X of $\mathbf{z}$ by $V(X)$. Let $X(\mathbf{m})$ be the set of $\mathbf{z}$ where $|z_k| \leqslant m_k$ $(k = 1, 2, \ldots)$. If, as $n \to \infty$, m_n is

252

monotone increasing, m_n/s_n monotone decreasing,

(50.1) $$s_n^2 \to \infty,$$

(50.2) $$m_n \cdot \log \log (s_n^2)/s_n^{-1} \to 0,$$

then for each $\varepsilon > 0$, and almost everywhere in $X(\mathbf{m})$, using V,

(50.3) $$|S_n| \leqslant (1+\varepsilon)s_n \sqrt{(2 \log \log (s_n^2))}$$

Note that if m_n is constant, (50.1) implies (50.2). We need many lemmas, and slight emendations of Kolmogoroff's proof.

LEMMA 50.1.

(50.4) $\quad (1-x/3)^{-1} \leqslant 1+x/2 \qquad (0 \leqslant x \leqslant 1),$

(50.5) $\quad 1-x/3-x^2/(3\cdot 4)-\ldots > 1-x/2 \qquad (0 \leqslant x \leqslant 1),$

(50.6) $\quad 1+x > \exp\{x(1-x)\} \qquad (x > 0),$

(50.7) $\quad 1-x < 1/(1-x^2/8) < 1+x \qquad (0 < x < 1/2),$

(50.8) $\quad (1+4x)(1-x)^{-2} < 1+24x \qquad (0 < x < 1/2).$

Proof. These easy estimations are obtained as follows.

$$(1-x/3)(1+x/2) = 1+x(1-x)/6 \geqslant 1 \qquad (0 \leqslant x \leqslant 1)$$

$$1-x/3-x^2/(3\cdot 4)- \ldots = 1-(x/3)\{1+(x/4)+x^2/(4\cdot 5)+ \ldots\}$$
$$> 1-(x/3)(1-1/4)^{-1} = 1-x/4 > 1-x/2 \qquad (0 \leqslant x \leqslant 1)$$

If $\qquad f(x) = \log(1+x)-x(1-x), \quad$ then $\quad f(0) = 0,$

$$f'(x) = -1+2x+1/(1+x) = (x+2x^2)/(1+x) > 0 \qquad (x > 0)$$

$$(1-x^2/8) < 1; \qquad (1+x)(1-x^2/8) = 1+x-(x^2/8)-(x^3/8)$$

$$= 1+x(1-x/8-x^2/8) > 1+29x/32 > 1 \qquad (0 < x < 1/2)$$

$$(1+24x)(1-x)^2 = 1+22x-47x^2+24x^3 = 1+4x+x(18-47x$$
$$+24x^2) \geqslant 1+4x+\tfrac{1}{2}x > 1+4x \qquad (0 < x < \tfrac{1}{2})$$

Let us now put

$$U_n = \max_{1 < k \leqslant n} S_k, \quad W_n(x) = V(\{z : S_n > x\}),$$

$$\overline{W}_n(x) = V(\{z : U_n > x\}), \quad m_n = \lambda_n s_n$$

LEMMA 50.2. *If* $0 \leqslant x\lambda_n \leqslant s_n$, *then* $W_n(x) < \exp\{-x^2(1-\theta_n)/(2s_n^2)\}$, $\theta_n = x\lambda_n/(2s_n)$.

Proof. Omitting suffixes k, n, take $a > 0$, $a\lambda s \leqslant 1$. Then since $|z| \leqslant \lambda s$,

$$\int_{-\infty}^{\infty} e^{az}\, dF = 1 + \frac{a^2}{2!}\sigma^2 + \sum_{n=3}^{\infty} \frac{a^n}{n!} \int_{-\infty}^{\infty} z^n\, dF$$

$$\leqslant 1 + \frac{a^2}{2!}\sigma^2 \left\{ 1 + \frac{a\lambda s}{3} + \frac{a^2\lambda^2 s^2}{3\cdot 4} + \ldots \right\} < 1 + \frac{a^2\sigma^2}{2} \bigg/ \left(1 - \frac{a\lambda s}{3}\right)$$

$$\leqslant 1 + \frac{a^2\sigma^2}{2}\left(1 + \frac{a\lambda s}{2}\right) < \exp\left\{\frac{a^2\sigma^2}{2}\left(1 + \frac{a\lambda s}{2}\right)\right\}$$

where we have used (50.4). Thus since $\lambda_k s_k$ is monotone increasing,

$$(50.9) \qquad \int_{-\infty}^{\infty} e^{az}\, dF_k < \exp\left\{\frac{a^2\sigma_k^2}{2}\left(1 + \frac{a\lambda_n s_n}{2}\right)\right\}$$

By (50.9) we have

$$\int_{-\infty}^{\infty} \ldots \int_{-\infty}^{\infty} \exp(aS_n)\, dF_1 \ldots dF_n = \prod_{k=1}^{n} \int_{-\infty}^{\infty} \exp(az_k)\, dF_k$$

$$(50.10) \qquad\qquad < \exp\left\{\frac{a^2 s_n^2}{2}\left(1 + \frac{a\lambda_n s_n}{2}\right)\right\}$$

Further, for all x, and using (50.10),

$$W_n(x)\, e^{ax} \leqslant \int_{-\infty}^{\infty} \ldots \int_{-\infty}^{\infty} \exp(aS_n)\, dF_1 \ldots dF_n \equiv \mu(\exp(aS_n))$$

$$(50.11) \qquad W_n(x) \leqslant \exp\left(-ax + \frac{a^2 s_n^2}{2}\left(1 + \frac{a\lambda_n s_n}{2}\right)\right)$$

We put $a = xs_n^{-2}$ $(x > 0)$, so that as $x\lambda_n \leqslant s_n$ we have $a\lambda_n s_n \leqslant 1$. Since $\lambda_k s_k$ is monotone increasing, then also $a\lambda_k s_k \leqslant 1$, and (50.11) gives the lemma.

LEMMA 50.3. *If* $x\lambda_n \geqslant s_n$, *then* $W_n(x) < \exp(-x/(4\lambda_n s_n))$.

Proof. In (50.11) we take $a = 1/(\lambda_n s_n)$. Then

$$W_n(x) \leqslant \exp\{-x/(\lambda_n s_n) + (1 + 1/2)/(2\lambda_n^2)\}, \quad 1/\lambda_n^2 \leqslant x/(\lambda_n s_n)$$

LEMMA 50.4. *If* $x\lambda_n \leqslant s_n$ *then* $W_n(x) < \exp(-x^2/(4s_n^2))$.

Use Lemma 50.2 with

$$\theta_n = x\lambda_n/(2s_n) \leqslant 1/2$$

LEMMA 50.5. *Under the conditions*

(50.12) $$x\lambda_n/s_n = \omega_n < 1/256,$$

(50.13) $$x^2/s_n^2 = \nu_n > 512,$$

then $W_n(x) > \exp\{-x^2(1+\varepsilon)/(2s_n^2)\}$, $\varepsilon = \max\{96\sqrt{(\log \nu_n/\nu_n)}, 192\sqrt{\omega_n}\}$.

Proof. For $\delta = \varepsilon/24$, then

(50.14) $$\delta^2 = \max (16 \log \nu_n/\nu_n, 64\omega_n)$$

Using (50.12; 50.13),

$$64\omega_n < 1/4, \quad (16 \log \nu_n)/\nu_n < (16 \log 512)/512 = (9 \log 2)/32 < 1/4$$

Hence by (50.14),

(50.15) $$0 < \delta < \tfrac{1}{2}$$

Let us take

(50.16) $$a = x/\{s_n^2(1-\delta)\}$$

(50.17) $$x/s_n^2 < a < 2x/s_n^2$$

From (50.12; 50.17),

$$a\lambda_n s_n < 2x\lambda_n/s_n$$

(50.18) $$a\lambda_n s_n < 2\omega_n < 1/128$$

Also by (50.16),

(50.19) $$\nu_n = x^2/s_n^2 = a^2 s_n^2(1-\delta)^2 < a^2 s_n^2$$

Using (50.18; 50.5; 50.6), and as for (50.9),

$$a\lambda_n s_n \leqslant 1,$$

$$\int_{-\infty}^{\infty} \exp (az)\, dF_k \geqslant 1 + \frac{a^2\sigma_k^2}{2}\left\{1 - \frac{a\lambda_n s_n}{3} - \frac{(a\lambda_n s_n)^2}{3\cdot 4} - \cdots\right\}$$

$$> 1 + \frac{a^2\sigma_k^2}{2}\left(1 - \frac{a\lambda_n s_n}{2}\right) > \exp\left\{\frac{a^2\sigma_k^2}{2}\left(1 - \frac{a\lambda_n s_n}{2}\right)\left(1 - \frac{a^2\sigma_k^2}{2} + \frac{a^3\sigma_k^2\lambda_n s_n}{2}\right)\right\}$$

$$> \exp\left\{\frac{a^2\sigma_k^2}{2}\left(1 - \frac{a\lambda_n s_n}{2} - \frac{a^2\sigma_k^2}{2}\right)\right\} \geqslant \exp\left\{\frac{a^2\sigma_k^2}{2}(1 - a\lambda_n s_n)\right\}$$

The last step follows since $|z_k| \leqslant \lambda_n^2 s_n^2$, so that

$$\sigma_k^2 \leqslant \lambda_n^2 s_n^2 = \lambda_n s_n / a$$

It follows that

(50.20) $\quad \mu(\exp{(aS_n)}) = \prod_{k=1}^{n} \int_{-\infty}^{\infty} \exp{(az_k)} \, dF_k > \exp\left\{\dfrac{a^2 s_n^2}{2}(1 - a\lambda_n s_n)\right\}$

By (50.14; 50.18; 50.20),

(50.21) $\quad a\lambda_n s_n < 2\omega_n < \delta^2/4, \quad \mu(\exp{(aS_n)}) > \exp\left\{\dfrac{a^2 s_n^2}{2}(1 - \delta^2/4)\right\}$

Now by (50.18), and then Lemma 50.3, as $y \to \infty$,

$$4a\lambda_n s_n < 1, \quad a < 1/(4\lambda_n s_n), \quad 0 \leqslant e^{ay} W_n(y) \leqslant \exp{(ay - y/(4\lambda_n s_n))} \to 0$$

$$\mu(\exp{(aS_n)}) = -\int_{-\infty}^{\infty} e^{ay} \, dW_n(y) = a \int_{-\infty}^{\infty} e^{ay} W_n(y) \, dy$$

(50.22) $\quad a\left\{\int_{-\infty}^{0} + \int_{0}^{x} + \int_{x}^{c} + \int_{c}^{g} + \int_{g}^{\infty}\right\} = a(J_1 + J_2 + J_3 + J_4 + J_5)$

where $x = as_n^2(1 - \delta)$, $c = as_n^2(1 + \delta)$, $g = 8as_n^2$. Now $W_n(y) = V(X)$ for some X in the space of all real sequences, so that $W_n(y) \leqslant 1$,

(50.23) $\qquad\qquad aJ_1 \leqslant a \int_{-\infty}^{0} e^{ay} \, dy = 1$

By Lemma 50.3 and (50.18), for $y \geqslant s_n/\lambda_n$,

$$W_n(y) < \exp{(-y/(4\lambda_n s_n))} < \exp{(-2ay)}$$

(50.24) $\qquad\qquad aJ_5 < a \int_{g}^{\infty} e^{-ay} \, dy = \left[-e^{-ay}\right]_{g}^{\infty} < 1$

By (50.13; 50.15; 50.19; 50.21),

$$\mu(\exp{(aS_n)}) > \exp\left\{\dfrac{a^2 s_n^2}{2}\left(1 - \dfrac{\delta^2}{4}\right)\right\} > \exp\left(\dfrac{a^2 s_n^2}{2} \cdot \dfrac{15}{16}\right)$$

$$> \exp\left(\dfrac{512 \cdot 15}{2 \cdot 16}\right) = \exp{(240)} > 8$$

Hence from (50.23; 50.24),

(50.25) $\qquad\qquad aJ_1 + aJ_5 < \tfrac{1}{4}\mu(\exp{(aS_n)})$

From (50.12; 50.14) and Lemma 50.2, if

$$y \leqslant 8as_n^2 \quad \text{then} \quad \theta_n = y\lambda_n/(2s_n) < \omega_n < \delta^2/8,$$
$$W_n(y) < \exp\{-y^2(1-\delta^2/8)/(2s_n^2)\},$$

(50.26) $\quad a(J_2 + J_4) < a \displaystyle\int \exp(u(y))\, dy \quad \text{over} \quad 0 \leqslant y \leqslant as_n^2(1-\delta),$

$$as_n^2(1+\delta) \leqslant y \leqslant 8as_n^2,$$

where $\quad u(y) = ay - y^2(1-\delta^2/8)/(2s_n^2), \quad u'(y) = a - y(1-\delta^2/8)/s_n^2$

with a maximum of $u(y)$ at

$$y = as_n^2/(1-\delta^2/8)$$

which by Lemma 50.1 (50.7) lies between x and c. Hence we need only look at

$$u(c) = a^2 s_n^2(1+\delta) - \tfrac{1}{2}a^2 s_n^2(1+\delta^2)(1-\tfrac{1}{8}\delta^2)$$
$$= \tfrac{1}{2}a^2 s_n^2\{1-\delta^2 + \tfrac{1}{8}\delta^2(1+\delta)^2\} < \tfrac{1}{2}a^2 s_n^2(1-\tfrac{1}{2}\delta^2)$$

since by (50.15), $(1+\delta^2) \leqslant 9/4$; and, more easily,

$$u(b) = a^2 s_n^2(1-\delta) - \tfrac{1}{2}a^2 s_n^2(1-\delta)^2(1-\tfrac{1}{8}\delta^2)$$
$$= \tfrac{1}{2}a^2 s_n^2\{1-\delta^2 + \tfrac{1}{8}\delta^2(1-\delta)^2\} < \tfrac{1}{2}a^2 s_n^2(1-\tfrac{1}{2}\delta^2)$$

Hence from (50.26),

(50.27) $\qquad a(J_2 + J_4) < a \displaystyle\int_0^g \exp\left(\tfrac{1}{2}a^2 s_n^2(1-\tfrac{1}{2}\delta^2)\right) dy$

$$< 8a^2 s_n^2 \exp\left(\tfrac{1}{2}a^2 s_n^2(1-\tfrac{1}{2}\delta^2)\right)$$

By (50.13; 50.14; 50.15; 50.19),

$$\log(32a^2 s_n^2) = \log(32v_n(1-\delta)^{-2}) \leqslant \log(128v_n) < \log v_n^2$$
$$= 2\log v_n \leqslant \tfrac{1}{8}v_n\delta^2 = \tfrac{1}{8}a^2 s_n^2(1-\delta)^2\delta^2$$
$$< \tfrac{1}{8}a^2 s_n^2\delta^2$$

(50.28) $\qquad \log(32a^2 s_n^2) < a^2 s_n^2\delta^2/8 < a^2 s_n^2\delta/2$

From (50.21; 50.27; 50.28),

$$a(J_2 + J_4) < \tfrac{1}{4}\exp\{\log(32a^2 s_n^2) + \tfrac{1}{2}a^2 s_n^2(1-\tfrac{1}{2}\delta^2)\}$$
$$< \tfrac{1}{4}\exp\{\tfrac{1}{2}a^2 s_n^2(1+\tfrac{1}{4}\delta^2 - \tfrac{1}{2}\delta^2)\}$$

(50.29) $\qquad a(J_2 + J_4) < \tfrac{1}{4}\mu(\exp(aS_n))$

From (50.21; 50.25; 50.29),

$$aJ_3 > \tfrac{1}{2}\mu(\exp{(aS_n)}) > \tfrac{1}{2}\exp{\{\tfrac{1}{2}a^2s_n^2(1-\tfrac{1}{4}\delta^2)\}}, \quad 0 < \delta < \tfrac{1}{2}$$

(50.30)
$$aJ_3 > \tfrac{1}{2}\exp{\{\tfrac{1}{2}a^2s_n^2(1-\delta)\}}$$

But as $W_n(y)$ is monotone decreasing in y,

(50.31)
$$aJ_3 = a\int_x^c e^{ay}W_n(y)\,dy < ae^{ac}W_n(x)\cdot 2as_n^2\delta$$

$$< 2a^2s_n^2 e^{ac}W_n(x)$$

From (50.8; 50.15; 50.28; 50.30; 50.31) and $24\delta = \varepsilon$,

$$W_n(x) > (4a^2s_n^2)^{-1}\exp{\{a^2s_n^2(1-\delta)/2 - a^2s_n^2(1+\delta)\}}$$
$$= (4a^2s_n^2)^{-1}\exp{\{-a^2s_n^2(1+3\delta)/2\}} = \exp{\{-\log{(4a^2s_n^2)}}$$
$$-a^2s_n^2(1+3\delta)/2\} > \exp{\{-a^2s_n^2(1+4\delta)/2\}}$$
$$> \exp{[-x^2(1+4\delta)/\{2s_n^2(1-\delta)^2\}]} > \exp{\{-x^2(1+24\delta)/(2s_n^2)\}}$$
$$= \exp{\{-x^2(1+\varepsilon)/(2s_n^2)\}}$$

giving Lemma 50.5.

LEMMA 50.6. $\mu((U_n - S_n)^2)$

$$\equiv \int_{-\infty}^{\infty}\ldots\int_{-\infty}^{\infty}(U_n - S_n)^2\,dF_1\ldots dF_n \leqslant s_n^2$$

Proof. $U_m = \max\limits_{1 < j < m} S_j = \max{(U_{m-1}, S_m)}$,

$$U_m - S_m = \max{(U_{m-1} - S_{m-1} - z_m, 0)}$$

If X is the set where the first term in the *max* is positive,

$$\mu((U_m - S_m)^2) = \mu((U_{m-1} - S_{m-1} - z_m)^2\,ch(X;\,.))$$
$$\leqslant \mu((U_{m-1} - S_{m-1} - z_m)^2) = \mu((U_{m-1} - S_{m-1})^2) + \sigma_m^2$$

the last step following since U_{m-1}, S_{m-1} are constant relative to z_m and since the integral of z_m relative to F_m is zero. By induction

$$\mu((U_n - S_n)^2) \leqslant \sum_{j=2}^{n}\sigma_j^2 < s_n^2$$

We can now turn to the proof of the theorem, supposing that $0 < \delta < \tfrac{1}{2}$, δ fixed. Since $s_n \to \infty$, $\lambda_n \to 0$, $\lambda_n \log\log{(s_n^2)} \to 0$, we can find a number N such that

(50.32) $$s_N^2 > e$$

(50.33) $$c(t) \equiv \log \log^{1/2} t, \quad c(s_N^2) > 4/\delta$$

(50.34) $$\lambda_N^2 < \delta/16$$

(50.35) $$\lambda_N c(s_N^2) < \sqrt{2\delta}/9 < \delta/4$$

For fixed N, $N(1)$, ..., $N(k-1)$, we choose $N(k)$ so that

(50.36) $$(s_{N(k)}/s_{N(k-1)})^2 \leqslant 1 + \delta/4$$

(50.37) $$(s_{N(k)+1}/s_{N(k-1)})^2 > 1 + \delta/4$$

By (50.34; 50.37),

$$(s_{N(k)}/s_{N(k-1)})^2 = (s_{N(k)+1}^2 - \sigma_{N(k)+1}^2)/s_{N(k-1)}^2$$
$$\geqslant (s_{N(k)+1}^2 - \lambda_{N(k)+1}^2 s_{N(k)+1}^2)/s_{N(k-1)}^2 > (1 + \delta/4)(1 - \delta/16) > 1 + \delta/8$$

By (50.32), and multiplying the inequalities together,

(50.38) $$s_{N(k)}^2 > (1 + \delta/8)^k$$

From (50.36), for

(50.39) $$\chi(t) = \sqrt{(2t \cdot \log \log t)}, \quad \chi(s_{N(k)}^2)/\chi(s_{N(k-1)}^2) < 1 + \delta/4$$

From the existence of at least one of the inequalities

$$S_n > \chi(s_n^2)(1 + \delta) \qquad (N(k-1) \leqslant n \leqslant N(k))$$

with (50.39), follow the inequalities

(50.40) $$U_{N(k)} > \chi(s_{N(k-1)}^2)(1 + \delta) > \chi(s_{N(k)}^2)(1 + \delta/4)$$

From Lemma 50.6,

$$V(\{z : U_n - S_n > \sqrt{m \cdot s_n}\}) \cdot m s_n^2 \leqslant \mu((U_n - S_n)^2) \leqslant s_n^2$$
$$V(\{z : U_n - S_n > \sqrt{m \cdot s_n}\}) \leqslant 1/m,$$
$$V(\{z : U_n - S_n \leqslant \sqrt{m \cdot s_n}\}) \geqslant 1 - 1/m$$

(50.41) $$U_n = S_n + O(s_n) = S_n + o(\chi(s_n^2)) \qquad \text{almost everywhere}$$

From (50.41), if (50.40) is true for an infinity of k, then, for these k after a certain stage,

(50.42) $$S_{N(k)} > \chi(s_{N(k)}^2)(1 + \delta/4)$$

The product measure of the set where (50.42) is true, is

$$V_k = W_{N(k)} [\chi(s^2_{N(k)}) (1+\delta/4)]$$

By (50.35) and Lemma 50.2,

$$\chi(s^2_{N(k)})\lambda_{N(k)} \leqslant s_{N(k)},$$
$$V_k < 2\exp\{-\chi^2(s^2_{N(k)}) (1+\delta/4)^2 (1-\theta_{N(k)})/(2s^2_{N(k)})\}$$
$$= 2\exp\{-c^2(s^2_{N(k)}) (1+\delta/4)^2 (1-\theta_{N(k)})\}$$

where by (50.35),

$$\theta_{N(k)} = \chi(s^2_{N(k)}) (1+\delta/4)\lambda_{N(k)}/(2s_{N(k)}) = 2^{-1/2}c(s^2_{N(k)}) (1+\delta/4)\lambda_{N(k)}$$
$$< \delta(1+\delta/4)/9 < \delta/8$$
$$V_k < 2\exp\{-c^2(s^2_{N(k)}) (1+\delta/4)^2 (1-\delta/8)\}$$
$$< 2\exp\{-c^2(s^2_{N(k)}) (1+\delta/4)\}$$

By (50.38),

$$V_k < 2\exp\{-c^2((1+\delta/8)^k) (1+\delta/4)\}$$
$$= 2\{\log(1+\delta/8)^k\}^{-1-\delta/4} = Ak^{-1-\delta/4}$$

where A is a constant depending on δ. Thus the sum of the V_k is finite, so that the set where (50.42) is true for some $k \geqslant k_0$, has variation that tends to 0 as $k_0 \to \infty$. Hence the theorem is proved.

11

FINITE DIMENSIONAL VECTOR SPACES

51. n-Dimensional Vectors

IN the notation of section 35 a *finite dimensional linear space T* is a space with the property that there is a finite set of linearly independent elements of T, such that all other elements of T are finite linear combinations of the elements of the finite set. Let these elements be $\mathbf{e}_1, \ldots, \mathbf{e}_n$, say. If $\mathbf{x} \in T$ then $\mathbf{x} = x_1\mathbf{e}_1 + \ldots + x_n\mathbf{e}_n$, for some scalars $x_1, \ldots, x_n$. Thus we can represent $\mathbf{x}$ by the vector $(x_1, \ldots, x_n)$ of its components or coordinates x_j, and $\mathbf{e}_1 = (1, 0, \ldots, 0)$, $\mathbf{e}_2 = (0, 1, 0, \ldots, 0)$, $\ldots$ We write $\mathbf{z} = (0, \ldots, 0)$, $a\mathbf{x} = (ax_1, \ldots, ax_n)$, $\mathbf{x}+\mathbf{y} = (x_1+y_1, \ldots, x_n+y_n)$, $\mathbf{xy} = (x_1y_1, \ldots, x_ny_n)$, also, where a is an arbitrary scalar. With these rules for operations on vectors we have set up a bijection between the $\mathbf{x} \in T$ and the $(x_1, \ldots, x_n)$ that preserves the algebraic operations of addition, and multiplication by a scalar. Thus we say that T is *algebraically isomorphic* to the space Z^n (if the scalars are arbitrary complex numbers) or R^n (if the scalars are all real.)

If f is a linear functional in T it has a simple form

$$(51.1) \qquad f(\mathbf{x}) = \sum_{i=1}^{n} x_j f(\mathbf{e}_j)$$

If f is bilinear we write $a_{jk} = f(\mathbf{e}_j, \mathbf{e}_k)$ and then

$$(51.2) \qquad f(\mathbf{x}, \mathbf{y}) = \sum_{j=1}^{n} \sum_{k=1}^{n} x_j y_k f(\mathbf{e}_j, \mathbf{e}_k) = \sum_{j,\,k=1}^{n} a_{jk} x_j y_k$$

Writing the a_{jk} as elements of a matrix A, the last expression is $\mathbf{x}A\mathbf{y}'$

in matrix notation. Similarly, if f is Hermitian then

(51.3)
$$f(\mathbf{x}, \mathbf{y}) = \sum_{j,\,k=1}^{n} x_j \bar{y}_k f(\mathbf{e}_j, \mathbf{e}_k)$$

The terms non-negative definite, positive definite, originated in matrix theory.

THEOREM 51.1. *If f is a bilinear non-negative definite functional in R^n,*

(51.4) $\quad (a_{jk} + a_{kj})^2 \leqslant 4 a_{jj} a_{kk}, \quad a_{jk} \equiv f(\mathbf{e}_j, \mathbf{e}_k) \quad (j, k = 1, 2, \ldots, n)$

Proof. We put $x = \mathbf{e}_j$, $y = \mathbf{e}_k$, in Theorem 26.1 (26.2). For the unit matrix,

(51.5)
$$\left(\sum_{j=1}^{n} |x_j y_j| \right)^2 \leqslant \sum_{j=1}^{n} x_j^2 \sum_{k=1}^{n} y_k^2$$

enabling us to deal with the Euclidean norm $\|\mathbf{x}\|_2 = \left\{ \sum_{j=1}^{n} x_j^2 \right\}^{1/2}$.
We write R^n as R_2^n.

If f is a Hermitian non-negative definite functional it is still biadditive, so that in Z^n,

(51.6)
$$\left\{ \sum_{j,\,k=1}^{n} (a_{jk} x_j \bar{y}_k + a_{kj} \bar{x}_j y_k) \right\}^2 \leqslant 4 \left\{ \sum_{j,\,k=1}^{n} a_{jk} x_j \bar{x}_k \right\} \left\{ \sum_{j,\,k=1}^{n} a_{jk} y_j \bar{y}_k \right\}$$

and with $\mathbf{x} = \mathbf{e}_j$, $\mathbf{y} = \mathbf{e}_k$, we again have (51.4).

The unit matrix case here leads to

(51.7)
$$\left\{ \sum_{j=1}^{n} |x_j y_j| \right\}^2 \leqslant \sum_{j=1}^{n} |x_j|^2 \sum_{k=1}^{n} |y_k|^2$$

and the *Euclidean norm* $\|\mathbf{x}\|_2$ with x_j^2 replaced by $|x_j|^2$, writing Z^n as Z_2^n.

More generally, we can consider the results of section 40, with X the set $1, 2, \ldots, n$, and $\mathcal{H}^+$ the set of all vectors with non-negative components. We choose L to be

$$L(|\mathbf{x}|) \equiv \sum_{j=1}^{n} |x_j|$$

for which the only 'null function' is the zero $\mathbf{z}$. Thus Theorem 40.3

(40.15) gives

$$(51.8) \quad \sum_{j=1}^{n} \Phi(a|x_j|) + \sum_{j=1}^{n} \Psi(b|y_j|) \geq ab \sum_{j=1}^{n} |x_j y_j| \quad (a > 0, b > 0)$$

Equality occurs in (51.8) if, and only if, it occurs for each j, so that, for a, b independent of j,

$$(51.9) \quad \varphi(a|x_j|) \leq b|y_j| \leq \varphi(a|x_j|+) \quad (j = 1, 2, \ldots, n)$$

Hölder's inequality, (40.21), gives

$$(51.10) \quad \left\{ \sum_{j=1}^{n} |x_j|^p \right\}^{1/p} \left\{ \sum_{j=1}^{n} |y_j|^q \right\}^{1/q} \geq \sum_{j=1}^{n} |x_j y_j|$$
$$(p > 1, \ 1/p + 1/q = 1)$$

and Minkowski's inequality, Theorem 40.4, shows that

$$\|x\|_p \equiv \left\{ \sum_{j=1}^{n} |x_j|^p \right\}^{1/p}$$

is a norm in R^n, Z^n, which are then written R_p^n, Z_p^n.

(51.11) Equality holds in (51.10) if, and only if, $a^p |x_j|^p = b^q |y_j|^q$ $(1 \leq j \leq n)$

We can write Minkowski's inequality in the form

$$\left\{ \sum_{j=1}^{n} |x_j + y_j|^p \right\}^{1/p} \leq \left\{ \sum_{j=1}^{n} (|x_j| + |y_j|)^p \right\}^{1/p} \leq \left\{ \sum_{j=1}^{n} |x_j|^p \right\}^{1/p}$$
$$+ \left\{ \sum_{j=1}^{n} |y_j|^p \right\}^{1/p}$$

The condition for equality in the second inequality, is found from (51.11), and then, for each j, $|x_j + y_j| = |x_j| + |y_j|$, if the first inequality is an equality. Thus we have that

(51.12) equality holds in Minkowski's inequality if, and only if, $a|x_j| = b|y_j|$ $(1 \leq j \leq n)$; with one or both of x_j, y_j zero, or x_j/y_j is a positive real number, for each $j = 1, 2, \ldots, n$.

In this case we can show that as $q \to \infty$,

$$(51.13) \quad \|x\|_q \to \|x\|_\infty = \sup_{1 \leq j \leq n} |x_j|$$
$$\left(\|x\|_\infty \leq \left\{ \sum_{j=1}^{n} |x_j|^q \right\}^{1/q} \leq n^{1/q} \|x\|_\infty \to \|x\|_\infty \right)$$

When we use $\|\mathbf{x}\|_\infty$ in R^n, Z^n, we write them as R_∞^n, Z_∞^n. Hölder's and a related inequality are

(51.14) $\|\mathbf{x}\|_p \cdot \|\mathbf{y}\|_q \geqslant \|\mathbf{xy}\|_1$, $\|\mathbf{x}\|_1 \|\mathbf{y}\|_\infty \geqslant \|\mathbf{xy}\|_1$

Corresponding to each norm $\|\mathbf{x}\|_p$ $(1 \leqslant p \leqslant \infty)$, there is a norm of each linear functional f on R^n, and on Z^n. From (51.1; 51.14), taking $y_j = f(\mathbf{e}_j)$, $= f_j$, say, we have

$$\text{norm}\,(f) = \sup |f(\mathbf{x})|/\|\mathbf{x}\|_p \leqslant \|\mathbf{f}\|_q$$

where $q = \infty$ when $p = 1$, and $q = 1$ when $p = \infty$. Actually equality occurs,

(51.15) $\text{norm}\,(f) = \|\mathbf{f}\|_q$,   where $f_j \equiv f(\mathbf{e}_j)$

$$(1 \leqslant p \leqslant \infty,\ 1/p + 1/q = 1)$$

For $p = 1$,   let $|f_k| = \|\mathbf{f}\|_\infty$.   Then $|f(\mathbf{e}_k)| = \|\mathbf{f}\|_\infty$,

$$\|\mathbf{e}_k\|_1 = 1$$

For $1 < p < \infty$ take

$$x_j = |f_j|^{q-1} \exp\left(-i\arg(f_j)\right) = |f_j|^q/f_j\ (f_j \neq 0),\quad x_j = 0\ (f_j = 0)$$

$$(j = 1, \ldots, n)$$

$$f(\mathbf{x}) = \sum_{j=1}^n |f_j|^q = \|\mathbf{f}\|_q^q,\quad \|\mathbf{x}\|_p^p = \sum_{j=1}^n |f_j|^{pq-p} = \|\mathbf{f}\|_q^q,$$

$$|f(\mathbf{x})|/\|\mathbf{x}\|_p = \|\mathbf{f}\|_q^{q-q/p} = \|f\|_q$$

For $p = \infty$ we take

$$x_j = |f_j|/f_j\ (f_j \neq 0),\quad x_j = 0\quad (f_j = 0)\quad (j = 1, 2, \ldots, n)$$

$$f(\mathbf{x}) = \sum_{j=1}^n x_j f_j = \sum_{j=1}^n |f_j| = \|\mathbf{f}\|_1,\quad \|\mathbf{x}\|_\infty = 1,$$

$$|f(\mathbf{x})|/\|\mathbf{x}\|_\infty = \|\mathbf{f}\|_1$$

52. Contraction Mappings in Real n-Dimensional Vector Spaces

All spaces R_p^n, Z_p^n ($1 \leqslant p \leqslant \infty$) are complete. For

$$\|\mathbf{x}\|_\infty \leqslant \|\mathbf{x}\|_p \leqslant n^{1/p} \|\mathbf{x}\|_\infty \qquad (1 \leqslant p < \infty)$$

so that $\|\mathbf{x}\|_p \to 0$ if, and only if, $\|\mathbf{x}\|_\infty \to 0$, i.e. if, and only if, for each fixed j, $x_j \to 0$. Thus the completeness of R_p^n, Z_p^n, follows from the completeness of R^1, $Z^1 = R_2^2$, and so from R^1 alone; and the fixed point theorem for contraction mappings follows (see section 16.)

Let $\mathbf{y} = A\mathbf{x}+\mathbf{b}$ be a mapping of R^n or Z^n into itself that uses a matrix A and a constant vector $\mathbf{b}$ (writing vectors as column vectors). Then a fixed point $\mathbf{x}$ satisfies $\mathbf{x} = A\mathbf{x}+\mathbf{b}$, $\mathbf{x}(I-A) = \mathbf{b}$, where I is the unit matrix. As might be expected, the conditions imposed on A to make a contraction mapping depend on the particular metric used. For

$$\|\mathbf{x}\|_1, \quad \varrho_1(\mathbf{x}, \mathbf{z}) = \sum_{j=1}^{n} |z_j - x_j|. \quad \text{If} \quad \mathbf{y} = A\mathbf{x}+\mathbf{b}, \quad \mathbf{w} = A\mathbf{z}+\mathbf{b},$$

$$\varrho_1(\mathbf{y}, \mathbf{w}) < a\varrho_1(\mathbf{x}, \mathbf{z}), \quad \text{then} \quad \varrho_1(\mathbf{y}, \mathbf{w}) = \varrho_1(A\mathbf{x}+\mathbf{b}, A\mathbf{z}+\mathbf{b})$$

$$= \varrho_1(A\mathbf{x}, A\mathbf{z}) = \sum_{j=1}^{n} \left| \sum_{k=1}^{n} a_{jk}(x_k - z_k) \right| \leqslant \sum_{j, k=1}^{n} |a_{jk}| \, |z_k - x_k|$$

$$= \sum_{k=1}^{n} \left\{ \sum_{j=1}^{n} |a_{jk}| \right\} |x_k - z_k| \leqslant \sup_k \sum_{j=1}^{n} |a_{jk}| \, \varrho_1(\mathbf{x}, \mathbf{z})$$

A sufficient condition for a contraction mapping, is therefore

$$(52.1) \qquad \sum_{j=1}^{n} |a_{jk}| < 1 \qquad (1 \leqslant k \leqslant n)$$

For $\quad \|\mathbf{x}\|_p, \quad \varrho_p(\mathbf{x}, \mathbf{z}) = \left\{ \sum_{j=1}^{n} |x_j - z_j|^p \right\}^{1/p}, \quad \varrho_p^p(\mathbf{y}, \mathbf{w})$

$$= \varrho_p^p(A\mathbf{x}, A\mathbf{z}) = \sum_{j=1}^{n} \left| \sum_{k=1}^{n} a_{jk}(x_k - z_k) \right|^p$$

$$\leqslant \sum_{j=1}^{n} \left(\sum_{k=1}^{n} |a_{jk}|^q \right)^{p/q} \sum_{k=1}^{n} |x_k - z_k|^p$$

We therefore obtain a sufficient condition as

$$(52.2) \qquad \sum_{j=1}^{n} \left(\sum_{k=1}^{n} |a_{jk}|^q \right)^{p/q} < 1$$

For $\|\mathbf{x}\|_\infty$, $\quad \varrho_\infty(\mathbf{x}, \mathbf{z}) = \sup_{1 < j < n} |x_j - z_j|, \quad \varrho_\infty(\mathbf{y}, \mathbf{w}) = \varrho_\infty(A\mathbf{x}, A\mathbf{z})$

$$= \sup_j \left| \sum_{k=1}^n a_{jk}(x_k - z_k) \right| \leqslant \sup_j \sum_{k=1}^n |a_{jk}| \, |x_k - z_k|$$

$$\leqslant \sup_j \sum_{k=1}^n |a_{jk}| \, \varrho_\infty(\mathbf{x}, \mathbf{z})$$

A sufficient condition for a contraction mapping is thus that

$$(52.3) \qquad\qquad \sum_{k=1}^n |a_{jk}| < 1 \qquad (all\ j)$$

For the metric ϱ_∞, this is also necessary. We take

$$x_k - z_k = |a_{jk}|/a_{jk}, \qquad (k = 1, \ldots, n)$$

for $j = 1, 2, \ldots, n$, in turn, to show this.

Finally, $\mathbf{y} = A\mathbf{x} + \mathbf{b}$ has a unique fixed point if, and only if, the determinant of $A - I$ is not zero, so that we have been finding sufficient conditions for the non-vanishing of that determinant; but none is necessary. This shows, at the same time, the usefulness and the limitations of the method of contraction mappings for a very simple space.

12

SEQUENCE SPACES

53. Real and Complex Sequence Spaces

MANY infinite dimensional spaces can be put in one-one correspondence with spaces of sequences by a bijection that preserves
addition, and multiplication by scalars, and then one can often
use results on finite dimensional spaces by letting the dimension
tend to infinity. Subsequently we shall give a few examples of this
process. We write

$$\mathbf{x} = \{x_n\}, \quad \mathbf{z} = \{0\}, \quad a\mathbf{x} = \{ax_n\}, \quad \mathbf{x}+\mathbf{y} = \{x_n+y_n\},$$
$$\mathbf{xy} = \{x_n y_n\}$$

where a is any real or complex number, while the sequence $\mathbf{e}^j$ is
that which has 1 in the jth place, and 0's elsewhere. A sequence $\mathbf{x}$ for
which there is an integer N such that $x_n = 0$ $(n > N)$, is by the
mathematician's usual economy of language, called a *finite sequence*.

If f is a linear functional of all finite sequences $\mathbf{x}$, then for these,

$$(53.1) \qquad\qquad f(\mathbf{x}) = \sum_{n=1}^{N} x_n f(\mathbf{e}^n)$$

But if the x_n are not 'zero for all but a finite number of n', the corresponding infinite series need not be convergent, and $f(\mathbf{x})$ need not
exist even if the series is convergent. To link the two properties we
need something like continuity or measurability on the space of
sequences. Continuity is dealt with in this chapter, measurability in
the next.

Similarly if f is a bilinear (or Hermitian) non-negative definite
functional, then $f^{1/2}(\mathbf{x}, \mathbf{x})$ will serve as a pseudonorm where it is
defined, while if $\mathbf{x}$ and $\mathbf{y}$ are finite sequences with the same N, then

267

in the bilinear case,

$$(53.2) \qquad f(\mathbf{x}, \mathbf{y}) = \sum_{j,\,k=1}^{N} a_{jk} x_j y_k, \qquad a_{jk} \equiv f(e^j, e^k)$$

where we can regard the a_{jk} as elements of an infinite matrix, with $j, k = 1, 2, \ldots$ Again, by using continuity or measurability conditions we can often ensure the existence of f in a substantial part of a pace of $(\mathbf{x}, \mathbf{y})$. In the Hermitian case,

$$(53.3) \qquad f(\mathbf{x}, \mathbf{y}) = \sum_{j,\,k=1}^{N} a_{jk} x_j \bar{y}_k$$

An example of a bilinear positive definite functional, is

$$f(\mathbf{x}, \mathbf{y}) = \sum_{n=1}^{\infty} x_n y_n$$

Let l_2 be the space of all real sequences $\mathbf{x}$ with finite $\|\mathbf{x}\|_2 = f^{1/2}(\mathbf{x}, \mathbf{x})$ This is the original *Hilbert space*. By (51.5), letting $n \to \infty$, and taking

$$(53.4) \qquad \mathbf{x}, \mathbf{y}, \in l_2, \qquad \left\{ \sum_{j=1}^{\infty} |x_j y_j| \right\}^2 \leqslant \|\mathbf{x}\|_2^2 \cdot \|\mathbf{y}\|_2^2$$

Similarly an example of a Hermitian positive definite functional, is

$$g(\mathbf{x}, \mathbf{y}) = \sum_{n=1}^{\infty} x_n \bar{y}_n$$

and we can write l_2 again for the space of all *complex* sequences $\mathbf{x}$ with finite $\|\mathbf{x}\|_2 = g^{1/2}(\mathbf{x}, \mathbf{x})$. Clearly, if $\mathbf{x}, \mathbf{y}$ are real, $f(\mathbf{x}, \mathbf{y}) = g(\mathbf{x}, \mathbf{y})$, so that g is an extension of f to complex sequences. Also we again obtain (53.4), this time from the limit of (51.7). In either case l_2 is a linear space, from

$$\sum_{j=1}^{\infty} |ax_j + by_j|^2 \leqslant \sum_{j=1}^{\infty} (|a|\,|x_j| + |b|\,|y_j|)^2 \leqslant |a|^2 \|\mathbf{x}\|_2^2 + |b|^2 \|\mathbf{y}\|_2^2$$
$$+ 2|ab|\,\|\mathbf{x}\|_2\,\|\mathbf{y}\|_2$$

More generally, let $\mathscr{H}^+$ be the space of $|\mathbf{x}| = \{|x_j|\}$, with L as

$$L(|\mathbf{x}|) \equiv \sum_{j=1}^{\infty} |x_j|$$

In this case the X of section 40 is the set of all positive integers. We can let $n \to \infty$ in (51.8) to obtain

(53.5) $\displaystyle\sum_{j=1}^{\infty} \Phi(a|x_j|) + \sum_{j=1}^{\infty} \Psi(b|y_j|) \geqslant ab \sum_{j=1}^{\infty} |x_j y_j| \quad (a > 0, \quad b > 0)$

(53.6) Equality holds in (53.5) if, and only if, for a, b independent of j,

$$\varphi(a|x_j|) \leqslant b|y_j| \leqslant \varphi(a|x_j|+) \quad (j = 1, 2, \ldots)$$

Let l_p be the space of sequences $\mathbf{x}$ for which

$$\|\mathbf{x}\|_p \equiv \left\{ \sum_{j=1}^{\infty} |x_j|^p \right\}^{1/p} < \infty$$

where $1 \leqslant p < \infty$. Letting $n \to \infty$ in (51.10) we have Hölder's inequality,

53.7) $\quad \|\mathbf{xy}\|_1 \leqslant \|\mathbf{x}\|_p \cdot \|\mathbf{y}\|_q \quad (p > 1, \quad 1/p + 1/q = 1)$

(53.8) Equality occurs in (53.7) if, and only if, for a, b independent of j,

$$a^p |x_j|^p = b^q |y_j|^q \quad (j = 1, 2, \ldots)$$

Minkowski's inequality now follows, in the form

(53.9) $\quad \|\mathbf{x} + \mathbf{y}\|_p \leqslant \||\mathbf{x}| + |\mathbf{y}|\|_p \leqslant \|\mathbf{x}\|_p + \|\mathbf{y}\|_p$

showing that $\|\mathbf{x}\|_p$ is a pseudonorm. Clearly it is a norm.

(53.10) If $p = 1$, equality occurs in (53.9) when, for each j, either $x_j = 0$, or $y_j = 0$, or both, or x_j/y_j is real and positive.

(53.11) If $p > 1$, equality occurs in (53.9) when $a|\mathbf{x}| = b|\mathbf{y}|$ and, for each j, either $x_j = 0$, or $y_j = 0$, or both, or $x_j/y_j = b/a$.

Let m be the space of *bounded* sequences, i.e. all for which

$$\|\mathbf{x}\|_\infty \equiv \sup_j |x_j| < \infty$$

269

Further, let c, c_0 be the respective spaces of convergent sequences, and of sequences tending to 0. These are subspaces of m, so that we can use $\|\mathbf{x}\|_\infty$. Not every point of even c_0 lies in the union of spaces $l_p (p \geqslant 1)$, for see *Ex. 53.1*. But it is obvious that (53.7) still holds when $p = 1$, $q = \infty$, or when $p = \infty$, $q = 1$.

THEOREM 53.1. *If $l_\infty = c_0$, each continuous linear functional f on l_p is given by the formula*

$$(53.12) \qquad f(\mathbf{x}) = \sum_{j=1}^\infty x_j f(\mathbf{e}^j) \qquad (1 \leqslant p \leqslant \infty)$$

(53.13) *with norm* $(f) = \|\mathbf{f}\|_q$, *where* $f_j \equiv f(\mathbf{e}_j)$ $\qquad (j = 1, 2, \ldots)$.

(53.14) *Conversely, if* $\|\mathbf{x}\|_p < \infty$, $\|\mathbf{f}\|_q < \infty$ $(1 \leqslant p \leqslant \infty, 1/p + 1/q = 1)$, *then*

$$\sum_{j=1}^\infty x_j f_j$$

is a continuous linear functional on l_p.

Proof. Let $\mathbf{x}^N$ be the vector constructed from $\mathbf{x}$ by

$$x_j^N = \begin{cases} x_j & (j \leqslant N) \\ 0 & (j > N) \end{cases}$$

Then as $N \to \infty$, since $l_\infty = c_0$,

$$\|\mathbf{x} - \mathbf{x}^N\|_p^p = \sum_{j=N+1}^\infty |x_j|^p \to 0 \qquad (1 \leqslant p < \infty),$$

$$\|\mathbf{x} - \mathbf{x}^N\|_\infty = \sup_{j > N} |x_j| \to 0$$

By continuity and (53.1) we have (53.12). For (53.13), by (51.15),

$$\text{norm } (f) = \sup |f(\mathbf{x})| / \|\mathbf{x}\|_p (\mathbf{x} \in l_p) \geqslant \sup |f(\mathbf{x}^N)| / \|\mathbf{x}^N\|_p (\mathbf{x}^N \in l_p),$$

$$= \|\mathbf{f}^N\|_q.$$

In all cases $\|\mathbf{f}^N\|_q \to \|\mathbf{f}\|_q$ as $N \to \infty$, so that

$$\text{norm } (f) \geqslant \|\mathbf{f}\|_q$$

By (51.15) again, given $M < \text{norm } (f)$, there are $\mathbf{x} \in l_p$ and an integer

N, with

$$|f(\mathbf{x})|/\|\mathbf{x}\|_p > M, \quad |f(\mathbf{x}^N)|/\|\mathbf{x}^N\|_p > M, \quad \|\mathbf{f}\|_q \geqslant \|\mathbf{f}^N\|_q > M$$

giving the opposite inequality and so (53.13). Then (53.14) follows by Hölder's inequality.

Ex. 53.1. Show that

$$\{\log^{-1}(n+1)\} \in c_0 \Big\backslash \bigcup_{p>1} l_p$$

54. Completeness in Real and Complex Sequence Spaces

In order to apply earlier theorems it is important to show that l_p, m, c, c_0 are complete.

THEOREM 54.1. *l_p is complete, using $\|\mathbf{x}\|_p$, for $1 \leqslant p < \infty$.*

Proof. If $\{\mathbf{x}^n\} \subseteq l_p$ ($\mathbf{x}^n = \{x_j^n\}$) is fundamental, then given $\varepsilon > 0$, there is an integer M with

$$(54.1) \qquad \sum_{j=1}^{\infty} |x_j^n - x_j^m|^p < \varepsilon^p \quad (m \geqslant M, \quad n \geqslant M)$$

Hence for each fixed j, $\{x_j^n\}$ is fundamental and so convergent to x_j, say. Also, for fixed N,

$$\sum_{j=1}^{N} |x_j^n - x_j^m|^p < \varepsilon^p \quad (m \geqslant M, \quad n \geqslant M),$$

$$\sum_{j=1}^{N} |x_j^n - x_j|^p \leqslant \varepsilon^p \quad (n \geqslant M)$$

Letting $N \to \infty$, we see that as $\varepsilon > 0$ is arbitrary, $\mathbf{x}^n \to \mathbf{x} \equiv \{x_j\}$. Also

$$\mathbf{x}^n - \mathbf{x} \in l_p \quad (n \geqslant M)$$

so that by linearity of l_p, $\mathbf{x} \in l_p$, and the result is proved.

THEOREM 54.2. *m, c, c_0 are complete, using $\|\mathbf{x}\|_\infty$.*

Proof. Let $\{\mathbf{x}^n\} \subseteq m$ ($\mathbf{x}^n = \{x_j^n\}$) be fundamental, so that for $\varepsilon > 0$, there is an M satisfying

$$\sup_j |x_j^n - x_j^m| < \varepsilon \quad (m \geqslant M, \quad n \geqslant M)$$

For each fixed j, then $\{x_j^n\}$ is fundamental, and so convergent to x_j, say,

(54.2)
$$|x_j^n - x_j^m| < \varepsilon \quad (m \geqslant M, \quad n \geqslant M),$$

$$|x^n - x_j| \leqslant \varepsilon \quad (n \geqslant M), \quad \sup_j |x_j^n - x_j| \leqslant \varepsilon$$

for $n \geqslant M$, and $\mathbf{x} \equiv \{x_j\}$ is a bounded sequence, and m is complete. To show that c is complete we take $\{\mathbf{x}^n\} \subseteq c$. Then $y^n = \lim_{j \to \infty} x_j^n$ exists, and from (54.2),

$$|y^n - y^m| \leqslant \varepsilon \quad (m \geqslant M, n \geqslant M)$$

and $\{y^n\}$ is fundamental, and so convergent, say to y. From (54.2) again,

$$\limsup_{j \to \infty} |y^n - x_j| \leqslant \varepsilon \quad (n \geqslant M), \quad \limsup_{j \to \infty} |y - x_j| \leqslant \varepsilon$$

As $\varepsilon > 0$ is arbitrary, $y = \lim_{j \to \infty} x_j$, $\mathbf{x} \in c$. If $\{\mathbf{x}^n\} \subseteq c_0$, then $y^n = y = 0$, $\mathbf{x} \in c_0$.

THEOREM 54.3. *Let* $f(\mathbf{x}) = \sum_{j=1}^{\infty} x_j y_j$ *exist for all* $\mathbf{x} \in X$, *where* $X = l_p$ $(1 \leqslant p < \infty)$, *m, c, or* c_0, *with the given norms. Then f is continuous*, norm $(f) < \infty$.

Proof. As f is the limit of continuous functions, the partial sums of the series, f is a Baire function, X being a Baire space since it is complete (Theorem 17.3). If N is an integer, the set X_N where $|f| \leqslant N$, is a Borel set (Theorem 19.5 (19.12)). The union of the X_N is X. Hence, for some N, X_N is of the second category. By Theorem 18.5, X_N is a Baire set, and by Theorem 29.4, X_N is a $D_1 - \mathcal{G}$-set. Hence there is a non-empty open neighbourhood G of the origin $\mathbf{z}$ with

$$G \subseteq D_1(X_N), \quad |f(\mathbf{x})| \leqslant 2N \quad (\mathbf{x} \in G)$$

As G contains a set $\|\mathbf{x}\| < \varepsilon$, for some $\varepsilon > 0$, we have f bounded and continuous.

55. The Summ ability of Sequences and Series

An interesting brief history of divergent series is given in Hardy (1949). These series are usually attacked by using some kind of smoothing process. For example, if $v_1 = 1$, $v_j = (-1)^{j+1} \cdot 2$, the infinite series is divergent, with partial sums $x_n = (-1)^{n+1}$ ($n = 1$, 2, ...). We smooth the partial sums, using

$$y_k = k^{-1}(x_1 + \ldots + x_k) = 0 \quad (k \text{ even}), \quad k^{-1} \ (k \text{ odd}),$$

$$y_k \to 0 \quad (k \to \infty)$$

This is the *first arithmetic* or *Çesaro* or *Hölder mean*. We could have used $z(u) = (1-u)\sum_{k=1}^{\infty} x_k u^k = (u-1)\sum_{k=1}^{\infty} (-u)^k = (1-u)\,u(1+u)^{-1}$ $\to 0 \ (u \to 1-)$, the *Abel mean*. Most smoothing processes on $\{x_k\}$ are linear and continuous,

(55.1) $$f(\mathbf{x}, u) = \sum_{k=1}^{\infty} a_k(u)\, x_k$$

where the parameter u takes positive integer values and tends to ∞, or u takes all real values in $[a, b)$, where b can be $+\infty$, and where $u \to b$. By a simple transformation we can assume $a = 1$, $b = \infty$, so that the notation '$u \geqslant 1$' is supposed to cover both cases. The coefficient $a_n(u)$ of x_k is called a *convergence factor*, and it is sometimes regarded as an element in an infinite matrix $\{a_k(u)\}$, particularly when u takes integer values alone.

The most convenient convergence factors are those that transform c into c, or a space of functions convergent as $u \to \infty$, which we also denote by c, and also that transform a substantial number of divergent sequences into sequences of c. Similarly we consider m, c_0, and the corresponding spaces of ultimately bounded functions, and of functions convergent to 0, for which we use the same symbols. For speed, we list the various conditions first, and then we write symbolically the statement:

'In order that the linear functional $f(\mathbf{x}, u)$ should transform the space X into (at least part of) the space Y, it is necessary and sufficient that (α) ...' as '$(X \to Y)(\alpha)$ ...'

(55.2) $$\sum_{k=1}^{\infty} |a_k(u)| < \infty, \quad a_k(u) = f(e_k, u),$$

(55.3) $$\lim_{u \to \infty} \sup \sum_{k=1}^{\infty} |a_k(u)| < \infty$$

(55.4) $\lim_{u \to \infty} a_j(u)$ exists, for each fixed positive integer j,

(55.5) $\lim_{u \to \infty} a_j(u) = 0$, for each fixed positive integer j,

(55.6) $$\lim_{u \to \infty} \sum_{k=1}^{\infty} a_k(u) \ \ exists,$$

(55.7) $$\lim_{u \to \infty} \sum_{k=1}^{\infty} a_k(u) = 1.$$

(55.8) $(c_0 \to m; \ c \to m; \ m \to m)$ (55.2) $(u \geqslant 1)$, (55.3).

Proof. Theorem 54.3 gives (55.2) necessary. Also, for each $\mathbf{x} \in c_0$,

$$\lim_{u \to \infty} \sup |f(\mathbf{x}, u)| < \infty.$$

By Theorems 34.1, 53.1, we have (55.3),

$$\lim_{u \to \infty} \sup \|\mathbf{f}(u)\|_1 = \lim_{u \to \infty} \sup \text{norm} \ (f(., u)) < \infty$$

For sufficiency, let $\mathbf{x} \in m$. Then

$$\sum_{k=1}^{\infty} |a_k(u)x_k| \leqslant \|\mathbf{x}\|_{\infty} \cdot \sum_{k=1}^{\infty} |a_k(u)| < \infty$$

$$\lim_{u \to \infty} \sup \left| \sum_{k=1}^{\infty} a_k(u)x_k \right| \leqslant \|\mathbf{x}\|_{\infty} \cdot \lim_{u \to \infty} \sup \sum_{k=1}^{\infty} |a_k(u)| < \infty$$

(55.9) $(c_0 \to c)$ (55.2) $(u \geqslant 1)$, (55.3) (55.4).

Proof. For (55.4), $e^j \in c_0$. Conversely, given $\varepsilon > 0$, there is an n depending on ε, such that

$$|x_k| < \varepsilon \ (k > n), \quad \left| \sum_{k=n+1}^{\infty} a_k(u)x_k \right| \leqslant \varepsilon \sum_{k=1}^{\infty} |a_k(u)| \leqslant \varepsilon M(u > u_0)$$

$$\lim_{u \to \infty} \sum_{k=1}^{n} a_k(u)x_k = \sum_{k=1}^{n} \left(\lim_{u \to \infty} a_k(u) \right) x_k$$

274

(55.10) $$\lim_{u \to \infty} f(\mathbf{x}, u) = \sum_{k=1}^{\infty} \left(\lim_{u \to \infty} a_k(u) \right) x_k \qquad (\mathbf{x} \in c_0)$$

(55.11) $(c_0 \to c_0)$ (55.2) $(u \geqslant 1)$, (55.3), (55.5).

Proof. For (55.5), $\mathbf{e}^j \in c_0$. Conversely, we use (55.10) with zero limits on the right.

The convergence factor $a_k(u)$ is said to be *efficient* for $\{x_k\}$ if there exist

$$f(\mathbf{x}, u) \equiv \sum_{k=1}^{\infty} a_k(u) \, x_k \, (u \geqslant 1), \qquad \lim_{u \to \infty} f(\mathbf{x}, u)$$

A *K-matrix* is defined to be a convergence factor efficient for every convergent sequence (Cooke (1950), p. 63).

(55.12) $(c \to c)$ (55.2) $(u \geqslant 1)$,   (55.3), (55.4), (55.6).

This was first proved for infinite lower semi-matrices by Kojima (1917) and extended to general infinite matrices by Schur (1920), written 1918.

Proof. After (55.9), take $x_k = 1$ (*all k*) for (55.6). For sufficiency, use (55.11),

$$\mathbf{x} \in c, \quad y = \lim_{k \to \infty} x_k, \quad y_k = x_k - y, \quad \mathbf{y} \in c_0,$$

$$f(\mathbf{x}, u) = y \sum_{k=1}^{\infty} a_k(u) + f(\mathbf{y}, u)$$

If a *K*-matrix preserves the limit of every convergent sequence, it is a *T-matrix* (Cooke (1950), p. 65), and is sometimes called *regular*.

(55.13) $(c \to c$, *limit preserved*) (55.2) $(u \geqslant 1)$, (55.3), (55.5), (55.7).

Sufficiency was first proved for infinite lower semi-matrices by Silverman (1913), written 1910. Necessity and sufficiency was proved for row-finite infinite matrices by Toeplitz (1911), and for general infinite matrices by Schur (1920).

Proof. After (55.11), for (55.7) put $x_k = 1$ (*all k*). For sufficiency follow (55.12).

(55.14) $(m \to c_0)$ (55.2) $(u \geqslant 0)$,   and

(55.15) $$\sum_{k=1}^{\infty} |a_k(u)| \to 0 \qquad (u \to \infty)$$

275

(Schur (1920), Satz III, 4′, p. 82) *Proof.* By (55.11) we have (55.3; 55.5). If

$$(55.16) \qquad \limsup_{u \to \infty} \sum_{k=1}^{\infty} |a_k(u)| > 0$$

then there are $M > \varepsilon > 0$ and a sequence $u_j \to \infty$, with

$$(55.17) \quad \varepsilon \leqslant \sum_{k=1}^{\infty} a_k(u_j) \leqslant M, \quad b(j, k) = a_k(u_j) \qquad (j = 1, 2, \ldots)$$

We define $\{x_k\}$ with $|x_k| = 1$ (*all* k) in the following way. By (55.17) there is a $k(1)$ with

$$(55.18) \qquad \sum_{k=k(1)+1}^{\infty} |b(1, k)| < \tfrac{1}{4}\varepsilon$$

From (55.17; 55.18), for

$$\text{sgn}\,(z) = z/|z|\ (z \neq 0), \quad \text{sgn}\,(0) = 1,$$
$$x_k = \text{sgn}^{-1}\,(b(1, k)) \qquad (1 \leqslant k \leqslant k(1))$$

$$(55.19) \quad \left| \sum_{k=1}^{\infty} b(1, k)x_k \right| \geqslant \sum_{k=1}^{\infty} |b(1, k)| - 2 \sum_{k=k(1)+1}^{\infty} |b(1, k)|$$
$$\geqslant \varepsilon - \tfrac{1}{2}\varepsilon = \tfrac{1}{2}\varepsilon$$

By (55.5; 55.17) we can choose $n_2 > n_1 = 1$, and then $k(2) > k(1)$, with

$$\sum_{k=1}^{k(1)} |b(n_2, k)| < \varepsilon/8, \qquad \sum_{k=k(2)+1}^{\infty} |b(n_2, k)| < \varepsilon/8,$$
$$x_k = \text{sgn}^{-1}\,(b(n_2, k))\,(k(1) < k \leqslant k(2))$$

$$(55.20) \quad \left| \sum_{k=1}^{\infty} b(n_2, k)x_k \right| \geqslant \sum_{k=k(1)+1}^{k(2)} |b(n_2, k)| - \sum_{k=1}^{k(1)} |b(n_2, k)|$$

$$- \sum_{k=k(2)+1}^{\infty} |b(n_2, k)| \geqslant \varepsilon - 2(\varepsilon/8) - 2(\varepsilon/8) = \varepsilon/2$$

and so on. Hence by (55.19; 55.20; ...) we define a bounded sequence whose transformed sequence is not in c_0. Hence (55.16; 55.17) are false and (55.15) true. The sufficiency is obvious.

An extension of the theorems of this section was given by Tamarkin (1935), Rogers (1946), in which we suppose that if **x** is in the space in question, there is a $v = v(\mathbf{x})$ such that (55.1) exists for all $u \geqslant v$. As c_0 is the smallest space here, it is sufficient to prove the following theorem, and then in other theorems, for the v_0 that exists, we need only consider all $u \geqslant v_0$.

THEOREM 55.1. *If to each* $\mathbf{x} \in c_0$ *there is a number* $v(\mathbf{x}) > 0$ *such that (55.1) exists for all* $u \geqslant v(\mathbf{x})$, *then there is a number* $v_0 \geqslant 0$ *such that (55.2) is true for all* $u \geqslant v_0$.

Proof. We follow the proof of the boundedness of $s_0(x)$, given in Theorem 34.2, noting that $|f(\mathbf{x}, u)|$ is a Baire function, the limit of the continuous function

$$\left| \sum_{k=1}^{n} a_k(u)x_k \right|$$

when the limit exists.

Let $a_k(u)$, $b_k(u)$ be two convergence factors with the same range of $u \geqslant 1$. For this purpose we can change the u in $a_k(u)$ from an integer to a continuous variable by defining

$$a_k(u) = a_k(j) \qquad (j \leqslant u < j+1, \; j = 1, 2, \ldots)$$

Let X be a family of $\mathbf{x}$, Then $a_k(u)$, $b_k(u)$ are said to be *absolutely equivalent for* X, if

$$f(\mathbf{x}, u) \equiv \sum_{k=1}^{\infty} a_k(u)x_k, \quad g(\mathbf{x}, u) = \sum_{k=1}^{\infty} b_k(u)x_k$$

exist for all $u \geqslant 1$, with

$$f(\mathbf{x}, u) - g(\mathbf{x}, u) \to 0 \qquad (u \to \infty)$$

for each $\mathbf{x} \in X$ (Cooke (1936; 1937) for the definition and Theorems 55.2, 55.3).

THEOREM 55.2. *In order that* $a_k(u)$, $b_k(u)$ *are absolutely equivalent for m, it is necessary and sufficient that (55.2) is true for* $a_k(u)$, $b_k(u)$ ($u \geqslant 1$), *and that (55.15) is true for* $a_k(u) - b_k(u)$.

Proof. Use Theorem 54.3 and (55.14).

THEOREM 55.3. *Let* $\{y_k\}$ *be a positive sequence, and let* X *be the family of all* $\mathbf{x}$ *with* $|x_k| \leqslant y_k$ (*all* k). *In order that* $a_k(u)$, $b_k(u)$ *are absolutely equivalent for* X, *it is necessary and sufficient that* $a_k(u)y_k$

and $b_k(u)y_k$ satisfy (55.2) $(u \geqslant 1)$, *and that* (55.15) *is true for* $\{a_k(u) - b_k(u)\}y_k$.

Proof. Use Theorem 55.2.

Instead of applying $a_k(u)$ to the sequence of partial sums of a series

$$(55.21) \qquad \sum_{n=1}^{\infty} c_n, \quad \text{with} \quad x_n = \sum_{j=1}^{n} c_j$$

we can apply $a_k(u)$ directly to the terms c_j, obtaining, for $\mathbf{c} = \{c_j\}$

$$(55.22) \qquad h(\mathbf{c}, u) = \sum_{n=1}^{\infty} a_n(u)c_n$$

We can study this by changing it to a transformation on $\{x_n\}$, using results already obtained, by applying a lemma of Abel and Hadamard (see Hadamard (1903)) or one due to Henstock (see Cooke (1950), p. 66). Here we use the former.

THEOREM 55.4 *(Abel and Hadamard). If* $\sum_{n=1}^{\infty} b_n c_n$ *converges for all convergent series* (55.21), *then*

$$(55.23) \qquad \sum_{n=1}^{\infty} |b_n - b_{n+1}| < \infty$$

Conversely, if (55.23) *is true, and if* (55.21) *is convergent to x, then the following are convergent.*

$$(55.24) \qquad \sum_{n=1}^{\infty} b_n c_n = b_1 x + \sum_{n=1}^{\infty} (b_n - b_{n+1})(x_n - x)$$

Proof. The proof (Kojima (1917), Schur (1920)), uses the transformation

$$(55.25) \qquad \sum_{j=1}^{n} b_j c_j = \sum_{j=1}^{n-1} (b_j - b_{j+1})x_j + b_n x_n$$

of the convergent sequence $\{x_n\}$ by the convergence factor

$$a_j(n) = b_j - b_{j+1}(j < n), \quad a_n(n) = b_n, \quad a_j(n) = 0 \quad (j > n)$$

We use (55.12), obtaining, for all n,

$$(55.26) \qquad \sum_{j=1}^{n-1} |b_j - b_{j+1}| + |b_n| \leqslant M$$

Hence (55.23). Conversely, if (55.23) is true, then

$$|b_n| = \left| b_1 + \sum_{j=1}^{n-1} (b_{j+1} - b_j) \right| \leqslant |b_1| + \sum_{j=1}^{\infty} |b_j - b_{j+1}|$$

and (55.26) is true. The other conditions of (55.12) are satisfied, giving the results.

Thus we can prove theorems due to Bosanquet (see Dienes (1931), pp. 394, 396), Bohr (1909), Carmichael (1918–19), Perron (1920), Hahn (1922), and Takenaka (1922).

Ex. 55.1. Show that the *unit matrix* $a_n(m) = 1$ $(m = n)$, $0(m \neq n)$ is a T-matrix, so that not every T-matrix can sum divergent series.

Ex. 55.2. The *Çesaro mean of order* $r(r \neq -1, -2, \ldots)$ is the $a_k(n)$ given by

$$A_0^r = 1, \quad A_n^r \cdot n! = (r+1)(r+2) \ldots (r+n);$$

$$a_k(n) \cdot A_n^r = A_{n-k}^{r-1} \quad (0 \leqslant k \leqslant n), \; 0(k > n)$$

Show that, for $r \geqslant 0$, $a_k(n)$ is a T-matrix. (Equate coefficients in

$$(1-z)^{-r}(1-z)^{-1} = (1-z)^{-r-1} = \sum_{n=0}^{\infty} A_n^r z^n \, (|z| < 1))$$

Ex. 55.3. Are there necessary and sufficient conditions for $(c \rightarrow c_0)$, $(m \rightarrow c)$.

56. The Summability of Power Series

Power series are very important, and their summability interesting. Let

$$f(z) \equiv \sum_{n=0}^{\infty} c_n(z-a)^n$$

be convergent in some circle $|z-a| < c$. Putting $\zeta = z-a$ we can assume $a = 0$. Then we use

$$s_n(z) \equiv \sum_{j=0}^{n} c_j z^j, \quad g(u, z) \equiv \sum_{n=1}^{\infty} a_n(u) s_{n-1}(z),$$

$$t(u, z) \equiv \sum_{n=1}^{\infty} a_n(u) z^n,$$

in the summability, with $u \geqslant 1$, $u \to \infty$. We say that $a_n(u)$ is *efficient for f at a point z*, if $\lim\limits_{u \to b-} g(u, z) = f(z)$.

LEMMA 56.1. *If the power series $\sum\limits_{j=0}^{\infty} c_j z^j$ is convergent for some $z \neq 0$, then for some M_1 depending only on z,*

(56.1) $|c_j z^j| \leqslant M_1$ *(all j)*,

(56.2) $|f(w) - s_{n-1}(w)| \leqslant M_1 q^n (1-q)^{-1}$ $(q = |wz^{-1}| < 1)$,

(56.3) $\left| g(u, w) - f(w) \sum\limits_{n=1}^{\infty} a_n(u) \right| \leqslant \sum\limits_{n=1}^{\infty} |a_n(u)| q^n M_1 (1-q)^{-1}.$

These results, analytic continuation, complex integration, and the calculus of residues, are assumed known. For example,

LEMMA 56.2. *If f(z) is convergent in $|z| < c$, and if $0 < h < c$, then*

$$c_n = \frac{1}{2\pi i} \int_{|z|=h} \frac{f(z)}{z^{n+1}} \, dz$$

THEOREM 56.1. *In order that, for each power series f(z) convergent in a circle C, $|z| < c$ (i.e. $C = S(0, c)$), g(u, z) should converge in C, and should tend to f(z) as $u \to \infty$, uniformly in each compact set contained in C, it is necessary and sufficient that*

(56.4) $\sum\limits_{n=1}^{\infty} a_n(u)$ *exists in $u \geqslant 1$, and tends to 1 as $u \to \infty$,*

(56.5) $\sum\limits_{n=1}^{\infty} |a_n(u)| q^n < \infty$ $(u \geqslant 1, \ 0 < q < 1)$,

(56.6) $\lim\limits_{u \to \infty} \sum\limits_{n=1}^{\infty} |a_n(u)| q^n = 0$ $(0 < q < 1)$.

Proof. We can use the methods of section 55, taking the series convergent for $z = 1$. Alternatively, we take $f(z) = 1$ *(all z)* for (56.4), and then

(56.7) $f(z) = (1-z)^{-1}$, $s_n(z) = (1 - z^{n+1})/(1-z)$,

$$g(u, z) = \sum\limits_{n=1}^{\infty} a_n(u)/(1-z) - t(u, z)/(1-z)$$

By (56.4) it is necessary that $t(u, z)$ should converge in $|z| < 1$, and should tend to 0 as $u \to \infty$, uniformly on the compact set $|z| = h$, where $h < 1$. We take $q < h < 1$,

$$\sum_{n=1}^{\infty} |a_n(u)| q^n = \sum_{n=1}^{\infty} \frac{q^n}{2\pi} \left| \int_{|z|=h} \frac{t(u, z)}{z^{n+1}} \, dz \right|$$

$$\leqslant \sum_{n=1}^{\infty} \left(\frac{q}{h}\right)^n \max_{|z|=h} |t(u, z)| \to 0$$

as $u \to \infty$, using Lemma 56.2.

For sufficiency let F be a non-empty compact set in C. As $|z|$ is continuous it attains its maximum on F, so that F lies in $S(0, c(1-2\varepsilon))$ for some $\varepsilon > 0$. Taking $r = 1 - \varepsilon$, so that f is convergent at $z = rc$, we use Lemma 56.1 with $q = (1-2\varepsilon)/(1-\varepsilon)$. We have

$$|c_j| \leqslant M_1 r^{-j} c^{-j}, \quad \sum_{j=1}^{n} a_j(u) \, s_{j-1}(z) = f(z) \sum_{j=1}^{n} a_j(u)$$

$$+ \sum_{j=1}^{n} a_j(u) \{s_{j-1}(z) - f(z)\}$$

Taking $|z| \leqslant c \, (1-2\varepsilon)$, the series are convergent as $n \to \infty$, with the result, from (56.3; 56.4; 56.6).

For summability outside the circle of convergence we look for a region in which f can be defined uniquely, so that we can specify the 'right' value to which $g(u, z)$ should tend. The easiest such region is found as follows. For each $z \neq 0$, the set of $qz \, (q \geqslant 0)$ is called a *ray r from the origin through z*. By power series in intersecting circles we can continue f in a unique way along r from $S(0, c)$, to all points $qz_r \, (0 \leqslant q < 1)$, but for no $q > 1$, for some point z_r (possibly at infinity) on r. If z_r is finite, it is a singularity of f, satisfying $|z_r| \geqslant c$. Let $D(f)$ be the starlike region that includes all such $qz_r \, (0 \leqslant q < 1)$, for all rays r. Then $D(f)$ is called the *star domain of f*. It is maximal for a family of f with the same $D(f)$, in the sense that if z_r is an isolated singularity of f, and if f itself does not change in value at $z \in D(f)$ near to z_r, as z moves in a circle round z_r, then $f + \log (z - z_r)$ does so and it has the same $D(f)$ as f. Thus we suppose that for

$z \in D(f)$, $a_n(u)$ should be efficient there when $g(z, u) \to f(z)$, the value obtained by analytic continuation along r. Now $D(f)$ is a union of parts of rays, and the method of analytic continuation ensures that $D(f)$ is open. For a more general starlike set we need a different proof.

THEOREM 56.2. (56.8) *Let F be a closed set in $|z| \geqslant 1$, \\F having a point with modulus > 1,*

(56.9)   *let F include the line $l = \{z : z = rl \, z \geqslant 1\}$,*

(56.10)   *if $z \in F$, $q > 1$, let $qz \in F$*

Then $E(f; F)$ is closed, where

$$E(f; F) \equiv \bigcup_r z_r F,$$

the union being for all rays r through the origin.

Proof. Let $w \in E'(f; F)$. Then points $z \in E(f; F)$ lie in $S(w; 1)$, and in a set $z_r F$, so that by (56.8),

$$|z| \geqslant |z_r|, \quad |z_r| \leqslant |w| + 1$$

$S(0, |w| + 1)$ is compact, so that if by considering $|z - w| < n^{-1}$, $n = 1, 2, \ldots$, we find a sequence of $z \to w$, then the corresponding sequence of z_r has a subsequence convergent to a point v. As each z_r is a singularity of f, so is v. The corresponding subsequence of $z \cdot z_r^{-1} \in F$ is convergent to wv^{-1}. Hence as F is closed,

$$wv^{-1} \in F, \quad w \in vF$$

If s is the ray through v, then $v = qz_s$, for some $q \geqslant 1$, and by (56.10) we have the theorem since

$$w \in z_s F, \quad w \in E(f; F), \quad E'(f; F) \subseteq E(f; F)$$

We put the open set $P(f; F) = \backslash E(f; F)$ as the *partial star domain of f relative to F*. Then f is uniquely defined in $P(f; F)$ since

$$l \subseteq F, \quad z_r l \subseteq z_r F, \quad P(f; F) \subseteq D(f)$$

By (56.8; 56.10),

(56.11) if $z \in P(f; F)$ then $qz \in P(f; F)$,   for all $0 \leqslant q < 1$

(56.12) $S(0, c) \subseteq P(f; F)$

Theorem 56.3. *In order that, for any power series f convergent in $S(0, c)$ for some $c > 0$, $g(u, z)$ should exist in $P(f; F)$ and converge to $f(z)$, uniformly in each compact set $C \subseteq P(f; F)$, as $u \to \infty$, it is necessary and sufficient that (56.4) holds and*

(56.13) $t(u, z)$ *converges in* $\backslash F$, *tending to* 0 *as* $u \to \infty$ *uniformly on every compact set in* $\backslash F$.

This theorem has a complicated history, essentially the same sufficiency results were proved independently by several people, beginning with Borel (1901), pp. 164 sqq. Dienes (1913) gave the $D(f)$ case, Buhl (1925) and Vermes the $P(f; F)$ case, with $t(u, z) = E(uz)/E(u)$, where $E(u)$ is a suitable integral (entire) function. Okada (1925), p. 68, § 3, Satz III, took $D(f)$ with the general $t(u, z)$ and proved the sufficiency. I took $P(f; F)$ and a general $t(u, z)$, and the combined proofs of Vermes and myself are in Cooke (1950), pp. 189–91.

Proof. After Theorems 56.1, 56.2, we use (56.7) to show that (56.13) is necessary, since the only singularity of $(1-z)^{-1}$ is a pole at $z = 1$.

For sufficiency we use

$$I_\eta \equiv \frac{1}{2\pi i} \int_\eta \frac{t(u, v^{-1}) f(wv)}{1-v} \, dv$$

where f is convergent in $S(0, c)$ $(c > 0)$, and where η is the circle $|v| = h$ for fixed $h > 0$. By (56.8; 56.13), since $\backslash F$ is open, the radius c_1 of convergence of $t(u, z)$ is greater than $|z|$, for each $z \in \backslash F$, and thus $c_1 > 1$. If $z \in P(f; F)$, open, there is an $\varepsilon > 0$ with $w \in P(f; F)$, if $|w - z| < 2\varepsilon$. We can take $|w|$ as near as we please to $|z| + 2\varepsilon$, so that as we can suppose c maximal, there is a singularity z_r on $|z_r| = c$, and by the size of c_1,

$$w \notin z_r F, \quad w \cdot z_r^{-1} \notin F, \quad c_1 > |w \cdot z_r^{-1}| = |w| \cdot c^{-1},$$

$$c \cdot c_1 \geqslant |z| + 2\varepsilon > |z| + \varepsilon$$

Hence we can choose h to lie in the range

(56.14) $\qquad c_1^{-1} < h < \min \{1; c(|z| + \varepsilon)^{-1}\}$

so that if $|w| < |z| + \varepsilon$, there are power series for $t(u, v^{-1})$, $f(wv)$, $(1-v)^{-1}$. Thus the coefficient of v^{-1} in the integrand of I_η is a convergent power series, giving

$$I_\eta = \sum_{n=1}^\infty a_n(u)\, s_{n-1}(w) = g(u, w)$$

We now deform η to become a contour σ round the real line from 0 to 1, so that the points of η lie inside or on σ, and we pass over a pole of the integrand at $v = 1$, with residue

$$-t(u, 1)\, f(w) = -f(w) \sum_{n=1}^\infty a_n(u)$$

We choose σ so that this is the only singularity of the integrand between η and σ, and so that the integrand is uniformly convergent to 0 on σ as $u \to \infty$. Then we show that

$$g(u, w) - f(w) \sum_{n=1}^\infty a_n(u) = I_\sigma \to 0$$

uniformly for w in a circle with centre z. If z lies in a compact set $C \subseteq P(f;\, F)$, we can cover C by such circles, and so by a finite number, and uniformity holds for C.

Thus in the rest of the proof we show that a suitable choice of σ is possible. The function $(1-v)^{-1}$ has only one singularity, at $v = 1$. Also, when $v \in \sigma$, the contour for v^{-1} lies on or within the circle $|z| = h^{-1}$, so that by (56.14), $t(u, v^{-1})$ is a power series in v^{-1}. The trouble lies in its uniform convergence as $u \to \infty$, and in the properties of $f(wv)$. Now z^{-1} is continuous, except at $z = 0$, so that F^{-1} is closed, except that $z = 0$ is missing. By (56.8), $F^{-1} \subseteq S(0,1)$. Let $z \in P(f;\, F)$. By (56.10), $z \notin y$. F for each $y \notin D(f)$, so that $y \notin zF^{-1}$, and $zF^{-1} \subseteq D(f)$. By Theorem 13.7 (13.15),

$$\varrho(zF^{-1}, \, \backslash D(f)) = 3\delta > 0, \quad \varrho(z_1, z_2) \equiv |z_1 - z_2|$$

We take σ a contour round F^{-1}, within δ of it, and $|w - z| \leqslant \delta$. Then $w\sigma$ has a greater distance than δ from $\backslash D(f)$, so that $w\sigma \subseteq D(f)$, and $f(wv)$ is uniquely definable for $v \in \sigma$. Further, σ^{-1} is a compact set lying in $\backslash F$, so that by (56.13), $t(u, v^{-1}) \to 0$ as $u \to \infty$, uniformly for $v \in \sigma$. Hence

$$|I_\sigma| \leqslant \max_\sigma |f(wv)/(1-v)| \max_\sigma |t(u, v^{-1})| \to 0 \qquad (u \to \infty)$$

the convergence being uniform in w for $|w-z| \leqslant \delta$.

Note that by a theorem of Vitali, if a sequence of regular functions is uniformly bounded in a circle, and convergent at a set of points with limit-point an interior point, then the sequence converges uniformly in the circle. Thus the weaker conditions of convergence of integrals are rather pointless here.

Also note that we require $g(u, z) \to f(z)$ in $P(f; F)$, saying nothing about points on the boundary of $D(f)$, where the power series for f can still converge. In fact $a_n(u)$ need not be a T-matrix (see Henstock (1947)).

Ex. 56.1. $t(u, z)$ is an integral (entire) function, if $\backslash F$ is unbounded.

Ex. 56.2. If c is the radius of convergence of f, and if $|w| > c$, then $|s_n(w)| < |w/c|^n M$, and $g(u, z)$ is convergent in $|z| < cc_1$.

Ex. 56.3. $\sum\limits_{n=1}^{\infty} z^n/n^2$ is convergent in $|z| \leqslant 1$, with a singularity at $z = 1$ that can be found by differentiation.

Ex. 56.4. In *Ex. 56.2* justify the following transformation by absolute convergence in $|z| < cc_1$.

$$\sum_{n=1}^{\infty} a_n(u)s_{n-1}(z) = \sum_{j=0}^{\infty} c_j z^j \sum_{n=j+1}^{\infty} a_n(u)$$

a transformation of the series itself.

Ex. 56.5. Let $h(z)$ be an integral (entire) function given by a power series in z with non-negative coefficients h_n ($n = 0, 1, 2, \ldots$), an infinity being positive. Prove that

(i) $h(u) \to \infty$ as $u \to \infty$, u real,

(ii) for each integer n, $h_n u^n/h(u) \to 0$ $(u \to \infty)$,

(iii) $t(u, z) \equiv h(uz)/h(u)$ satisfies the conditions of Theorem 56.1,

(iv) if $t(u, z) \to 0$ for a particular z, then $t(u, qz) \to 0$ for each $q \in [0,1)$,

(v)   if $h(u, z) \to 0$ as $u \to \infty$, uniformly for z in each compact set F contained in an open set G, then $t(u, z)$ satisfies (56.13), for $F = \backslash(G_1 \cup S)$, where S is the set $|z| < 1$, and where G_1 is the set of qz for all $z \in G$, all q in $0 \leqslant q < 1$.

Ex. 56.6. $h(z) = e^z$ in *Ex. 56.5* gives the *Borel polygon of summability*.

57. Hausdorff Summability

In this book we have dealt with general, as opposed to special, infinite matrices. But the subfamily of Hausdorff matrices has points of interest. Here, u takes integer values 0, 1, 2, ... and we write $a_n(u)$ as a_{un}, for $n = 0, 1, 2, \ldots$ If $A = (a_{un})$ and $B = (b_{un})$ are two such functions of u, n, written in matrix form, we write $AB = C$ when it is possible to define the c_{un} as

$$c_{un} = \sum_{j=0}^{\infty} a_{uj} b_{jn}$$

This idea is taken directly from matrix algebra, with finite series replaced by infinite ones, so that convergence is required. Let d denote the *diagonal matrix* (d_{un}) with $d_{un} = 0$ $(u \neq n)$, $d_{nn} = d_n$ $(n = 0, 1, \ldots)$. If $d_n = 1$ *(all n)* we write d as I, the *unit (infinite) matrix*. Then if $AB = I$ we write $B = A^{-1}$. Let Δ denote the *difference matrix* with elements

$$\Delta_{un} = (-1)^n \binom{u}{n} \quad (0 \leqslant n \leqslant u), \quad = 0 \quad (n > u); \quad \Delta^2 \equiv \Delta\Delta = C,$$

with

$$c_{un} = \sum_{j=0}^{u} \Delta_{uj} \Delta_{jn}, \quad \sum_{n=0}^{\infty} c_{un} x^n = \sum_{j=0}^{u} \Delta_{uj} \sum_{n=0}^{j} \Delta_{jn} x^n = \sum_{j=0}^{u} \Delta_{uj} (1-x)^j = x^u$$

Comparing coefficients of x^n, we have $C = I$ and $\Delta = \Delta^{-1}$.

The matrix $\Delta d\Delta$ is called the *Hausdorff matrix relative to* $\{d_n\}$. If its elements are a_{un}, then $a_{un} = 0$ $(n > u)$, while for $n \leqslant u$,

$$a_{un} = \sum_{j=n}^{u} \Delta_{uj} d_j \Delta_{jn} = \sum_{j=n}^{u} (-1)^{j+n} d_j \binom{u}{j} \binom{j}{n}$$

Rearranging the factorials and putting $k = j - n$,

$$\binom{u}{j}\binom{j}{n} = \binom{u}{n}\binom{u-n}{j-n}, \qquad a_{un} = \binom{u}{n}\sum_{k=0}^{u-n}(-1)^k\binom{u-n}{k}d_{k+n}$$

$$= (-1)^{u-n}\binom{u}{n}\Delta^{u-n}d_n,$$

the last being in the forward difference notation.

If e is a diagonal matrix with diagonal using $\{e_n\}$, then

$$(\Delta\, d\,\Delta)(\Delta e\,\Delta) = (\Delta\, d)(\Delta\Delta)(e\,\Delta) = \Delta\, de\,\Delta$$

since the sums of non-zero terms are finite. Thus the product of two Hausdorff matrices is another of the same type.

The Hausdorff matrix $A = \Delta\, d\Delta$ sends c_0 into m, if, and only if,

(57.1) $$\sum_{n=0}^{\infty}\binom{u}{n}\left|\sum_{k=0}^{u-n}(-1)^k\binom{u-n}{k}d_{k+n}\right| \leqslant M$$

for some $M > 0$ independent of $u = 0, 1, 2 \ldots$

THEOREM 57.1. *If $g(t)$ is of bounded variation and*

(57.2) $$d_n = \int_0^1 t^n\, dg(t) \qquad (n = 0, 1, 2, \ldots)$$

then (57.1) *is true.*

Proof. If $V(t)$ is the variation of $g(t)$ in $[0, t]$,

$$a_{un} = \binom{u}{n}\sum_{k=0}^{u-n}(-1)^k\binom{u-n}{k}\int_0^1 t^{k+n}\, dg(t) = \binom{u}{n}\int_0^1 t^n(1-t)^{u-n}\, dg(t)$$

$$\sum_{n=0}^{\infty}|a_{un}| \leqslant \sum_{n=0}^{\infty}\binom{u}{n}\int_0^1 t^n(1-t)^{u-n}\, dV(t) = V(1) < \infty$$

To prove the converse we need more definitions. If f is defined on $[0, 1]$, a *Bernstein polynomial* $B_n(f)$ *for* f, is

$$B_n(f) = \sum_{j=0}^{n}f(j/n)\binom{n}{j}x^j(1-x)^{n-j}$$

The *moment* of a polynomial $P(x) = \sum_{j=0}^{m}b_j x^j$ is defined to be

$$M(P) = \sum_{j=0}^{m}b_j d_j; \quad M(x^m) = d_m$$

If $\{d_n\}$ satisfies (57.2), then clearly

$$(57.3) \qquad M(P) = \int_0^1 P(t)\, dg(t)$$

By the binomial theorem,

$$(57.4) \qquad a_{un} = M\left(\binom{u}{n} x^n (1-x)^{u-n}\right)$$

THEOREM 57.2. *If* (57.1) *is true, then*

$$(57.5) \qquad d_n = \lim_{k \to \infty} M(B_k(x^n)) \qquad (n = 0, 1, 2, \ldots)$$

Proof. First, we have

$$M(B_k(1)) = M\left(\sum_{j=0}^k \binom{k}{j} x^j (1-x)^{k-j}\right) = M(1) = d_0$$

$$(57.6) \qquad \sum_{n=0}^k a_{kn} = d_0$$

For $k > n > 0$, $m = j+n$, the binomial theorem gives

$$x^n = x^n((1-x)+x)^{k-n} = \sum_{j=0}^{k-n} \binom{k-n}{j} x^{j+n}(1-x)^{k-j-n}$$

$$= \sum_{m=n}^k \frac{(k-n)!\, m!}{(m-n)!\, k!} \binom{k}{m} x^m (1-x)^{k-m}$$

$$= \sum_{m=n}^k \frac{m(m-1)\ldots(m-n+1)}{k(k-1)\ldots(k-n+1)} \binom{k}{m} x^m (1-x)^{k-m}$$

But by definition and (57.4),

the Bernstein polynomial

$$B_k(x^n) = \sum_{m=0}^k \left(\frac{m}{k}\right)^n \binom{k}{m} x^m (1-x)^{k-m}$$

$$d_n - M(B_k(x^n)) = \sum_{m=n}^k \left\{\frac{m(m-1)\ldots(m-n+1)}{k(k-1)\ldots(k-n+1)} - \left(\frac{m}{k}\right)^n\right\} a_{km}$$

$$- \sum_{m=0}^{n-1} \left(\frac{m}{k}\right)^n a_{km}, \quad \left|\sum_{m=0}^{n-1} \left(\frac{m}{k}\right)^n a_{km}\right| \le \left(\frac{n}{k}\right)^n M$$

Further, for $0 \leqslant y \leqslant 1$; $j = 0, 1, \ldots, n-1$; $k \geqslant n$; and then $y = m/k$;

$$0 \leqslant y - \frac{ky-j}{k-j} = \frac{(1-y)j}{k-j} \leqslant \frac{n-1}{k-n+1},$$

$$0 \leqslant y^n - \frac{ky(ky-1)\ldots(ky-n+1)}{k(k-1)\ldots(k-n+1)} \leqslant \frac{n(n-1)}{k-n+1}$$

$$\left| d_n - M\big(B_k(x^n)\big) \right| \leqslant n(n-1) M/(k-n+1) + (n/k)^n M \to 0$$

$$(k \to \infty)$$

giving the result.

THEOREM 57.3. *The Hausdorff matrix $A = \Delta d\Delta$ sends c_0 into m, if, and only if, (57.2) is true.*

Proof. We have already shown that (57.2) implies (57.1) and $c_0 \to m$. In turn, this implies (57.1) and (57.5). To complete the theorem we show that (57.5) implies (57.2). We use (57.6), defining

$$g_k(0) = 0, \quad g_k(1) = d_0, \quad g_k(x) = \sum_{m < kx} a_{km} \quad (0 < x < 1)$$

$$M\big(B_k(x^n)\big) = \sum_{m=0}^{k} (m/k)^n a_{km} = \int_0^1 t^n \, dg_k(t),$$

$$d_n = \lim_{k \to \infty} \int_0^1 t^n \, dg_k(t)$$

The variation of $g_k(t)$ in $[0, 1)$ is

$$\sum_{m=0}^{k} |a_{km}| \leqslant M$$

independent of k, so that by Helly's theorem (Theorem 39.8) there is a subsequence $\{k(j)\}$ of integers for which $g_{k(j)}(t) \to g(t)$ pointwise, with $g(t)$ of bounded variation, and by Theorem 39.7 we have (57.2) for this g.

THEOREM 57.4. *If $f(x)$ is continuous in $0 \leqslant x \leqslant 1$ then $\lim_{n \to \infty} B_n[(f)] = f(x)$ uniformly in $[0, 1]$.*

Proof. For fixed $x \in [0, 1]$ and a fixed integer p, set

$$\varepsilon_p(x) = \max \{|f(x) - f(m/p)| : m = 1, 2, \ldots; |m - px| < p^{3/4}\}.$$

By the uniform continuity of f, the upper bound ε_p of $\varepsilon_p(x)$ in $[0, 1]$ tends to 0 as $p \to \infty$. Let $\sum'$ be a summation over all m in $0 \leqslant m \leqslant p$ with $|m-px| < p^{3/4}$, and let $\sum''$ be a summation over the other m in $0 \leqslant m \leqslant p$. As f is bounded by some $M > 0$,

$$f(x) - B_p[f] = \sum'[f(x)-f(m/p)] \binom{p}{m} x^m(1-x)^{p-m}$$

$$+ \sum''[f(x)-f(m/p)] \binom{p}{m} x^m(1-x)^{p-m}$$

$$|f(x) - B_p[f]| \leqslant \sum' \varepsilon_p \binom{p}{m} x^m(1-x)^{p-m} + 2M \sum'' \binom{p}{m} x^m(1-x)^{p-m}$$

$$\sum' \varepsilon_p \binom{p}{m} x^m(1-x)^{p-m} \leqslant \varepsilon_p \to 0.$$

The second sum is more difficult to majorize. We have

$$\sum'' \binom{p}{m} x^m(1-x)^{p-m} < p^{-3/2} \sum_{m=0}^{p} (m-px)^2 \binom{p}{m} x^m(1-x)^{p-m}$$

$$\sum_{m=0}^{p} (px-m)^2 \binom{p}{m} x^m(1-x)^{p-m} =$$

$$= \sum_{m=0}^{p} (p^2x^2 - (1-2px)m + m(m-1)) \binom{p}{m} x^m(1-x)^{p-m}$$

$$= p^2x^2 + (1-2px)px + p(p-1)x^2 = px - px^2 \leqslant \tfrac{1}{4}p,$$

$$\sum'' \binom{p}{m} x^m(1-x)^{p-m} \leqslant \tfrac{1}{4} p^{-1/2} \to 0.$$

Hence the result. The Weierstrass approximation theorem for continuous functions is a corollary.

58. The Combined Summability of Bounded and Zero-one Sequences

The summability of a given bounded sequence by a T-matrix $a_n(u)$ can often be made to depend on the summability by $a_n(u)$ of sequences of integers 0 and 1 alone, from a set S depending on the given sequence but not on $a_n(u)$. When the bounded sequence has only a finite set of limit-points, Cooke and Barnett (1948), Theorem I, Corollary, prove that a finite set S exists, each of its sequences corresponding to a limit-point, and conversely, and that the result can be extended to the case where the bounded sequence $\{z_n\}$ has a countable infinity of limit-points of a restricted type. After a seminar on this and other matter at Birkbeck College, London, I produced Theorem I of Cooke and Barnett (1948), in which a function $g_n(x)$ is constructed from $a_n(u)$ and $\{z_k\}$. It was assumed that $g_n(x) \to g(x)$ (say) for all x of an interval, which corresponds to a continuum number of points in S. Subsequently, in Henstock (1950), Theorem 2, $g_n \to g$ almost everywhere; then the example of § 2 was produced, imitating something like *Ex. 46.1;* finally leading to the mean convergence of g_n to g, in Theorem 1, for which S is countable, and a new 'limit under the integral sign' was needed. Hill (1951) shows more simply that S can always be countable, and his proof can be simplified. Here we give the integration proof as well, as it has points of interest, and connects with Dowidar and Petersen (1963), p. 1, Theorem 1. Restricting their work to real sequences they assume g_n pointwise convergent, replacing z_k by $f(z_k)$, where f is continuous; and then assume non-negative a_{nk} with $g_n \to g$ in an everywhere dense set.

We combine the theorems of Cooke and Barnett, Henstock, Hill, Dowidar and Petersen, to obtain the following result.

THEOREM 58.1. *Let* $\mathbf{z} \equiv \{z_j\}$ *be a given bounded sequence of complex numbers. Then there is a countable sequence of* 0, 1 *sequences, depending only on* $\mathbf{z}$, *such that the summability of each of these by any convergence factor* $a_n(u)$ *implies the summability of* $f(\mathbf{z}) \equiv \{f(z_n)\}$ *for each continuous function f.* This has not yet been proved in full generality. Hill's proof deals with $f(z) \equiv z$, and Henstock's with $f(x+iy) \equiv f_1(x)+f_2(y)$. The full theorem could need integration by parts in two dimensions, as arises in the theory of Section 63, and isolated in *Ex. 63.1,* but for simplicity we deal with the easy case.

Proof. First let $f(z) \equiv z$, with $z_n = x_n+iy_n$ for real x_n, y_n ($n = 1, 2, \ldots$). There is an integer $b > 0$, independent of n, with

$$|x_n| < b, \quad |y_n| < b \quad (n = 1, 2, \ldots)$$

291

For real x let $[x]$ be the integer m with $m \leqslant x < m+1$. Then for each $r = 1, 2, \ldots$, let

$$\mathbf{x}_r = \{x_{rn}\}, \quad x_{rn} = [rx_n]/r, \quad \|\mathbf{x}-\mathbf{x}_r\|_\infty \leqslant 1/r$$
$$\mathbf{y}_r = \{y_{rn}\}, \quad y_{rn} = [ry_n]/r, \quad \|\mathbf{y}-\mathbf{y}_r\|_\infty \leqslant 1/r$$

Now $[rx_n]$ takes a finite number of values in $-rb, -rb+1, \ldots, rb$. If m is one of them let $\mathbf{x}_{rm}$ be the 0,1 sequence given by

$$x_{rmn} = \begin{cases} 1 & ([rx_n] = m) \\ 0 & ([rx_n] \neq m) \end{cases}$$

and similarly for $\mathbf{y}_{rm}$. Then each $\mathbf{x}_r$, $\mathbf{y}_r$ is summable by $a_n(u)$, if all $\mathbf{x}_{rm}$, $\mathbf{y}_{rm}$ are summable, since

$$\mathbf{x}_r = \sum_{m=-rb}^{rb} m\mathbf{x}_{rm}/r, \quad \mathbf{y}_r = \sum_{m=-rb}^{rb} m\mathbf{y}_{rm}/r; \quad \mathbf{z}_r = \mathbf{x}_r + i\mathbf{y}_r$$

$$\left| \sum_{n=1}^{\infty} a_n(u)z_n - \sum_{n=1}^{\infty} a_n(u)z_{rn} \right| \leqslant \sum_{n=1}^{\infty} |a_n(u)| \cdot 2/r$$

For the second proof let $\xi_1 = -b$, $\xi_2 = b$, $\xi_3, \ldots, \xi_m, \ldots$, and $\xi_1^* = -b$, $\xi_2^* = b$, $\xi_3^*, \ldots, \xi_m^*, \ldots$ be two sequences each distinct and dense in $(-b, b)$. Let the convergence factor $a_n(u)$ be efficient for the countable number of 0, 1 sequences $\mathbf{w}^m = \{w_n^m\}$, where

$$w_n^{2m-1} = \begin{cases} 1 & (x_n \leqslant \xi_m), \\ 0 & (x_n > \xi_m), \end{cases} \quad w_n^{2m} = \begin{cases} 1 & (y_n \leqslant \xi_m^*), \\ 0 & (y_n > \xi_m^*) \end{cases}$$

We prove that $a_n(u)$ sums $\{f(z_n)\} = \{f_1(x_n)+f_2(y_n)\}$. The ξ_m, ξ_m^* are independent of $\{z_n\}$, but the $\mathbf{w}^m$ depend on all three sequences. Clearly the theorem is true if, and only if, it is true for real sequences $\{x_n\}$ and continuous functions f of the real variable x, which is the reason for the restriction to a special form of f. Thus we omit $\{\xi_m^*\}$, and replace $\mathbf{w}^{2m-1}$ by $\mathbf{w}^m$. We need not assume $a_n(u)$ and $f(x)$ real. As f is continuous on $[-b, b]$,

(58.1) $$k = \sup_{|x| \leqslant b} |f(x)| < \infty$$

Since $|x_n| < b$, and by absolute convergence of the second series,

$$(58.2) \qquad \sum_{n=1}^{\infty} |a_n(u) f(x_n)| \leqslant k \sum_{n=1}^{\infty} |a_n(u)| \leqslant kM(u) < \infty$$

We are given that $a_n(u)$ is efficient for $\mathbf{w}^m$, so that if

$$g(u, x) = \sum \{a_n(u) : x_n \leqslant x\}, \qquad g(u, \xi_m) = \sum_{n=1}^{\infty} a_n(u) w_n^m$$

$$(58.3) \qquad \lim_{u \to \infty} g(u, \xi_m) = g(\xi_m) \qquad (m = 1, 2, \ldots) \qquad \text{say}$$

Since $\qquad |x_n| < b, \quad \xi_1 = -b, \quad \xi_2 = b,$

$$(58.4) \qquad g(-b) = \lim_{u \to \infty} g(u, -b) = 0,$$

$$g(b) = \lim_{u \to \infty} g(u, b) = \lim_{u \to \infty} \sum_{n=1}^{\infty} a_n(u) = 1$$

Using points of $\{\xi_m\}$ alone, let $-b = t_0 < t_1 < \ldots < t_n = b$ be a division of $[-b, b]$. Then

$$(58.5) \qquad \sum_{j=1}^{n} |g(t_j) - g(t_{j-1})| = \lim_{u \to \infty} \sum_{j=1}^{n} |g(u, t_j) - g(u, t_{j-1})|$$

$$\leqslant \lim_{u \to \infty} \sup M(u) = M < \infty$$

Here, M is independent of the division, so that as $\{\xi_m\}$ is dense in $(-b, b)$, we can define

$$h(-b) = 0, \; h(b) = 1, \quad h(x) = \lim g(\xi_m) \qquad (-b < x < b)$$

where $\xi_m \to x-$. From (58.4; 58.5) and an arbitrary division

$$(58.6) \qquad -b = v_0 < v_1 < \ldots < v_n = b, \quad \sum_{j=1}^{n} |h(v_j) - h(v_{j-1})| \leqslant M$$

and h is of bounded variation. We prove that

$$(58.7) \qquad \int_{-b}^{b} |h(x) - g(u, x)| \, dx \to 0 \qquad (u \to \infty)$$

We put $v(j) = v_j$, and v as the norm of the division, and use Theorem 39.6.

$$(58.8) \qquad \sum_{j=1}^{n} \int_{v(j-1)}^{v(j)} |h(v(j-1)) - h(x)| \, dx \leqslant vM$$

293

By definition of h and by continuity of the integrals we can choose $t(j)\,(j = 0, 1, \ldots, n)$ from $\{\xi_m\}$, so that

$$-b = t(0) = v(0) < t(1) < v(1) < t(2) < v(2)$$

$$< \ldots < t(n) < v(n) = b$$

$t(j) - t(j-1) \leqslant v(j = 1, 2, \ldots, n)$ with $t(j)$ so near to $v(j)$ $(j = 1, 2, \ldots$ $n)$ that from (58.8),

$$\sum_{j=1}^{n} \left| g(t(j-1)) - h(v(j-1)) \right| (v(j) - v(j-1)) \leqslant vM$$

$$\sum_{j=1}^{n} \int_{v(j-1)}^{v(j)} \left| g(t(j-1) - h(x)) \right| dx \leqslant 2vM$$

(58.9) $\quad \displaystyle\sum_{j=1}^{n} \int_{t(j-1)}^{t(j)} \left| g(t(j-1)) - h(x) \right| dx + \int_{t(n)}^{b} \left| g(t(n)) - h(x) \right| dx \leqslant 3vM$

But each $t(j)$ is a ξ_m, so that by (58.3) there is a u_0 depending on $t(0)$, $\ldots$, $t(n)$, such that for all $u \geqslant u_0$, (58.9) gives

(58.10) $\quad \displaystyle\sum_{j=1}^{n} \int_{t(j-1)}^{t(j)} \left| g(u, t(j)) - h(x) \right| dx$

$$+ \int_{t(n)}^{b} \left| g(u, t(n)) - h(x) \right| dx \leqslant 4vM$$

From Theorem 39.6,

$$\sum_{j=1}^{n} \int_{t(j-1)}^{t(j)} \left| g(u, t(j)) - g(u, x) \right| dx + \int_{t(n)}^{b} \left| g(u, t(n)) - g(u, x) \right| dx \leqslant vM$$

This with (58.10) shows that the integral in (58.7) is less than $5vM$, for all $u \geqslant u_0$. But that integral does not contain $t(0), \ldots, t(n)$, so that u_0 can be taken for just one division of the type given, with norm less than v, and u_0 depends on v alone. Hence (58.7), and $g(u, .)$ converges in mean to h.

We now find an integral expression for the sum

$$s(u) = \sum_{k=1}^{\infty} a_k(u) f(x_k), \quad = \int_{-b}^{b} f(x)\, dg(u, x)$$

(See Theorem 39.3 (39.5)). Theorem 39.7 shows that $s(u)$ tends to a limit as $u \to \infty$, so that $a_n(u)$ sums $\{f(x_k)\}$

In another language, $\lim_{u \to \infty} s(u)$ is an operator on the continuous functions f of x in $-b \leqslant x \leqslant b$, that has a simple spectral resolution

$$\lim_{u \to \infty} s(u) = \int_{-b}^{b} f(x) \, dh(x)$$

where $h(-b) = 0$, $h(b) = 1$, and h is of bounded variation, but not necessarily monotone.

To show that (58.7) is the most that can be expected and that $g(u, x)$ need not always tend to a limit almost everywhere, we take the example in Henstock (1950), § 2, pp. 30–1. Let u take integer values, and put

$$a_{3n-2}(n) = 1 = a_{3n-1}(n), \quad a_{3n}(n) = -1,$$
$$a_k(n) = 0 (k \neq 3n-2, 3n-1, 3n; n = 1, 2, \ldots)$$

Then $a_k(n)$ is a T-matrix. Further, let $\{\xi_j\}$ be the set of points

$$\pm(2m+1)2^{-n} (n = -1 = m; \text{ and } m = 0, 1, \ldots, N-1$$
$$= 2^n - 1; \; n = 0, 1, 2, \ldots)$$

and let $\{x_n\}$ be defined by

$$x_{3N+3m+1} = 0, \quad x_{3N+3m+2} = (m+\varepsilon_n)/N, \quad x_{3N+3m+3} = (m+1-\varepsilon_n)/N$$

for $0 \leqslant m < N$, $\varepsilon_n > 0$, $n = 0, 1, 2, \ldots$ We then obtain

$$g(N+m, x) = \begin{cases} 0 & (x < 0) \\ 1 & (0 \leqslant x < (m+\varepsilon_n)/N) \\ 2 & ((m+\varepsilon_n)/N \leqslant x < (m+1-\varepsilon_n)/N) \\ 1 & (x \geqslant (m+1-\varepsilon_n)/N) \end{cases}$$

Thus for $x \geqslant 0$, $g(N+m, x) = 1$ except for an interval in $(m/N, (m+1)/N)$. Hence

$$(q \geqslant 0, n > s) g(N+m, q \cdot 2^{-s}) = 1, \quad g(\xi_m) = \begin{cases} 1 & (\xi_m \geqslant 0), \\ 0 & (\xi_m < 0), \end{cases}$$

$$h(x) = \begin{cases} 1 & (x > 0) \\ 0 & (x \leqslant 0) \end{cases}$$

But the set of x for which $g(n, x)$ oscillates between 1 and 2 as $n \to \infty$, is

$$\bigcap_{n=1}^{\infty} \bigcup_{m=0}^{N-1} ((m+\varepsilon_n)/N, (m+1-\varepsilon_n)/N)$$

a $\mathcal{G}_\delta$-set with measure or variation

$$\geq 1-2 \sum_{n=0}^{\infty} \varepsilon_n > 0$$

for suitable choice of $\{\varepsilon_n\}$. Thus $g(n, x)$ does not 'tend to a limit almost everywhere'. A similar example can be constructed to show that $g(n, x)$ need not tend to a limit anywhere, except at $-b$, b, even though $s(n)$ tends to a limit. However, a special set of conditions ensures convergence almost everywhere.

THEOREM 58.2 (Henstock (1950), Theorem 2, p. 31; Dowidar and Petersen (1963), p. 3, Theorem 2). *If all $a_n(u) \geq 0$, and if, for a dense set of points $\xi_1 = -b$, $\xi_2 = b$, $\xi_3, \ldots, \xi_m, \ldots$, we have $g(u, \xi_m) \to$*
$\to g(\xi_m)(u \to \infty)$, with $g(-b) = 0$, $g(b) = 1$, then $\lim\limits_{u \to \infty} g(u, x)$ exists for all but a countable number of points in $[-b, b]$.

Proof. If $\xi_m < x \leq \xi_n$, $t_1 < t_2$, then, since $a_n(u) \geq 0$,

(58.11) $\quad g(u, \xi_m) \leq g(u, \xi_n)$, $\quad g(\xi_m) \leq g(\xi_n)$, $\quad h(x) \leq g(\xi_n)$,

$$h(t_1) \leq h(t_2)$$

and h is monotone increasing from 0 to 1. By Theorem 39.3, h has an at most countable set of discontinuities. Now let $\xi_m < t_1 < t_2 < \xi_n < t_3$. Then

$$g(u, \xi_m) \leq g(u, t_2) \leq g(u, \xi_n)$$

$$g(\xi_m) \leq \liminf_{u \to \infty} g(u, t_2) \leq \limsup_{u \to \infty} g(u, t_2) \leq g(\xi_n)$$

$$h(t_1) \leq \liminf_{u \to \infty} g(u, t_2) \leq \limsup_{u \to \infty} g(u, t_2) \leq h(t_3)$$

$$h(t_2-) \leq \liminf_{u \to \infty} g(u, t_2) \leq \limsup_{u \to \infty} g(u, t_2) \leq h(t_2+),$$

$$\lim_{u \to \infty} g(u, x) = h(x)$$

at each point of continuity of h, and so the theorem is proved.

Dowidar and Petersen (1963), p. 2, Proposition 1, and a result of Hill (1944), are included in the following theorem.

THEOREM 58.3. *If X is an arbitrary separable subset of the space of bounded sequences, there is a sequence $\{u_j\}$ of u for which $a_n(u_j)$ sums all $\mathbf{x} \in X$, and all $f(\mathbf{x})$, where f is any continuous function.*

Proof. If $\mathbf{x} \in X$ we construct the $g(u, x)$ of Theorem 58.1. For some u_0, they are of uniformly bounded variation for $u \geqslant u_0$, with $g(u, -b) = 0$ if $|x_j| < b$. Applying Helly's theorem (Theorem 39.8), there is a subsequence $\{u_j^1\}$ for which $g(u_j^1, x)$ is pointwise convergent in $[-b, b]$ to a function $g(x)$ of bounded variation. Using Theorem 58.1, $\mathbf{x}$ and $f(\mathbf{x})$ are summed, for a single $\mathbf{x} \in X$.

We can repeat for each member in turn of a sequence $\{\mathbf{x}_j\}$ from X, taking successive subsequences, so that the diagonal sequence $\{u_j\}$ is such that $a_n(u_j)$ sums all $\mathbf{x}_j$ $(j = 1, 2, \ldots)$. Now a separable subset X of a topological space, is defined to be one that contains a countable set Y with $\overline{Y} \supseteq X$. Thus we choose the $\mathbf{x}_j \in Y$, so that $\{\mathbf{x}_j\}$ is dense in X, and $f(\mathbf{x}_j)$ dense in $f(X)$ by continuity, and

$$\left| \sum_{n=1}^{\infty} a_n(u_j) \{f(x_{jn}) - f(x_n)\} \right| \leqslant \sum_{n=1}^{\infty} |a_n(u_j)| \sup_q |f(x_{jq}) - f(x_q)| \to 0$$

$$\text{as} \quad \sup_q |x_{jq} - x_q| \to 0$$

Hence the result.

THEOREM 58.4 (Dowidar and Petersen (1963), p. 3, Proposition 2). *If, for every continuous f in $[-b, b]$, and for some function h of bounded variation in $[-b, b]$ and independent of f, we have*

$$\lim_{u \to \infty} s(u) = \lim_{u \to \infty} \sum_{n=1}^{\infty} a_n(u) f(x_n) = \int_{-b}^{b} f(x) \, dh(x)$$

then for a sequence $\{u_j\}$ tending to infinity with j,

$$h(x) = \lim_{j \to \infty} g(u_j, x) + h(a)$$

except possibly for a countable set of x, where $g(u, x)$ is the function of Theorem 58.1.

Proof. As in Theorem 58.3, for some $\{u_j\}$ independent of f,

$$\lim_{j \to \infty} s(u_j) = \int_{-b}^{b} f(x) \, dg(x), \qquad g(x) \equiv \lim_{j \to \infty} g(u_j, x);$$

$$\int_{-b}^{b} f(x) \, d\{g(x) - h(x)\} = 0$$

We take a bounded sequence of continuous functions that is point-wise convergent to the function

$$j(x) = 1(x \leqslant t), \quad j(x) = 0 \qquad (x > t)$$

for some t in $(-b, b)$, and Lebesgue's bounded convergence theorem (Theorem 46.2) with an extension from $\mu \geqslant 0$ to $|\mu|$ of bounded variation) shows that

$$\int_{-b}^{b} j(x) \, d\{g(x) - h(x)\} = 0, \qquad g(t+) - h(t+) + h(a) = 0,$$

$$h(t+) = g(t+) + h(a)$$

Hence, except at a countable set of points,

$$h(t) = h(t+) = g(t+) + h(a) = g(t) + h(a)$$

THEOREM 58.5 (Dowidar (1961)). *Given a sequence $\{x_n\} \subseteq [0,1]$, the limit-points being dense in $[0,1]$, and given a function g of bounded variation on $[0,1]$, with $g(0+) = g(0) = 0$, $g(1) = 1$, there is a T-matrix $\{a_{un}\}$ that sums $\{x_n\}$ and $\{f(x_n)\}$, for any function f continuous on $[0,1]$, with*

$$\lim_{u \to \infty} \sum_{n=1}^{\infty} a_{un} f(x_n) = \int_{0}^{1} f(x) \, dg(x)$$

Proof. Let $r_j = k/(l+1)$ when $j = \frac{1}{2}l(l+1) + k$ $(1 \leqslant k \leqslant l+1, l \geqslant 1)$; $r_1 = \frac{1}{2}$.
From $\{x_n\}$ we choose a subsequence $\{x_{n(j)}\}$ with

$$|x_{n(j)} - r_j| < j^{-1}, \quad n(1) < n(2) < \ldots;$$

$$a_{l, n(j)} = \binom{l+1}{k} \int_{0}^{1} x^k (1-x)^{l+1-k} \, dg(x)$$

for the same range of j, k, and $a_{ln} = 0$ for all other values of n.

Clearly

$$\lim_{l \to \infty} a_{ln} = 0$$

for each fixed integer n. Further, by the binomial theorem,

$$\sum_{n=0}^{\infty} a_{ln} = \sum_{k=1}^{l+1} \binom{l+1}{k} \int_0^1 x^k (1-x)^{l+1-k} \, dg(x)$$

$$= \int_0^1 \sum_{k=1}^{l+1} \binom{l+1}{k} x^k (1-x)^{l+1-k} \, dg(x)$$

$$= \int_0^1 \{1 - (1-x)^{l+1}\} \, dg(x) \to g(1) - g(0+) = 1$$

$$(l \to \infty)$$

Similarly, if $V(x)$ is the variation of $g(x)$ in $[0, x]$,

$$\sum_{n=0}^{\infty} |a_{ln}| \le \sum_{k=1}^{l+1} \binom{l+1}{k} \int_0^1 x^k (1-x)^{l+1-k} \, dV(x)$$

$$\le V(1) < \infty \, (\text{all } l)$$

Also we have

$$\sum_{j=1}^{\infty} a_{ln(j)} f(r_j) = \sum_{k=1}^{l+1} \int_0^1 f\left(\frac{k}{l+1}\right) \binom{l+1}{k} x^k (1-x)^{l+1-k} \, dg(x)$$

$$= \int_0^1 \{B_l(f) - f(0) (1-x)^{l+1}\} \, dg(x) \to \int_0^1 f(x) \, dg(x)$$

$$-f(0) \{g(0 +) - g(0)\}$$

The last step follows by Theorem 57.4 and then uniform convergence under the integral sign. Finally,

$$|x_{n(j)} - r_j| \to 0, \quad |f(x_{n(j)}) - f(r_j)| \to 0$$

$$\lim_{l \to \infty} \sum_{n=1}^{\infty} a_{ln} f(x_n) = \lim_{l \to \infty} \sum_{j=1}^{\infty} a_{ln(j)} f(x_{n(j)}) = \int_0^1 f(x) \, dg(x)$$

13

SEQUENCES, MEASURE AND VARIATION

59. The Summability of 0,1 Sequences and Category

This chapter deals with more specialized topics, first the theory of 0,1 sequences in connection with category, then 0,1 sequences and measure, in each case using a mapping from 0,1 sequences to points of $0 \leqslant x \leqslant 1$; finally, the similar problem in connection with measure and general bounded sequences is tackled. We begin with a result of Steinhaus (1911). See also Maddox (1967).

THEOREM 59.1. *If $a_n(u)$ is a T-matrix, there is a 0,1 sequence not summed by it.*

Proof. By taking the real part of $a_n(u)$, we can assume that $a_n(u)$ is real. By (55.3),

$$(59.1) \qquad \sum_{n=1}^{\infty} |a_n(u)| \leqslant M \qquad (u \geqslant U)$$

For convenience let us put

$$A(m, n, u) = \sum_{j=m}^{n} |a_j(u)|$$

By (55.7; 59.1) we can choose $u_1 \geqslant U$, and then n_1, so that

$$(59.2) \qquad \sum_{n=1}^{\infty} a_n(u) \geqslant \tfrac{3}{4} \ (all \ u \geqslant u_1), \quad A(n_1+1, \infty, u_1) < 1/24$$

If $x_n = 1$ for $1 \leqslant n \leqslant n_1$, then

$$\sum_{n=1}^{\infty} a_n(u_1)x_n \geqslant \sum_{n=1}^{\infty} a_n(u_1) - 2A(n_1+1, \infty, u_1) > 2/3$$

Next, by (55.5; 59.1), we can choose $u_2 > u_1+1$, and then $n_2 > n_1$, so that

$$A(1, n_1, u_2) < 1/6, \quad A(n_2+1, \infty, u_2) < 1/6$$

If $x_n = 0$ for $n_1 < n \leqslant n_2$, then

$$\left| \sum_{n=1}^{\infty} a_n(u_2)x_n \right| \leqslant A(1, n_1, u_2) + A(n_2+1, \infty, u_2) < 1/3$$

Next, by (55.5; 59.1), we choose $u_3 > u_2+1$, and then $n_3 > n_2$, so that

$$A(1, n_2, u_3) < 1/48, \quad A(n_3+1, \infty, u_3) < 1/48$$

If $x_n = 1$ for $n_2 < n \leqslant n_3$, then by (59.2), first part,

$$\sum_{n=1}^{\infty} a_n(u_3)x_n \geqslant \sum_{n=1}^{\infty} a_n(u_3) - 2A(1, n_2, u_3) - 2A(n_3+1, \infty, u_3) > 2/3$$

And so on. Such a sequence $\{x_n\}$ is not summed by $a_n(u)$, since $u_j \to \infty$.

Hill (1945) has built on this result in the following way. A 0,1 sequence $\{x_n\}$ corresponds to an infinite binary decimal

$$x = 0 \cdot x_1 x_2 \ldots x_n \ldots, \quad 0 \leqslant x \leqslant 1$$

The correspondence is not a bijection, since, for example,

$$0 \cdot 0111 \ldots = 0 \cdot 1000 \ldots$$

But no trouble is caused by this since such infinite decimals correspond to numbers $m \cdot 2^{-n}$ for integers m, n, these numbers being countable. Thus for topology on the space of 0,1 sequences we can use the corresponding metric topology of $[0, 1]$. Let Y be the space of all $x \in [0, 1]$ that are not of the form $m \cdot 2^{-n}$ for any integers m, n. Given a T-matrix $a_n(u)$, let $X \subseteq Y$ be the set of infinite decimals for which the corresponding sequences are summed.

THEOREM 59.2 (59.3) $f(x, u)$ is continuous in Y, where

$$f(x, u) = f(0 \cdot x_1 x_2 \ldots; u) = \sum_{n=1}^{\infty} a_n(u) x_n \quad (u \geqslant U)$$

(59.4) X is of the first category in Y.

301

Proof. The continuity of $f(x; u)$ in Y follows from (59.1), since, for each N,

$$\left| \sum_{n=1}^{\infty} a_n(u)\, y_n - \sum_{n=1}^{\infty} a_n(u)\, x_n \right| \le M \cdot \sup_{n \le N} |y_n - x_n| + 2 \sum_{m=N+1}^{\infty} |a_n(u)|$$

This need not hold in $\backslash Y$ since there are two $\{x_n\}$ to each $x \in \backslash Y$. For $v > u \ge U$ let $F(\varepsilon, u, v)$ denote the set of $x \in Y$ for which

$$|f(x, v) - f(x, u)| \le \varepsilon$$

Then $F(\varepsilon, u, v)$ is closed in Y since $f(x, u)$ and $f(x, v)$ are continuous in Y. Thus the intersection $F(\varepsilon, u)$ of the $F(\varepsilon, u, v)$, for all $v > u$, is also closed in Y. Now for $x \in X$, $f(x, u)$ is convergent, and so fundamental, as $u \to \infty$, so that X lies in the union $F(\varepsilon)$ of the $F(\varepsilon, u)$, for $u = U, U+1, U+2, \ldots$ If X is of the second category, so is $F(\varepsilon)$. Hence, for some u, $F(\varepsilon, u)$ is dense in an interval $(a, b) \subseteq$ $\subseteq (0,1)$, and $F(\varepsilon, u) \supseteq (a, b) \cap Y$. Let y be the infinite decimal for the sequence in Theorem 59.1 that is not summable by $a_n(u)$. Then $y \in Y$, as all $x \in \backslash Y$ are summable, so that there is an $x \in (a, b) \cup Y$ with

$$x_n = y_n \quad (n \ge N) \quad \text{(some } N), \quad f(x, v) - f(y, v) \to 0 \quad (v \to \infty)$$

by (55.5). Hence also $f(x, v)$ ultimately oscillates by at least $1/3$, as $v \to \infty$, and $x \notin F(\varepsilon, u)$, if $0 < \varepsilon < 1/3$. This contradiction shows that $F(\varepsilon)$ $(0 < \varepsilon < 1/3)$ and so X, are of the first category in Y.

THEOREM 59.3. *No sequence of T-matrices exists for which every 0,1 sequence is summed by at least one member of the sequence.*

Proof. A countable number of sets X of the first category, is still of the first category, while Y is of the second category.

Every 0,1 sequence is summed by some T-matrix, for if $x \in Y$, $\{x_u\}$ has an infinity of zeros, and $a_n(u)$ can be zero for them, and so sum x to I. Thus *the collection of T-matrices with different X is not countable.*

60. 0,1 Sequences and the Borel Property

As in the previous section we represent the 0,1 sequences as infinite binary decimals in [0,1]; but we replace category by measure mX. This can be defined from Lebesgue outer measure, using the function $l(a, b) = b - a$ of intervals. Alternatively we use the variation, since

$$mX = V (l; A; [0,1]; X)$$

For proof we use Henstock (1963c), p. 121, Theorem 49.1; p. 49, Theorem 28.1; and the Carathéodory definition of measurable sets. As the measure and variation of a countable set are both 0, the double representation of some decimals makes no difference to the results. Thus we can restrict our attention to Y, the set of all x in [0,1] that are not equal to $r \cdot 2^{-n}$ for any integers r, n. Again we suppose that $X \subseteq Y$ is the set of sequences summable by $a_n(u)$.

THEOREM 60.1. *A T-matrix $a_n(u)$ either sums almost none of the 0,1 sequences (i.e. $mX = 0$) or else sums almost all (i.e. $mX = 1$) to the value $\frac{1}{2}$.*

Proof. We use the set $F(\varepsilon)$ of Theorem 59.2, the set where $f(x, u)$ ultimately oscillates not more than ε as $u \to \infty$. It is a union of closed sets relative to Y. By using Lebesgue's bounded convergence theorem repeatedly, we see that if W is an open interval, an open set, a closed set, or $F(\varepsilon)$, then l and $l \cdot ch(W;.)$ are integrable in [0,1], so that for mW denoting $V(l; A; [0,1]; W)$, which is the $V(l; [0,1]; W)$ of Henstock (1963c), p. 80, Theorem 35.3, we see that, for x almost everywhere in $F(\varepsilon)$, and each $\varepsilon' > 0$,

$$m((x-\delta, x+\delta) \cap F(\varepsilon)) > 2\delta(1-\varepsilon') \quad (all \ \delta \ in \ 0 < \delta < \delta_0 = \delta_0(\varepsilon'))$$

(60.1)

Let us say that $x, y \in Y$ are *linked*, if $x_n = y_n$ $(n \geq N)$, for some integer N. By (55.5), if $x \in F(\varepsilon)$, and if y is linked to x, then $y \in F(\varepsilon)$. Thus if $F(\varepsilon)$ is of positive variation or measure there is a point x satisfying (60.1), and then all y linked to x also satisfy (60.1), for δ additionally satisfying $(y-\delta, y+\delta) \subseteq (0,1)$. Taking $x-\delta$ linked to x, a finite number of $(y-\delta, y+\delta)$ abut and cover [0,1], apart

303

from a finite number of isolated points, and an interval at each end of length $< 2\delta$. Hence

$$mF(\varepsilon) > (1-\varepsilon')(1-4\delta) \quad (all \; \varepsilon' > 0, \; \delta > 0), \quad mF(\varepsilon) = 1,$$

$$X = \bigcap_{n=1}^{\infty} F(1/n).$$

By Henstock (1963c), p. 61, Theorem 31.2 (31.9), and p. 54, second part of Theorem 28.6, we can write the variation of l for $F(\varepsilon)$ as an integral, and then obtain $mX = 1$ if $mX > 0$. A similar proof follows by Lebesgue methods.

In the case $mX = 1$, $f(x, u)$ tends to some limit function $f(x)$ almost everywhere, where $f(x) = f(y)$ when x is linked to y. To show f constant,

$$\{x : s < f(x) < t\} = \bigcup_{N=1}^{\infty} \bigcap_{n>N} \{x : s < f(x, n) < t\} \cap X \quad (s < t)$$

so that the first set is $K \cap X$, where K is a $G_{\delta\sigma}$-set. If $mK > 0$, then similar arguments show that $mK = 1$. Taking $s = r \cdot 2^{-n}$, $t = (r+2) \cdot 2^{-n}$, we see that for each n there is just one r with $mK > 0$. The intervals $[r \cdot 2^{-n}, (r+2) 2^{-n}]$ have the finite intersection property and so have a point c in common, and $f(x) = c$ almost everywhere. Finally, as $1-x$ has the representation

$$0 \cdot (1-x_1)(1-x_2)\ldots \quad when \quad x = 0 \cdot x_1 x_2 \ldots, \quad f(x)+f(1-x) = 1,$$

$$2c = 1, \quad c = \tfrac{1}{2}$$

We say that a T-matrix $a_n(u)$ has the *Borel property*, if

$$(60.2) \qquad \sum_{n=1}^{\infty} a_n(u) x_n \to \tfrac{1}{2} \quad (u \to \infty)$$

for *almost all* 0,1 sequences $\{x_n\}$ (i.e. $f(x) = \tfrac{1}{2}$ *almost everywhere*). Thus either a T-matrix $a_n(u)$ has the Borel property, or else it sums almost none of the 0,1 sequences.

To proceed further, it is convenient to use the functions of Rademacher (1922). For $n = 1, 2, 3, \ldots, 0 \leqslant x \leqslant 1$

$$R_{n-1}(x) = \begin{cases} (-1)^k & (k < 2^n x < k+1, \quad k = 0, 1, \ldots, 2^n-1) \\ 0 & (otherwise) \end{cases}$$

Then we have the convenient results

(60.3) $x = 0 \cdot x_1 x_2 \ldots \in Y, \quad x = \frac{1}{2}(1 - R_{n-1}(x)) \quad (n = 1, 2, \ldots)$

(60.4) $f(x, u) \equiv \sum_{n=1}^{\infty} a_n(u) x_n = \frac{1}{2} \sum_{n=1}^{\infty} a_n(u) - \frac{1}{2} \sum_{n=1}^{\infty} a_n(u) R_{n-1}(x)$

The last series is convergent since if

(60.5) $AR(u; x) \equiv \sum_{n=1}^{\infty} a_n(u) R_{n-1}(x),$

$$|AR(u; x)| \leqslant \sum_{n=1}^{\infty} |a_n(u)| \, |R_{n-1}(x)| \leqslant \sum_{n=1}^{\infty} |a_n(u)|$$

Further, for an integer k depending on x, we have by cancellation,

(60.6) $0 \leqslant s_n(x) \equiv \int_0^x R_{n-1}(t) \, dt \leqslant \int_{k \cdot 2^{-n}}^{(k+1) \cdot 2^{-n}} 1 \, dt = 2^{-n}$

$$(k \leqslant 2^n x < k+1)$$

(60.7) $\int_0^1 R_m(x) \, R_n(x) \, dx = \begin{cases} 1 & (m = n) \\ 0 & (m \neq n) \end{cases}$

(60.8) More generally, if $m(1), \ldots, m(n)$ are distinct integers and $j(1), \ldots, j(n)$ are integers,

$$\int_0^1 R_{m(1)}(x)^{j(1)} \ldots R_{m(n)}(x)^{j(n)} \, dx = \begin{cases} 1 & (\text{all } j(1), \ldots, j(n) \text{ even}) \\ 0 & (\text{at least one of } j(1), \ldots, j(n) \text{ odd}) \end{cases}$$

For (60.7), if $n > m$ then $R_n(x)$ is periodic, a multiple period being the length of the intervals on which $R_m(x)$ is constant, so that the integral over such an interval is 0 by cancellation due to R_n. Hence the result when $n > m$, and so when $m > n$. When $m = n$, $R_m(x) = R_n(x) = 1$ except at the ends of the intervals, and the result follows. Then (60.8) follows in a similar way, it being easy to see that we need only take the case $j(1) = 1 = \ldots = j(n)$.

305

THEOREM 60.2. *In order that the real T-matrix $a_n(u)$ should have the Borel property it is necessary that*

$$(60.9) \qquad A(u) \equiv \sum_{n=1}^{\infty} a_n^2(u) < \infty \qquad (u \geqslant 1)$$

$$(60.10) \qquad \lim_{u \to \infty} A(u) = 0$$

Proof. To prove the necessity, we have

$$AR^2(u; t) = \sum_{n=1}^{\infty} \sum_{j=1}^{\infty} a_n(u) \, a_j(u) \, R_{n-1}(t) \, R_{j-1}(t)$$

the double series converging absolutely in [0,1] by (55.2), with the $|R_n|$ bounded by 1. By Henstock (1963c), Theorem 37.1, p. 85, we can integrate term-by-term. Using (60.7),

$$\int_0^1 AR^2(u; t) dt = \sum_{n=1}^{\infty} a_n^2(u)$$

finite for $u \geqslant 1$. If $a_n(u)$ has the Borel property we use (60.4) for $AR(u; t) \to 0$, so that the integral above tends to 0, by Lebesgue's bounded convergence theorem.

This T-matrix theorem is due to Hill (1951). Garreau (1951) gives an example to show that (60.9; 60.10) are not sufficient. He defines a matrix G by putting $g_{11} = 1$, $g_{1n} = 0$ $(n > 1)$ in the first row. For the second row he permutes the 1, 0, to obtain $g_{21} = 0$, $g_{22} = 1$, $g_{2n} = 0$ $(n > 2)$. In the next $\binom{4}{2}$ rows the first 4 elements are the permutations of $\frac{1}{2}, \frac{1}{2}, 0, 0$, and the rest are 0. Proceeding in this way, for $k = 1, 2, \ldots$, we have $\binom{2k}{k}$ rows, in each of which the first $2k$ elements are the permutations of k numbers k^{-1}, and k numbers 0, and later elements are 0. Here,

$$(60.11) \qquad \sum_{n=1}^{\infty} g_{un}^2 = k^{-1} \left(u = \sum_{j=1}^{k-1} \binom{2j}{j} + r, \quad 1 \leqslant r \leqslant \binom{2k}{k} \right)$$

and (60.9; 60.10) are satisfied, while clearly G is a T-matrix.

Now let the first $2k$ elements of the 0,1 sequence $\{x_n\}$ consist of $(k+j)$ 1's and $(k-j)$ 0's. If $j \geqslant 0$, there is some nth row of the matrix

306

that contains 0's and $1/k$'s, such that all $1/k$'s correspond to 1's of the sequence, giving a sum

$$G_n(x) \equiv \sum_{j=1}^{\infty} g_{nj} x_j = 1$$

There is also some Nth row such that all 0's in $x_1, \ldots, x_{2k}$ correspond to $1/k$'s and then $G_N(x) = j/k$. This follows since there are only $(k-j)$ 0's. Thus the oscillation of $G_n(x)$, for rows containing $1/k$'s, is at least $1 - j/k$. If $j < 0$ we interchange 0's and 1's of the sequence and have an oscillation of at least $1 - |j|/k$. Thus a 0,1 sequence $\{x_n\}$ is summable by G, if, and only if, $|j|/k \to 1$ as $k \to \infty$. But the matrix H of the first arithmetic mean, is

$$h_{ur} = \begin{cases} 1/u & (1 \leqslant r \leqslant u) \\ 0 & (otherwise) \end{cases} \qquad \sum_{r=1}^{\infty} h_{2k,r} x_r = \frac{k+j}{2k} = \frac{1}{2} + \frac{j}{2k}$$

while H has the Borel property. This is proved by using Theorem 60.3. Hence $j/k \to 0$ almost everywhere as $k \to \infty$, and G cannot have the Borel property, and (60.9; 60.10) are not sufficient.

Cooke (1950), p. 223, 12, points out that if H^* is obtained from H by repeating rows an arbitrary number of times, so that H^* is a T-matrix, then H^* also has the Borel property, and yet $\sum_{r=1}^{\infty} (h_{ur}^*)^2 \to 0$ arbitrarily slowly. Thus the examples of Garreau and Cooke show that no condition that depends on the rapidity of convergence of sums of squares, can be necessary and sufficient for the matrix to have the Borel property. However, there are sufficient conditions that we consider after examining the Rademacher functions in more detail.

LEMMA 60.1 (*Stirling's formula*). $(2\pi)^{1/2} k^{k+\frac{1}{2}} e^{-k} \leqslant k! \leqslant (2\pi)^{1/2} k^{k+\frac{1}{2}} e^{-k}(1+1/4k)$, *the last bracket being* $\leqslant 5/4$.

The proof is left to the reader!

LEMMA 60.2.

$$\int_0^1 |AR(u; x)|^{2j} dx \leqslant M_j \|a(u)\|_2^{2j} \qquad where \qquad M_j \leqslant \left(\frac{e}{4}\right)^j \frac{(2j)!}{j!},$$

$$\|a(u)\|_2^2 \equiv \sum_{n=1}^{\infty} a_{un}^2$$

307

Proof. By the multinomial theorem,

$$\int_0^1 |AR(u;x)|^{2j}\,dx = \int_0^1 \left(\sum_{n=1}^\infty a_n(u)R_{n-1}(x)\right)^{2j} dx$$

$$= \sum \int_0^1 (a_{n(1)}(u)\,R_{n(1)-1}(x))^{j(1)} \cdots$$

$$\cdots (a_{n(m)}(u)\,R_{n(m)-1}(x))^{j(m)}\,\frac{(2j)!}{j(1)!\cdots j(m)!}\,dx$$

where the last sum is over all positive integers $j(1), \ldots, j(m)$ with sum $2j$, and over all distinct $n(1), \ldots, n(m)$. The series is absolutely convergent, by (55.2), so that we can integrate term-by-term and use (60.8). Then the only terms left are those with $j(1), \ldots, j(m)$ equal to $2k(1), \ldots, 2k(m)$, and

$$\int_0^1 |AR(u;x)|^{2j}\,dx = \sum a_{n(1)}(u)^{2k(1)} \cdots$$

$$\cdots a_{n(m)}(u)^{2k(m)}\,\frac{(2j)!}{(2k(1))!\cdots(2k(m))!}$$

the sum being over all positive integers $k(1), \ldots, k(m)$ with sum j, and over all distinct positive integers $n(1), \ldots, n(m)$. For a similar summation, since

$$\|a(u)\|_2^{2j} = \sum a_{n(1)}(u)^{2k(1)} \cdots a_{n(m)}(u)^{2k(m)}\,\frac{j!}{k(1)!\cdots k(m)!}$$

the lemma is proved if M_j is bounded by the given number, where

$$M_j \equiv \sup \frac{(2j)!}{j!}\cdot\frac{k(1)!\cdots k(m)!}{(2k(1))!\cdots(2k(m))!}$$

By Lemma 60.1,

$$M_j \leqslant \frac{(2j)!}{j!}\left(\frac{e}{4}\right)^j \sup\left(\frac{5}{4\sqrt2}\right)^m \frac{1}{k(1)^{k(1)}\cdots k(m)^{k(m)}} \leqslant \left(\frac{e}{4}\right)^j \frac{(2j)!}{j!}$$

Lemma 60.3. $\displaystyle\int_0^1 \exp(b\cdot AR(u;x)^2)\,dx \leqslant (1-be\,\|a(u)\|_2^2)^{-1}$

$$(\text{all } b < e^{-1}\|a(u)\|_2^{-2})$$

308

Proof. From Lemma 60.2, and then Lemma 60.1,

$$\int_0^1 \exp\left(b \cdot AR(u;x)^2\right) dx = \sum_{j=0}^{\infty} \int_0^1 \frac{b^j}{j!} AR(u;x)^{2j} dx$$

$$\leqslant \sum_{j=0}^{\infty} \left(\frac{be}{4}\right)^j \frac{(2j)!}{(j!)^2} \|a(u)\|_2^{2j} \frac{(2j)!}{(j!)^2} \leqslant \frac{5(2j)^{2j+1/2}e^{-2j}}{4(2\pi)^{1/2}j^{2j+1}e^{-2j}} = \frac{5 \cdot 4^j}{4\pi^{1/2}j^{1/2}} \leqslant 4^j$$

$$\int_0^1 \exp\left(b \cdot AR(u;x)^2\right) dx \leqslant \sum_{j=0}^{\infty} \left(be \|a(u)\|_2^2\right)^j$$

giving the result.

LEMMA 60.4. *If* $\|a(u)\|_2^2 \leqslant M$ *for* $u = 1, 2, \ldots$, *and if* $b_u > 0$,

$$\sum_{u=1}^{\infty} b_u < \infty, \text{ then } c(u;x) \equiv \exp\left(b \cdot AR(u;x)^2\right) = O(b_u^{-1})$$

almost everywhere in $(0, 1)$, *where* b *is any fixed number less than* $(eM)^{-1}$.

Proof. By Lemma 60.3, for each integer u, and for each $N > 0$, the set of x where $c(u;x) \geqslant N/b_u$, has variation not greater than $(1-beM)^{-1}b_u N^{-1}$. Hence the set of x where $c(u;x) < N/b_u$, for all integers u, has variation not less than

$$1-(1-beM)^{-1} \sum_{u=1}^{\infty} b_u N^{-1} = 1-KN^{-1}$$

for some $K > 0$. Taking all $N > 0$ we obtain the lemma.

THEOREM 60.3. *A T-matrix* $a_n(u)$ *has the Borel property if it satisfies*

$$(60.12) \qquad \sum_{u=1}^{\infty} \exp\left(-\delta \cdot \|a(u)\|_2^{-2}\right) < \infty, \quad \text{for each } \delta > 0$$

or, equivalently, if, for each fixed $\delta > 0$, *there is some* $\{b_u\}$ *satisfying*

$$(60.13) \quad b_u > 0, \quad \sum_{u=1}^{\infty} b_u < \infty, \quad \|a(u)\|_2^2 = \delta\{\log(b_u^{-1})\}^{-1}$$

These are equivalent since $b_u = \exp\left(-\delta \|a(u)\|_2^{-2}\right)$. (60.12) is due to Hill (1951), (60.13) independently due to Henstock (1955), p. 255, Theorem (ii).

Proof. To prove Theorem 60.3 we put

$$c_{un} = \delta^{-1/2} \log^{1/2}(b_u^{-1}) \cdot a_n(u) = a_n(u) \cdot \|a(u)\|_2^{-1}, \quad \|c(u)\|_2 = 1$$

If $CR(u; x)$ is the $AR(u; x)$ for $\{c_{un}\}$, then by Lemma 60.4.

$$\exp\left(b \cdot CR(u; x)^2\right) \leqslant Ab_u^{-1}$$

almost everywhere in $(0, 1)$, where b is any number $< e^{-1}$, and for the same points,

$$b \cdot \delta^{-1} \log\left(b_u^{-1}\right) AR(u; x)^2 \leqslant \log A + \log\left(b_u^{-1}\right)$$

$$|AR(u; x)| \leqslant \delta^{1/2} b^{-1/2}\left(1 + (\log A) \cdot (\log\left(b_u^{-1}\right))^{-1}\right)^{1/2}$$

$$\lim_{u \to \infty} \sup |AR(u; x)| \leqslant \delta^{1/2} b^{-1/2}$$

and this for each $\delta > 0$. Hence $AR(u; x) \to 0$ almost everywhere in $(0, 1)$, and $a_n(u)$ has the Borel property.

From Lemma 60.4 and Garreau's example, we can obtain information on the rate of growth of $AR(u;x)$ as $u \to \infty$ (see Henstock (1955)).

THEOREM 60.4. *If $a_n(u)$ is a T-matrix, and if $\varepsilon > 0$, there is a $u_0 > 0$, depending on $a_n(u)$, x, ε, such that, for almost all $x \in (0, 1)$,*

(60.14) $\quad |AR(u; x)| \leqslant (K + \varepsilon) \|a(u)\|_2 \cdot \log^{1/2} u (u \geqslant u_0)$

(60.15) *where K is a constant that can be taken as low as $e^{1/2}$, but cannot be lower than* $\log^{-1/2} 4$.

Proof. Replacing $a_n(u)$ in Lemma 60.4 by c_{un}, with $b_u = u^{-1} \log^{-2} (u+1)$, we see that for some $N = N(x) > 0$, depending on x for almost all $x \in (0, 1)$, and for each fixed $b < e^{-1}$, we have

$$\exp\left(b \cdot CR(u; x)^2\right) \leqslant Nu \cdot \log^2 (u+1) \qquad (u = 1, 2, \ldots)$$

$$CR(u; x)^2 \leqslant b^{-1} \log N + b^{-1} \log u + 2b^{-1} \log \log (u+1)$$

As b is any number less than e^{-1}, while N depends on b, x, we see that

$$|CR(u; x)| \leqslant (e^{1/2} + \varepsilon) \log^{1/2} u,$$

$$|AR(u; x)| \leqslant (e^{1/2} + \varepsilon) \|a(u)\|_2 \cdot \log^{1/2} u$$

giving (60.14) and the first part of (60.15). The second part follows from Garreau's example and Lemma 60.1 (Stirling's formula). For

$$\frac{16 \cdot 2^{2k}}{25(\pi k)^{1/2}} \leqslant \binom{2k}{k} \leqslant \frac{5}{4} \cdot \frac{2^{2k}}{(\pi k)^{1/2}},$$

$$\frac{16}{25(\pi k)^{1/2}} \left(\frac{4^k-1}{3}\right) \leqslant \sum_{j=1}^{k-1} \binom{2j}{j} \leqslant \frac{5}{4\pi^{1/2}} \left(\frac{4^k-1}{3}\right)$$

By this and (60.11)

$$\frac{16}{25(\pi k)^{1/2}} \left(\frac{4^k-1}{3}\right) \leqslant u \leqslant \frac{5}{\pi^{1/2}} 4^k,$$

$$\log N_1 - \tfrac{1}{2}\log k + k \log 4 \leqslant \log u \leqslant \log N_2 + k \log 4,$$

$$\log u/(k \log 4) \to 1(u \to \infty), \quad \sum_{n=1}^{\infty} g_{un}^2 = k^{-1}$$

and we have the second result in (60.15). The exact value of K is unknown. $K \leqslant \sqrt{2}$ by improving Lemma 60.2.

61. Measure and Variation in the Space of Bounded Sequences

One of the objects of this section is to extend Theorems 34.1, 34.2. We began by using multiplicative functionals $f(s; x)$ defined for all $x \in T$, all $s \geqslant 1$, s taking all such real number values, or integer values only. We then considered $f(s; x)$ to be defined for all $x \in T$ and all $s \geqslant s_0(x)$, where $s_0(x)$ can vary with x. With mild restrictions on f it turned out that we can replace $s_0(x)$ by a constant. We now go deeper, and use a measure or variation on the range $s \geqslant 1$. The two problems we wish to consider, may be written for a general T as follows.

Using the ordinary measure or variation on $(1, \infty)$, *is it possible to have necessary and sufficient conditions on* f *in order that* $\operatorname*{ess\,lim\,sup}_{s \to \infty} |f(s; x)| < \infty$ *for all* $x \in T$, *where in taking the essential limit we omit a set of* s *of measure or variation zero that can possibly depend on* x?

Replacing $+\infty$ by a finite $b > 0$, we suppose that $1 \leqslant s < b$, and then can use a one-sided approximate limit like the two-sided limit of Saks (1937), pp. 218–19. *Is it possible to have necessary and sufficient conditions in order that* $\lim_{s \to b-} \sup \text{ap } |f(s; x)| < \infty$ *for all* $x \in T$?

In both problems our hypotheses involve each fixed $x \in T$, and all s in a set contained in $s \geqslant 1$, and initially varying with x. By some means we have to turn this into one involving a fixed set of s, and for each such s, a set of x 'thick' enough for our purpose. We use Fubini's theorem, and so need a measure or variation on T, and then there arise two more problems.

Let a measure or variation V be defined on T, and let $f(x)$ be multiplicative and measurable on T. If f is finite on a set of positive variation, does it follow that f is finite almost everywhere on T, and is given by some simple formula? More generally, for the same T let $f(x, y)$ be a bimultiplicative and non-negative definite real functional of $x, y \in T$ with $f(x, x)$ measurable, and finite on a set of positive variation. Can we prove that $f(x, y)$ and $f(x, x)$ are finite with simple formulae, almost everywhere?

Naturally, in this fourth problem we must have some rule to proceed from values $f(x, x)$ to values $f(x, y)$, so that we assume that

$$(61.1) \qquad f(x \cdot y, \, x \cdot y^{-1}) = f(x, x) - f(y, y)$$

the left side existing when the right exists. Note that if

$$(61.2) \qquad f(y^{-1}, y^{-1}) = f(y, y)$$

we can replace y by y^{-1} in (61.1) to show that

$$(61.3) \qquad f(x \cdot y, \, x \cdot y^{-1}) = f(x \cdot y^{-1}, \, x \cdot y)$$

If $T = R^n$, with the usual algebraic, topological, and measure or variation structures, then in the third problem we can prove f finite *everywhere* in T and possibly a similar result holds in the fourth problem. The results of Theorem 32.10 (32.36; 32.37) for convex functions can be used here. From a functional analysis point of view, R^n is a rather trivial space. But, as is pointed out in Henstock (1963a), pp. 319–20, the methods may fail in a more complicated T.

A space just a little more complicated than R^n, is the space m of bounded sequences, which we can assume real, since if $\{z_n\}$ is a complex sequence we can write $w_{2n-1} = \mathrm{rl}\, z_n$, $w_{2n} = \mathrm{im}\, z_n$ ($n = 1$, $2, \ldots$) and use $\{w_n\}$ instead. In m the group operation is addition, $\{x_n\} + \{y_n\} = \{x_n + y_n\}$, while the volume $\mu(I)$ of the interval I that is the Cartesian product of real intervals $[x_n, y_n]$ ($n = 1, 2, \ldots$), is taken to be

$$\mu(I) = \prod_{n=1}^{\infty} (y_n - x_n)$$

In order that this volume be finite, it is usual to deal only with the 'unit cube' W, the Cartesian product of $[-\frac{1}{2}, \frac{1}{2}]$ for $n = 1, 2, \ldots$ For each $\mathbf{y} \in M$ we can then consider the unit cube neighbourhood $\mathbf{y} + W$ of $\mathbf{y}$. The theory of section 21 relative to measure, needs that for some set $E \subseteq W$, and so for W itself, E is strongly-$\bar{p}_9$ (δ) relative to itself, i.e. (for $E = W$)

$$\mu(W^{\mathbf{v}}) \equiv \mu(W \cap (\mathbf{v} + W)) \geqslant \delta \cdot \mu(W) \, (\mathbf{v} \in G(\delta) \in \mathcal{G}_0)$$

In particular we require that for $\mathbf{v} = \{v_n\} \in G(\delta)$

$$\mu(W \cap (\mathbf{v} + W)) = \prod_{n=1}^{\infty} \{1 - |v_n|\} > 0, \quad \sum_{n=1}^{\infty} |v_n| < \infty$$

by the convergence of the infinite product, and $G(\delta) \subseteq c$. As c is a complete linear subspace of m, using $\|\mathbf{v}\|_{\infty}$, then $\bar{c} = c$, and the closure of $D(G(\delta))$ is contained in c. Thus $D(G(\delta))$ is not even dense in W. To tackle the theorems of this section on necessity of conditions we seem to need far stronger tools than are provided by those of Banach-Steinhaus type, such tools being given in Henstock (1955; 1956). This section is based on those papers.

A further extension is to the space T of functions continuous on a compact set, with Wiener measure. See Graves (1951), and Fau Dyk Tin and Silov, G.E. (1966). But this theory is too long to be described here.

As in section 48, for $\mathbf{x} \in m$ let

$$\mathbf{x}'_n = \{x_1, \ldots, x_n, 0, 0, \ldots\}, \quad \mathbf{x}''_n = \{0, \ldots, 0, x_{n+1}, \ldots\},$$
$$\mathbf{x}'_n + \mathbf{x}''_n = \mathbf{x}$$

Let W_n be the set of $\mathbf{x}'_n$, for $\mathbf{x} \in W$, W_n^* the corresponding set of $\mathbf{x}''$, and μ_n the n-dimensional measure on W_n, i.e.

$$\mu_n(X) = \mu(X \times W_n^*) \qquad (X \subseteq W_n)$$

Also, as usual, we define the first integral as

$$\int_X f \, d\mu = \int_W f \cdot ch(X; .) \, d\mu \qquad (X \subseteq W)$$

THEOREM 61.1. *If $f(\mathbf{x}, \mathbf{z})$ is a bilinear non-negative definite function of $\mathbf{x}, \mathbf{z} \in m$ for which*

(61.4) $\quad a_{jn} \equiv f(\mathbf{t}^j, \mathbf{t}^n) \quad$ *exists, for* $\quad j, n = 1, 2, \ldots, \quad$ *where*

$$t_n^j = 0 \; (n \neq j), \quad 1 \; (n = j);$$

(61.5) $\quad a_j(\mathbf{y}) \equiv f(\mathbf{t}^j, \mathbf{y}), \quad b_j(\mathbf{y}) \equiv f(\mathbf{y}, \mathbf{t}^j) \quad$ *exist, for* $\quad j = 1, 2, \ldots,$

where $\quad \mathbf{y} \in m \quad$ *is fixed,*

(61.6) $$\Gamma \equiv \sum_{n=1}^{\infty} a_{nn} < \infty,$$

(61.7) $$\sum_{n=1}^{\infty} a_n^2(\mathbf{y}) < \infty, \quad \sum_{n=1}^{\infty} b_n^2(\mathbf{y}) < \infty,$$

(61.8) $$\lim_{n \to \infty} f(\mathbf{x}'_n, \mathbf{x}''_n) = \lim_{n \to \infty} f(\mathbf{x}''_n, \mathbf{x}'_n) = 0$$

almost everywhere in W,

(61.9) $\lim\limits_{n \to \infty} f(\mathbf{x}''_n + \mathbf{y}, \mathbf{x}''_n + \mathbf{y}) = K, \; for \; some \; constant \; K \geq 0, \; almost$

everywhere in W, then $f(\mathbf{x}+\mathbf{y}, \mathbf{x}+\mathbf{y})$ is measurable for $\mathbf{x} \in W$, and definable (finite) for almost all $\mathbf{x} \in W$ by the formula

(61.10) $\quad f(\mathbf{x}+\mathbf{y}, \mathbf{x}+\mathbf{y}) = \sum\limits_{j, n=1}^{\infty} a_{jn} x_j x_n + \sum\limits_{n=1}^{\infty} \{a_n(\mathbf{y}) + b_n(\mathbf{y})\} x_n + K.$

Proof. The integral of an odd power of x over $[-\frac{1}{2}, \frac{1}{2}]$ is 0. Thus, putting

$$f_n(\mathbf{x}) \equiv f(\mathbf{x}'_n, \mathbf{x}'_n) = \sum_{j, k=1}^{n} a_{jk} x_j x_k \qquad (n \geq 1)$$

314

we have, for $m > n$,

$$\int_W \{f_m(x) - f_n(x)\}^2 \, d\mu = \int_W \left\{ \sum_{j,\,k=n+1}^{m} + \sum_{j=1}^{n} \sum_{k=n+1}^{m} \right.$$

$$+ \sum_{j=n+1}^{m} \sum_{k=1}^{n} \bigg\}^2 \, d\mu = \int_W \left[\left\{ \sum_{j,\,k=n+1}^{m} a_{jk} x_j x_k \right\}^2 + \left\{ \sum_{j=1}^{n} \sum_{k=n+1}^{m} (a_{jk} \right. \right.$$

$$+ a_{kj}) x_j x_k \bigg\}^2 \bigg] \, d\mu = \int_W \left[\left\{ \sum_{n<j\leqslant m} a_{jj} x_j^2 + \sum_{n<j<k\leqslant m} (a_{jk} + a_{kj}) x_j x_k \right\}^2 \right.$$

$$+ \left\{ \sum_{1<j\leqslant n<k\leqslant m} (a_{jk} + a_{kj}) x_j x_k \right\}^2 \bigg] \, d\mu = \sum_{n<j\leqslant m} a_{jj}^2/80$$

$$+ 2 \sum_{n<j<k\leqslant m} a_{jj} a_{kk}/144 + \sum_{n<j<k\leqslant m} (a_{jk} + a_{kj})^2/144$$

$$+ \sum_{1<j\leqslant n<k\leqslant m} (a_{jk} + a_{kj})^2/144.$$

By using Theorem 26.1 (26.2) we have

$$(61.11) \qquad \int_W \{f_m(x) - f_n(x)\}^2 \, d\mu \leqslant \sum_{n<j\leqslant m} a_{jj}^2/80$$

$$+ \sum_{n<j<k\leqslant m} a_{jj} a_{kk}/24 + \sum_{1<j\leqslant n<k\leqslant m} a_{jj} a_{kk}/36 \leqslant \sum_{j=1}^{m} a_{jj} \sum_{k=n}^{m} a_{kk}/36$$

Hence by (61.6) there is an $n(j)$ such that if

$$g_j(\mathbf{x}) \equiv f_{n(j)}(\mathbf{x}), \quad \int_W \{f_m(\mathbf{x}) - g_j(\mathbf{x})\}^2 \, d\mu < 4^{-j} \qquad (m > n(j))$$

$$h_j \equiv \int_W |g_{j+1}(\mathbf{x}) - g_j(\mathbf{x})| \, d\mu \leqslant \left\{ \int_W |g_{j+1}(\mathbf{x}) \right.$$

$$\left. - g_j(\mathbf{x})|^2 \, d\mu \int_W 1^2 \, d\mu \right\}^{1/2} < 2^{-j}$$

$$\sum_{j=1}^{\infty} h_j < 1$$

Hence by Lebesgue's monotone convergence theorem, Theorem 46.1,

$$\sum_{j=1}^{\infty} |g_{j+1}(\mathbf{x}) - g_j(\mathbf{x})| < \infty, \quad g(\mathbf{x}) \equiv \lim_{j \to \infty} g_j(\mathbf{x})$$

exists almost everywhere in W, and by Fatou's lemma, Theorem 46.2, and using (61.11),

$$\int_W \{g(\mathbf{x}) - f_n(\mathbf{x})\}^2 \, d\mu = \int_W \left\{ \lim_{j \to \infty} f_{n(j)}(\mathbf{x}) - f_n(\mathbf{x}) \right\}^2 d\mu$$

$$\leq \lim_{j \to \infty} \inf \int_W \{f_{n(j)}(\mathbf{x}) - f_n(\mathbf{x})\}^2 \, d\mu \leq \sum_{k=n}^{\infty} a_{kk} \Gamma/36$$

Thus $f_n(\mathbf{x}) \to g(\mathbf{x})$ in mean with index 2, and

$$\int_W g^2(\mathbf{x}) \, d\mu < \infty$$

By the Cauchy–Schwartz–Buniakowsky inequality for integrals,

$$G(X) \equiv \int_X g(\mathbf{x}) \, d\mu$$

exists, for each μ-measurable set $X \subseteq W$. Let $\mathbf{x} \in W$, let n be an integer, and let $I(n)$ denote the interval containing $\mathbf{x}$ of the form

$$k_j \leq 2^n x_j \leq k_j + 1 \; (1 \leq j \leq n), \quad -\tfrac{1}{2} \leq x_j \leq \tfrac{1}{2} \quad (j > n)$$

where k_j is an integer depending on $\mathbf{x}$ and n. We have

$$\int_{I(n)} \{g(\mathbf{x}) - f_n(\mathbf{x})\} \, d\mu = \lim_{m \to \infty} \int_{I(n)} \{f_m(\mathbf{x}) - f_n(\mathbf{x})\} \, d\mu$$

$$= \lim_{m \to \infty} \int_{I(n)} \left\{ \sum_{jr=n+1}^{m} a_{jr} x_j x_r + \sum_{j=1}^{n} \sum_{r=n+1}^{m} (a_{jr} + a_{rj}) x_j x_r \right\} d\mu$$

$$= \lim_{m \to \infty} \sum_{j=n+1}^{m} \mu_n(I(n)) a_{jj}/12 = \mu_n(I(n)) \sum_{j=n+1}^{\infty} a_{jj}/12$$

$$\int_{I(n)} f_n(\mathbf{x}) \, d\mu = \sum_{j,r=1}^{n} a_{jr} \int_{I(n)} x_j x_r \, d\mu_n = \sum_{j=1}^{n} a_{jj} 2^{-n(n-1)} \cdot 3^{-1} \{(k_j+1)^3$$

$$- k_j^3\} \, 2^{-3n} + \sum_{1 < j < r \leq n} (a_{jr} + a_{rj}) \, 2^{-n(n-2)} 2^{-1} \{(k_j+1)^2 - k_j^2\} \cdot 2^{-1}\{(k_r$$

$$+ 1)^2 - k_r^2\} \, 2^{-4n} = \sum_{j=1}^{n} a_{jj} \cdot 2^{-2n}(k_j^2 + k_j + 3^{-1}) \, \mu_n(I(n))$$

$$+ \sum_{1 < j < r \leq n} (a_{jr} + a_{rj}) \, 2^{-2n}(k_j + 2^{-1}) \cdot (k_r + 2^{-1}) \, \mu_n(I(n))$$

$$G(I(n))/\mu_n(I(n)) = f(\mathbf{z}^{(n)}, \, \mathbf{z}^{(n)}) + \sum_{j=1}^{n} a_{jj} \cdot 2^{-2n} \cdot (12)^{-1} + \sum_{j=n+1}^{\infty} a_{jj}(12)^{-1}$$

where $z^{(n)}$ is the midpoint of $I(n)$. Also

$$\left|f(z^{(n)}, z^{(n)}) - f_n(x)\right|^2 = \left|\sum_{j,r=1}^{n} a_{jr}\left(z_j^{(n)} z_r^{(n)} - x_j x_r\right)\right|^2$$

$$\leqslant \sum_{j,r=1}^{n} (a_{jr} + a_{rj})^2 \cdot n^2 \cdot 2^{-2n-1} \leqslant n^2 \cdot 2^{-2n}\Gamma^2,$$

$$\left|f(z^{(n)}, z^{(n)}) - f_n(x)\right| \leqslant n \cdot 2^{-n} \cdot \Gamma$$

Hence we have

(61.12) $\qquad G\big((I(n))/\mu_n(I(n))\big) - f_n(x) \to 0 \qquad (n \to \infty)$

To show that $f_n(x)$ tends to a limit almost everywhere, and so tends to $g(x)$ almost everywhere, we need only show that G is differentiable almost everywhere, in the sense that the ratio in (61.12) tends to a limit. I omit the proof as it can be found in Saks (1937), pp. 152–5, on noting that a set of measure zero is a set of variation zero.

Similarly we can prove that

$$c_n(x) \equiv \sum_{j=1}^{n} a_j(y)\, x_j, \qquad d_n(x) \equiv \sum_{j=1}^{n} b_j(y)\, x_j$$

tend to a limit almost everywhere, using (61.5; 61.7). Thus

$$\lim_{n \to \infty} f(x'_n, y), \qquad \lim_{n \to \infty} f(y, x'_n)$$

exist for x almost everywhere in W, and also

$$f(x+y, x+y) = \lim_{n \to \infty} f(x'_n + x''_n + y, x'_n + x''_n + y)$$

$$= \lim_{n \to \infty} \{f(x'_n, x'_n) + f(x'_n, x''_n) + f(x''_n, x'_n) + f(x'_n, y)$$

$$+ f(y, x'_n) + f(x''_n + y, x''_n + y)\}$$

$$= \sum_{j,k=1}^{\infty} a_{jk} x_j x_k + \sum_{j=1}^{\infty} \{a_j(y) + b_j(y)\}\, x_j + K$$

giving (61.10).

We can prove a converse when (61.1) holds, so that $f(x, z)$ is symmetric by (61.3), for $f(x, x)$ and $f(z, z)$ existing, since (61.2) is true in this case.

Lemma 61.1 (Henstock (1955), p. 240, Lemmas 1,2; Henstock (1956), p. 487, Lemma 1(3.3)) *If the μ-measurable $X \subseteq W$ has variation V, then for some $k > 0$,*

$$(61.13) \qquad \int_X x_n^2 \, d\mu \geqslant \max\left(kV^4, \tfrac{1}{4}V - \tfrac{1}{6}\right),$$

$$(61.14) \qquad \sum_{n=1}^{\infty} \left\{\int_X x_n \, d\mu\right\}^2 \leqslant \tfrac{1}{12}\min\left(V, 1-V\right),$$

$$(61.15) \qquad \sum_{j<n} \left\{\int_X x_j x_n \, d\mu\right\}^2 \leqslant \tfrac{1}{144}\min\left(V, 1-V\right).$$

Proof. Let $\mathbf{x}_n^1$ denote the $\mathbf{y}$ with $y_j = x_j$ ($j < n$), $y_j = x_{j+1}$ ($j \geqslant n$), let $V_1(\mathbf{x}_n^1)$ be the variation, in the x_n-direction, of that part of X for which $\mathbf{x}_n^1$ is fixed, and let V_2 be the variation $\mu(Y)$ of the set Y of $\mathbf{x}_n^1$ for which

$$V_1(\mathbf{x}_n^1) \geqslant \delta V$$

Then the variation of the remaining set of $\mathbf{x}_n^1$ is $1 - V_2$. In the integral of the characteristic function of X we separate the variable x_n. Then by Fubini's theorem (the generalization of Henstock (1963c), p. 110, Theorem 44.3, as $(R, \mathcal{S}, \mathcal{A})$ is a product division space) we have

$$\delta V(1 - V_2) + V_2 \geqslant V, \; V_2(1 - \delta V) \geqslant (1 - \delta)\, V$$

The least value of the integral in (61.13) occurs when the x_n form an interval symmetrical about $x_n = 0$, in which case, for the section with a given $\mathbf{x}_n^1$, the interval has length $V_1(\mathbf{x}_n^1)$. Hence by Fubini's theorem,

$$\int_X x_n^2 \, d\mu \geqslant V_2 \delta^3 V^3 / 12 \geqslant \delta^3(1 - \delta)\, V^4 / \{12(1 - \delta V)\} \geqslant kV^4$$

For example, $\delta = \tfrac{3}{4}$ gives $k = 9/1024$. For the second estimate in (61.13) let $Y = W \backslash X$. Then

$$\int_X x_n^2 \, d\mu = \int_W - \int_Y > \tfrac{1}{12} - \int_Y \left(\tfrac{1}{2}\right)^2 d\mu = \tfrac{1}{12} - \tfrac{1}{4}(1 - V)$$

(61.14; 61.15) are inequalities of Bessel type. Let $c(x)$ be the characteristic function of X. Then for real numbers a_n,

$$0 \leqslant \int_W \left\{c(x) - \sum_{j=1}^n a_j x_j\right\}^2 d\mu = V - 2\sum_{j=1}^n a_j \int_X x_j \, d\mu + \sum_{j=1}^n a_j^2 / 12$$

318

The first inequality in (61.14) follows on taking

$$a_j = 12 \int_X x_j \, d\mu$$

with $n \to \infty$. Then the second inequality follows from

$$\int_X x_n \, d\mu = \int_W - \int_Y = -\int_Y x_n \, d\mu$$

Similarly, for real numbers a_{jn}, we obtain (61.15) from

$$0 \leqslant \int_W \left\{ c(x) - \sum_{1 < j < n \leqslant N} a_{jn} x_j x_n \right\}^2 d\mu = V - 2 \sum_{1 < j < n \leqslant N} a_{jn} \int_X x_j x_n \, d\mu$$

$$+ \sum_{1 < j < n \leqslant N} a_{jn}^2 / 12^2; \qquad a_{jn} = 144 \int_X x_j x_n \, d\mu$$

$$\int_X x_j x_n \, d\mu = \int_W - \int_Y = -\int_Y x_j x_n \, d\mu \qquad (j \neq n)$$

THEOREM 61.2. *Let f be a bilinear non-negative definite function of* **x**, **z** $\in m$ *satisfying* (61.1), *and let $X \in W$ be the set of* **x** *where the measurable* $f(\mathbf{x}+\mathbf{y}, \mathbf{x}+\mathbf{y})$ *exists. If $\mu(X) > 0$, then $\mu(X) = 1$, and f satisfies* (61.4;...; 61.9), *while, for almost all* **x** $\in W$, $f(\mathbf{x}, \mathbf{t}^n)$ $(n = 1, 2, \ldots)$ *and* $f(\mathbf{x}, \mathbf{y})$ *exist. Further, with the other hypotheses, $f(\mathbf{x}, \mathbf{x})$ exists almost everywhere in W if, and only if, $f(\mathbf{y}, \mathbf{y})$ exists.*

Proof. Let $j < n$, and let $\mathbf{x}_{jn}^2$ be the point $\mathbf{y} \in W$ with

$$y_k = x_k \quad (1 \leqslant k < j), \quad y_k = x_{k+1} \quad (j \leqslant k < n-1),$$

$$y_k = x_{k+2} \quad (k \geqslant n-1); \quad X_1 \subseteq X, \quad X_{jn}(\mathbf{x}_{jn}^2) \equiv \{(x_j, x_n) : \mathbf{x} \in X\},$$

$$X_{1jn}(\mathbf{x}_{jn}^2) \equiv \{(x_j, x_n) : \mathbf{x} \in X_1\}$$

the last sets being for fixed $\mathbf{x}_{jn}^2$. By Fubini's theorem,

$$(61.16) \qquad \int_W \mu_2(X_{1jn}(x_{jn}^2)) \, d\mu = \mu(X_1)$$

As $X_{1jn} \subseteq X_{jn}$, if, for a set of $\mathbf{x} \in X$ of positive variation,

$$(61.17) \qquad \mu_2(X_{jn}(\mathbf{x}_{jn}^2)) = 0$$

we can take X_1 as this set of positive variation and contradict (61.16). Hence (61.17) is false for almost all $\mathbf{x} \in X$, and the plane sets X_n

contain distinct points of the form

$$(x_j, x_n), \quad (x_j+b_k, x_n) \quad (k = 1, 2),$$
$$(x_j+b_3, x_n+b_4) \quad (b_3 b_4 \neq 0)$$

for almost all $(x_j, x_n) \in X_{jn}$. Thus by (61.1), if $\mathbf{x}$ is the corresponding point in W, there exist

$$f(2\mathbf{x}+2\mathbf{y}+b_k\mathbf{t}^j, b_k\mathbf{t}^j) \quad (k = 1, 2),$$
$$f(2\mathbf{x}+2\mathbf{y}+b_3\mathbf{t}^j+b_4\mathbf{t}^n, b_3\mathbf{t}^j+b_4\mathbf{t}^n)$$

By linearity we can remove the second b_k from the first term, and a_{jj} exists, and then from the second term we have the existence of

$$f(b_3\mathbf{t}^j+b_4\mathbf{t}^n, b_3\mathbf{t}^j+b_4\mathbf{t}^n)-f(b_3\mathbf{t}^j, b_3\mathbf{t}^j) = f(2b_3\mathbf{t}^j+b_4\mathbf{t}^n, b_4\mathbf{t}^n)$$

Subtracting $b_4^2 f(\mathbf{t}^n, \mathbf{t}^n)$ and then dividing by $2b_3b_4$ we have a_{jn}. Further

(61.18) $$f(\mathbf{x}+\mathbf{y}, \mathbf{t}^j) \quad (j = 1, 2, \ldots)$$

exists for almost all $(x_j, x_n) \in X_{jn}$, and so for almost all $\mathbf{x} \in X$. Thus for

$$x \in X_2 \subseteq X, \quad \mu(X \backslash X_2) = 0,$$
$$f(\mathbf{x}+\mathbf{y}+\mathbf{w}, \mathbf{x}+\mathbf{y}+\mathbf{w}) = f(\mathbf{x}+\mathbf{y}, \mathbf{x}+\mathbf{y})+2f(\mathbf{x}+\mathbf{y}, \mathbf{w})+f(\mathbf{w}, \mathbf{w})$$

exists, where $\mathbf{w}$ is an arbitrary finite linear combination of the $\mathbf{t}^j$ independent of X_2, and X_2 is cylindrical of every finite order. Hence by Theorem 48.1, $\mu(X_2) > 0$ becomes $\mu(X_2) = 1$. Further, changing $\mathbf{x}$ to $-\mathbf{x}$ in (61.18), we see that $a_j(\mathbf{y}) = b_j(\mathbf{y})$ exists, the equality following from (61.3); and also $f(\mathbf{x}, \mathbf{t}^j)$ exists, for almost all $\mathbf{x} \in W$, with $j = 1, 2, \ldots$ Also $f(\mathbf{x}+\mathbf{y}, \mathbf{x}+\mathbf{y})$ exists for almost all $\mathbf{x} \in W$, so that if we change $\mathbf{x}$ to $-\mathbf{x}$, we see that $f(\mathbf{x}, \mathbf{y})$ exists for almost all $\mathbf{x} \in W$.

We now have to show that $(61.6; \ldots; 61.9)$ are necessary. We choose a set $X_3 \subseteq W$ in which $f(\mathbf{x}+\mathbf{y}, \mathbf{x}+\mathbf{y}) < N$. Since $\mu(X) = 1$ we can choose N so large that $\mu(X_3) > 0.99$, using Theorem 44.9. For a particular $\mathbf{x}_n''$ we put

$$X(n) = \{\mathbf{x}_n' : \mathbf{x}_n'+\mathbf{x}_n'' \in X_3\}$$

Then by Jessen's theorem, Theorem 48.2,

(61.19) $$\lim_{n \to \infty} \mu_n(X(n)) = \mu(X_3), \quad V = \mu_n(X(n)) > 0.99$$

$$\lim_{n \to \infty} \int_{X(n)} f(\mathbf{x}_n'+\mathbf{x}_n''+\mathbf{y}, \mathbf{x}_n'+\mathbf{x}_n''+\mathbf{y}) \, d\mu_n = \int_{X_2} f(\mathbf{x}+\mathbf{y}, \mathbf{x}+\mathbf{y}) \, d\mu$$

$$(61.20) \qquad \int_{X(n)} f(\mathbf{x}_n'+\mathbf{x}_n''+\mathbf{y},\ \mathbf{x}_n'+\mathbf{x}_n''+\mathbf{y})\, d\mu_n < N$$

This is true for $n > n_0$, where n_0 depends on the $\mathbf{x}$ almost everywhere in W that gives the $\mathbf{x}_n''$. We now split up f into parts that have already been shown to exist.

$$f(\mathbf{x}_n'+\mathbf{x}_n''+\mathbf{y},\ \mathbf{x}_n'+\mathbf{x}_n''+\mathbf{y}) = f(\mathbf{x}_n',\mathbf{x}_n')+2f(\mathbf{x}_n''+\mathbf{y},\mathbf{x}_n')+f(\mathbf{x}_n''+\mathbf{y},\mathbf{x}_n''+\mathbf{y})$$

$$(61.21) \qquad = \sum_{j,\,k=1}^{n} a_{jk}\,x_j x_k + 2\sum_{j=1}^{n} a_j(\mathbf{x}_n''+\mathbf{y})\,x_j + f(\mathbf{x}_n''+\mathbf{y},\ \mathbf{x}_n''+\mathbf{y})$$

For simplicity let us denote the last term by Δ_n, and also put

$$(61.22) \qquad \Gamma_n \equiv \sum_{j=1}^{n} a_{jj};\quad \sum_{j=1}^{n} a_j(\mathbf{x}_n''+\mathbf{y})^2 \leqslant \Gamma_n \Delta_n$$

(By (61.19; ...; 61.22) and Lemma 61.1,

$$N > \sum_{j,\,k=1}^{n} a_{jk}\int_{X(n)} x_j x_k\, d\mu_n + \sum_{j=1}^{n} 2a_j(\mathbf{x}_n''+\mathbf{y})\int_{X(n)} x_j\, d\mu_n + \Delta_n V$$

$$\geqslant \sum_{j=1}^{n} a_{jj}\int_{X(n)} x_j^2\, d\mu_n - \sum_{1<j<k<n} 2|a_{jk}|\left|\int_{X(n)} x_j x_k\, d\mu_n\right|$$

$$- \sum_{j=1}^{n} 2|a_j(\mathbf{x}_n''+\mathbf{y})|\left|\int_{X(n)} x_j\, d\mu_n\right| + \Delta_n V \geqslant \Gamma_n(\tfrac{1}{4}V-\tfrac{1}{6})$$

$$-2\left\{\sum_{1<j<k<n} a_{jk}^2 \sum_{1<j<k<n}\left(\int_{X(n)} x_j x_k\, d\mu_n\right)^2\right\}^{1/2}$$

$$-2\left[\sum_{j=1}^{n} a_j(\mathbf{x}_n''+\mathbf{y})^2\right]^{1/2}\left[\sum_{j=1}^{n}\left(\int_{X(n)} x_j\, d\mu_n\right)^2\right]^{1/2} + \Delta_n V$$

$$\geqslant \Gamma_n(\tfrac{1}{4}V-\tfrac{1}{6}) - 2^{1/2}\left(\sum_{j,\,k=1}^{n} a_{jj}a_{kk}\right)^{1/2}\{\tfrac{1}{12}(1-V)\}^{1/2}$$

$$-2\Gamma_n^{1/2}\Delta_n^{1/2}(1-V)^{1/2}(12)^{-1/2} + \Delta_n V = 97\Gamma_n(1200)^{-1}$$

$$-\Gamma_n(600)^{-1/2} - 2\Gamma_n^{1/2}\Delta_n^{1/2}(1200)^{-1/2} + 99\Delta_n(100)^{-1}$$

$$= \Gamma_n\{97(1200)^{-1}-(600)^{-1/2}-(1200)^{-1/2}\}+\Delta_n\{99(100)^{-1}$$

$$-(1200)^{-1/2}\}+(\Gamma_n^{1/2}-\Delta_n^{1/2})^2\,(1200)^{-1/2}$$

$$> \Gamma_n\left(\frac{97}{1200}-\frac{40+50}{1200}\right)+\Delta_n\left(\frac{99}{100}-\frac{40}{1200}\right) = \frac{7}{1200}\Gamma_n+\frac{1148}{1200}\Delta_n$$

321

Thus we obtain

(61.23) $\Gamma_n < 200\,N, \quad \Delta_n < 2N$

which gives (61.6) on letting $n \to \infty$. Also the integral

$$\int_W f(\mathbf{x}+\mathbf{y}, \mathbf{x}+\mathbf{y})\,d\mu = \lim_{n \to \infty} \int_{W_n} f(\mathbf{x}_n'+\mathbf{x}_n''+\mathbf{y}, \mathbf{x}_n'+\mathbf{x}_n''+\mathbf{y})\,d\mu_n$$

$$= \lim_{n \to \infty} \left\{ \sum_{j=1}^n a_{jj}/12 + f(\mathbf{x}_n''+\mathbf{y}, \mathbf{x}_n''+\mathbf{y}) \right\}$$

and by (61.23) with $a_{jj} \geqslant 0$, we have the existence of

$$\lim_{n \to \infty} f(\mathbf{x}_n''+\mathbf{y}, \mathbf{x}_n''+\mathbf{y})$$

almost everywhere in W. It is cylindrical of every finite order, so that (61.9) is true. Thus

(61.24) $\displaystyle \int_W f(\mathbf{x}+\mathbf{y}, \mathbf{x}+\mathbf{y})\,d\mu = \sum_{j=1}^{\infty} a_{jj}/12 + K$

Since $f(\mathbf{x}, \mathbf{y})$ exists, for almost all $\mathbf{x} \in W$, (61.7) follows by using the functional $f^*(\mathbf{x}, \mathbf{w}) = f(\mathbf{x}, \mathbf{y})f(\mathbf{w}, \mathbf{y})$, which satisfies all conditions on the original $f(\mathbf{x}+\mathbf{y}, \mathbf{w}+\mathbf{y})$ with $y_j = 0$ (*all j*)

There remains (61.8). From Theorem 61.1, $f(\mathbf{x}_n', \mathbf{x}_n')$ and $f(\mathbf{x}_n', \mathbf{y})$ tend to limits almost everywhere in W as $n \to \infty$. But by (61.21), $f(\mathbf{x}_n', \mathbf{x}_n'')$ tends to a limit almost everywhere. As in the first part of the proof, for some $g = g(\mathbf{x}) \neq 0$, and almost everywhere in $\mathbf{x}$, there exists

$$\lim_{n \to \infty} f(\mathbf{x}_n'+g\mathbf{t}^j, \mathbf{x}_n''), \quad \lim_{n \to \infty} f(\mathbf{t}^j, \mathbf{x}_n'')$$

The last limit is cylindrical of every finite order, and so is constant almost everywhere. Changing $\mathbf{x}$ to $-\mathbf{x}$, we see that the limit must be 0 almost everywhere. Thus if $\mathbf{w}$ is any finite linear combination of the $\mathbf{t}^j$,

$$\lim_{n \to \infty} f(\mathbf{x}_n'+\mathbf{w}, \mathbf{x}_n'') = \lim_{n \to \infty} f(\mathbf{x}_n', \mathbf{x}_n'')$$

and this limit is also cylindrical of every finite order, and hence is constant almost everywhere. Substituting (61.21) into (61.24) and using what we have proved, we have the constant 0 since

$$\int_W \lim_{n \to \infty} f(\mathbf{x}'_n, \mathbf{x}''_n) \, d\mu = 0$$

This result requires a little care. First, Δ_n is bounded by $2N$, so that the limit of its integral is K. Secondly, the integral of the limit of $f(\mathbf{x}'_n, \mathbf{x}'_n)$ is the limit of the integral, $\lim_{n \to \infty} \Gamma_n/12$, by Theorem 61.1, giving the result. We cannot argue directly from

$$\int_W f(\mathbf{x}'_n, \mathbf{x}''_n) \, d\mu = 0$$

since the integrand might not be majorized.

If $f(\mathbf{y}, \mathbf{y})$ exists, and since $f(\mathbf{x}, \mathbf{y})$ exists for almost all $\mathbf{x}$, we have the existence of $f(\mathbf{x}, \mathbf{x})$ almost everywhere from

$$f(\mathbf{x}+\mathbf{y}, \mathbf{x}+\mathbf{y}) - f(\mathbf{y}, \mathbf{y}) = f(\mathbf{x}+2\mathbf{y}, \mathbf{x})$$

Similarly, if $f(\mathbf{x}, \mathbf{x})$, $f(\mathbf{x}+\mathbf{y}, \mathbf{x}+\mathbf{y})$ exist for almost all $\mathbf{x} \in W$, they exist simultaneously for almost all $\mathbf{x}$, so that $f(2\mathbf{x}+\mathbf{y}, \mathbf{y})$ exist, and the existence of $f(\mathbf{y}, \mathbf{y})$ follows from the existence of $f(\mathbf{x}, \mathbf{y})$ for almost all $\mathbf{x}$.

THEOREM 61.3. *A necessary and sufficient condition on a real double sequence $\{a_{mn}\}$ satisfying*

$$\sum_{m, n=1}^{N} a_{mn} x_m x_n \geqslant 0 \qquad (all \ \mathbf{x} \in W; \ N = 1, 2, \ldots),$$

in order that

$$\sum_{m, n=1}^{\infty} a_{mn} x_m x_n \equiv \lim_{N \to \infty} \sum_{m, n=1}^{N} a_{mn} x_m x_n$$

should exist for almost all $\mathbf{x} \in W$, is that

$$\sum_{j=1}^{\infty} a_{jj} < \infty.$$

This is a special case of Theorems 61.1, 61.2 in which $\mathbf{y}$ is zero and (61.5; 61.7; 61.9) are automatically satisfied.

THEOREM 61.4. *Let $f(\mathbf{x})$ be a linear functional of points $\mathbf{x} \in m$, and let*

$\mathbf{y}$ *be fixed in m. If* $f(\mathbf{x}+\mathbf{y})$ *is measurable and exists for* $\mathbf{x} \in X \subseteq W$ *with* $\mu(X) > 0$, *then*

(61.25) $f(\mathbf{x})$ *exists for almost all* $\mathbf{x} \in W$, *and* $f(\mathbf{y})$ *exists;*

(61.26) $f(\mathbf{t}^n)$ *exists for* $n = 1, 2, \ldots;$

(61.27) $\displaystyle\sum_{n=1}^{\infty} |f(\mathbf{t}^n)|^2 < \infty;$

(61.28) $\displaystyle\lim_{n \to \infty} f(\mathbf{x}_n'') = 0$ *almost everywhere in* W.

Conversely, if $f(\mathbf{y})$ *exists, and if* $f(\mathbf{x})$ *satisfies* (61.26; 61.27; 61.28), *then* $f(\mathbf{x}+\mathbf{y})$ *is defined for almost all* $\mathbf{x} \in W$ *by the formula*

(61.29) $\displaystyle\sum_{n=1}^{\infty} f(\mathbf{t}^n)x_n + f(\mathbf{y}).$

Proof. For the first part we replace $f(\mathbf{x}+\mathbf{y}, \mathbf{x}+\mathbf{y})$ in Theorem 61.2 by $f^2(\mathbf{x}+\mathbf{y})$, since we can clearly assume f real. Then (61.25; 61.26; 61.27) occur easily. If $f(\mathbf{y}) \neq 0$ we substitute $-\mathbf{x}$ for $\mathbf{x}$ in the present form of (61.9), and subtract to obtain, almost everywhere in W,

$$\lim_{n \to \infty} f(\mathbf{x}_n'') f(\mathbf{y}) = 0, \quad \lim_{n \to \infty} f(\mathbf{x}_n'') = 0$$

If $f(\mathbf{y}) = 0$, we note that $f(\mathbf{x})$ exists almost everywhere in W, and

$$\lim_{n \to \infty} f^2(\mathbf{x}_n'') = K$$

almost everywhere in W, giving (61.28) if $K = 0$. If $K \neq 0$ we use (61.8) to obtain, almost everywhere in W,

$$\lim_{n \to \infty} f(\mathbf{x}_n') = 0, \quad f(\mathbf{x}) = \lim_{n \to \infty} f(\mathbf{x}) = \lim_{n \to \infty} \{f(\mathbf{x}_n')$$
$$+f(\mathbf{x}_n'')\} = \lim_{n \to \infty} f(\mathbf{x}_n'')$$

The last limit is cylindrical of every finite order, so that $f(\mathbf{x})$ is constant, and so 0, almost everywhere, and $K = 0$, contrary to hypothesis. Hence (61.28) is always true. For the converse we need only follow the proof in Theorem 61.1 that involves $c_n(\mathbf{x})$, replacing $a_j(\mathbf{y})$ by $f(\mathbf{t}^j)$.

LEMMA 61.2. *For almost all* $\mathbf{x} \equiv \{x_n\} \in W$ *and for each bounded sequence* $\{y_n\}$ *we have, as* $n \to \infty$,

$$(61.30) \qquad \sum_{j=1}^{n} x_j = O(n^{1/2} \log \log n);$$

$$(61.31) \qquad \sum_{j=1}^{n} |x_j| = \tfrac{1}{4}n + O(n^{1/2} \log \log n),$$

$$(61.32) \qquad \sum_{j=1}^{n} x_j^2 = \tfrac{1}{12}n + O(n^{1/2} \log \log n),$$

$$(61.33) \qquad \sum_{j=1}^{n} x_j y_j = O(n^{1/2} \log \log n),$$

$$(61.34) \qquad \sum_{j=1}^{n} (x_j + y_j)^2 = \tfrac{1}{12}n + \sum_{j=1}^{n} y_j^2 + O(n^{1/2} \log \log n).$$

Proof. These results can be proved by Kolmogoroff's law of the iterated logarithm, Theorem 50.1. In each case we have a function $f(x_j)$ with

$$I(f) = \int_{-1/2}^{1/2} f(x) \, dx, \qquad \int_{-1/2}^{1/2} \{f(x) - I(f)\} \, dx = 0$$

and we can take

$$z_j = f(x_j) - I(f); \qquad \sigma_j^2 \equiv \sigma^2 = \int_{-1/2}^{1/2} \{f(x) - I(f)\}^2 \, dx$$

$$|x_j| \leqslant \tfrac{1}{2}, \; |z_j| \leqslant M \; \textit{independent of } j = 1, 2, \ldots$$

The conditions of the theorem are satisfied, and $I(f)$ appears as the coefficient of n.

We can now deal with the following interesting example.

$$f_1(\mathbf{x}, \mathbf{y}) \equiv \lim_{n \to \infty} n^{-1} \sum_{j=1}^{n} x_j y_j$$

Then $f_1(\mathbf{x}, \mathbf{y})$ is non-negative definite, bilinear, symmetric, and measurable in $(\mathbf{x}, \mathbf{y})$, and in $\mathbf{x}$ for each fixed $\mathbf{y}$, with $f_1(\mathbf{x}, \mathbf{x})$ measurable. But for almost all $\mathbf{x} \in W$ we have some seemingly contradictory properties. From (61.33), $f_1(\mathbf{x}, \mathbf{y}) = 0$ for each $\mathbf{y} \in m$. It follows by Fubini's theorem that $f_1(\mathbf{x}, \mathbf{y}) = 0$ for almost all $(\mathbf{x}, \mathbf{y}) \in W \times W$, using the product variation. Secondly, from (61.32), $f_1(\mathbf{x}, \mathbf{x}) = 1/12$, which shows that the line $\mathbf{x} = \mathbf{y}$, of product variation zero, is in some

325

sense a line singularity of $f_1(\mathbf{x}, \mathbf{y})$. Further, from (61.34), $f_1(\mathbf{x}+\mathbf{y}, \mathbf{x}+\mathbf{y}) \geq 1/12$ for each fixed $\mathbf{y} \in m$, while combining (61.32; 61.34), $f_1(\mathbf{x}+\mathbf{y}, \mathbf{x}+\mathbf{y}) = 1/6$ for almost all $\mathbf{y} \in W$. We can use

$$f_1(\mathbf{x}-\mathbf{y}, \mathbf{x}-\mathbf{y})^{1/2}$$

as a pseudometric in at least part of W, and the last results show that W is not separable under this pseudometric. Of course there are easier examples of non-separable spaces. Also the constant K in Theorem 61.1 (61.9) is, for f_1, given by $K = 1/6$ for almost all $\mathbf{y} \in W$.

Having cleared up the preliminary results, we can now tackle the further problems on convergence factors.

THEOREM 61.5. *Let $f(t, \mathbf{x})$ be linear in $\mathbf{x}$ and measurable in $(t, \mathbf{x})$ for $t \geq 0$ and $\mathbf{x} \in W$, such that there is a set $A(\mathbf{x})$ of t, depending on $\mathbf{x}$, and of variation zero for almost all $\mathbf{x} \in W$, with the property that $f(t, \mathbf{x})$ exists when $t \notin A(\mathbf{x})$. Then, for almost all t,*

$$(61.35) \qquad \|f(t, .)\|_2^2 \equiv \sum_{n=1}^{\infty} f^2(t, t'') < \infty$$

and for $\mathbf{x}$ in a set depending on t and lying almost everywhere in W,

$$(61.36) \qquad \lim_{n \to \infty} f(t, \mathbf{x}_n'') = 0$$

and conversely.

Proof. Fubini's theorem shows that the set B of all $(t, \mathbf{x})$, with $t \in A(\mathbf{x})$, has product variation zero, so that the intersection of B by a space $t = constant$, is also of variation zero for almost all constants in $t \geq 0$. Then Theorem 61.4 gives (61.35; 61.36), and also the converse on using Fubini's theorem again.

THEOREM 61.6. *If in Theorem 61.5,*

$$(61.37) \qquad \lim_{t \to \infty} \sup |f(t, \mathbf{x})| < \infty \qquad (t \notin A(\mathbf{x})), \quad then$$

$$(61.38) \qquad \text{ess} \lim_{t \to \infty} \sup \|f(t, .)\|_2 < \infty$$

Here, for almost all $\mathbf{x} \in W$, there are numbers $M = M(\mathbf{x})$, $N = N(\mathbf{x})$, with $f^2(t, \mathbf{x}) \leq N$ for almost all $t \geq M$. Hence there are a set X of $\mathbf{x}$ of variation greater than 0·99, and two numbers M_0, N_0, such that if $x \in X$ then

$$M(x) \leqslant M_0, \quad N(x) \leqslant N_0$$

By Fubini's theorem and (61.23), for almost all $t \geqslant M_0$,

(61.39) $\|f(t, \cdot)\|_2^2 \leqslant 200N_0$

which gives (61.38).

THEOREM 61.7. *If in Theorem 61.5,*

(61.40) $\lim\limits_{t \to \infty} f(t, \mathbf{x}) \qquad (t \notin A(\mathbf{x}))$

exists for almost all $\mathbf{x} \in W$, *then* (61.38) *is true, and*

(61.41) $g_n \equiv \text{ess} \lim\limits_{t \to \infty} f(t, \mathbf{t}^n) \qquad (n = 1, 2, \ldots)$

exist; and from these conclusions we can prove that

(61.42) $$\sum_{n=1}^{\infty} g_n^2 < \infty$$

Proof. The set of $\mathbf{x}$ where the essential limit of $f(t, \mathbf{x})$ exists, has complement of variation zero, so that as in the proof of Theorem 61.2 we can find $\mathbf{x}$ and $\mathbf{x} + a\mathbf{t}^n (a \neq 0)$ in the set, giving (61.41). Then, for each integer n,

$$\sum_{j=1}^{n} g_j^2 = \text{ess} \lim\limits_{t \to \infty} \sum_{j=1}^{n} f^2(\mathbf{t}, \mathbf{t}^j) \leqslant 200N_0$$

and (61.42) follows on letting $n \to \infty$.

THEOREM 61.8. *If in Theorem 61.5, for almost all* $\mathbf{x} \in W$,

(61.43) $\lim\limits_{t \to \infty} f(t, \mathbf{x}) = 0 \qquad (t \notin A(\mathbf{x}))$

(61.44)   *then* $\quad \text{ess} \lim\limits_{t \to \infty} \|f(t, \cdot)\|_2 = 0.$

Proof. Given $\varepsilon > 0$, we can take $N_0 = \varepsilon$ in Theorem 61.6, and then use (61.39). Theorems 61.5, $\ldots$, 61.8 are Henstock (1955), p. 245, Theorem 3 (i, ii, iii, iv).

We now consider the one-sided approximate limit as $t \to b-$, where $b > 0$ is some fixed number. The *upper* and *lower thicknesses* of a set $A \subseteq (0, b)$, relative to the variation in $(0, b)$ as $t \to b-$, are respectively defined as

$$\lim_{h \to 0} \sup h^{-1}\mu_1(A \cap (b-h, b)), \quad \lim_{h \to 0} \inf h^{-1}\mu_1(A \cap (b-h, b)).$$

When equal, the value is the *thickness* of A; while A is *thick* if its thickness is 1, and A is *thin* if its thickness is 0. There should be no confusion between these thick and thin sets and those given in Chapter 2. Note that

$$(61.45) \qquad 0 \leqslant h^{-1}\mu_1(A \cap (b-h, b)) \leqslant 1$$

$$\lim_{t \to b-} \sup \text{ap } f(t) = c, \quad \lim_{t \to b-} \inf \text{ap } f(t) = d,$$

if the sets of t, respectively for which $f(t) < c+\varepsilon$, $f(t) > d-\varepsilon$, are thick for each $\varepsilon > 0$, but for no $\varepsilon < 0$. If $c = d$, we write

$$\lim_{t \to b-} \text{ap } f(t) = c$$

There are appropriate modifications for infinite c or d. The approximate limit of Saks (1937), pp. 218–19 uses values $t > b$ as well. If we had taken $b = +\infty$, we would have needed $(t, +\infty)$ to have finite variation, say $V(t)$, for some $t_0 \geqslant 0$, and all $t \geqslant t_0$. Using $v = V(t_0)$, we could map $[t_0, +\infty)$ on to $(0, v]$ by using $u = V(t)$, reducing the approximate upper and lower limits to those as $u \to 0+$, similar to the ones given.

THEOREM 61.9. *Let $f(t, \mathbf{x})$ be linear in $\mathbf{x}$, and measurable in $(t, \mathbf{x})$, for $\mathbf{x} \in W$, and for t in a thick set A_1 independent of $\mathbf{x}$. If, for almost all $\mathbf{x} \in W$, $f(t, \mathbf{x})$ exists when t lies in a thick set $A(\mathbf{x})$ depending on $\mathbf{x}$, then for t in a thick set B independent of $\mathbf{x}$,*

$$(61.46) \qquad \|f(t, .)\|_2 < \infty,$$

and, almost everywhere in W,

$$(61.47) \qquad \lim_{n \to \infty} f(t, \mathbf{x}_n'') = 0 \qquad (t \in B).$$

Conversely, (61.46; 61.47) are sufficient for $f(t, \mathbf{x})$ to exist almost everywhere in W, for t in a thick set.

Proof. The following sets are measurable for almost all values of the variables concerned, by the measurability of f, and the variations of the sets are also measurable in the given variables. We need only use Fubini's theorem.

$$Y(h) \equiv \{(t, \mathbf{x}): b - h \leqslant t < b, \ t \in A_1, \ \mathbf{x} \in W, \ f(t, \mathbf{x}) \ does \ not \ exist\}$$

$$A(h, \mathbf{x}) \equiv \{t : (t, \mathbf{x}) \in Y(h)\} \ (\mathbf{x} \in W), \quad X(t) \equiv \{\mathbf{x} : (t, \mathbf{x}) \in Y(h)$$

$$(b - h \leqslant t < b, t \in A_1)\}$$

(61.48) $$\lim_{h \to 0} h^{-1}\mu_1(A(h, \mathbf{x})) = 0$$

for almost all $\mathbf{x} \in W$. By Fubini's and Lebesgue's bounded convergence theorems

$$A \equiv (b - h, b) \cap A_1; \quad \int_A \mu(X(t)) \, dt = \mu(Y(h))$$

$$= \int_W \mu_1(A(h, \mathbf{x})) \, d\mu < \delta h$$

We have used (61.45; 61.48), and the result is true for $0 < h < h_1(\delta)$. Hence those t in $(b - h, b) \cap A_1$ for which $X(t)$ is not measurable, or for which $\mu(X(t)) \geqslant \frac{1}{2}$, form a set of variation smaller than $2\delta h$. As A_1 is thick, we take all $\delta > 0$ to prove that for each t in a thick set B, there is a set of $\mathbf{x} \in W$, of variation greater than $\frac{1}{2}$, in which $f(t, \mathbf{x})$ exists. By the necessity of Theorem 61.4 (61.26; 61.27) we prove that $\| f(t, .)\|_2$ is finite when $t \in B$. For the converse we can use Fubini's theorem and the sufficiency in Theorem 61.4.

THEOREM 61.10. *In Theorem* 61.9, *if, almost everywhere in* W,

(61.49) $$\lim_{t \to b-} \sup ap \, |f(t, \mathbf{x})| < \infty$$

(61.50)   *then* $$\lim_{t \to b-} \sup ap \, \|f(t, .)\|_2 < \infty$$

(61.51)   *i. e.* $\| f(t, .)\|_2 \leqslant M$ ($t \in B$, *a thick set*).

Proof. Replacing '$f(t, \mathbf{x})$ does not exist', in the definition of the set $Y(h)$ of Theorem 61.9, by '$f^2(t, \mathbf{x}) \geqslant N$ or does not exist', we obtain sets $Y(N, h)$, $A(N, h, \mathbf{x})$, $X(N, t)$, and for $N > N_1(\mathbf{x})$,

$$\lim_{h \to 0} h^{-1}\mu_1(A(N, h, \mathbf{x})) = 0$$

for almost all $\mathbf{x} \in W$. Thus we can find a set $X \subseteq W$ with $N_1(\mathbf{x}) < N_0$, for some fixed N_0, with $\mu(X) > 0.995$. Then for

$$0 < h < h_1(\delta), \quad A = A_1 \cap (b-h, b)$$

$$\int_A \mu(X(N_0, t) \cap X) \, dt = \int_X \mu_1(A(N_0, h, \mathbf{x})) \, d\mu < \delta h$$

Those $t \in A_1 \cap (b-h, b)$ for which $X(N_0, t) \cap X$ is not measurable, or has variation not less than 0.005 form a set of variation less than $200 \, \delta h$, and the remaining set of $t \in (b-h, b)$ has variation greater than $(1 - 200\delta)h$. As A_1 is thick, we take all $\delta > 0$, and obtain that for each t in a thick set B there is a set of $x \in W$ of variation greater than $0.995-0.005 = 0.99$, in which $f^2(t, \mathbf{x}) \leqslant N_0$. By (61.23), (61.39) is true, which gives (61.50).

THEOREM 61.11. *In Theorem 61.9, if, almost everywhere in W,*

$$(61.52) \qquad \lim_{t \to b-} \text{ap } f(t, \mathbf{x})$$

exists, then (61.50) is true, and there exist

$$(61.53) \qquad g_n^* = \lim_{t \to b-} \text{ap } f(t, \mathbf{t}^n) \qquad (n = 1, 2, \ldots), \qquad \text{with}$$

$$(61.54) \qquad \sum_{n=1}^{\infty} (g_n^*)^2 < \infty$$

The proof of this is formally the same as that of Theorem 61.7.

THEOREM 61.12. *In Theorem 61.9, if, almost everywhere in W,*

$$(61.55) \qquad \lim_{t \to b-} \text{ap } f(t, \mathbf{x}) = 0$$

$$(61.56) \qquad \text{then } \lim_{t \to b-} \text{ap } \| f(t, .) \|_2 = 0$$

Proof. Here, $N_1(x) = 0$ almost everywhere in W, so that in (61.39) we can take $N_0 > 0$ as small as we please, giving (61.56). Note that Theorems 61.8, 61.12 correspond to (55.14), the result of Schur. Theorems 61.9, $\ldots$, 61.12 are Henstock (1955), p. 246, Theorem 4 (i, ii, iii, iv). The conditions in Theorems 61.5, 61.9 are necessary and sufficient. But the necessary conditions in the rest of Theorems 61.5, $\ldots$, 61.12 are not sufficient, and the fault does not lie in the omission of a condition like (61.36; 61.47), but in the existence of an analogue of Theorem 60.4. We begin with an analogue of Lemma 60.2.

LEMMA 61.3. *Let* $f(\mathbf{x})$ *be real, linear, and measurable, existing almost everywhere in* W. *Then for each integer* $j > 0$,

$$\int_W f^{2j}(\mathbf{x})\,d\mu \leqslant M_j \|f\|_2^{2j}, \quad M_j \leqslant \left(\frac{e}{16}\right)^j \frac{(2j)!}{j!}$$

Proof. By Theorem 61.4 (61.29) with $\mathbf{y}$ zero and $a_n \equiv f(t^n)$, we have

$$\int_W f^{2j}(\mathbf{x})\,d\mu = \int_W \left(\sum_{n=1}^\infty a_n x_n\right)^{2j} d\mu = \int_W \sum (a_{n_1} x_{n_1})^{j_1} \dots (a_{n_m} x_{n_m})^{j_m}$$
$$\cdot \frac{(2j)!}{j_1! \dots j_m!}\, d\mu$$

where the last sum is over all positive integers $j_1, \dots, j_m$ with sum $2j$, and over all non-coincident values of $n_1, \dots, n_m$. By using the methods of the proof of necessity in Theorem 61.2 we can show that term-by-term integration is permissible. The integral of an odd power of x_n is 0, so that we can put $j_r = 2k_r$, to obtain

$$\int_W f^{2j}(\mathbf{x})\,d\mu = \sum a_{n_1}^{2k_1} \dots a_{n_m}^{2k_m} \frac{(2j)!}{(2k_1)! \dots (2k_m)!}$$
$$\cdot \frac{2^{-2j}}{(2k_1+1)\dots(2k_m+1)}$$

with sum over all positive integers $k_1, \dots, k_m$ with sum j, and over all non-coincident values of $n_1, \dots, n_m$. Now

$$\|f\|_2^{2j} = \sum a_{n_1}^{2k_1} \dots a_{n_m}^{2k_m} \frac{j!}{k_1! \dots k_m!}$$

so that, as in the proof of Lemma 60.2,

$$M_j \equiv \sup \frac{(2j)!}{2^{2j}j!} \cdot \frac{k_1! \dots k_m!}{(2k_1+1)! \dots (2k_m+1)!}$$
$$\leqslant \sup \frac{(2j)!}{2^{2j}j!} \cdot \frac{k_1^{k_1+1/2} \dots k_m^{k_m+1/2}\, e^{-j}(5/4)^m}{2^{2j+3/2 m} k_1^{2k_1+3/2} \dots k_m^{2k_m+3/2}\, e^{-2j-m}(\frac{9}{4})^m}$$
$$\leqslant \sup \left(\frac{e}{16}\right)^j \frac{(2j)!}{j!} \left(\frac{5e}{9 \cdot 2^{3/2}}\right)^m < \left(\frac{e}{16}\right)^j \frac{(2j)!}{j!}$$

since $25e^2 < 648$.

Next we have an analogue of Lemma 60.3.

LEMMA 61.4. *If f is real, linear, and measurable, existing almost everywhere in W, then, for each fixed $c < 4/(e \|f\|_2^2)$, $c \geqslant 0$,*

$$\int_W \exp\left(cf^2(\mathbf{x})\right) d\mu \leqslant (1 - ce\|f\|_2^2/4)^{-1}$$

For proof follow the proof of Lemma 60.3. The inversion of summation and integration is justified since everything is non-negative.

The analogue of Lemma 60.4 now follows by an analogous proof.

LEMMA 61.5. *If f is real, linear, and measurable, existing almost everywhere in W, and if $\|f_n\|_2^2 \leqslant M$ $(n = 1, 2, \ldots)$, then for arbitrary*

$$(61.57) \quad b_n > 0, \quad \sum_{n=1}^{\infty} b_n < \infty, \quad \exp\left(cf_n^2(\mathbf{x})\right) = O(b_n^{-1})$$

almost everywhere in W, where c is any fixed number less than $4/(eM)$.

Lemmas 61.3, 61.4, 61.5 are given in Henstock (1955), p. 249, Lemma 5; p. 250, Lemma 6; p. 248, Theorem 6, while p. 248, Theorem 5, is as follows.

THEOREM 61.13. *Let $\{f_n(\mathbf{x})\}$ be a sequence of linear functionals that are real and measurable and exist almost everywhere in W. Then, for almost all $\mathbf{x}$,*

$$(61.58) \quad \lim_{n \to \infty} \sup |f_n(\mathbf{x})| \cdot \|f_n\|^{-1} \cdot \log^{-1/2} n \leqslant K$$

where K is an absolute constant independent of $\{f_n(\mathbf{x})\}$, and

$$(61.59) \quad \frac{1}{64\log 4} \leqslant K^2 \leqslant \frac{e}{4}$$

Proof. Taking $f_n/\|f_n\|_2$ for f_n, we can assume that $\|f_n\|_2 = 1$ for all n. In Lemma 61.5 we put $b_n^{-1} = n \log^2(n+1)$, so that, for almost

332

all $\mathbf{x} \in W$, and for $A > 0$ depending on $\mathbf{x}$,

$$\exp\left(cf_n^2(\mathbf{x})\right) \leqslant An \log^2 (n+1),$$

$$cf_n^2(\mathbf{x}) \leqslant \log A + \log n + 2 \log \log (n+1)$$

$$f_n^2(\mathbf{x})/\log n \leqslant c^{-1}(1 + \log A/\log n + 2 \log \log (n+1)/\log n) \qquad (n > 1)$$

$$\limsup_{n \to \infty} f_n^2(\mathbf{x})/\log n \leqslant c^{-1} \qquad (c < 4/e)$$

Hence (61.58) with $K \leqslant e/4$. To complete the proof of (61.59) we take the values of $b_{mn} = f_n(t^n)$ to be those in Garreau's matrix (see Theorem 60.2 and the discussion), as in Henstock (1955), p. 253. The computation in Theorem 60.4 gives

(61.60) $$\|f_n\|_2^2 \cdot \log n/\log 4 \to 1 \qquad (n \to \infty)$$

Given $\mathbf{x} \in W$ and a positive integer k, let there be at least k integers in $1 \leqslant j \leqslant 2k$ for which $x_j \geqslant 0$, let A_k be the sum of the k greater ones of these x_j, with B_k the sum of the rest of the $x_j \geqslant 0$, and $-C_k$ the sum of the $x_j < 0$. If $\mathbf{x}, k$ do not satisfy the condition, then $-\mathbf{x}, k$ do so, and we define A_k, B_k, C_k for $-\mathbf{x}, k$ instead. Then by Lemma 61.2 (61.30; 61.31),

$$(A_k + B_k - C_k)/k = \pm \sum_{j=1}^{2k} x_j/k \to 0.$$

$$(A_k + B_k + C_k)/k = \sum_{j=1}^{2k} |x_j|/k \to \tfrac{1}{2}$$

$$(A_k + B_k)/k \to \tfrac{1}{4} \qquad (k \to \infty)$$

almost everywhere in W. Now in one row of the matrix, all k^{-1} occur with the terms of A_k, giving a sum $\pm A_k/k$. Hence by (61.60),

$$|f_n(\mathbf{x})| = A_k/k \geqslant (A_k + B_k)/(2k) \to 1/8, \qquad K \geqslant 1/(8 \log^{1/2} 4)$$

Ex. 61.1. If $\displaystyle\sum_{n=1}^{\infty} a_n x_n$ is convergent almost everywhere in W, then $\displaystyle\sum_{n=1}^{\infty} |a_n|^2 < \infty$ and conversely.

Ex. 61.2. A linear functional is bounded in l_2 if, and only if, it can be extended almost everywhere in W.

333

Ex. 61.3. If, for each $\mathbf{x}$ of a set of positive variation in W, $\sum\limits_{j=1}^{\infty} x_j h_j(y)$ is convergent in a set of real numbers y depending on $\mathbf{x}$, and of positive variation, with measurable $h_j(y)$, prove that there is a set of y of positive variation in which $\sum\limits_{j=1}^{\infty} h_j^2(y) < \infty$.

Ex. 61.4. Considering $f(\mathbf{x}, \mathbf{x}) \equiv ||\mathbf{x}||_2^2$, show that $\mu(l_2 \cap W) = 0$, and show that the same result is true if W is replaced by $\mathbf{y} + W$, for any $\mathbf{y} \in m$.

14

THE SPACE OF CONTINUOUS FUNCTIONS ON A FIXED COMPACT SET

62. Norms on the Space

Let T be a compact set, and $\mathcal{C}(T)$ the space of all functionals continuous on T. As in *Ex. 43.14* we can take as intervals the closures of non-empty open sets in T. If $\mu \geqslant 0$ is an interval function we can define the generalized Riemann integral H of 1 with respect to μ, which we suppose exists and satisfies $H(I) > 0$ for each interval $I \subseteq T$. We can also define the linear functional

$$L(f) \equiv \int_T f(t)\, d\mu \qquad (f \in \mathcal{C}(T))$$

This integral exists by the integrability of 1 with respect to μ and the uniformity of continuity of f (Theorem 13.6 (13.12)), where f is bounded, by the same theorem, (13.11). Thus we can define the norms $L(|f|^p)^{1/p}$ ($p \geqslant 1$), with

$$\|f\|_p = L(|f|^p)^{1/p}, \quad \|f\|_\infty = \sup_{t \in T} |f(t)|$$

When we use the norm $\|f\|_p$ we denote $\mathcal{C}(T)$ by $\mathcal{C}^p(T)$ $(1 \leqslant p \leqslant \infty)$.

THEOREM 62.1.

(62.1) *Given* $\varepsilon > 0$, *there is an interval* I *on which*

$$|f(t)| > \|f\|_\infty - \varepsilon; \quad (\|f\|_\infty - \varepsilon)\, H(I)^{1/p} \leqslant \|f\|_p \leqslant \|f\|_\infty\, H(T)^{1/p}$$
$$(1 \leqslant p < \infty).$$

(62.2) *The only null function* f *for* L *has* $f(t) = 0 (t \in T)$.

Proof. In (62.1) there is nothing to prove if $\|f\|_\infty = 0$. Otherwise there are a $t \in T$ with $|f(t)| > \|f\|_\infty - \frac{1}{2}\varepsilon$, and a neighbourhood G of t within which the same inequality holds. Thus by continuity, if

$$I = \bar{G}, \quad x \in I, \quad \text{then} \quad |f(x)| \geqslant \|f\|_\infty - \frac{1}{2}\varepsilon > \|f\|_\infty - \varepsilon$$

and the further inequalities follow easily. Then (62.2) follows from (62.1), and all our pseudonorms are norms.

THEOREM 62.2. *If* $T = [-1, 1]$, $H(a, b) = b - a$, *then* $\mathcal{C}^p[-1, 1]$ *is not complete, for* $1 \leqslant p < \infty$.

Proof. We show that $\{x_n\}$ is fundamental but not convergent, where

$$x_n(t) = \text{arc tan } nt \quad (-1 \leqslant t \leqslant 1)$$

(62.3) $0 < \text{arc tan } mt < \text{arc tan } nt < \pi/2 \quad (m < n, t > 0)$

Further, given $\varepsilon > 0$, there is an $A > 0$ such that

$$\pi/2 - \varepsilon < \text{arc tan } t < \pi/2 \quad (t \geqslant A)$$

From this and (62.3),

(62.4) $\pi/2 - \varepsilon < \text{arc tan } nt < \pi/2 \quad (t \geqslant A/n)$

$0 < \text{arc tan } nt - \text{arc tan } mt < \varepsilon \quad (n > m, t \geqslant A/m)$

$$\int_{-1}^{1} |x_n(t) - x_m(t)|^p \, dt = 2 \int_0^1 = 2 \int_0^{A/m} + 2 \int_{A/m}^1$$

$$\leqslant 2(\pi/2)^p A/m + 2\varepsilon^p(1 - A/m)$$

$$\lim_{m, n \to \infty} \sup \int_{-1}^{1} |x_n(t) - x_m(t)|^p \, dt \leqslant 2\varepsilon^p$$

This is true for each $\varepsilon > 0$, so that the lim sup $= 0$, and the sequence is fundamental. To show that $\{x_n\}$ is not convergent in $\mathcal{C}^p[-1, 1]$, we put

$$x(t) = \begin{cases} \pi/2 & (t > 0) \\ 0 & (t = 0) \\ -\pi/2 & (t < 0) \end{cases}$$

and use (62.4). Then

$$\int_{-1}^{1} |x_n(t) - x(t)|^p \, dt = 2 \int_{0}^{1} |\arctan nt - \pi/2|^p \, dt = 2 \int_{0}^{A/n} + 2 \int_{A/n}^{1}$$

$$\leqslant 2(\pi/2)^p \cdot A/n + 2\varepsilon^p (1 - A/n),$$

$$\lim_{n \to \infty} \sup \int_{-1}^{1} |x_n(t) - x(t)|^p \, dt \leqslant 2\varepsilon^p,$$

and the lim sup is 0. Hence $\lim x_n = x \notin \mathcal{C}^p[-1, 1]$. Further, if in the $\|.\|_p$ norm

$$y = \lim_{n \to \infty} x_n, \quad \left\{ \int_{-1}^{1} |y(t) - x(t)|^p \, dt \right\}^{1/p}$$

$$\leqslant \left\{ \int_{-1}^{1} |y(t) - x_n(t)|^p \, dt \right\}^{1/p} + \left\{ \int_{-1}^{1} |x_n(t) - x(t)|^p \, dt \right\}^{1/p} \to 0$$

as $n \to \infty$, and $y(t) = x(t)$ except in a set of measure or variation zero, so that $y(t)$ cannot be continuous at $t = 0$.

THEOREM 62.3. *The space $\mathcal{C}^\infty(T)$ is complete.*

Proof. Given a fundamental sequence $\{x_n\} \subseteq \mathcal{C}^\infty(T)$, and $\varepsilon > 0$, there is an N with

$$\sup_{t \in T} |x_n(t) - x_m(t)| < \varepsilon \qquad (n > m \geqslant N)$$

so that for each fixed $t \in T$, $\{x_n(t)\}$ is fundamental,

$$|x_n(t) - x_m(t)| < \varepsilon \qquad (n > m \geqslant N)$$

Hence $x_n(t)$ tends to a limit, say, $x(t)$. Letting $n \to \infty$,

$$|x(t) - x_m(t)| \leqslant \varepsilon \qquad (m \geqslant N)$$

This is true for each $t \in T$, with N independent of t. Hence

(62.5) $$\sup_{t \in T} |x(t) - x_m(t)| \leqslant \varepsilon \qquad (m \geqslant N)$$

and $\{x_n\}$ converges to x in norm $\|.\|_\infty$. To show that $x \in \mathcal{C}(T)$, let $t \in T$, and $x(t) = y$. Since $x_N(t)$ is continuous, there is a

337

neighbourhood G of t with

$$|x_N(t) - x_N(u)| < \varepsilon (u \in G), \quad |x(t) - x(u)| \leqslant |x(t) - x_N(t)|$$

$$+ |x_N(t) - x_N(u)| + |x_N(u) - x(u)| < 3\varepsilon$$

using (62.5). As $\varepsilon > 0$ is arbitrary, we have the continuity of x.

More generally we can consider Orlicz norms. The only result beyond section 41 that we need consider, however, is that $\|f\|_\Phi < \infty$ for each $f \in \mathcal{C}[T]$. To prove this, we have $\varphi(a)$ finite for $a > 0$ small enough, and

$$\|f/A\|_\Phi^* = L(\Phi(|f|/A)) < \infty \ (A > \|f\|_\infty/a); \quad f/A \in L_\Phi^*,$$

$$f \in L_\Phi.$$

THEOREM 62.4. *The trigonometric polynomials are dense in $\mathcal{C}^\infty[0, 2\pi]$.*

Proof. By Theorem 57.4 and a linear transformation, the polynomials in x are dense in $\mathcal{C}^\infty [0, 2\pi]$. The Fourier series of x^n is easily shown to be convergent, so that by taking the first n terms of the series, where n is arbitrary, the *trigonometric polynomials*, of the form

$$\tfrac{1}{2}a_0 + (a_1 \cos x + b_1 \sin x) + (a_2 \cos 2x + b_2 \sin 2x) + \ldots$$

$$+ (a_n \cos nx + b_n \sin nx)$$

are dense in the set 1, x, x^2, ..., and so in $\mathcal{C}^\infty [0, 2\pi]$.

Alternatively it can easily be shown that the first arithmetic mean of the first n partial sums of the Fourier series of $f \in \mathcal{C}^\infty [0, 2\pi]$ tends to f in $\| . \|_\infty$ as $n \to \infty$ (Fejér).

63. Continuous Linear Functionals on $\mathcal{C}^\infty(\mathbf{T})$, and on the Space of Denjoy Integrable Functions

We now come to the Riesz representation theorem, which gives the expression of all continuous linear functionals on $\mathcal{C}^\infty(T)$ as integrals. F. Riesz (1909) is the earliest paper, for $T = [0, 1]$.

THEOREM 63.1. *Every continuous linear functional $\mathcal{F}$ defined on*

338

$\mathcal{C}^\infty(T)$, *where T is compact, is of the form*

$$F(f) = \int_T f(t) \, d\mu$$

where μ is an interval function of bounded variation, and conversely.

Proof. Our intervals here are the closures of non-empty open sets of T, and for ordinary topologies, their characteristic functions are not continuous. It therefore becomes necessary to proceed a little way out of $\mathcal{C}^\infty(T)$. Let $\mathcal{X}$ be the family of characteristic functions of all $X \subseteq T$ that satisfy

(63.1) $I^\circ \subseteq X \subseteq I$

for some interval I of T. By the Hahn–Banach theorem (if $\mathcal{F}$ is real), with the Bohnenblust–Sobczyk–Soukhomlinoff extension (if $\mathcal{F}$ is complex), $\mathcal{F}$ can be extended from $\mathcal{C}^\infty(T)$ to $\mathcal{X}_1$ as a continuous linear functional with the same norm, where $\mathcal{X}_1$ is the smallest linear space that contains $\mathcal{C}^\infty(T)$ and $\mathcal{X}$. See Theorems 33.5, 35.1, 35.2, in combination. In the extension we can well order $\mathcal{X}_1$ so that the characteristic functions of intervals follow directly after the functions of $\mathcal{C}^\infty(T)$, and we use $N \equiv$ norm $(\mathcal{F})$, and

$$m \equiv \sup \{-\|x(t)+z(t)\|_\infty \cdot N - \mathcal{F}(x)\},$$
$$M \equiv \inf \{\|x(t)+z(t)\|_\infty \cdot N - \mathcal{F}(x)\}$$

where $z \in \mathcal{X}$ is the next function, and the sup and inf are for all $x < z$ in the well ordering. By the definition of $\|.\|_\infty$ and by inductive hypothesis, if z is the characteristic function of an interval I, and if X satisfies (63.1), m and M are unaltered if we replace $z(t)$ by the characteristic function of X; so that we can choose $\mathcal{F}(ch(X;.)) = \mathcal{F}(ch(I;.))$ for all X satisfying (63.1), and in order to extend $\mathcal{F}$ to $\mathcal{X}_1$ we need only run through $\mathcal{X}$. We put

$$\mu(I) = \mathcal{F}(ch(I;.)) = \mathcal{F}(ch(X;.)) \qquad (I^\circ \subseteq X \subseteq I)$$

first showing that μ is of bounded variation. Let Q, with union E, be a partial division of a division $\mathcal{D}$ of T. By linearity and boundedness, since the interiors of intervals of $\mathcal{D}$ are disjoint, these

339

intervals being $I_1, \ldots, I_n$ and putting in turn

$$X = I_1, \quad I_2 \backslash I_1, \ldots, I_n \Big\backslash \bigcup_{j < n} I_j$$

$$(Q) \sum \mu(I) = (Q) \sum \mathcal{F}(ch(X; .)) = \mathcal{F}(ch(E; .))$$

$$\left| (Q) \sum \mu(I) \right| \leqslant \text{norm}\,(\mathcal{F}), \quad (D) \sum |\mu(I)| \leqslant 4 \cdot \text{norm}\,(\mathcal{F})$$

by the argument of Theorem 44.6, first part. Thus μ is of bounded variation. By Theorem 13.6 (13.12), for each $f \in \mathcal{C}(T)$ we can find a division $\mathcal{D}'$ such that on each interval I of each $\mathcal{D} \preccurlyeq \mathcal{D}'$, the oscillation of f is less than $\varepsilon > 0$. Taking $x \in I^\circ$, we have

$$\left| \mathcal{F}(f) - \mathcal{F}((\mathcal{D}) \sum f(x)\, ch(X; .)) \right| \leqslant \text{norm}\,(\mathcal{F}) \cdot \varepsilon$$

$$\mathcal{F}((\mathcal{D}) \sum f(x)\, ch(X; .)) = (\mathcal{D}) \sum f(x)\, \mathcal{F}(ch(X; .))$$

$$= (\mathcal{D}) \sum f(x)\, \mu(I)$$

and the result follows by definition of the integral. In fact here we could have used the Moore–Pollard definition of the integral using $\mathcal{D} \preccurlyeq \mathcal{D}'$.

Conversely, the integral is a linear functional (see Henstock (1963c), p. 27, Theorem 19.1, for the simple case) that has

$$|\mathcal{F}(f)| \leqslant \sup |f(t)| \cdot V(\mu; \mathcal{A}; T), \quad \text{norm}\,(\mathcal{F}) \leqslant V(\mu; \mathcal{A}; T)$$

so that the integral is also continuous. We have

$$\text{norm}\,(\mathcal{F}) = V(\mu; \mathcal{A}; T)$$

since in the extension from $\mathcal{C}^\infty(T)$ to $\mathcal{K}_1$ the norm is unchanged, while we can take

$$f = (\mathcal{D}) \sum ch(X; .)\, \text{sgn}\, \mu(I) \in \mathcal{K}_1, \quad \mathcal{F}(f) = (\mathcal{D}) \sum |\mu(I)|$$

since $x \in I^\circ$, and we have

$$\text{norm}\,(\mathcal{F}) \geqslant (\mathcal{D}) \sum |\mu(I)|$$

Alexiewicz (1948) uses this representation to find the general form of continuous linear functionals on the space of Denjoy integrable functions, for T a finite closed interval on the real line. We generalize and let T be a Cartesian product of compact intervals $[a_j, b_j]$ on the real line, so that we write $\mathbf{s} \in T$ in the form $\mathbf{s} = \{s_j\}$. Let $R(\mathbf{s})$ be the interval consisting of the Cartesian product of $[a_j, s_j]$, and let

$$IR(f; s) \equiv \int_{R(s)} f(t)\, d\mu_1$$

where f is integrable in some sense, and where $\mu_1 \geqslant 0$ is continuous. By Tychonoff's theorem (Theorem 13.8), T also is compact. If T is a finite Cartesian product we can use the integration of *Ex. 43.3*, or a Cartesian product of integration processes corresponding to those of *Ex. 43.9*. These correspond respectively to the special and general integrals of Denjoy over finite dimensional compact intervals, and we can prove that

(63.2) $IR(f; s)$ is continuous for $s \in T$

(63.3) the function $f(t; s)$, equal to $f(t)$ for all $t \in R(s)$, and 0 otherwise, is integrable relative to $\mu_1 \cdot \mu$, where μ_1 is connected to t, μ to s, and where μ is any integrable interval function of bounded variation on T. If T is a countable Cartesian product we can use the integration of *Ex. 43.12*, and it is likely that (63.2; 63.3) are still satisfied.

We denote by $\mathcal{D}(T)$ the space of functions f having finite $IR(f; s)$ that satisfy (63.2; 63.3).

THEOREM 63.2. *For the given* T, $\mathcal{D}(T)$, *every continuous linear functional* $\mathcal{F}$ *defined on* $\mathcal{D}(T)$, *is of the form*

$$\mathcal{F}(f) = \int_T f(t)\, g(t)\, d\mu_1$$

where g *is of bounded variation, and conversely.*

Proof. By (63.2), $IR(f; s) \in \mathcal{C}(T)$, so that for norm we use

$$\|f\|^* = \sup_{s \in T} |IR(f; s)| = \|IR(f; \cdot)\|_\infty$$

We denote by $\mathcal{C}\mathcal{I}$ the subspace of $\mathcal{C}(T)$ consisting of all such $IR(f; s)$. The norm of f in $\mathcal{D}(T)$ is the norm of $IR(f; s)$ in $\mathcal{C}\mathcal{I}$, so that $\mathcal{F}$ is a continuous linear functional on $\mathcal{C}\mathcal{I}$ with the same norm. By the Hahn–Banach theorem (for real $\mathcal{F}$), and the Bohnenblust–Sobczyk–Soukhomlinoff extension (for complex $\mathcal{F}$), $\mathcal{F}$ can be extended to $\mathcal{C}(T)$ as a continuous linear functional with the same norm. Hence by Theorem 63.1 there is a finitely additive interval function μ of bounded variation for which

$$\mathcal{F}(f) = \int_T IR(f; \mathbf{s})\, d\mu$$

Using (63.3) and Fubini's theorem, we have

$$\mathcal{F}(f) = \int_T f(\mathbf{t})\, \mu\big(R^*(\mathbf{t})\big)\, d\mu_1$$

where $R^*(\mathbf{t})$ is the set of all $\mathbf{s}$ for which $\mathbf{t} \in R(\mathbf{s})$, $\mathbf{s} \in T$, so that $R^*(\mathbf{t})$ is the Cartesian product of closed real intervals $t_j \leqslant s_j \leqslant b_j$. Then

$$g(\mathbf{t}) = \mu\big(R^*(\mathbf{t})\big)$$

is of bounded variation, with variation the same as μ. As the norm of $\mathcal{F}$ is unchanged throughout, we have

$$\text{norm}\,(\mathcal{F}) = V(\mu; \mathcal{A}; T)$$

which is also the variation of g. The converse follows from Theorem 63.1.

Alexiewicz (1948) considers a second norm on the space that will not be considered here.

In connection with $\mathcal{eA}$, Mazurkiewicz (1931) has given the following theorem.

THEOREM 63.3. *If $\mathcal{C}$ is the space of continuous functions on the real line with period 1, and with value 0 at $t = 0$, the set $\mathcal{M}$ of functions of $\mathcal{C}$ that have no finite derivative to the right at any point, is of the second category in $\mathcal{C}$, and $\mathcal{C}\backslash\mathcal{M}$ is of the first category.*

Proof. For $k = 1, 2, \ldots$, let U_{k1} be the set of $f \in \mathcal{C}$ such that, (63.4) for all t there are two points t_j with $t + 1/k \leqslant t_j \leqslant t + 3/k$ ($j = 1, 2$),

(63.5) $\qquad \delta(f; t, t_1, t_2) = \dfrac{f(t_1) - f(t)}{t_1 - t} - \dfrac{f(t_2) - f(t)}{t_2 - t} > \dfrac{1}{2}$

Let U_{k2} be the set of functions $g \in \mathcal{C}$ satisfying an inequality analogous to (63.5), namely, for (63.4) we have

(63.6) $\qquad\qquad\qquad \delta(g; t, t_1, t_2) > 1$

Let U_{k3} be the open set of $h \in \mathcal{C}$ such that, for at least one $g \in U_{k2}$,

(63.7) $$\|h-g\|_\infty < 1/(8k)$$

For $j = 1, 2, 3$, we put

(63.8) $$V_{nj} = \bigcup_{k=n}^\infty U_{kj}; \qquad \bigcap_{n=1}^\infty V_{n1} \subseteq \mathcal{M}$$

Now suppose that (63.4; 63.6; 63.7) hold. Then, for the same t_1, t_2,

$$\delta(h; t, t_1, t_2) > \delta(g; t, t_1, t_2) - \{|g(t_1)-h(t_1)|+|g(t)-h(t)|\}/(t_1-t)$$
$$-\{|g(t_2)-h(t_2)|+|g(t)-h(t)|\}/(t_2-t) > 1-4k/(8k) = 1/2$$

(63.9) $$U_{k3} \subseteq U_{k1}, \qquad V_{n3} \subseteq V_{n1}$$

where V_{n3} is open since U_{k3} is open. By (63.8; 63.9),

(63.10) $$\bigcap_{n=1}^\infty V_{n3} \subseteq \mathcal{M}$$

To show that V_{n3} is dense in $\mathcal{C}$, let $f \in \mathcal{C}$, $\varepsilon > 0$. By Theorem 62.4 there is a trigonometric polynomial $f_1(t)$ in $\cos(2\pi t)$, $\sin(2\pi t)$, such that $\|f-f_1\|_\infty < \frac{1}{2}\varepsilon$. Let n be an integer, $\eta = \|df_1/dt\|_\infty$, $k > n$ an integer greater than $3(2\eta+1)/\varepsilon$, and put, for a suitable integer q,

$$f_2(t) = f_1(t)+\tfrac{1}{2}\varepsilon \sin(2\pi kt), \qquad kt_1 = q+2\tfrac{1}{4},$$
$$kt_2 = q+2\tfrac{3}{4}(q < kt \le q+1)$$

Then we have

(63.11) $$\|f-f_2\|_\infty < \varepsilon$$

(63.12) $$t+1/k \le (q+2)/k < t_1 < t_2 < (q+3)/k \le t+3/k$$
$$\sin(2\pi kt_1) = 1, \qquad \sin(2\pi kt_2) = -1$$

(63.13) $$\delta(f_2; t, t_1, t_2) > \tfrac{1}{2}\varepsilon\{1-\sin(2\pi kt)\}/(t_1-t)$$
$$+\tfrac{1}{2}\varepsilon\{1+\sin(2\pi kt)\}/(t_2-t)-2\eta > \tfrac{1}{2}\varepsilon(k/3) \times$$
$$\times \{1-\sin(2\pi kt)+1+\sin(2\pi kt)\}-2\eta = \tfrac{1}{2}\varepsilon \cdot 2k/3-2\eta > 1$$

From (63.12; 63.13),

$$f_2 \in U_{k2} \subseteq U_{k3} \subseteq V_{n3}$$

so that from (63.11), V_{n3} is dense in $\mathcal{C}$. Since V_{n3} is an open set, $\mathcal{C}\backslash V_{n3}$ is nowhere dense in $\mathcal{C}$. By (63.10), $\mathcal{C}\backslash\mathcal{M}$ is of the first category, since

$$\mathcal{C}\backslash\mathcal{M} \subseteq \bigcup_{n=1}^{\infty} \mathcal{C}\backslash V_{n3}$$

while $\mathcal{C}$ is of the second category since it is complete.

Sargent (1950), p. 289, observes that for T on the real line, each function of $\mathcal{C}\mathcal{J}$ has a finite derivative in a subset of T of positive variation (or measure). This follows from *Ex. 43.10*, in the case of the general Denjoy integral, by using Henstock (1963c), p. 78, Theorem 35.1. It follows from Theorem 63.3 that $\mathcal{C}\mathcal{J}$ is of the first category in $\mathcal{C}_0[a, b]$, when $T = [a, b]$, where $\mathcal{C}_0[a, b]$ is the subset of $\mathcal{C}[a, b]$ for which each $f(a) = 0$. Further, by Theorem 62.4, $\mathcal{C}\mathcal{J}$ is dense in $\mathcal{C}_0[a, b]$, so that by Theorem 12.7 (12.30), $\mathcal{C}\mathcal{J}$ is of the first category in itself. It is for this reason that Sargent introduces her β-spaces; from *Ex. 31.1*, $\mathcal{C}\mathcal{J}$ is a β-space. However, Sargent (1953), pp. 448–9, shows that we cannot deal with Lebesgue integrals in a similar way. Her proof is given in Theorem 63.4.

THEOREM 63.4. *If $\mathcal{A}\mathcal{C}$ is the subspace of $\mathcal{C}[a, b]$ consisting of all functions of $\mathcal{C}[a, b]$ that are absolutely continuous on $[a, b]$, then $\mathcal{A}\mathcal{C}$ is both an α-group and an α-subgroup of $\mathcal{C}[a, b]$.*

Proof. Let functions $g_n(t)$ be uniformly bounded, continuous, and of bounded variation on $[a, b]$, but with

$$\limsup_{n \to \infty} V(g_n; \mathcal{A}; [a, b]) = +\infty$$

For example, we could have

$$g_n(t) = \sin\{2\pi n(t-a)/(b-a)\}$$

Then from integration by parts, the functional

$$\mathcal{F}_n(f) \equiv \int_a^b f(t)\, dg_n(t) = [f(t)\, g_n(t)]_a^b - \int_a^b g_n(t) f'(t)\, dt$$

$$(n = 1, 2, \ldots)$$

344

satisfies

$$\lim_{n \to \infty} \sup |\mathcal{F}_n(f)| < \infty \qquad (f \in \mathcal{A}\mathcal{C}),$$

$$\text{norm } (\mathcal{F}_n) = V(g_n; \mathcal{A}; [a, b]) \to \infty$$

using $\|f\|_\infty$ for the norm on f. Hence by Theorem 34.1, $\mathcal{A}\mathcal{C}$ cannot be a β-group and so must be an α-group. Also, by Theorem 34.3, $\mathcal{A}\mathcal{C}$ is an α-subgroup of $\mathcal{C}[a, b]$.

It follows that the norm $\|f\|_\infty$ is not suitable for the space $\mathcal{A}\mathcal{C}$ and in the next chapter it will be shown that a better norm is

$$\int_a^b |f'(t)|\, dt$$

since for this norm, $\mathcal{A}\mathcal{C}$ is complete and so a Baire space.

Ex. 63.1. Show that for T the real interval $[a, b]$, the transformation of integrals in Theorem 63.2 is of the form

$$\int_a^b \left\{ \int_a^x f(t)\, d\mu_1 \right\} d\mu = \int_a^b f(t)\, \mu([t, b])\, d\mu_1$$

Substituting t for h_1 and

$$j(t) = \int_c^t f(t)\, dt, \; g(t) = \mu([c, t]) \qquad \text{(fixed } c < a)$$

show that we obtain the formula for integration by parts. Is there a similar result for $n = 2$?

64. Differential and Integral Equations and Contraction Mappings

We begin with the equation in real x,

(64.1) $$dy/dx = K(x, y)$$

This can be generalized to the case of simultaneous differential equations of the type

(64.2) $\quad dy_j(x)/dx = K_j(x, y_1(x), \ldots, y_n(x)) \qquad (j = 1, 2, \ldots, n)$

Clearly, if we put $\mathbf{y}(\mathbf{x})$ as the vector function of x with components

23*

$y_j(x)$, and if $\mathbf{K}(x, \mathbf{y}(x))$ denotes the vector function with components $K_j(x, y_1(x), \ldots, y_n(x))$, we can write equations (64.2) as

(64.3) $$dy/dx = \mathbf{K}(x, \mathbf{y})$$

of the same form as (64.1). If (64.3) has a unique solution $\mathbf{y}(x)$ in a neighbourhood $(a-\varepsilon, a+\varepsilon)$ of some real number a, then $\mathbf{K}(x, \mathbf{y}(x))$ must be equal to $d\mathbf{y}(x)/dx$, which can be integrated. Thus we obtain

(64.4) $$\mathbf{y}(x) - \mathbf{y}(a) = \int_a^x \mathbf{K}(t, \mathbf{y}(t))\, dt$$

which is an integral equation. Some equations are already in integral form, for example, the *Volterra integral equation*

(64.5) $$y(x) = g(x) + \lambda \int_a^x K(x, z)\, y(z)\, dz \qquad (a \leqslant x \leqslant b)$$

where λ is an arbitrary constant, and g is continuous in $a \leqslant x \leqslant b$. The *Fredholm inhomogeneous linear integral equation of the second kind*, is

(64.6) $$y(x) = g(x) + \lambda \int_a^b K(x, z)\, y(z)\, dz \qquad (a \leqslant x \leqslant b)$$

where λ, g are as in (64.5). These equations generalize to two types.

THEOREM 64.1. *The integral equation*

(64.7) $$\mathbf{y}(x) = \mathbf{g}(x) + \lambda \int_a^b \mathbf{K}(x, z, \mathbf{y}(z))\, dz \qquad (a \leqslant x \leqslant b)$$

where the constant λ, the continuous $\mathbf{g}(x)$, and the kernel $\mathbf{K}(x, z, \mathbf{y})$, are all given, has one and only one solution $\mathbf{y}(x)$, if

(64.8) $$|\mathbf{K}(x, z, \mathbf{y}_1) - \mathbf{K}(x, z, \mathbf{y}_2)|_\infty \leqslant M\, |\mathbf{y}_1 - \mathbf{y}_2|_\infty$$

(64.9) $$|\lambda|\, M(b-a) < 1$$

(64.10) $$|\mathbf{K}(x, z, \mathbf{y}(z)|_\infty \leqslant M_1\, |||\mathbf{y}|_\infty||_\infty$$

where M, M_1 are constants, $\mathbf{K}$ continuous in x, and where

$$Y(x) = |\mathbf{y}(x)|_\infty \equiv \sup_{1 < j < n} |y_j(x)|, \qquad \|Y(x)\|_\infty = \sup_{a < x < b} Y(x)$$

Proof. Because of (64.10) we can take limits with respect to x under the integral sign. For scalars y, K, we can use Theorem 46.2 while

346

for vectors **y, K** we only need a slight generalization. Thus the integral is continuous in x, so that if

$$(64.11) \quad \mathbf{u}(x) = \mathbf{A}(x, \mathbf{y}) = \mathbf{g}(x) + \lambda \int_a^b \mathbf{K}(x, z, \mathbf{y}(z)) \, dz \quad (a \leqslant x \leqslant b)$$

then $\mathbf{u}(x)$ is continuous, and the mapping $\mathbf{u}(x) = \mathbf{A}(x, \mathbf{y})$ maps the n-fold Cartesian product of $\mathcal{C}[a, b]$ into itself. Next, **A** is a contraction mapping.

$$\mathbf{u}(x) = \mathbf{A}(x, \mathbf{y}), \quad \mathbf{w}(x) = \mathbf{A}(x, \mathbf{v}); \quad |\mathbf{u}(x) - \mathbf{w}(x)|_\infty$$

$$\leqslant |\lambda| \int_a^b \left| \mathbf{K}(x, z, \mathbf{y}(z)) - \mathbf{K}(x, z, \mathbf{v}(z)) \right|_\infty dz \leqslant |\lambda| M \int_a^b |(\mathbf{y}(z)$$

$$- \mathbf{v}(z)|_\infty \, dz \leqslant |\lambda| M (b-a) \left\| \, |\mathbf{y}(x) - \mathbf{v}(x)|_\infty \right\|_\infty,$$

$$\left\| \, |\mathbf{u}(x) - \mathbf{w}(x)|_\infty \right\|_\infty \leqslant |\lambda| M (b-a)| \left\| \, |\mathbf{y} - \mathbf{v}|_\infty \right\|_\infty$$

We have used (64.8). Hence by (64.9), **A** is a contraction mapping. Also by Theorem 62.3, $\mathcal{C}^\infty[a, b]$ is a complete metric space, so that the same is true for the n-fold Cartesian product. Hence by Theorem 16.1, (64.7) has one and only one solution.

THEOREM 64.2. *The integral equation*

$$(64.12) \quad \mathbf{y}(x) = \mathbf{g}(x) + \lambda \int_a^x \mathbf{K}(x, z, \mathbf{y}(z)) \, dz$$

where the constant λ, the continuous $\mathbf{g}(x)$, and the kernel $\mathbf{K}(x, z, \mathbf{y})$, are given, has one and only one solution in $[a-d, a+d]$, if (64.8) holds,

(64.13) *if $\mathbf{K}$ is continuous in x with $|\mathbf{K}(x, z, \mathbf{y})|_\infty \leqslant M_1$, in a neighbourhood G of the point $(a, a, \mathbf{g}(a))$,*

(64.14) *and if $(x, z, \mathbf{y}) \in G$ when $|x-a| \leqslant d$,*

$$|z-a| \leqslant d, \quad |\mathbf{y} - \mathbf{g}(x)|_\infty \leqslant M_1|\lambda| \, d$$

Proof. Instead of (64.11) we use

347

$$(64.15) \qquad \mathbf{u}(x) = \mathbf{A}(x, \mathbf{y}) = \mathbf{g}(x) + \lambda \int_a^x \mathbf{K}(x, z, \mathbf{y}(z)) \, dz$$

$$(|x - a| \leqslant d)$$

while in place of $\mathcal{C}[a, b]$ we use the space $\mathcal{C}^*$ of $y_j \in \mathcal{C}[a-d, a+d]$ with

$$|\mathbf{y}(x) - \mathbf{g}(x)|_\infty \leqslant M_1 |\lambda| \, d$$

Then for $\mathbf{y} \in \mathcal{C}^*$, $|x - a| \leqslant d$, we use (64.13) to show that the integral in (64.12) is continuous in x, so that $\mathbf{u}(x)$ is continuous. By (64.15; 64.13),

$$|\mathbf{u}(x) - \mathbf{g}(x)|_\infty = |\lambda| \left| \int_a^x \mathbf{K}(x, z, \mathbf{y}(z)) \, dz \right|_\infty \leqslant M_1 |\lambda| \, d$$

$$(|x - a| \leqslant d)$$

and $u \in \mathcal{C}^*$. Also $\mathcal{C}^*$ is complete under the norm $\big\| |\mathbf{y}(x)|_\infty \big\|_\infty$ (replacing $[a, b]$ by $[a-d, a+d]$), by a modification of Theorem 62.3, while $\mathbf{A}(x, \mathbf{y})$ is a continuous operator on $\mathbf{y}$, since from (64.8),

$$|\mathbf{A}(x, \mathbf{y}_1) - \mathbf{A}(x, \mathbf{y}_2)|_\infty \leqslant |\lambda| \, M |x - a| \cdot \big\| |\mathbf{y}_1 - \mathbf{y}_2|_\infty \big\|_\infty$$

$$\leqslant |\lambda| \, Md \big\| |\mathbf{y}_1 - \mathbf{y}_2|_\infty \big\|_\infty$$

Finally we show that for some integer n, $\mathbf{A}^n$ is a contraction mapping. For if

$$\mathbf{u}(x) = \mathbf{A}(x, \mathbf{y}), \quad \mathbf{w}(x) = \mathbf{A}(x, \mathbf{v}); \qquad |\mathbf{u}(x) - \mathbf{w}(x)|_\infty$$

$$= |\lambda| \left| \int_a^x \{\mathbf{K}(x, z, \mathbf{y}(z)) - \mathbf{K}(x, z, \mathbf{v}(z))\} \, dz \right|_\infty$$

$$\leqslant |\lambda| M \int_a^x |\mathbf{y}(z) - \mathbf{v}(z)|_\infty \, dz$$

where the integration is over $[x, a]$ if $x < a$,

$$\leqslant |\lambda| \, M |x - a| \cdot \big\| |\mathbf{y}(x) - \mathbf{v}(x)|_\infty \big\|_\infty$$

Applying this repeatedly, we have by induction

$$|\mathbf{A}^n(x, \mathbf{y}) - \mathbf{A}^n(x, \mathbf{v})|_\infty \leqslant |\lambda|^n M^n |x - a|^n \big\| |\mathbf{y}(x) - \mathbf{v}(x)|_\infty \big\|_\infty / n!$$

Clearly $\mathbf{A}^n$ is a contraction mapping as soon as

$$(|\lambda| \, Md)^n < n!$$

348

which occurs for some n by the convergence of the exponential series. Applying Theorem 16.2 we obtain what we require.

For examples the reader could specialize the sufficient conditions given for the two general cases, to suit the various special equations given at the beginning of the section.

15

SPACES OF MEASURABLE FUNCTIONS, AND INTEGRABILITY CONDITIONS

65. Lebesgue and Orlicz Spaces of Functions

We now come to that part of functional analysis that involves spaces of measurable functions, and linear functionals on those spaces in the form of integrals. Let T be a base space for generalized Riemann integration, using (generalized) intervals $I \subseteq T$, the I forming a family $\mathscr{S}$. Let $\mu \geqslant 0$ be a fixed interval function. We require 1 to be integrable with respect to μ over each of a sequence $\{T_n\}$ of subsets of T with union T, where each T_n is an elementary set, a finite union of non-overlapping intervals. Then if f is a real or complex valued function of the associated points of the intervals $I \in \mathscr{S}$, we can consider the integral

$$(65.1) \qquad L(f) \equiv \int_T f \, d\mu$$

Naturally, for $L(f)$ to exist, f has to be μ-measurable in general, and then if $L(|f|)$ exists, so does $L(f)$. But we are using a non-absolute integration, $L(f)$ sometimes exists when $L(|f|)$ does not. Integrals of Lebesgue type correspond to a specialization of μ, together with the requirement that both $L(f)$ and $L(|f|)$ exist.

The functional L is linear and non-negative, so that the theory of sections 40,41 applies.

(65.2) A function f is a null function for L, if, and only if, the set of points x where $f(x) \neq 0$, has μ-variation zero (i.e. $f = 0$ almost everywhere).

This follows from Theorem 44.11 (44.13), since a null function f for L is precisely one for which $L(|f|) = 0$.

(65.3) Thus L satisfies condition (40.8).

As usual, we now replace the space of μ-measurable functions by the space of cosets of these functions modulo those functions that are zero almost everywhere, the L for each coset being the L for any function in that coset, if the L exists. It is clear that we lose nothing by using the ordinary mathematical contraction of denoting by f the coset of all functions equivalent to f, modulo the null functions.

We denote by L_p the Lebesgue space of all functions f that are μ-measurable, with $|f|^p$ integrable relative to μ in T, where $p \geqslant 1$ is constant. From

$$|f+g|^{p-1} \leqslant (|f|+|g|)^{p-1} \leqslant (\max(2|f|, 2|g|))^{p-1}$$
$$\leqslant 2^{p-1}(|f|^{p-1}+|g|^{p-1})$$

and since the μ-measurability of $f+g$ follows from the μ-measurability of f and g, it follows that if $f, g \in L_p$, Minkowski's inequality holds, and $L(|f^p|)^{1/p}$ is a norm on L_p; and L_p is a linear space. By the theorem on mean convergence, Theorem 46.3, L_p is complete, for $1 \leqslant p < \infty$. Further, ess sup has its usual meaning, namely, the supremum on neglecting a set of μ-variation zero. Then we define the space L_∞ of those μ-measurable functions that have a finite essential supremum, and L_∞ is also complete. For by the union of sets of variation zero, if

$$f_n \in L_\infty \ (n = 1, 2, \ldots), \quad \|f_m - f_n\|_\infty \to 0$$

the norm being the essential supremum, there is a fixed set X of variation zero with

$$|f_m(x) - f_n(x)| \leqslant \|f_m - f_n\|_\infty \qquad (x \in \backslash X)$$

and we can use the proof of Theorem 62.3, omitting references to continuity.

THEOREM 65.1. *If $f \in L_p$ ($1 \leqslant p \leqslant \infty$), and L_q is the complementary space, so that $1/p + 1/q = 1$ in all cases, then over all $g \in L_q$ with $\|g\|_q \leqslant 1$, we have*

$$\|f\|_p = \sup \left| \int_T fg \, d\mu \right| = \sup \int_T |fg| \, d\mu$$

351

Proof. By Hölder's inequality, both integrals are not greater than $\|f\|_p$, since $\|g\|_q \leqslant 1$. Thus we need only prove the opposite inequality when $\|f\|_p > 0$. When $p = 1$, $q = \infty$, we take $g(x) = 1/\text{sgn} f(x)$, with $\|g\|_\infty = 1$, and

$$\int_T fg \, d\mu = \int_T |f| \, d\mu = \|f\|_1$$

If $1 < p < \infty$, so that $1 < q < \infty$ and $p-1 = p/q$, we put

$$g(x) = |f(x)|^{p-1}/\{\|f\|_p^{p-1} \text{ sgn} f(x)\}; \qquad |g(x)|^q = |f(x)|^p/\|f\|_p^p,$$

$$\|g\|_q = 1$$

$$\int_T fg \, d\mu = \int_T \{|f(x)|^p/\|f\|_p^{p-1}\} \, d\mu = \|f\|_p$$

If $p = \infty$, $q = 1$, we take arbitrary $\varepsilon > 0$. By definition of $\|f\|_\infty$, the set X^* where $|f(x)| > \|f\|_\infty - \varepsilon$, has positive (possibly infinite) variation. Now 1 is integrable with respect to μ over each T_n, their countable union being T, so that μ is of bounded variation on each T_n (by Henstock (1963c), p. 60, Theorem 31.2, for the simple Riemann-complete integration). Hence, for some integer n, $X = X^* \cap T_n$ has finite non-zero variation, and we define

$$g(x) = (V(\mu; \mathcal{A}; E; X) \text{ sgn} f(x))^{-1} (x \in X),$$

$$g(x) = 0 (x \notin X).$$

By Henstock (1963c) pp. 90–1, Theorem 38.2 (38.5), $\|g\|_1 = 1$, and also

$$\int_T fg \, d\mu = \int_T |f(x)| \, ch(X; x) \, d\mu/V(\mu; \mathcal{A}; E; X) \geqslant \|f\|_\infty - \varepsilon$$

giving the result.

This theorem recalls the definition of the norm in Orlicz spaces, to which we now turn, remembering sections 40, 41. As should be clear, $\mathcal{H}$ here is the space of μ-measurable functions, and we assume that $\varphi(t; x)$ is such that $\Phi(t; |f(t)|)$ and $\Psi(t; |f(t)|)$ are μ-measurable, for every μ-measurable function f. A simple sufficient condition seems to be that $\varphi(t; ch(I; t))$ is μ-measurable, for each interval I. Then the definitions and theorems follow for this case as in section 41; and

352

there are also some special results given below, for the case when φ is independent of t.

THEOREM 65.2 (65.4) *If* $\|f\|_\Phi = 0$, *then* $f = 0$ *almost everywhere, and conversely.*

(65.5) *If* $\|f\|_\Phi$ *is finite, then* $f(x)$ *and* $\varphi(|f(x)|/\|f\|_\Phi)$ *are finite almost everywhere.*

(65.6)   *If* $0 < \|f\|_\Phi < \infty$, *then* $\|(f/\|f\|_\Phi)\|_\Phi^* \leqslant 1$

(65.7) *If* f *is bounded and* μ-*measurable, and zero in* $\backslash T_n$, *for some integer* n, *then* $f \in L_\Phi$.

(65.8) *If* $f \in L_\Phi$, $g \in L_\Psi$, *and* f, g *are* μ-*measurable, then* $fg, |fg|$ *are integrable relative to* μ *in* T, *and*

$$\left| \int_T fg \, d\mu \right| \leqslant \int_T |fg| \, d\mu \leqslant \|f\|_\Phi \cdot \|g\|_\Psi$$

The last result is Hölder's inequality for Orlicz spaces. *Proof.* For (65.4) we use *Ex. 41.2*, but cannot use it directly since if I denotes the function identically equal to 1, I need not be integrable with respect to μ in T. Thus we use $I \cdot ch(T_n; .)$, and find that $f \cdot ch(T_n; .) = 0$ almost everywhere. Taking $n = 1, 2, \ldots$ gives (65.4). For (65.5) we find similarly that

$$L(|f| \cdot ch(T_n; .)) < \infty, \quad |f| \cdot ch(T_n; .) < \infty$$

almost everywhere, giving the first result on taking $n = 1, 2, \ldots$ For the second result, we note that it follows from the first if $\varphi(x)$ is finite for all x. If, however, $\varphi(x)$ is finite for all $x < c$, but tends to infinity as $x \to c-$, then $\psi(x) \to c$ as $x \to \infty$, with $\psi(x) < c$ for all finite x. Hence

(65.9) $\Psi(x) = cx\{1 - \varepsilon(x)\}, \quad \varepsilon(x) > 0(x \geqslant 0), \quad \varepsilon(x) \to 0 \quad x \to \infty$

Let $|f(x)| \geqslant c\|f\|_\Phi$ on a set X_1 not of variation zero, so that by intersection with T_n if necessary, we can assume that

(65.10) $0 < \mu_1(X_1) \equiv V(\mu; \mathcal{A}; T; X_1) < \infty$,   defining

$$\varepsilon^* = \max\left[1/2, 1 - \varepsilon(2/\{c\mu_1(X_1)\})\right],$$

$$g(x) = \{c\mu_1(X_1)\varepsilon^*\}^{-1} ch(X_1; x)$$

Then by (65.9),

$$\int_T \Psi(|g|)d\mu = \mu_1(X_1)\, \Psi(\{c\mu_1(X_1)\,\varepsilon^*\}^{-1})$$

$$= (\varepsilon^*)^{-1}[1 - \varepsilon(\{c\mu_1(X_1)\,\varepsilon^*\}^{-1})]$$

$$\leqslant (\varepsilon^*)^{-1}[1 - \varepsilon(\{c\mu_1(X_1)(1/2)\}^{-1})] \leqslant 1$$

$$\int_T |fg|\,d\mu = \int_T \frac{|f|\,ch(X_1;x)}{c\mu_1(X_1)\,\varepsilon^*}\,d\mu \geqslant \frac{\|f\|_\Phi}{\varepsilon^*} > \|f\|_\Phi$$

This gives a contradiction, so that (65.10) is false and (65.5) true.

The remaining case is when $\varphi(c)$ is finite, and $\varphi(x)$ infinite for all $x > c$. We now have $\psi(x) = c$ for all $x > \varphi(c)$, and instead of (65.9) $x < \gamma(c)$, and instead of (65.9) we use $\Psi(x) \leqslant cx\ (x > 0)$, taking $\varepsilon^* = 1$, and $|f(x)| > c\|f\|_\Phi$ in X_1. Thus we prove that $|f(x)| \leqslant c\|f\|_\Phi$ almost everywhere, and (65.5) is again true.

To prove (65.6) let f and $\varphi(|f|/\|f\|_\Phi)$ exist in the set X, with $\setminus X$ of variation zero. By the case, Theorem 40.1 (40.2), of equality in Young's inequality, if $X_n \to X$ as $n \to \infty$, where each X_n has

(65.11) $0 < \mu_1(X_n) < \infty$, $a(x) = |f(x)|\, ch(X_n; x)/\|f\|_\Phi$

$$b(x) = \varphi(a(x)) = \varphi(|f(x)|/\|f\|_\Phi)\, ch(X_n; x)$$

both bounded, then

(65.12) $$\Phi(a(x)) + \Psi(b(x)) = a(x)\, b(x)$$

The right side has a finite integral on T since it is bounded there, and zero in $\setminus X_n$ with $\mu_1(X_n)$ finite. Hence from (65.12) and Theorem 41.4 (41.13),

$$\|b\|_\Psi^* < \infty, \|a\|_\Phi^* + \|b\|_\Psi^* = \int_T a(x)\, b(x)\, d\mu = \int_T \frac{|f_{(x)}|b_{(x)}}{\|f\|_\Phi}\, ch(X; x)\, d\mu$$

$$\leqslant \max(1, \|b\|_\Psi^*)$$

If $\|b\|_\Psi^* > 1$ then $\|a\|_\Phi^* = 0$. If $\|b\|_\Psi^* \leqslant 1$, then

$$\|a\|_\Phi^* \leqslant \|a\|_\Phi^* + \|b\|_\Psi^* \leqslant 1$$

Hence in either case

$$\int_T \Phi(|f(x)|/\|f\|_\Phi)\, ch(X_n; x)\, d\mu \leqslant 1$$

and we have (65.6) on letting $n \to \infty$ and using our version of Lebesgue's monotone convergence theorem, Theorem 46.1.

For (65.7), $\Phi(a)$ is finite when $a > 0$ is small enough. As f is bounded there is a large constant $A > 0$ for which $|f(x)|/A < a$. As f is zero in $\backslash T_n$ and as $\mu_1(T_n) < \infty$,

$$\int_T \Phi(|f(x)|/A)\, d\mu < \infty, \quad f/A \in L_\Phi^* \subseteq L_\Phi, \quad f \in L_\Phi$$

Clearly we can interchange f and g, Φ and Ψ, in the above results.

For (65.8), if $\|g\|_\Psi = 0$, then by (65.4) for g, $g = 0$ almost everywhere, and the proof is trivial. If $\|g\|_\Psi > 0$ we use (65.6) for g, and the definition of $\|f\|_\Phi$, to obtain

$$\int_T |fg|\, d\mu = \int_T \frac{|fg|}{\|g\|_\Psi}\, d\mu\, \|g\|_\Psi \leqslant \|f\|_\Phi \cdot \|g\|_\Psi$$

THEOREM 65.3 *If there are constants* $M > 0$, $y \geqslant 0$, *with*

(65.13) $$\Phi(2x) \leqslant M\Phi(x) \qquad (all\ x \geqslant y),$$

and if 1 *is integrable over* T *in the case when* $y > 0$, *then* $L_\Phi^* = L_\Phi$

Proof. From Theorem 41.4 (41.10), we have $L_\Phi^* \subseteq L_\Phi$. Thus let $f \in L_\Phi$. We write $f = f_1 + f_2$, where $f_1(x) = f(x)$ in the set where $|f(x)| \leqslant y\|f\|_\Phi$, and $f_1(x) = 0$ elsewhere. If $y = 0$ then $f_1 = 0$. If $y > 0$ then $\Phi(|f_1|)$ is bounded, and so integrable on T, relative to μ, as 1 is supposed integrable on T. Now for some integer $j > 0$, we have $\|f\|_\Phi \leqslant 2^j$, so that if $f_2(x) \neq 0$,

$$\Phi(|f_2(x)|) \leqslant \Phi(|f(x)|\, 2^j/\|f\|_\Phi) \leqslant M^j \Phi(|f(x)|/\|f\|_\Phi)$$

By Theorem 65.2 (65.6), $\Phi(|f_2(x)|)$ is integrable relative to μ in T. Since

$$\Phi(0) = 0, \quad \Phi(|f(x)|) = \Phi(|f_1(x)|) + \Phi(|f_2(x)|), \quad f \in L_\Phi^*$$

THEOREM 65.4. *If* $\lim_{x \to \infty} \psi(x) = c < \infty$, *then* $L_\Phi \subseteq L_\infty$, $L_\Psi \supseteq L_1$. *If also* 1 *is integrable on* T *the* $\subseteq$, $\supseteq$ *are* = *signs.*

Proof. If $f \in L_\Phi$, then by the proof of Theorem 65.2, $|f(x)| \leq$ $\leq c\|f\|_\Phi$ almost everywhere, $f \in L_\infty$, and $\|f\|_\infty \leq c \cdot \|f\|_\Phi$.
Further, taking all f with $\|f\|_\Phi \leq 1$,

$$\|g\|_\Psi = \sup \int_T |fg| \, d\mu \leq \int_T |g| \, d\mu \cdot \operatorname{ess sup} |f| \leq \int_T |g| \, d\mu \cdot c,$$

$$\|g\|_\Psi \leq c\|g\|_1$$

proving that $L_\Psi \supseteq L_1$.

If also 1 is integrable on T, and if $f \in L_\infty$, then for some constant $a > 0$, $a|f(x)| \leq \frac{1}{2}c$ almost everywhere, and

$$af \in L_\Phi^* \subseteq L_\Phi, \quad f \in L_\Phi, \quad L_\Phi = L_\infty$$

If $g \in L_\Psi$, then $L(|fg|)$ is finite for all $f \in L_\Phi$, in particular, for $f(x) = 1$ *(all x)*. Thus

$$L(|g|) < \infty, \quad g \in L_1, \quad L_\Psi = L_1$$

THEOREM 65.5. L_Φ *is complete, i.e. if $f_n(x) \in L_\Phi$ $(n = 1, 2, \ldots)$, and as m, $n \to \infty$ $\lim \|f_m - f_n\|_\Phi = 0$, then there exists a function $f(x) \in L_\Phi$ with $\lim_{n \to \infty} \|f_n - f\|_\Phi = 0$. This function f is uniquely determined almost everywhere.*

Proof. Given $\varepsilon > 0$ and a g with $\|g\|_\Psi^* \leq 1$, there is an $N(\varepsilon)$ independent of g, with

(65.14) $$\int_T |f_n - f_m| \cdot |g| \, d\mu \leq \varepsilon \quad (m, n \geq N(\varepsilon))$$

We choose $a > 0$ such that

$$V(\mu; \mathcal{A}; T_1) \, \Psi(a) \leq 1$$

Writing $g = a \cdot ch(T_1; x)$, we have $\|g\|_\Psi^* \leq 1$, so that from (65.14),

$$\int |f_n - f_m| \, d\mu \leq \varepsilon/a \quad (m, n \geq N(\varepsilon))$$

for integration over T_1, so that by mean convergence with index 1 (Theorem 46.3) there is a subsequence $\{f_n^{(1)}\}$ such that some function f is the limit almost everywhere in T_1. Similarly, by mean convergence with index 1 over T_2, there is a subsequence $\{f_n^{(2)}\}$ of $\{f_n^{(1)}\}$

with $f = \lim\limits_{n \to \infty} f_n^{(2)}$ almost everywhere in T_2, and so on. Hence, almost everywhere in T, $f = \lim\limits_{n \to \infty} f_n^{(n)}$. By Fatou's lemma, Theorem 46.2, we let f_n in (65.14) pass through the sequence $\{f_n^{(n)}\}$ to give

$$(65.15) \qquad \int_T |f-f_m|\,|g|\,d\mu \leqslant \varepsilon \qquad (m \geqslant N(\varepsilon))$$

where $N(\varepsilon)$ is independent of the g with $\|g\|_\Psi^* \leqslant 1$. Hence $f-f_m \in L_\Phi$, so that as L_Φ is linear, $f \in L_\Phi$, and $\|f-f_m\|_\Phi \leqslant \varepsilon$ for $m \geqslant N(\varepsilon)$. The uniqueness almost everywhere of f follows as in Theorem 46.3.

THEOREM 65.6. *If* $f, f_n \in L_\Phi$, *and* $g, g_n \in L_\Psi$, *for* $n = 1, 2, \ldots,$ *with*

$$\|f-f_n\|_\Phi \to 0, \quad \|g-g_n\|_\Psi \to 0, \quad then$$

$$\int_T f_n g_n \, d\mu \to \int_T fg \, d\mu$$

Proof. For by Theorem 65.2 (65.8),

$$fg - f_n g_n = (f-f_n)\,g + f(g-g_n) - (f_n-f)\,(g_n-g)$$

$$\left| \int_T fg \, d\mu - \int_T f_n g_n \, d\mu \right| \leqslant \|f-f_n\|_\Phi \cdot \|g\|_\Psi + \|f\|_\Phi \cdot \|g-g_n\|_\Psi$$

$$+ \|f_n-f\|_\Phi \cdot \|g_n-g\|_\Psi$$

THEOREM 65.7. *Let* T *be a* β-*group with norm homogeneous for positive integers, and let* $y(f; s)$ *be a function of* $f \in T$, $s \geqslant 0$. *If, for each fixed* $f \in T$, $y(f;.) \in L_\Phi(0, \infty)$, *and if, for each fixed* $s \geqslant 0$, $y(., s)$ *is a continuous multiplicative functional on* T, *then* $H(f) \equiv y(f;.)$ *sends* T *into* $L_\Phi(0, \infty)$, *and* $H(.)$ *is a continuous multiplicative operator from* T *to* $L_\Phi(0, \infty)$.

Tatchell (1953), Lemmas 1, 6, takes T a Banach space, while Sargent (1955), p. 405, Lemma 5, takes T a β-space, both with $L_\Phi = L_1$ or L_∞.

Proof. In view of Theorem 33.4 (33.11; 33.12), since L_Φ is a group with norm $\|f\|_\Phi$ homogeneous for positive integers, we need only prove that

$$\|H(f)\|_\Phi = \|y(f;.)\|_\Phi$$

is lower semi-continuous in f. If $f_n \to f$ then $y(f_n, s) \to y(f, s)$ for each $s \geqslant 0$, by continuity. By Fatou's lemma (see Theorem 46.2), for each g with $\|g\|_{\Psi}^{*} \leqslant 1$, we have

$$\int_{s=0}^{\infty} |y(f; s)|\,|g|\,d\mu = \int_{0}^{\infty} \lim_{n \to \infty} |y(f_n; s)|\,|g|\,d\mu$$

$$\leqslant \lim_{n \to \infty} \inf \int_{0}^{\infty} |y(f_n; s)|\,|g|\,d\mu \leqslant \lim_{n \to \infty} \inf \|y(f_n; \cdot)\|_{\Phi},$$

$$\|y(f; \cdot)\|_{\Phi} \leqslant \lim_{n \to \infty} \inf \|y(f_n; \cdot)\|_{\Phi}$$

This gives the lower semi-continuity, and so the theorem.

66. Integrability of Products, and Similar Theorems

In the next chapter we consider integrals of the form

(66.1) $$y(s) = \int_{1}^{\infty} K(s, t) f(t)\,dt$$

(66.2) $$y(s) = \int_{1}^{\infty} K(s, t)\,df(t)$$

Formally, the first is connected with Silverman–Toeplitz matrix summability, while the second is connected with gamma matrix summability. For if we take $f(t) = f(n)$ $(n \leqslant t < n+1)$, for $n = 1, 2, \ldots$, the first becomes

$$y(s) = \sum_{n=1}^{\infty} f(n) \int_{n}^{n+1} K(s, t)\,dt$$

while if K is continuous in t, the second becomes

$$y(s) = \sum_{n=1}^{\infty} K(s, n+1)\,\{f(n+1) - f(n)\}$$

$$= \sum_{n=1}^{\infty} K(s, n+1)\,u_n \qquad \left(f(n) = \sum_{j=1}^{n-1} u_j\right)$$

Thus we might expect the necessary and sufficient conditions on $K(s, t)$ to be generalizations of conditions in Chapter 12; in fact the theory of that chapter is a guide for research on the two types of integrals.

However, the theory of (66.1) is far behind the theory of matrix transformations, while that of (66.2) is rarely considered. One reason is that integrals are used in (66.1; 66.2) while matrix transformations only need infinite series, over which there is no controversy in connection with the limit process used. But the integral signs in (66.1; 66.2) can represent Cauchy–Riemann and Cauchy–Riemann–Stieltjes integrals, they can represent Cauchy–Lebesgue and Cauchy–Radon integrals, they can represent the special or general Denjoy and Denjoy–Stieltjes integrals, or they can be still more general. In this respect the generalized Riemann and variational integrals are a great help because of their unifying influence in the theory of integration, and in any case they arose out of work connected with summability in integrals. But sometimes the simpler kind is not strong enough to deal with (66.2), as we shall see later.

A second difficulty is that, whereas the sum to n terms of an infinite series is definable by elementary algebra and needs no limit process, the integral over a finite interval is defined by a limit. Replacing the interval $[1, +\infty]$ of integration in (66.1; 66.2) by $[1, a]$, we have first to consider the integrability of $K(s, t) f(t)$ relative to t, or the integrability of $K(s, t)$ relative to $f(t)$, over $[1, a]$, for each fixed s in the range of s. Part of the discussion of the second needs an integration by parts, so that we have an integrability of $f(t)$ relative to $K(s, t)$. These considerations first lead to a discussion of the integral

$$(66.3) \qquad \int_T f(t) \, d\mu$$

We look for properties of μ in order that (66.3) should exist, for all f in a space of functions. The theory includes part of Henstock (1955b, 1957a), and the theory that uses Lebesgue integration, in which (66.3) becomes

$$(66.4) \qquad \int_T f(t) \, k(t) \, d\mu \qquad (\mu \geqslant 0)$$

where k is μ-measurable in T, and where also $|f(t) \, k(t)|$ is assumed integrable in T. The latter follows since we can replace $f(t)$ by

24

$f(t)/\mathrm{sgn}\, k(t)$ in the Lebesgue spaces used in that part of the theory. We also include the work of Sargent on Denjoy integrals, in which both modulus and amplitude of $f(t)$ are concerned in assigning $f(t)$ to the space of functions used.

The first theorem could be given for n-dimensional intervals T, but for simplicity we assume $n = 1$.

THEOREM 66.1. *The necessary and sufficient conditions on μ in order that (66.3) should exist for all bounded Baire functions $f(t)$ on $[a, b] = T$, are that*

(66.5) 1 *is integrable with respect to μ to $H(x)$ over $[a, x]$, for all x in $a \leqslant x \leqslant b$*

(66.6) $H(x-)$ *exists in $a < x \leqslant b$, $H(x+)$ exists in $a \leqslant x < b$, both being of bounded variation in those ranges, where*

$$H(x-) = \lim_{u \to 0+} H(x-u) = H(x) - \lim_{u \to 0+} \mu(x-u, x)$$
$$H(x+) = \lim_{u \to 0+} H(x+u) = H(x) + \lim_{u \to 0+} \mu(x, x+u);$$

and for

$$(66.7) \begin{cases} j(a) = -H(a+) = \lim_{u \to 0+} -\mu(a, a+u), \\ j(b) = H(b) - H(b-) = \lim_{u \to 0+} \mu(b-u, b), \\ j(x) = H(x) - \tfrac{1}{2}\{H(x+) + H(x-)\} \\ \quad = \lim_{u \to 0+} \tfrac{1}{2}\{\mu(x-u, x) - \mu(x, x+u)\} \ (a < x < b), \end{cases}$$

the set of points u in $a < u < b$ where $j(u) \neq 0$, can be divided into two sequences $\{u_n\}$, $\{v_n\}$, with the properties

$$(66.8) \qquad \sum_{n=1}^{\infty} |j(u_n)| < \infty,$$

(66.9) $j(v_n) \to 0$ *as $n \to \infty$, and surrounding each v_n there is an open interval $\overline{I}(v_n) \equiv (v_n, \overline{v}_n) \subseteq (a, b)$ such that each point of (a, b) can lie in an at most finite number of the $I(v_n)$,*

(66.10) *there is a strictly increasing bounded function χ such that*

$$\chi(\overline{v}_n+) - \chi(v_n) \geqslant |j(v_n)|, \quad \chi(v_n) - \chi(v_n-) \geqslant |j(v_n)|$$

Conversely, if j satisfies (66.8; ... ; 66.10), *where each u for which* $j(u) \neq 0$, *is either a u_n or a v_n, for some n, then for all bounded f in* $[a, b]$,

$$(66.11) \qquad \int_a^x f \, dj = \left[fj \right]_a^x = f(x) \, j(x) - f(a) \, j(a) \qquad (a < x \leqslant b)$$

If also μ satisfies (66.5; 66.6) *for the j of* (66.7), *then* (66.3) *exists for all bounded Baire functions f, and is equal to*

$$(66.12) \qquad \int_a^b f \, dH_1 + \left[fj \right]_a^b \qquad (H_1 \equiv H - j)$$

Proof. We prove the necessity of the conditions in easy stages.

Lemma 66.1. H(x), H(x−), H(x+) exist in the given ranges with the given values.

Proof. (66.5) is obvious, so that we can replace μ by H in (66.3) by Theorems 44.11 (44.14), 44.6. From Henstock (1963c), p. 33, Theorem 21.2 (21.12),

$$(66.13) \qquad \int_u^x f(t) \, dH - f(x) \{H(x) - H(u)\} \to 0$$

$$(u \to x-, a \leqslant u < x \leqslant b)$$

so that for $f(t) = 0 (t < x)$, $f(t) = 1 (t \geqslant x)$ and for $a \leqslant u < x \leqslant b$,

$$\int_a^x f(t) \, dH = \int_a^u + \int_u^x = \int_u^x,$$

$$\int_a^x = \lim_{u \to x-} \int_u^x = \lim_{u \to x-} \{H(x) - H(u)\}$$

Thus $H(x−)$ exists, finite, in $a < x \leqslant b$. Similarly $H(x+)$ exists, finite, in $a \leqslant x < b$. A second application of Henstock (1963c), p. 33, Theorem 21.2 (21.12; 21.13) gives the values in terms of μ.

LEMMA 66.2. *Let $\{x(n)\}$ be a strictly increasing or strictly decreasing sequence in (a, b). Then*

$$\sum_{n=1}^{\infty} \left| H(x(n+1)-) - H(x(n)-) \right| < \infty$$

Proof. We can assume that the sequence is strictly increasing.

For convergent

$$\sum_{n=1}^{\infty} c_n, \quad f(t) \equiv \sum_{x(n)<t} c_n$$

is a bounded Baire function, with $f(a) = 0$ since $x(1) > a$. We use (66.13) repeatedly, taking $x(n-1) < u < x(n)$. Then

$$\int_{x(n-1)}^{x(n)} f(t)\, dH = \lim_{u \to x(n)} \left\{ \int_{x(n-1)}^{u} + \int_{u}^{x(n)} = \lim_{u \to x(n)} \left[f(x(n-1)) \times \right. \right.$$
$$\times \{H(u) - H(x(n-1))\} + f(x(n))\{H(x(n)) - H(u)\} \right]$$
$$= f(x(n-1))\{H(x(n)) - H(x(n-1))\} + c_n\{H(x(n)) - H(x(n)-)\}$$
$$\int_{a}^{x(n)} f(t)\, dH = \sum_{j=1}^{n} c_j\{H(x(n)) - H(x(j)-)\}$$

If $v = \lim_{n \to \infty} x(n)$ then $a < v \leqslant b$, and

$$\int_{a}^{v} f(t)\, dH = \lim_{n \to \infty} \left\{ \int_{a}^{x(n)} + \int_{x(n)}^{v} \right\} = \lim_{n \to \infty} \left[\sum_{j=1}^{n} c_j\{H(x(n)) \right.$$
$$- H(x(j)-))\} + f(v)\{H(v) - H(x(n))\} \right] = \lim_{n \to \infty} \left[\sum_{j=1}^{n} c_j\{H(v) \right.$$
$$- H(x(j)-)\} + \sum_{j=n+1}^{\infty} c_j\{H(v) - H(x(n))\} \right]$$

We thus have a transformation of the type (55.22), in which $h(\mathbf{c}, n)$ tends to a limit whenever (55.21) is convergent. The condition that corresponds to (55.2; 55.3), is that for all integers n, and for fixed M,

$$\sum_{j=2}^{n} |H(x(j)-) - H(x(j-1)-)| + |H(x(n)) - H(x(n)-)| \leqslant M$$

giving the lemma.

LEMMA 66.3. $H(x-)$ is of bounded variation in $(a, b]$.

Proof. Since for $a \leqslant u < x \leqslant b$, $|H(x-) - H(u-)|$ is subadditive, taking $H(a-) = H(a)$, $V(v, w) \equiv V(H(x-); \mathcal{A}; [v, w]) = \sup (\mathcal{D}) \sum |H(x-) - H(u-)|$ $(a \leqslant v < w \leqslant b)$ for all divisions $\mathcal{D}$ of $[v, w]$ formed of intervals $[u, x]$, and not just those from an

$S \in \mathcal{A}$ and complete in $[v, w]$. If the lemma is false, then either

$$V(a, \tfrac{1}{2}(a+b)) = +\infty, \quad \text{or} \quad V(a, \tfrac{1}{2}(a+b)) < +\infty,$$
$$V(\tfrac{1}{2}(a+b), b) = +\infty$$

We then choose the intervals $[a, \tfrac{1}{2}(a+b)]$, $[\tfrac{1}{2}(a+b), b]$, respectively, and we can repeat the process, obtaining a monotone decreasing sequence $[x_n, y_n]$ of closed intervals contained in the compact $[a, b]$. Let c be the common point of the sequence. Then we can suppose that $y_n > c$ and $V(c, y_n) = +\infty$ for $n = 1, 2, \ldots$. For otherwise $x_n < c$, $V(x_n, c) = +\infty$, and we have a similar proof.

$$|H(x-) - H(c-)| \rightarrow |H(c+) - H(c-)| < \infty \qquad (x \rightarrow c+)$$

so that there are integers M, N with

$$|H(x-) - H(c-)| \leqslant M \qquad (c < x \leqslant y_N)$$

There is a division $\mathcal{D}_N$ of $[c, y_N]$ with

$$(\mathcal{D}_N) \sum |H(x-) - H(u-)| > M+1$$

By subadditivity we can suppose that $\mathcal{D}_N$ includes $[c, y_n]$ for some $n > N$, by splitting an interval $[c, x]$ if necessary. Removing $[c, y_n]$ from $\mathcal{D}_N$, we have a finite monotone decreasing sequence $z_1 > \ldots$ $\ldots > z_m = y_n$ of points greater than c, with

$$\sum_{j=1}^{m-1} |H(z_{j+1}-) - H(z_j-)| > 1$$

There are similarly a division $\mathcal{D}_n$ of $[c, y_n]$, that includes an interval $[c, y_r]$ for some $r > n$, with

$$(\mathcal{D}_n) \sum |H(x-) - H(u-)| > M+1$$

and so points $z_m > z_{m+1} > \ldots > z_s = y_r$, with

$$\sum_{j=1}^{s-1} |H(z_{j+1}-) - H(z_j-)| > 2$$

and so on. Thus Lemma 66.2 is falsified, unless Lemma 66.3 is true.

Similarly $H(x+)$ is of bounded variation in $[a, b)$, so that the same is true of H_1.

LEMMA 66.4. $\displaystyle\int_a^x f \, dH_1$ exists in $a \leqslant x \leqslant b$.

363

Proof. By Theorem 39.2, the integral exists when f is continuous. If $\{f_n\}$ is a sequence of bounded Baire functions, with $\|f_n\|_\infty \leqslant M$, independent of n, then for all u, t, x in $a \leqslant u < x \leqslant b, u \leqslant t \leqslant x$, and all integers n, $f_n(t)\{H_1(x)-H_1(u)\}$ lies between $\pm MV$ $(H_1; \mathcal{A}; [u, x])$, this interval function being finite by Lemma 66.3, and finitely additive, and so integrable. Hence by Theorem 46.2, if

$$f(x) = \lim_{n \to \infty} f_n(x) \qquad (a \leqslant x \leqslant b)$$

the integrability of f follows from the integrability of the f_n. Hence the lemma, by the definition of the Baire functions.

LEMMA 66.5. $\int_a^x f\, dj = \left[fj \right]_a^x$ *exists, and* $j(u) \neq 0$ *at a countable number of points* $\{w_n\}$ *in* (a, b), *and*

$$j(w_n) \to 0.$$

Proof. By hypothesis and Lemma 66.4, the given integral exists. Also $j(x-) = 0$ in $a < x \leqslant b$, and $j(x+) = 0$ in $a \leqslant x < b$, so that, for each $\varepsilon > 0$, the set of u, where $|j(u)| \geqslant \varepsilon$, has no limit point in $[a, b]$, and so is finite. Hence the results on j follow, while $j = 0$ at an everywhere dense set of points in $[a, b]$, and the value of the integral follows from Henstock (1963c), p. 34, Theorem 22.2.

LEMMA 66.6. *The function j satisfies* (66.8; 66.9; 66.10).

Proof. We take $f(w_n) = 1/\text{sgn } j(w_n)$, and $f(t) = 0$ otherwise, so that f is a bounded Baire function. By the value of the integral in Lemma 66.5,

$$f(x)\{j(x)-j(u)\}-\{f(x)j(x)-f(u)j(u)\} = \{f(u)-f(x)\}j(u)$$

$$(x > u \quad \text{or} \quad x < u)$$

is an interval function of variation zero in $[a, b]$, with associated points x. Hence given $\varepsilon > 0$, there is an $\mathbf{S} \in \mathcal{A}$ and complete in $[a, b]$ with

(66.14) $\qquad \chi(v) \equiv V(\{f(u)-f(x)\}j(u); \mathbf{S}; [a, v])$

$$+ \tfrac{1}{2}\varepsilon(v-a)/(b-a), \quad \chi(b) < \varepsilon$$

Then χ is strictly increasing. If x is not in the sequence $\{w_n\}$, but $u = w_n$, there is a $\delta(x)$ depending on S, with $0 < \delta(x) < \varepsilon$, and by definition of f, such that

(66.15) $\qquad |\chi(x) - \chi(w_n)| \geq |j(w_n)| \qquad (|x - w_n| \leq \delta(x))$

We now define the points v_n in $[a, b]$ as those for which

(66.16) $\quad |j(v_n)| > \chi(v_n +) - \chi(v_n), \quad |j(v_n)| > \chi(v_n) - \chi(v_n -)$

The other points $\{u_n\}$ of $\{w_n\}$ satisfy

$$\sum_{n=1}^{\infty} |j(u_n)| \leq \sum_{n=1}^{\infty} \{\chi(u_n +) - \chi(u_n -)\} \leq \chi(b) < \varepsilon$$

which gives (66.8). Also if, for some x, v_n, we have $|x - v_n| \leq \delta(x)$, then (66.15) holds with v_n for w_n. There is a non-uniformity. If v_n approaches the fixed x, then (66.15) is eventually true. But if v_n is fixed and x tends to v_n then by (66.16) eventually (66.15) is false, and the variable $\delta(x)$ is now less than $|x - v_n|$. Let $\underline{v}_n$ be the supremum of all $x < v_n$ satisfying (66.15) for $w_n = v_n$. If no such x, we put $\underline{v}_n = a$. Let $\bar{v}_n$ be the infimum of all $x > v_n$ satisfying (66.15) for $w_n = v_n$, and if no such x, we put $\bar{v}_n = b$. Then $\underline{v}_n < v_n < \bar{v}_n$. Also, for $\underline{v}_n > a$, $\bar{v}_n < b$.

(66.17) $\quad \chi(v_n) - \chi(\underline{v}_n -) \geq |j(v_n)|, \quad \chi(\bar{v}_n +) - \chi(v_n) \geq |j(v_n)|$

For those v_n with $\underline{v}_n = a$ or $\bar{v}_n = b$, or both, we can put jumps of χ at a, b, so that (66.17) is true for all v_n, since $j(v_n) \to 0$ as $n \to \infty$, and so is bounded. Hence (66.10) is true. Further,

$$\chi(v_n) - \chi(u) < |j(v_n)| \, (\underline{v}_n < u < v_n), \quad \chi(u) - \chi(v_n) < |j(v_n)|$$
$$(v_n < u < \bar{v}_n)$$

(66.18) $\qquad \chi(\bar{v}_n -) - \chi(\underline{v}_n +) \leq 2|j(v_n)| \to 0 \qquad (n \to \infty)$

If a point $x \in (a, b)$ lies in an infinity of the $I(v_n) \equiv (\underline{v}_n, \bar{v}_n)$, then by (66.18), and since χ is strictly increasing, there is an infinite sequence of n for which $\underline{v}_n \to x$, $\bar{v}_n \to x$, so that the corresponding subsequence of $\{v_n\}$ also tends to x, and eventually $|v_n - x| \leq \delta(x)$, and $x \notin I(v_n)$. This contradiction proves (66.9), the final result in the proof of necessity.

It is pointed out in Henstock (1957a), p. 108, Theorem 6(48), that the set $\{v_n\}$ is *scattered*. This is the nomenclature of J. E. Little-wood, others being *zerstreute* (F. Hausdorff), *separierte* (G. Cantor), *clairsemé* (A. Denjoy). But not all $j(v_n)$, with $\{v_n\}$ scattered, satisfy (66.8; 66.9; 66.10).

To prove that the conditions of Theorem 66.1 are sufficient, we begin with the following lemma.

LEMMA 66.7. *Let H_k be the set of points of (a, b) lying in at most k intervals of a sequence $\{I_n\}$ of open intervals in (a, b). Then all the intervals I_n that cover at least one point of H_k can be arranged into, at most, $3k$ sets of non-overlapping intervals.*

Proof. There is a sequence $\{x_r\}$ of points of H_k with closure containing H_k. Each I_n covering a point of H_k will then also cover at least one x_r, and conversely, so that we now concentrate on the $\{x_r\}$. We put the qth interval of $\{I_n\}$ covering x_1 into the set S_q. Then $1 \leqslant q \leqslant k$, as $x_1 \in H_k$. Suppose that the intervals I_n covering $x_1, \ldots, x_{r-1}$ have been arranged into sets $S_q (1 \leqslant q \leqslant 3k)$ of non-overlapping intervals, and let x_r lie between x_s and x_t, for $s < r$, $t < r$, with no $x_q (q < r)$ between x_s and x_t. Then at most k intervals I_n cover x_s, and at most k cover x_t, so that at least k of the sets $S_1, \ldots, S_{3k}$, say, $T_1, \ldots, T_k$, will be free from intervals I_n covering x_s or x_t, and so will contain no I_n lying in (x_s, x_t). The intervals I_n covering x_r that have not already been put into sets S_q, are at most k in number, cannot cover x_s nor x_t, and so must lie between x_s and x_t, and hence may be put into some or all of $T_1, \ldots, T_k$. Similarly if

$$x_r < \min_{q < r} x_q, \quad \text{or} \quad x_r > \max_{q < r} x_q$$

in which case one of x_s, x_t is missing. Hence by induction it is true for all $\{x_r\}$, and so for H_k.

LEMMA 66.8. *Let χ be bounded and monotone increasing in $[a - \varepsilon, b + \varepsilon]$, for some $\varepsilon > 0$, and let j, χ satisfy (66.8; 66.9; 66.10). Then for all bounded f in $[a, b]$, (66.11) is true.*

Proof. Let the discontinuities of χ in $[a, b]$ occur at $x_1, x_2, \ldots$

Then

$$\sum_{n=1}^{\infty} \{\chi(x_n+) - \chi(x_n-)\} \leqslant \chi(b+) - \chi(a-) < \infty$$

Thus, given $\varepsilon > 0$, there is an integer N with

(66.19) $$\sum_{n=N}^{\infty} \{\chi(x_n+) - \chi(x_n-)\} < \varepsilon$$

Then there is an integer m such that, for $n > m$, v_n is not one of the points $x_q(1 \leqslant q < N)$. In Lemma 66.7 we put $I_n = I(v_n)$. By (66.9), then

$$(a, b) = \bigcup_{k \geqslant 0} H_k$$

By definition the H_k are monotone increasing in k, and they are closed. For let $u \in (a, b) \backslash H_k$, and let J be the intersection of the first $(k+1)$ intervals $I(v_n)$ covering u. Then $J \subseteq (a, b) \backslash H_k$, and J is an open interval.

Now the characteristic functions of open intervals, open sets, and closed sets, can be successively proved integrable with respect to χ, with values equal to the corresponding variations of the sets. Hence by Theorem 44.9, we can take k so large that

(66.20) $$V(\chi; A; [a, b]; (a, b) \backslash H_k) < \varepsilon$$

By Lemma 66.7 there are $3k$ sets S_q, of non-overlapping intervals $I(v_n)$ that together cover $H_k \backslash H_0$. Since χ is finite and monotone increasing, there is an integer $t > m$, depending on ε, such that, for each q in $1 \leqslant q \leqslant 3k$,

(66.21) $$\sum \{\chi(\bar{v}_n+) - \chi(\underline{v}_n-)\} < \varepsilon/(3k)$$

where the sum is taken over those intervals of S_q with $n > t$. By (66.8) we can also arrange that

(66.22) $$\sum_{n > t} |j(u_n)| < \varepsilon$$

Let S be the open set formed from those intervals of the S_q with $n > t$ and $1 \leqslant q \leqslant 3k$. Then by adding an at most countable number of points to $\{(a, b) \backslash H_k\} \cup S$, open since H_k is closed, we obtain a union U of open non-abutting intervals. We write

(66.23) $\quad \chi_1(x) = \sum_1 \{\chi(z+) - \chi(y-)\} + \varepsilon(x-a)/(b-a) + \sum_2 2\,|j(u_n)|$

where $\sum_1$ denotes summation over the constituent intervals (y, z) of $U \cap (a, x)$, changing $z+$ to z if $z = x$; and where $\sum_2$ denotes summation over all $n > t$ with $u_n < x$, adding $|j(u_q)|$ if $q > t$ and $x = u_q$. Then χ_1 is strictly increasing, and from $(66.19; \ldots 66.22)$,

(66.24) $\qquad\qquad\qquad \chi_1(b) - \chi_1(a) < 6\varepsilon$

By definition the points of H_0 do not lie in any interval $I(v_n)$. If $n > t$ and if $I(v_n)$ covers a point of $H_k \backslash H_0$, then $I(v_n)$ lies in one of the S_q, and so in S, and so in U. Hence $\chi(v_n) - \chi(v_n-)$ occurs in $\sum_1$ for $x = v_n$. If $n > t$ and if $I(v_n)$ does not cover a point of $H_k \backslash H_0$, then $I(v_n) \subseteq (a, b) \backslash H_k \subseteq U$, and again, $\chi(v_n) - \chi(v_n-)$ occurs in $\sum_1$ for $x = v_n$. Thus by (66.23),

(66.25) $\quad \chi_1(v_n) - \chi_1(\underline{v}_n-) \geqslant \chi(v_n) - \chi(\underline{v}_n-) \geqslant |j(v_n)| \qquad (n > t)$

Similarly for the result with $\bar{v}_n+$, so that χ_1 satisfies (66.10) for all $n > t$, as well as (66.24).

Let $\{y_n\}$ be the sequence of distinct points that includes the points of $\{u_n\}$, $\{v_n\}$, $\{\underline{v}_n\}$, $\{\bar{v}_n\}$, and no more, and let $x \notin \{y_n\}$. We choose $\delta(x) > 0$ so that $(x - \delta(x), x + \delta(x))$ does not include

$$u_1, \ldots, u_t, \quad v_1, \ldots, v_t, \quad z_1, \ldots z_r$$

where the z_j are those v's with $x \in I(z_j)$ $(1 \leqslant j \leqslant r)$. Then by (66.25),

$$\chi_1(x) - \chi_1(v_n) \geqslant \chi_1(\bar{v}_n) - \chi_1(v_n) \geqslant |j(v_n)| \qquad (x > v_n > x - \delta(x))$$

since $\bar{v}_n < x$. If $x > u_n > x - \delta(x)$ then $n > t$, and by (66.23),

$$\chi_1(x) - \chi_1(u_n) \geqslant |j(u_n)|$$

If $v \notin u_n$, $v \notin v_n$, for any n, then $j(v) = 0$. Hence

(66.26) $\quad \chi_1(x) - \chi_1(v) \geqslant |j(v)| \qquad (x > v > x - \delta(x),\ x \notin \{y_n\})$

Similarly for all v in $x < v < x + \delta(x)$, $x \notin \{y_n\}$. To deal with the case when $x = y_n$ for some n we note that from (66.9), $j(v_n) \to 0$

as $n \to \infty$, so that $j(v_n) \to 0$ as $v_n \to y_n \equiv y_{(n)}$. Hence we need only take

$$\chi_2(x) = \chi_1(x) + \sum_{y(n) < x} \varepsilon \cdot 2^{-n} \qquad (x \notin \{y_n\})$$

$$\chi_2(y_n) = \chi_2(y_n-) + \varepsilon \cdot 2^{-2n} \qquad (n = 1, 2, \ldots)$$

and we can choose $\delta(y_n)$ suitably. From (66.24),

(66.27) $$\chi_2(b) - \chi_2(a) < 7\varepsilon$$

Now let $|f| \leqslant M$, and let $\mathcal{D}$ be a division of $[a, b]$ that uses $\delta(x)$. Then

$$|(\mathcal{D}) \sum f(x)\{j(v) - j(u)\} - [fj]_a^b| \leqslant (\mathcal{D}) \sum |f(x)\{j(v) - j(u)\} - [fj]_u^v|$$

so that if x' denotes the opposite end of the interval from the associated point x, we have from (66.26), and the similar results for $\{y_n\}$,

$$(\mathcal{D}) \sum |f(v) - f(u)| \cdot |j(x')| \leqslant 2M(\mathcal{D}) \sum \{\chi_2(v) - \chi_2(u)\}$$
$$= 2M\{\chi_2(b) - \chi_2(a)\} < 14M\varepsilon$$

It follows that f is integrable relative to j, with (66.11).

To complete the proof of Theorem 66.1 we need only note Lemmas 66.4, 66.8.

The following result is new, and shows when we can dispense with $j(t)$.

THEOREM 66.2. *If $T = [a, b]$, the necessary and sufficient conditions on μ in order that (66.3) should exist for all Baire functions f such that, for some countable set X, f is bounded in $[a, b]\backslash X$, are that (66.5) is true, and (66.28) that H has only a finite number of discontinuities, and is of bounded variation.*

Proof. After Lemma 66.1, we can take $f = 0$ except at a sequence $\{y(n)\}$ of points that is strictly increasing to some $y \leqslant b$. If, for all n,

(66.29) $$H(y(n)+) - H(y(n)-) \neq 0$$

we put

$$f(y(n)) = 1/\{H(y(n)+) - H(y(n)-)\}$$

369

Then as in Lemma 66.1, but taking $y(n) < x < z < y(n+1)$, with $x \to y(n)$, and $z \to y(n+1)$, we have

$$\int_{y(n)}^{y(n+1)} f \, dH = f(y(n))\{H(y(n)+) - H(y(n))\}$$
$$+ f(y(n+1))\{H(y(n+1)) - H(y(n+1)-)\}$$

$$\int_a^y f \, dH$$

$$= \lim_{n \to \infty} \left[\sum_{j=1}^n f(y(j))\{H(y(n)+) - H(y(n)-)\} + f(y)\{H(y) - H(y')\} \right]$$

$$= +\infty$$

where $y(n) < y' < y(n+1)$. It follows that we cannot have (66.29) for a strictly increasing sequence $\{y(n)\}$; and similarly for a strictly decreasing sequence, so that

$$H(x+) \neq H(x-)$$

at only a finite number of points of (a, b). Then Lemma 66.3 shows that H_1 is of bounded variation, and we have the function j. In Lemma 66.4 we can allow f to be unbounded in an X, since all but a finite number of points are of H_1-variation zero, and Lemma 66.5 follows for the wider class of f. If $j(x) \notin 0$ for an infinity of $x \in (a, b)$, there are either a strictly increasing sequence or a strictly decreasing sequence $\{y(n)\}$ tending to y, with $j(y(n)) \neq 0$, or both. Say, the first. We put $f = 0$ except for

$$f(y(n)) = n/j(y(n)) \qquad (n = 1, 2, \ldots)$$

$$\int_a^y f \, dj = \lim_{n \to \infty} \left\{ \int_a^{y(n)} + \int_{y(n)}^y \right\}$$

$$= \lim_{n \to \infty} \{f(y(n))j(y(n)) - f(a)j(a) + f(y)j(y) - f(y)j(y(n))\}$$

$$= \lim_{n \to \infty} n = +\infty$$

Similarly, for a strictly decreasing sequence, so that $j(x) \neq 0$ only for a finite number of points. Hence $H = H_1 + j$ is of bounded variation, and we have the necessity of the theorem. For the sufficiency, f is bounded almost everywhere since H is discontinuous at only a finite number of points, and the sufficiency in Theorem 66.1 gives the sufficiency here.

67. The Integrability of a Product of Functions in Lebesgue and Orlicz Spaces

In section 66 we have used the space of bounded Baire functions. Here we expand it to L_Φ, the smallest being L_∞, the space of all functions bounded except possibly in a set of μ-variation zero, where $\mu \geqslant 0$ is a fixed interval function for which 1 is integrable with respect to μ in elementary sets T_n ($n = 1, 2, \ldots$) with union T. If $T = [a, b]$, if μ has only a finite number of discontinuities, and if f is a Baire function bounded in $[a, b]\backslash X$ for some countable X, then $f \in L_\infty$. If

$$(67.1) \qquad \int_T f(x)\, d\mu_0$$

exists for all $f \in L_\infty$, then Theorem 66.2 shows that 1 is integrable with respect to μ_0 to a function H_0 of bounded variation, with only a finite number of discontinuities. Thus the limitation in the following theorem is reasonable.

THEOREM 67.1. *If $T = [a, b]$, the necessary and sufficient condition on μ_0, given continuous and of bounded variation, in order that (67.1) should exist for all $f \in L_\infty$, relative to a μ satisfying the conditions above, is that there is a function $k(t) \in L_1$ with $\mu_0 - k\mu$ of variation zero.*

Proof. The indefinite integral H_0 of 1 in T exists, and we can replace μ_0 by H_0, and H_0 is also of bounded variation. If its variation is $V \equiv V(H_0; \mathcal{A};.)$, then V is continuous since μ_0 is continuous, by Henstock (1963c), p. 53, Theorem 28.5, and p. 57, Theorem 30.1. Hence by Henstock (1963c), p. 77, Theorem 34.5,

$$H_0 = \int s\, dV, \qquad |s| \leqslant 1$$

371

where s is the derivative of H_0 relative to V, and (67.1) becomes

(67.2)
$$\int_a^b f(x)\, s(x)\, dV$$

Let X be a V-measurable set of μ-variation zero but with positive V-variation. Since V is continuous we can divide $[a, b]$ into smaller intervals, and so X into disjoint sets $X_1, X_2, \ldots$, each V-measurable, with positive V-variation and zero μ-variation. Let $f = 0$ in$\backslash X$, and

$$f(x) = 1/\{s(x)\, V(V; \mathcal{A}; [a, b]; X_n)\} \qquad (x \in X_n, n = 1, 2, \ldots)$$

Then $f \in L_\infty$, f is V-measurable, and

$$\int_a^b f(x)\, s(x)\, dV \geqslant \sum_{j=1}^\infty 1 = +\infty$$

Hence if $V(\mu; \mathcal{A}; E; X) = 0$ and X is V-measurable, then $V(V; \mathcal{A}; E; X) = 0$. The proof of Henstock (1963c), p. 77, Theorem 34.5, completes the proof.

After Theorem 67.1 it is now reasonable to replace (67.1) by

(67.3)
$$\int_T f(t)\, k(t)\, d\mu$$

where $(T, \mathcal{S}, \mathcal{A})$ is a decomposable division space, $\mu \geqslant 0$, 1 is integrable in elementary sets $T_n\, (n = 1, 2, \ldots)$ with union T, and k is μ-measurable.

THEOREM 67.2. *In order that $f(t)\, k(t)$ be integrable in T with respect to μ, for each $f \in L_\Psi$, it is necessary and sufficient that $k \in L_\Phi$.*

Proof. For sufficiency we use Theorem 65.2 (65.8). For the necessity we first replace f by $f/\mathrm{sgn}\, k$, also in L_Ψ, to show that $|f(t)k(t)|$ is integrable with respect to μ in T. We define

$$k_n(t) = \begin{cases} k(t) & (|k(t)| \leqslant n,\ t \in T_n) \\ 0 & (\textit{otherwise}) \end{cases}$$

By Theorem 65.2 (65.7), $k_n \in L_\Phi$, and by (65.8),

$$y_n(f) \equiv \int_T k_n(t)\, f(t)\, d\mu$$

372

is a bounded, and so continuous, linear functional on L_Ψ. Further, in order to be integrable, $k(t)f(t)$, and so $k(t)$, have to be finite almost everywhere. Hence, almost everywhere,

$$\lim_{n \to \infty} k_n(t) = k(t), \quad |k_n(t)f(t)| \leqslant |k(t)f(t)|$$

and by our form of Lebesgue's majorized convergence theorem,

$$\lim_{n \to \infty} y_n(f) = \int_T k(t)f(t)\, d\mu, \, = y(f)$$

say. By Theorem 65.5, L_Ψ is complete, so that by Theorem 34.1 there is a constant M independent of $n, f \in L_\Psi$, such that

$$|y_n(f)| \leqslant M \, \|f\|_\Psi$$

We now take f with $\|f\|_\Psi^* \leqslant 1$, so that by Theorem 41.4 (41.10), $\|f\|_\Psi \leqslant 2$, and

$$|y_n(f)| \leqslant 2M, \quad |y(f)| \leqslant 2M, \quad \|k\|_\Phi = \sup \int_T |k(t)f(t)|\, d\mu \leqslant 2M$$

on replacing f by $f/\mathrm{sgn}\, k$. Hence $k \in L_\Phi$.

There is a similar theorem for L_p, L_q spaces, that is included in this theorem.

68. The Integrability of a Product of Functions, one of which is Integrable

We now turn to the space $\mathscr{E}\mathscr{I}$ of integrals $IR(f; s)$ of section 63, and the corresponding space $\mathscr{D}(T)$ of integrable functions f with respect to a fixed continuous $\mu_1 \geqslant 0$. For simplicity we take T as the real line or a subset of it, so that the definitions simplify.

Let $T = [a, b]$, a finite or infinite interval, and write

$$IR(f; s) \equiv \int_a^s f(t)\, d\mu_1$$

where $\mu_1 \geqslant 0$ is a fixed continuous function of intervals, the integral being a generalized Riemann integral using the integration of *Ex. 43.3* or *Ex. 43.9*, which correspond respectively to the special and general integrals of Denjoy over T. The space $\mathcal{D}(T)$ is the space of all f for which $IR(f; b)$ exists, so that $IR(f; s)$ exists for all s in $a < s \leqslant b$ (Theorem 44.5) and is continuous in s. (For *Ex. 43.3* see Henstock (1963c), p. 33, Theorem 21.2 (21.12; 21.13) as μ_1 is continuous.)

Let μ be an arbitrary interval function of bounded variation on T for which 1 is integrable in T. Then the function $f(t; s)$, equal to $f(t)$ for all $t \in [a, s]$, and 0 otherwise, is easily proved integrable with respect to $\mu_1 \cdot \mu$, where μ_1 is connected to t, μ to s, for each $f \in \mathcal{D}(T)$, and Fubini's theorem holds. (For *Ex. 43.3* see Henstock (1963c), pp. 106–11.) Thus (63.2; 63.3) hold for the case of *Ex. 43.3*, and there are similar proofs for *Ex. 43.9*.

We cannot use a Lebesgue or Orlicz norm on $\mathcal{D}(T)$ as the space is too large, and contains functions for which such a norm does not exist. However, we can use the norm $\|f\|^* = \|IR(f; .)\|_\infty$, using the space $\mathcal{QI}$ of functions $r(s) = IR(f; s)$, for all $f \in \mathcal{D}(T)$. By (63.2), $\mathcal{QI}$ is a subspace of the space $\mathcal{Q}(T)$ of continuous functions on T. But, as is pointed out in section 63, $\mathcal{QI}$ is of the first category in $\mathcal{Q}(T)$ and in itself, and the ordinary Banach–Steinhaus methods will not work. However, Sargent (1953) points out that $\mathcal{QI}$ is a β-space (see *Ex. 31.1*).

The following theorem has affinities with Theorem 63.2, which in this case says that every continuous linear functional $\mathcal{F}$ on $\mathcal{D}(T)$ has the form

$$\mathcal{F}(f) = \int_T f(t)\, g(t)\, d\mu_1$$

for some g of bounded variation. Note that by Theorem 44.11 it would be enough to say that g is *EBV*, i.e. there is a function $g_1(t)$ of bounded variation on T, such that $\{g(t) - g_1(t)\}\, \mu_1$ has variation zero.

THEOREM 68.1. (Sargent (1948)) *In order that $k(t)f(t)$ is integrable in T for all $f(t)$ integrable in T, both with respect to μ_1, it is necessary and sufficient that k is EBV.*

Proof. Since $L_1 \subseteq \mathcal{D}(T)$, Theorem 67.2 gives $k \in L_\infty$. Thus we can

374

use the notation of section 41, putting

$$\text{ess-sup}_{U} k(t) \equiv \inf_{h} \sup_{U} h(t), \quad \text{ess-inf}_{U} k(t) \equiv \sup_{h} \inf_{U} h(t)$$

for all h for which $\{k(t)-h(t)\}\,\mu_1$ is of variation zero in the interval U.

Let $\{t(n)\}$ be an arbitrary strictly increasing sequence in $[a, b]$, and

$$M_n \equiv \text{ess-sup}_{U} k(t), \quad m_n \equiv \text{ess-inf}_{U} k(t)$$

$$(U = [t(n), t(n+1)], \quad n = 1, 2, \ldots).$$

Then for each n there are distinct μ_1-measurable subsets X_n, Y_n, of $(t(n), t(n+1))$ of equal positive μ_1-variation v_n, such that

$$k(t) \geqslant \tfrac{3}{4}M_n + \tfrac{1}{4}m_n \quad (t \in X_n),$$

$$k(t) \leqslant \tfrac{1}{4}M_n + \tfrac{3}{4}m_n \quad (t \in Y_n)$$

Let us put

$$t_0 = \lim_{n \to \infty} t(n), \quad N_n = \sum_{j=1}^{n} (M_j - m_j)$$

$$(n = 1, 2, \ldots) \quad (\text{supposed} > 0)$$

$$f(t) = \begin{cases} (v_n N_n)^{-1} & (t \in X_n, n = 1, 2, \ldots) \\ -(v_n N_n)^{-1} & (t \in Y_n, n = 1, 2, \ldots) \\ 0 & (\text{otherwise}) \end{cases}$$

Then f is μ_1-measurable and bounded in $[a, c]$, for each c in $t(1) < c < t_0$, and for $t(n) \leqslant c \leqslant t(n+1)$,

$$\left| \int_a^c f\,d\mu_1 \right| \leqslant \left| \sum_{j=1}^{n-1} \int_{t(j)}^{t(j+1)} f\,d\mu_1 \right| + \left| \int_{t(n)}^{c} f\,d\mu_1 \right|$$

$$\leqslant \left| \sum_{j=1}^{n-1} (v_j N_j)^{-1}(v_j - v_j) \right| + 2(v_n N_n)^{-1} v_n = 2N_n^{-1}$$

We now use the integrability by continuity property of Denjoy integrals as in Henstock (1963c), p. 113, Theorem 46.1, the property that ensures that $\mathcal{C\!\mathcal{A}}$ is a β-space. If $N_n \to +\infty$ as $n \to \infty$, then f is integrable in $[a, b]$ with respect to μ_1, and $f \in \mathcal{D}(T)$. On the other hand,

$$\int_a^{t(n+1)} fk \, d\mu_1 = \sum_{j=1}^n \int_{t(j)}^{t(j+1)} fk \, d\mu_1 \geqslant \sum_{j=1}^n v_j(v_j N_j)^{-1} \{(\tfrac{3}{4} M_j + \tfrac{1}{4} m_j)$$

$$- (\tfrac{1}{4} M_j + \tfrac{3}{4} m_j)\} = \tfrac{1}{2} \sum_{j=1}^n N_j^{-1}(M_j - m_j)$$

$$= \tfrac{1}{2} \sum_{j=1}^n (N_j - N_{j-1}) N_j^{-1} \qquad \text{(where } N_0 = 0\text{)},$$

$$\sum_{j=r}^n (N_j - N_{j-1}) N_j^{-1} \geqslant (N_n - N_r) N_n^{-1} = 1 - N_r \cdot N_n^{-1} > \tfrac{1}{2}$$

$$(n \geqslant n_0(r)).$$

Hence for $r = 1$ the sum tends to infinity with n, contradicting the requirement that fk is to be integrable with respect to μ_1 in T.

Hence $\{N_n\}$ is bounded as $n \to \infty$. Similarly for each strictly decreasing sequence in $[a, b]$. The theorem follows from these results as in Lemma 66.3.

For the sufficiency we need only use Henstock (1963c), p. 99, Theorem 40.2, or the analogue for the case of *Ex. 43.9*, for finite intervals and then take limits.

It might be possible to use the fact that $\mathcal{QA}$ is a β-space to prove directly that

$$\mathcal{F}(f) = \int_a^b kf \, d\mu_1$$

is a continuous linear functional on $\mathcal{D}(T)$. This result follows from Theorem 68.1 on integrating by parts (Henstock (1963c), p. 69 for *Ex. 43.3* with $b - a < \infty$). For if k_1 is of bounded variation with $(k - k_1)\mu_1$ of variation zero,

$$\mathcal{F}(f) = \int_a^b k_1 f \, d\mu_1 = \int_a^b k_1 d \left(\int_a^t f \, d\mu_1 \right) = k_1(b) \int_a^b f \, d\mu_1$$

$$- \int_a^b IR(f; s) \, dk_1(s),$$

$$|\mathcal{F}(f)| \leqslant \|f\|^*(|k_1(b)| + V(k_1; \mathcal{A}; T)),$$

$$\text{norm } (\mathcal{F}) \leqslant |k_1(b)| + V(k_1; \mathcal{A}; T)$$

By Theorem 63.2, for some g of bounded variation, with $g(b) = 0$,

$$\int_c^b kf \, d\mu_1 = (\mathcal{F}(f)) = \int_a^b gf \, d\mu_1, \quad \text{norm}\,((\mathcal{F}) = V(g; \mathcal{A}; T)$$

Since μ_1 is continuous we can choose f as the characteristic function of an arbitrary elementary set E in $[a, b]$, to obtain by Theorem 44.11,

$$\int_E (k - g) \, d\mu_1 = 0, \quad V((k - g)\mu_1; \mathcal{A}; T) = 0,$$

$$V(\mu_1; \mathcal{A}; T; X) = 0$$

where X is the set where $k \neq g$. Thus $k = g$ almost everywhere, g is a k_1 with $k_1(b) = 0$, and as norm $(\mathcal{F})$ is the variation of g we have

$$\text{norm}\,((\mathcal{F}) = \inf\,(|k_1(b)| + V(k_1; \mathcal{A}; [a, b]))$$

the inf being taken over all $k_1 = k$ almost everywhere, it being attained for $k_1 = g$. Sargent (1950) denotes this infimum by a symbol like $V_e(k; \mathcal{A}; [a, b])$, the *essential variation of k over* $[a, b]$.

The Cauchy–Lebesgue integral lies between the Lebesgue and Denjoy integrals over $[0, \infty)$. A function f is *Cauchy–Lebesgue integrable with respect to μ_1 in* $[0, \infty)$, if f and $|f|$ are integrable with respect to μ_1 on $[0, a]$, for each $a > 0$, and if there exists

$$\lim_{a \to \infty} \int_0^a f \, d\mu_1$$

We then write $f \in \mathcal{CL}\,[0, \infty)$

THEOREM 68.2 (*Sargent (1952), p. 412, Theorem 3, with $\lambda = 0$; Lorentz (1947), p. 258). In order that $fk \in \mathcal{CL}\,[0, \infty)$ for each $f \in \mathcal{CL}$ $[0, \infty)$ it is necessary and sufficient that there is a $b > 0$ such that k is essentially bounded in $[0, b]$ (i.e. $k \in L_\infty\,[0, b]$), and that k is of essentially bounded variation in $[b, \infty)$.*

Proof. For the necessity we use unbounded sequences $\{t(n)\}$ and follow the proof of Theorem 68.1. If there is no such $b > 0$, then we can have $N_n \to \infty$, so that the constructed $f \in \mathcal{CL}\,[0, \infty)$, but $fk \notin \mathcal{CL}\,[0, \infty)$. For the sufficiency, $fk \in L\,[0, a]$ for each $a > 0$. If k_1 is of bounded variation in $[b, \infty)$ with $k = k_1$ almost everywhere, then as in the discussion after Theorem 68.1, for $c > a \geqslant b$,

$$\left| \int_0^c fk \, d\mu_1 - \int_0^a fk \, d\mu_1 \right| = \left| \int_a^c fk_1 \, d\mu_1 \right|$$

$$\leqslant \sup_{v > a} \left| \int_a^v f \, d\mu_1 \right| \{|k_1(b)| + V(k_1; \mathcal{A}; [b, \infty))\}$$

and we have a fundamental sequence as $f \in \mathcal{QL} \, [0, \infty)$. Hence the result.

69. Integrability Conditions with a Variable Integrand

We now study conditions to be imposed on $k(t)$ in order that

(69.1) $$y(f) \equiv \int_a^b k(t) \, df(t)$$

should exist for all $f \in BV \, [a, b]$, the space of functions of bounded variation on $[a, b]$. In summability theorems using such integrals (e.g. Lorentz (1947)), the integral is usually taken to be a Riemann–Stieltjes integral, but here we take it to be a generalized Riemann integral. In a sense this is the dual problem to that considered in section 66, where f is fixed and k varies.

THEOREM 69.1. *If (69.1) exists for all $f \in BV \, [a, b]$, then $k(t)$ is bounded, and if $\|k\|_\infty$ denotes the bound, then*

(69.2) $\quad |y(f)| \leqslant \|k\|_\infty \, V(f; \mathcal{A}; [a, b])$, $\quad$ norm $(y) = \|k\|_\infty$,

while k is f-measurable for each $f \in BV[a, b]$. For example, k can be a bounded Baire function, but there are bounded non-Baire k.

Proof. Let $\{t(n)\}$ be a strictly increasing sequence in $[a, b]$, and put

$$f(t) = \sum \{a(n) : t(n) < t\}, \quad \sum_{n=1}^{\infty} |a(n)| < \infty$$

Then as in Lemmas 66.1, 66.2,

$$y(f) = \sum_{n=1}^{\infty} k(t(n)) \, a(n)$$

The series is convergent for all *absolutely* convergent series $\sum\limits_{n=1}^{\infty} |a(n)|$, so that we cannot use the lemma of Abel and Hadamard (Theorem 55.4). If $k(t(n))$ is unbounded as $n \to \infty$, then for strictly increasing integers $\{n_j\}$,

$$\left| k(t(n_j)) \right| > 2^j$$

and $y(f)$ does not exist for the absolutely convergent series with

$$a(n_j) = 2^{-j} \quad (j = 1, 2, \ldots), \quad a(n) = 0 \quad \textit{(otherwise)}$$

Hence $\{k(t(n))\}$ is bounded. Similarly for each strictly decreasing sequence in $[a, b]$. Thus to prove k bounded we need only use continued bisection. Then the first part of (69.2) follows easily. For the second part let f have a jump 1 at a point t in $[a, b)$. Then

$$y(f) = k(t), \quad |k(t)| = |y(f)| \leqslant \text{norm } (y) \cdot V\,(f; \mathscr{A}; [a, b])$$

$$= \text{norm } (y), \quad \|k\|_\infty \leqslant \text{norm } (y)$$

There is equality because of the first part.

For an example of a bounded non-Baire k that is f-measurable for each $f \in BV[a, b]$ we need only take the characteristic function of an analytic, but not Borel, set.

16

INTEGRAL SUMMABILITY RESULTS WITH A FIXED INTEGRATOR

70. Summability to Zero

In this chapter we study integral summability results of the following types.

$$(70.1) \quad y(f; s) = \int_0^\infty k(s; t) f(t) \, d\mu \to \lim_{t \to \infty} f(t) \qquad (s \to \infty)$$

$$(70.2) \qquad\qquad y(f; s) \to \int_0^\infty f(t) \, d\mu \qquad (s \to \infty)$$

Taking $f(t) = 0 \, (t > u)$ in (70.1), the limit is 0, and an auxiliary result appears, namely,

$$(70.3) \qquad y(f; s) = \int_T k(s, t) f(t) \, d\mu \to 0 \qquad (s \to \infty)$$

where T has been generalized from $[0, \infty)$ to a general decomposable division space. We study this problem in the present section, making it more definite by supposing that $\mu \geqslant 0$ with 1 integrable in elementary sets $T_n \, (n = 1, 2, \ldots)$, with union T. We also suppose that f lies in some space $\mathcal{F}$ of functions, and we then have to determine the properties of $k(s; t)$ in order that (70.3) is true for all $f \in \mathcal{F}$.

Lebesgue (1909) uses $T = [a, b]$ and his own integral, and shows that his work includes earlier work on Fourier–Dirichlet (p. 86), Poisson (p. 87), Fejér (p. 88), and Weierstrass (p. 90) integrals. Perhaps much of Lebesgue's work on his integral resulted from his interest in such singular integrals.

THEOREM 70.1 (*Agnew* (1939), *p.* 704, *Theorem* 6.1, *for* L_∞). *If, for*

380

all $f \in L_\Phi$,

(70.4) $\displaystyle \sup_s |y(f; s)| = \sup_s \left| \int_T k(s, t) f(t) \, d\mu \right| < \infty$

then there are finite constants M, N, such that

(70.5) $\|k(s; .)\|_\Psi < \infty$ (all s), $\displaystyle \sup_{s > N} \|k(s; .)\|_\Psi = M$

and conversely.

Proof. By Theorem 65.2 (65.8), (70.5) is sufficient for (70.4). To prove it necessary we note first that $y(f; s)$ is to exist for each s, and each $f \in L_\Phi$. By Theorem 67.2 the norm of the continuous linear functional $y(f; s)$ is $\|k(s; .)\|_\Psi < \infty$, for each s.

THEOREM 70.2. If we have (70.3) for all $f \in L_\Phi$, then (70.5) is true, with

(70.6) $\displaystyle \lim_{s \to \infty} \int_T ch(X; .) k(s, t) \, d\mu = 0$

for each T_n and for each μ-measurable set $X \subseteq T_n$; and conversely.

Proof. For the necessity, (70.6) follows on taking $f = ch(X; .) \in L_\Phi$, since $X \subseteq T_n$ is μ-measurable. For the sufficiency we see from (70.6) that (70.3) is true for all $f \in L_\Phi$ that take only a finite number of values, and are zero in $\backslash T_n$ for some integer n. By Theorem 47.2, such functions are dense in L_Φ, with norm $\| . \|_\Phi$, so that by (70.5) the result is true from

$$|y(f; s) - y(f_n; s)| = |y(f - f_n; s)| \leqslant \|f - f_n\|_\Phi \cdot \|k(s; .)\|_\Psi$$
$$\leqslant M \|f - f_n\|_\Phi$$
$$\lim_{s \to \infty} \sup |y(f; s)| = \lim_{s \to \infty} \sup |y(f; s) - y(f_n; s)| \leqslant M \|f - f_n\|_\Phi$$

Hence the result.

LEMMA 70.1. The space $\mathcal{U}$ of all characteristic functions $ch(X; .)$ of μ-measurable sets X, is complete for the norm $V(X) \equiv V(\mu; \mathcal{A}; T; X)$.
Here we have

$$\varrho(X, Y) \equiv V((X \backslash Y) \cup (Y \backslash X)) \equiv V(d(X, Y))$$

381

Proof. Let $\{ch(X_n; .)\}$ be a fundamental sequence in $\mathcal{V}$. Then, given $\varepsilon > 0$, there is an integer N for which

$$V\big(d(X_m, X_n)\big) < \varepsilon \qquad (m, n \geqslant N)$$

When $\varepsilon = 2^{-j}$ let $N = N(j)$, and put

$$X = \limsup_{j \to \infty} X_{N(j)} = \bigcap_{k=1}^{\infty} \bigcup_{j=k}^{\infty} X_{N(j)}$$

Then $\quad X \backslash X_{N(j)} \subseteq \bigcup_{k=j+1}^{\infty} X_{N(k)} \backslash X_{N(j)} \subseteq \bigcup_{k=j+1}^{\infty} X_{N(k)} \backslash X_{N(k-1)},$

$$V(X \backslash X_{N(j)}) \leqslant \sum_{k=j}^{\infty} 2^{-k} = 2^{1-j}, \quad X_{N(j)} \backslash X \subseteq \bigcup_{k=j+1}^{\infty} X_{N(k-1)} \backslash X_{N(k)},$$

$$V(X_{N(j)} \backslash X) \leqslant \sum_{k=j}^{\infty} 2^{-k} = 2^{1-j}, \quad V\big(d(X, X_{N(j)})\big) \leqslant 2^{2-j}$$

so that X is the limit of $\{X_{N(j)}\}$ in the given norm, and hence the limit of the whole sequence since it is fundamental. Hence the result.

THEOREM 70.3 (*Lebesgue* (1909), *p.* 57) *If* $T = T_1 = [a, b]$, *and if* $L_\Phi = L_\infty$, *then* (70.6) *can be replaced by*

$$(70.7) \qquad \lim_{s \to \infty} \int_a^b ch([u, v]; t)\, k(s; t)\, d\mu = 0$$

for each fixed u, v *in* $a \leqslant u < v \leqslant b$;

$$(70.8) \qquad \int_a^b ch(X; .)\, |k(s; t)|\, d\mu \leqslant M(N; \varepsilon)$$

for all $s \geqslant N$ *and all* μ-*measurable sets* $X \subseteq [a, b]$ *with*

$$V(X) \equiv V(\mu; \mathcal{A}; [a, b]; X) < \varepsilon,$$

(70.9) *where for some function* $N = N(\varepsilon)$, $M(N(\varepsilon), \varepsilon) \to 0$ *as* $\varepsilon \to 0$.

Proof. To show that (70.7; 70.8; 70.9) are sufficient for (70.6), we use Theorem 47.1 and Henstock (1963c), Theorem 31.2 (31.9), p. 61, to prove that if $X \subseteq [a, b]$ is μ-measurable, then given $\varepsilon > 0$, there is an elementary set $E \subseteq [a, b]$ with $V\big(d(X, E)\big) < \varepsilon$. Then by (70.8), for $s \geqslant N$,

$$\left| y\big(ch(X;.);\, s\big) - y\big(ch(E;.);\, s\big) \right| = \left| y\big(ch(X;.) - ch(E;.);\, s\big) \right|$$

$$\leqslant \int_a^b ch\big(d(X, E)\big)\, |k(s;\, t)|\, d\mu \leqslant M(N;\, \varepsilon)$$

As E is a finite union of closed intervals, (70.7; 70.9) complete the proof of (70.6) in this case.

Conversely, (70.7) follows from (70.6), while $M(1;\, \varepsilon)$ is finite from (70.5), since here, $L_{\psi} = L_1$. Thus there remain (70.8; 70.9).

Let $\mathcal{O}$ be the set of characteristic functions of μ-measurable sets X, and let $\mathcal{O}_N$ be the set of $f \in \mathcal{O}$ with $|y(f;\, s)| < \tfrac{1}{4}\varepsilon\, (\text{all } s \geqslant N)$. By (70.6),

$$\mathcal{O} = \bigcup_{N=1}^{\infty} \mathcal{O}_N$$

while by the absolute continuity of the integral (Henstock (1963c), p. 98, Theorem 40.1), each $\mathcal{O}_N$ is the intersection for $s \geqslant N$ of closed sets, and so is closed. Further, by Lemma 70.1, $\mathcal{O}$ is a complete metric space. Hence for some integer N, $\mathcal{O}_N$ contains a sphere with centre $f_0 \in \mathcal{O}$ and radius $\delta > 0$, where f_0 is the characteristic function of some μ-measurable set X_0. Taking

$$X \subseteq [a, b], \quad ch(X;.) \in \mathcal{O}, \quad V(X) < \delta, \quad X_1 \equiv X \cup X_0,$$

$$X_2 \equiv X_0 \backslash X$$

we then have

$$d(X_0, X_1) = X \backslash X_0 \subseteq X, \quad d(X_0, X_2) = X \cap X_0 \subseteq X,$$

$$V\big(d(X_0, X_j)\big) < \delta \quad (j = 1, 2)$$

$$ch(X;\, x) = ch(X_1;\, x) - ch(X_2;\, x) = f_1 - f_2,$$

$$f_j \in S(f_0, \delta) \quad (j = 1, 2)$$

$$\left| y\big(ch(X;.);\, s\big) \right| \leqslant |y(f_1;\, s)| + |y(f_2;\, s)| \leqslant \tfrac{1}{2}\varepsilon \quad (s \geqslant N)$$

Finally, for real k, we need only take $X_3(s)$, $X_4(s)$ as the respective sets where $k(s;\, t)$ is positive and is negative, and

$$\int_a^b ch(X;\, x)\, |k(s;\, t)|\, d\mu \leqslant \sum_{j=3,\, 4} \left| \int_a^b ch\big(X \cap X_j(s)\big)\, k(s;\, t)\, d\mu \right| \leqslant \varepsilon$$

For complex k we take real and imaginary parts separately. Hence (70.8; 70.9). For this method of proof I have followed Zygmund (1959), p. 167, proof of Theorem (9.13).

THEOREM 70.4 (*Lebesgue* (1909), L_1 *on p. 52, L_2 on p. 55). If, for all $f \in L_\Phi \neq L_\infty$, we have* (70.3), *with $T = T_1 = [a, b]$, then* (70.6) *can be replaced by* (70.7).

Proof. If $\|g\|_\Psi^* \leqslant 1$, then by Theorem 41.4 (41.10), $\|g\|_\Psi \leqslant 2$, so that if $X \subseteq [a, b]$ is a μ-measurable set, and if $\Phi(\alpha) < \infty$,

$$\left| \int_a^b \alpha \cdot ch(X; .) g \, d\mu \right| \leqslant \|\alpha(ch(X; .))\|_\Phi^* \cdot \|g\|_\Psi \leqslant 2\Phi(\alpha) V(X),$$

$$\|ch(X; .)\|_\Phi \leqslant 2\Phi(\alpha) V(X)/\alpha$$

Thus, to prove sufficiency of (70.7), we begin as in Theorem 70.3,

$$|y(ch(X; .); s) - y(ch(E; .); s)| \leqslant \int_a^b ch(d(X, E)) |k(s; t)| \, d\mu$$

$$\leqslant \|ch(d(X, E); .)\|_\Phi \int_a^b \Psi(|k(s; t)|) \, d\mu \leqslant M \cdot 2\Phi(\alpha) V(d(X, E))/\alpha \to 0$$

$$(\varepsilon \to 0)$$

Then (70.7) gives (70.6), remembering (70.5). Conversely, (70.7) follows from (70.6).

Lebesgue (1909) also considers simply discontinuous functions on p. 59.

THEOREM 70.5. *In* Theorem 70.4 *we can replace $[a, b]$ by $[a, \infty)$, with $T_n = [a, n]$.*

Proof. After Theorem 70.4 we need only prove the sufficiency of (70.5; 70.7), with all u, v in $a \leqslant u < v$. If $\|f\|_\Phi^* < \infty$, then

$$\left| \int_u^\infty f \cdot k(s; .) \, d\mu \right| \leqslant \int_u^\infty \Phi(|f|) \, d\mu \cdot \|k(s; .)\|_\Psi \leqslant M \int_u^\infty \Phi(|f|) \, d\mu \to 0$$

$$(u \to \infty)$$

Hence by Theorem 70.4. A similar result holds when $L_\Phi = c_0$.

Ex. 70.1. If $f \in L_1$, $k(s; t) = e^{ist}$, prove the Riemann–Lebesgue theorem that

$$\lim_{s \to \infty} \int_0^\infty e^{ist} f(t) \, dt = 0$$

$$\left(\text{Use Theorem 70.4,} \int_u^v e^{ist} \, dt = \frac{e^{isv} - e^{isu}}{is} \to 0 \right)$$

71. Summability to the Limit of a Function

Next we consider (70.1). Agnew (1939) allows the right side to be $a(f) \cdot \lim_{t \to \infty} f(t)$, for some constant $a(f)$ depending on f *ab initio*, in his Theorem 9.2, p. 719. Hill (1936) replaces $[0, \infty)$, by $[0, \eta]$, with $l = \lim_{t \to \eta -} f(t)$ on the right. Obvious modifications can be made to theorems to include this point of view. M. M. Day (1939) replaces $[0, \infty)$ by an n-dimensional interval, the results including part of Parker (1950). Here, for simplicity, we restrict the discussion to $f[0, \infty)$.

THEOREM 71.1. (*Agnew* (1939), *Theorem* 9.4, *pp.* 720–721). *If, for all* $f \in L_\infty$ *for which* $l = \lim_{t \to \infty} f(t)$ *exists, we have*

(71.1) $\quad \lim_{s \to \infty} y(f; s) \equiv \lim_{s \to \infty} \int_0^\infty k(s; t) f(t) \, d\mu = a(f) \cdot \lim_{t \to \infty} f(t)$

for some constant $a(f)$ *depending possibly on* f, *then*

(71.2) $\qquad \| k(s; .) \|_1 \equiv \int_0^\infty | k(s; t) | \, d\mu < \infty \qquad (each\ s)$

(71.3) $\qquad \qquad \limsup_{s \to \infty} \| k(s; .) \|_1 < \infty$

(71.4) $\qquad \qquad \lim_{s \to \infty} \int_0^\infty k(s; t) \, d\mu = b$

(71.5) *for each* $c > 0$, *and each* μ-*measurable set* $X \subseteq [0, c]$,

$$\lim_{s \to \infty} \int_0^\infty k(s; t) \, ch\,(X; t) \, d\mu = 0$$

Alternatively to (71.5), *we can have the following:*

(71.6)   *for each fixed u, v in* $0 \leqslant u < v$

$$\lim_{s \to \infty} \int_u^v k(s; t) \, d\mu = 0$$

(71.7)   *there is a function* $N(\varepsilon)$ *of all* $\varepsilon > 0$, *such that if*

$$M(N; \varepsilon) \equiv \sup \int_0^\infty |k(s; t)| \, ch \, (X; t) \, d\mu$$

for all $s \geqslant N$, *all bounded* μ-*measurable sets* X *with* $V(X) \equiv V(\mu; \mathcal{A};$
$[0, \infty); X) < \varepsilon$, *then* $M(N(\varepsilon), \varepsilon) \to 0$ *with* ε.
If $a(f) = 0$ *always, we can omit* (71.4).
Conversely, if k *satisfies* (71.2) *to* (71.8), *then* (71.1) *occurs with*
$a(f) = b$ *for all such* f.

Proof. All except (71.4) have been proved necessary in section 70, while we can take $f_1(t) = 1$ (*all t*) to obtain (71.4) with $b = a(f_1)$. Conversely, if l is the limit of f, then, given $\varepsilon > 0$, there is a u with

$$|f(t) - l| \leqslant \varepsilon \qquad (t \geqslant u),$$

$$\left| y(f; s) - l \int_0^\infty k(s; t) \, d\mu \right| = |y(f - l; s)| \leqslant \left| \int_0^u \right| + \varepsilon M,$$

$$l \int_0^\infty k(s; t) \, d\mu \to bl$$

A result similar to the above, and new except when $L_\Phi = L_1$, is as follows.

THEOREM 71.2. *If, for all* $f \in L_\Phi \neq L_\infty$ *for which* $l = \lim_{t \to \infty} f(t)$
exists, we have (71.1), *then* (71.4; 71.6) *are true, with*

(71.8) $\|k(s; .)\|_\Psi < \infty$ (*each s*), $\limsup_{s \to \infty} \|k(s; .)\|_\Psi < \infty$

and conversely.
The various details have already been proved.
Ex. 71.1. (Agnew (1939), pp. 702–3, Theorem 5.3). Neither

(71.9) $\lim_{s \to \infty} k(s; t) = 0$ $(t > 0)$,   nor

386

(71.10) $$\lim_{s \to \infty} \int_0^u |k(s; t)| \, dt = 0 \qquad (\text{fixed } u > 0)$$

is necessary in Theorem 71.1, nor in Theorem 71.2 for $L_\Phi = L_1$. (Take

$$k(s; t) = \begin{cases} e^{ist}/(1+t^2) & (0 \leqslant t < s) \\ 1 & (s \leqslant t < s+1) \\ e^{is(t-1)}/\{1+(t-1)^2\} & (s+1 \leqslant t) \end{cases}$$

If $f \in L_1[0, h]$, $\limsup\limits_{t \to \infty} |f(t)| < \infty$, then $y(f; s)$ exists. For each $s \geqslant 0$,

$$\|k(s; .)\|_\infty \leqslant 1, \quad \|k(s; .)\|_1 = \int_0^\infty \frac{dt}{1+t^2} + \int_s^{s+1} 1 \, dt = \frac{\pi}{2}+1$$

while for each $s > u > 0$, by *Ex. 70.1* (the Riemann–Lebesgue theorem),

$$\int_0^u k(s; t) \, dt = \int_0^u \frac{e^{ist}}{1+t^2} \, dt \to 0 \qquad (s \to \infty);$$

$$\int_0^\infty k(s; t) \, dt = 1 + \int_0^\infty \frac{e^{ist}}{1+t^2} \, dt \to 1$$

so that since $\mu(a, b) = b-a$ is continuous, k satisfies the conditions of Theorems 71.1, 71.2 for $\|.\|_1$. But this k does not satisfy (71.9; 71.10).

72. Convergence Factors in Integrals of Lebesgue and Denjoy Depth

This section deals with (70.2). Clearly we have to assume the integrability of f, and first we also assume the integrability of $|f|$, both relative to $\mu \geqslant 0$ over T. Then we have

(72.1) $$\int_T \{k(s; t) - 1\} f(t) \, d\mu \to 0$$

so that we need only rewrite the results of section 70 in the main.

THEOREM 72.1. *In order that (70.2) holds for all $f \in L_\Phi$, it is neces-*

387

sary and sufficient that

(72.2) $\|k(s;.)-1\|_{\Psi} < \infty,$ $\displaystyle\limsup_{s \to \infty} \|k(s;.)-1\|_{\Psi} < \infty$

(72.3) $\displaystyle\lim_{s \to \infty} \int_T ch(X;.)\, k(s;t)\, d\mu = \int_T ch(X;.)\, d\mu$

for each T_n over which 1 is integrable, with T the union of the T_n, and for each μ-measurable set $X \subseteq T_n$. The 1 in (72.2) can be omitted if $T = T_1$.

THEOREM 72.2. *When $T = [0, \infty)$, $T_n = [0, n)$, then (72.3) can be replaced by*

(72.4) $\displaystyle\lim_{s \to \infty} \int_0^\infty k(s;t)\, ch\,([u, v];.)\, d\mu = \int_0^\infty ch\,([u, v];.)\, d\mu$

$$(each\ 0 \leqslant u < v),$$

when $L_\Phi \neq L_\infty$. (Sargent (1955), p. 405, for $L_\Phi = L_1$.) There is the usual addition when $L_\Phi = L_\infty$.

Results involving Denjoy type integrals give something more than section 70.

THEOREM 72.3 (*Sargent (1953), p. 450, Theorem 6*). *In order that $y(f; s)$ be defined for $s \geqslant 0$ and f integrable in $[0, \infty)$, with (70.2), it is necessary and sufficient that, for each s, $k(s;t)$ is of essentially bounded variation for $t \in [0, \infty)$, with essential variation $V_e(s) = \lim_{u \to \infty} V_e(k(s;.),\ \mathcal{A},\ [0, u])$, V_e after the 'lim' sign denoting the essential variation over $[0, u]$; with (72.5)*

$$\sup_{s \to \infty} V_e(s) < \infty$$

and with (72.3).

Proof. In section 68 it is proved that if

$$y\,(f; s; u) \equiv \int_0^u k(s;t)f(t)\, d\mu_1,$$

norm $(y) = V_e(k(s;.),\ \mathcal{A},\ [0, u]) \equiv \inf\,(|k_1(u)| + V(k_1;\ \mathcal{A};\ [0, u]))$ the inf being over all $k_1 = k$ almost everywhere. Thus it is easy to see that for $y(f; s) = \lim_{u \to \infty} y(f; s; u)$, the norm is $V_e(s)$, and we have (72.5) from Theorem 34.1 (34.3). Conversely, we need only show that step functions are dense in the space of integrable f, which follows from (47.4) with $f = f_j$. The proof then proceeds as usual.

THEOREM 72.4. (*Sargent* (1955), p. 407, Theorem 1) *In order that, for all $f \in \mathcal{D}\ [0, \infty)$ $y(f; s)$ is defined and measurable for all $s \geqslant 0$, it is necessary and sufficient that $V_e(k(s; .))$ is finite for each $s \geqslant 0$, and that* (72.6)

$$k_2(s; t) = \text{ess} \lim_{u \to 0+} k(s; t+u)$$

is measurable for $s \geqslant 0$, for each fixed $t \geqslant 0$. As usual, 'ess lim' means that we let $t+u \to t+$ in a set X with $\backslash X$ of μ-variation zero. We also need μ continuous.

Proof. For the necessity of (72.6), let $t \geq 0$. Then as k is of essentially bounded variation, if H is the integral of 1 with respect to μ,

$$
\begin{aligned}
k_2(s; t) &= \lim_{u \to 0+} \int_t^{t+u} k(s; v)\, d\mu / H(t, t+u) \\
&= \lim_{u \to 0+} y\big(ch([t, t+u]; .); s\big) / H(t, t+u)
\end{aligned}
$$

the numerator of the last fraction being given measurable in s. Hence, taking $u = 1/n$, $n = 1, 2, \ldots$, $k_2(s; t)$ is measurable in s for each fixed $t \geqslant 0$. Conversely, by Henstock (1963c), p. 80, Theorem 35.3, as in the proof of p. 78, Theorem 35.1 (35.3), $k(s; t) = k_2(s; t)$ almost everywhere in t, so that as a function of bounded variation is Riemann integrable relative to the continuous μ,

$$\int_u^v k(s; t)\, d\mu = \int_u^v k_2(s; t)\, d\mu$$

$$= \lim_{n \to \infty} \sum_{j=1}^n k_2\big(s; u+j(v-u)/n\big)\, H(u+(j-1)(v-u)/n,\ u+j(v-u)/n)$$

Thus $y(f; s)$ is measurable in $s \geqslant 0$, if f is a step function in t. As step functions are dense in $\mathcal{D}[0, \infty)$ (see (47.4) with $f = f_j$), the converse follows.

THEOREM 72.5. (*Sargent* (1955), p. 407, Theorem 2). *In order that, for all $f \in \mathcal{D}\ [0, \infty)$, $y(f; s)$ be defined, measurable, and essentially bounded on $s \geqslant 0$, when μ is continuous, it is necessary and sufficient* *that the conditions of Theorem 72.4 are satisfied, with*

(72.7)
$$\text{ess sup}_{s \geqslant 0} V_e(k(s; \cdot)) < \infty$$

Proof. To show that (72.7) is sufficient for essential bounded-ness, we have

$$|y(f; s)| \leqslant V_e(k(s; \cdot)) \, \|IR(f; \cdot)\|_\infty$$

as in section 68. To show that (72.7) is necessary we use Theorem 65.7 with $L_\Phi = L_\infty$, showing that $y(\cdot, \cdot)$ is a continuous linear transformation of $\mathcal{D}[0, \infty)$ into L_∞. Thus there is an M such that for all $f \in \mathcal{D}[0, \infty)$,

$$|y(f; s)| \leqslant M \, \|IR(f; \cdot)\|_\infty$$

almost everywhere in s, i.e. for all s except for a set $X(f)$ of variation zero. We can take a countable family of step functions dense in $\mathcal{D}[0, \infty)$, so that the union X of the $X(f_n)$ for this family is still of variation zero. Then if $f \in \mathcal{D}[0, \infty)$ we can choose a sequence out of the countable family, say, $\{f_n\}$, that tends to f in the given norm, which means that

$$\sup_s |IR(f-f_n; s)| \to 0$$

$$|y(f; s)| = \lim_{n \to \infty} |y(f_n; s)| \leqslant M \lim_{n \to \infty} \|IR(f_n; \cdot)\|_\infty = M \, \|IR(f; \cdot)\|_\infty$$

$$(s \notin X)$$

$$V_e(k(s; \cdot)) = \text{norm} \, (y(\cdot; s)) \leqslant M \qquad (s \notin X)$$

giving (72.7).

THEOREM 72.6. (*Sargent* (1955), p. 408, Theorem 3). *In order that, for each* $f \in \mathcal{D}[0, \infty)$, $y(f; s)$ *be defined for each* $s \geqslant 0$, *and* $y(f; \cdot) \in L_1$, *when* μ *is continuous, it is necessary and sufficient that* $V_e(k(s; \cdot)) < \infty$ $(s \geqslant 0)$ *and, for the* k_2 *of Theorem 72.4*

(72.8)
$$k_2(\cdot, t) \in L_1 \qquad (t \geqslant 0),$$

$$\sup_t \|k_2(\cdot, t)\|_1 \equiv \sup_t \int_0^\infty |k_2(\cdot, t)| \, d\mu < \infty ;$$

(72.9) *for each bounded* μ-*measurable set* X,

$$k_3(X; t) = \int_{s=0}^\infty k_2(s; t) \, ch \, (X; s) \, d\mu$$

390

is a function of t of bounded variation on $[0, \infty)$, *and over all such X,*

(72.10) $$\sup_X V(k_3(X; t); \mathcal{A}; [0, \infty)) < \infty$$

Proof. For the necessity, after Theorem 72.4, and $L_\Phi = L_1$ in Theorem 65.7, there is a constant M such that, for $f \in \mathcal{D}\ [0, \infty)$

$$\int_0^\infty |y(f; \cdot)|\ d\mu_1 \leq M \|IR(f; \cdot)\|_\infty$$

For each $u \geq 0$, $v > 0$, we put

$$f_v(t) = ch([u, u+v]; t)/H(u, u+v), \quad \|IR(f_v; \cdot)\|_\infty = 1$$

by continuity of μ; and by Fatou's lemma,

$$\int_0^\infty |k_2(s; u)|\ d\mu_1 = \int_0^\infty \lim_{v \to 0+} \left| \int_u^{u+v} k(s; t)\ d\mu/H(u, u+v) \right|\ d\mu_1$$

$$= \int_0^\infty \lim_{v \to 0+} |y(f_v; s)|\ d\mu_1 \leq \lim_{v \to 0+} \inf \int_0^\infty |y(f_v; s)|\ d\mu_1 \leq M$$

Hence (72.8) is proved. Now let X be a bounded μ_1-measurable set in $s \geq 0$. We prove that $k_3(X; t)$ is of bounded variation by taking $0 \leq \alpha_1 < \beta_1 < \alpha_2 < \beta_2 < \ldots \ldots < \alpha_r < \beta_r < \infty$, with

$$d = \min_{1 < j < n} (\beta_j - \alpha_j, \alpha_{j+1} - \beta_j, \beta_n - \alpha_n),$$

$$z_v(t) = \sum_{j=1}^r ch([\beta_j, \beta_j+v]; t)/H(\beta_j, \beta_j+v)$$

$$- \sum_{j=1}^r ch([\alpha_j, \alpha_j+v]; t)/H(\alpha_j, \alpha_j+v),$$

$$\|IR(z_v; \cdot)\|_\infty = 1(0 < v \leq d), \quad \left| \sum_{j=1}^r \{k_3(X; \beta_j) - k_3(X; \alpha_j)\} \right|$$

$$= \left| \int_0^\infty \sum_{j=1}^r \{k_2(s; \beta_j) - k_2(s; \alpha_j)\} ch(X; \cdot)\ d\mu_1 \right|$$

$$\leq \int_0^\infty \left| \sum_{j=1}^r \{k_2(s; \beta_j) - k_2(s; \alpha_j)\} \right|\ d\mu_1 = \int_0^\infty \lim_{v \to 0+} |y(z_v; s)|\ d\mu_1$$

$$\leq \lim_{v \to 0+} \inf \int_0^\infty |y(z_v; s)|\ d\mu_1 \leq M \|IR(z_v; \cdot)\|_\infty = M$$

i.e. for each such X, the variation of $k_3(X; t)$ on $[0, \infty)$ is not greater than M, giving (72.10).

To prove that the conditions are sufficient, first, (72.8) implies the μ_1-measurability of $k_2(s; t)$ in $s \geqslant 0$ for each $t \geqslant 0$, so that from Theorem 72.4, $y(f; s)$ is defined and measurable on $[0, \infty)$ for each $f \in \mathcal{D}[0, \infty)$. Also, if $z(t)$ is a step function in $\mathcal{D}[0, \infty)$, so that $z(t)$ is zero for t large enough, we can replace k by k_2 in $y(z; s)$, giving by Fubini's theorem,

$$\int_0^\infty |y(z; s)| \, d\mu_1 \leqslant \int_0^\infty d\mu_1 \int_0^\infty |z(t) \, k_2(s; t)| \, d\mu$$

$$= \int_0^\infty |z(t)| \, d\mu \int_0^\infty |k_2(s; t)| \, d\mu_1 < \infty$$

Further, from Fubini's theorem again, for a bounded μ_1-measurable set X,

$$\int_0^\infty y(z; s) \, ch(X; s) \, d\mu_1 = \int_0^s z(t) \, d\mu \int_0^\infty k_2(s; t) \, ch(X; s) \, d\mu_1$$

$$\left| \int_0^\infty y(z: s) \, ch(X; s) \, d\mu_1 \right| \leqslant \|IR(z; \, .)\|_\infty \, V(k_3(X; \, .); \, \mathcal{A}; [0, \infty))$$

$$\leqslant M \, \|IR(z; \, .)\|_\infty$$

Letting X be in turn the subsets of any bounded interval $[0, a]$ in which $y(z; s)$ is positive and negative, we see that, for any step function z,

$$\int_0^\infty |y(z; s)| \, d\mu_1 = \lim \int_0^u |y(z; s)| \, d\mu_1 \leqslant 2M \, \|IR(z; \, .)\|_\infty$$

We now take $f \in \mathcal{D}[0, \infty)$ and step functions z_n tending to f in the norm. By continuity of $y(f; s)$ in f for each s,

$$y(f; s) = \lim_{n \to \infty} y(z_n; s),$$

$$\int_0^\infty |y(f; s)| \, d\mu_1 \leqslant \lim_{n \to \infty} \inf \int_0^\infty |y(z_n; s)| \, d\mu_1$$

$$\leqslant 2M \lim_{n \to \infty} \|IR(z_n; .)\|_\infty = 2M \, \|IR(f; \, .)\|_\infty$$

and $y(f; \, .) \in L_1[0, \infty)$ for each $f \in \mathcal{D}[0, \infty)$

Tatchell (1953), p. 262, Theorem 2, gives similar results for $f \in L_1 [0, \infty)$.

Ex.72.1. Let $T = [0, 1]$, $f \in L_1 [0, 1]$, $k \in L_\infty [0, 1]$, with k periodic with period 1. Then prove that

$$(72.11) \qquad \lim_{s \to \infty} \int_0^1 k(sx) f(x) \, dx = \int_0^1 k(x) \, dx \int_0^1 f(x) \, dx$$

(Zygmund (1959), p. 49, Theorem (4.15)).

Ex. 72.2. Let $T = [0, 1]$, $f \in L_1 [0, 1]$, $k \in L_\infty [0, \infty)$,

$$(72.12) \qquad \lim_{s \to \infty} \frac{1}{s} \int_0^s k(x) \, dx = l$$

Prove that

$$(72.13) \qquad \lim_{s \to \infty} \int_0^1 k(sx) f(x) \, dx = l \int_0^1 f(x) \, dx$$

and prove the converse. (Keogh (1960), p. 284, Theorem 1). (We need only prove

$$\lim_{s \to \infty} \int_0^u k(st) \, dt = 0$$

for each fixed u in $0 < u \leqslant 1$, on replacing k by $(k - l)$. For the converse take $f = 1$.)

Ex. 72.3. $T = [0, 1]$, $f \in L_\Phi [0, 1] \neq L_\infty [0, 1]$, $k \in L_\Psi [0, a]$ *(all $a > 0$)*, and (72.12),

$$(72.14) \qquad \int_0^s \Psi(|k(x)|) \, dx = O(s)$$

Then prove (72.13). ($L_\Phi = L_p$ in Zygmund (1959), p. 376, notes to Chapter II, §4, and k periodic; Keogh (1960), p. 286, Theorem 2, with general k).

17

INTEGRAL SUMMABILITY RESULTS
WITH A VARIABLE INTEGRATOR

73. Integrators of Bounded Variation

In this chapter we study the functionals

$$(73.1) \qquad y(f; s) = \int_0^\infty k(s; t) \, df(t)$$

where the $k(s; t)$ are fixed, and the f are members of some family of functions. First we use the space $BV[0, \infty)$ of functions f of bounded variation on $[0, \infty)$, so that $\lim_{t \to \infty} f(t)$ exists.

LEMMA 73.1. *The space $BV[0, \infty)$ is a complete normed linear space with*

$$\|f\|_{BV} = V(f; \mathcal{A}; [0, \infty))$$

Proof. The space is linear since if a, b are constants, and $x > y \geqslant 0$,

$$|\{af(x) + bg(x)\} - \{af(y) + bg(y)\}|$$
$$\leqslant |a| \, |f(x) - f(y)| + |b| \, |g(x) - g(y)|$$
$$V(af + bg; \mathcal{A}; [0, \infty)) \leqslant |a| \, V(f; \mathcal{A}; [0, \infty)) + |b| \, V(g; \mathcal{A}; [0, \infty))$$

If, given $x > 0$, the right side of

$$(73.2) \qquad |f(x) - f(0)| \leqslant V(f; \mathcal{A}; [0, \infty))$$

is zero, then $f(x) = f(0)$ i.e. to ensure that the variation is a norm we should take equivalence classes E, for which $f, g \in E$ if, and only if, $f - g$ is constant. To prove completeness, let $\{f_n\} \subseteq BV[0, \infty)$ be such that for all $\varepsilon > 0$,

$$V(f_m - f_n; \mathcal{A}; [0, \infty)) < \varepsilon \qquad (m, n \geq N = N(\varepsilon))$$

By (73.2), for each $x \geq 0$, $\{f_n(x) - f_n(0)\}$ is a fundamental sequence, and so tends to a limit, say, $f(x)$, with $f(0) = 0$. Further, if $0 = t_0 < t_1 < \ldots < t_r$

$$\sum_{j=1}^{r} |f_m(t_j) - f(t_j) - f_m(t_{j-1}) + f(t_{j-1})|$$

$$= \lim_{n \to \infty} \sum_{j=1}^{r} |f_m(t_j) - f_n(t_j) - f_m(t_{j-1}) + f_n(t_{j-1})|$$

$$\leq \lim_{n \to \infty} \inf V(f_m - f_n; \mathcal{A}; [0, \infty)) \leq \varepsilon$$

$$V(f_m - f; \mathcal{A}; [0, \infty)) \leq \varepsilon$$

and $f \in BV[0, \infty)$, with $f_m \to f$ in the norm.

Banach (1932), p. 134, and Lorentz (1947), p. 263, use Riemann–Stieltjes integrals in dealing with (73.1), the former requiring

(73.3) $$\qquad y(f; s) \to \int_0^\infty k(t) \, df(t)$$

for some function $k(t)$, and the latter requiring

(73.4) $$\qquad \lim_{s \to \infty} y(f; s) = \lim_{t \to \infty} f(t) - f(0)$$

It is easy to see that (73.4) is the special case of (73.3) in which $k(t)$ is identically 1, while if we write a new $k(s; t)$ in place of the old $k(s; t) - k(t)$, we reduce both to the form

(73.5) $$\qquad y(f; s) \equiv \int_0^\infty k(s; t) \, df(t) \to 0 \qquad (s \to \infty)$$

Here we shall use generalized Riemann integration instead of Riemann–Stieltjes integration, so that we can also include some results of Lee (1965), in particular, p. 5, Theorem 2. Lee uses the space $\mathcal{B}$ of all vector interval functions $\mathbf{h}$ that are variationally integrable and VB^* in an elementary set E. Then the integral H of $\mathbf{h}$ lies in $BV(E)$, while

$$\int_E f \, d\mathbf{h} = \int_E f \, dH$$

in the sense that if either integral exists, so does the other, and they are equal. It follows that if we study (73.5) we can produce the results of Lee (1965), and analogues of the results of Banach (1932), Lorentz (1947).

THEOREM 73.1. *In order that* $y(f; s)$ *should exist for all* $f \in BV[0, \infty)$, *all* $s \geqslant 1$, *and that* (73.5) *should hold, it is necessary and sufficient that* (73.6) $k(s; t)$ *is f-measurable in* $t \geqslant 0$, *for each fixed* $s \geqslant 1$, *and for each* $f \in BV[0, \infty)$

(73.7) $\|k(s; .)\|_\infty \equiv \sup_{t > 0} |k(s; t)| < \infty$ (*each fixed* $s \geqslant 1$)

(73.8) $\qquad\qquad \limsup_{s \to \infty} \|k(s; .)\|_\infty < \infty$

(73.9) $\qquad \lim_{s \to \infty} k(s; t) = 0$ (*each fixed* $t \geqslant 0$)

Proof. Theorem 69.1 gives (73.6; 73.7), with

$$\text{norm } (y(.; s)) = \|k(s; .)\|_\infty$$

By Lemma 73.1 and Baire's category theorem (Theorem 17.3), $BV[0, \infty)$ is a Baire space. Then Theorem 34.2 gives (73.8). Finally, to prove (73.9) we need only take an f with a jump 1 at t, that is constant elsewhere.

For the sufficiency, after Theorem 69.1, which gives the existence of $y(f; s)$, we note that there is a $u > 0$ for which

$$V(f; \mathcal{A}; [u, \infty)) < \varepsilon;$$

$$\left| \int_u^\infty k(s; t)\, df(t) \right| \leqslant \|k(s; .)\|_\infty \varepsilon \leqslant M\varepsilon \qquad (s \geqslant v)$$

Also, by our form of Lebesgue's convergence theorem, splitting f as a difference of two monotone increasing functions,

$$\lim_{s \to \infty} \int_0^u k(s; t)\, df(t) = \int_0^u 0\, df(t) = 0$$

Hence we have (73.5).

In the theorem involving (73.3) we need only add to the conditions of Theorem 73.1 the conditions that $k(t)$ also satisfies (73.6; 73.7).

Ex. 73.1. Let m, $\mathcal{C}(E)$, $BV(E)$ be respectively the Banach spaces

396

of bounded functions, of continuous functions, and of functions of bounded variation, all on E, an elementary set. In order that $y(f;.) \in m$, $\mathcal{C}(E)$, or $BV(E)$, for all $f \in BV[0, \infty)$, it is necessary and sufficient that $k(., t) \in m$, $\mathcal{C}(E)$, or $BV(E)$, for each $t \geqslant 0$, and that

$$\sup \left(\|k(.;t)\|; \; t \geqslant 0 \right)$$

The last norm is the usual one for m, $\mathcal{C}(E)$, $BV(E)$, respectively. (Lee (1965), p. 6, Theorem 3, for $t \in E$ replacing $t \geqslant 0$).

74. Bounded Baire Function Integrators

The study of (73.4) has been most interesting to me for many years. Having been given the task by Dr. (later, Professor) P. Dienes of research in integration theory, and having been introduced by Dr. R. G. Cooke to the theory of summability for infinite series, it was clear that a translation of much of the latter theory into terms involving integrals would prove interesting. In particular, we have that the necessary and sufficient conditions on numbers a_{mk} in order that

$$\sum_{k=1}^{\infty} a_{mk} b_k$$

should exist for all integers $m \geqslant 1$, and should tend as $m \to \infty$, to

$$\sum_{k=1}^{\infty} b_k$$

whenever this exists, are that

$$\lim_{m \to \infty} a_{mk} = 1, \quad \text{for each fixed } k = 1, 2, 3, \ldots$$

(74.1) $$\sum_{k=1}^{\infty} |a_{m_{k+1}} - a_{mk}| \leqslant M \quad (m = 1, 2, 3, \ldots)$$

where M is independent of m. See Theorem 55.4 and the subsequent discussion.

To generalize this problem we can replace a_{mk} by $k(s; t)$ and

$$s_n = b_1 + b_2 + \ldots + b_n \quad \text{by} \quad f(t)$$

obtaining (73.4). It was obvious to me in 1944 that to (74.1) corresponds the condition that $k(s; t)$ is of bounded variation in t, uniformly for $s \geqslant 1$, and that to prove that $k(s; t)$ is of bounded variation in t for each fixed s, one has to take functions f that are not of bounded variation, or else one could only prove that $k(s; t)$ is bounded in t for each fixed s. Theorem 68.1 proves that $k(s; t)$ is of essentially bounded variation, Dr. Sargent using Denjoy integrals for f, which is therefore ACG or ACG^*, in the notation of integration theory. I wished to use the family of bounded Baire functions f; but then the choice of a suitable integral proved difficult, and finally in 1953 I used the Ward integral, integrated by parts (see Henstock (1955b)). Ward's integral includes the elementary Stieltjes integral, and the modification by Moore and Pollard. If the Lebesgue–Stieltjes (Radon) integral exists, so does the Ward integral, and a simple relation concerning discontinuities of f connects them. Further, the Ward integral is included in the Riemann–complete integral. It follows that if the last integral does not exist, neither can the others. But if the integral $y(f; s)$ exists for the function f that is 0 at the rationals and 1 at the irrationals, then $k(s; t)$ must be constant in t (see Henstock (1963c), p. 73, *Ex. 33.4*). Thus the integration breaks down even in this simple case, and in Henstock (1955b) I use

$$(74.2) \qquad y(f; s) = \lim_{u \to \infty} y(f; s; u),$$

$$y(f; s; u) \equiv [k(s; .) f(.)]_0^u - \int_0^u f(t)\, dk(s; t)$$

where now we could write the last integral in the generalized Riemann form. We therefore require $y(f; s; u)$ to exist, for each bounded Baire function f, so that the conditions on $k(s; t)$ in t for each fixed s, can be found from Theorem 66.1, in which theorem we can put $H(t) = k(s; t)$. It is then clear that $k(s; t)$ is equal to a function of bounded variation, except for a countable number of points t, for each fixed s. The values of $k(s; t)$ at the exceptional points make no difference to the value of $y(f; s)$ and so can be disregarded. Alternatively, we can proceed in either of two ways. We can widen the family of f to include all Baire functions f such that, for some countable set X, f is bounded in $[0, \infty) \backslash X$, and use Theorem 66.2; or we can suppose that

(74.3) $$\liminf_{u \to t} k(s; u) \leqslant k(s; t) \leqslant \limsup_{u \to t} k(s; u)$$

which condition is true in any case except for a countable set of t. The last is used in Henstock (1955b). In either of the last two cases we prove that $k(s; t)$ is of bounded variation in t. Assuming that we have proved this in some way, we can turn from integrability to summability problems.

THEOREM 74.1. *In order that the $y(f; s)$ of (74.2), with the k satisfying (74.3), shall itself satisfy (73.4) for all bounded Baire functions f for which $\lim_{t \to \infty} f(t)$ exists, it is necessary and sufficient that*

(74.4) $V(s) \equiv V(k(s; .); \mathcal{A}; [0, \infty)) < \infty$ *(each fixed s)*

(74.5) $$\limsup_{s \to \infty} V(s) < \infty$$

(74.6) $k(s, t-) \to 1$ *(fixed t in $(0, \infty)$)*,

$\qquad\qquad k(s; t+) \to 1$ *(fixed t in $[0, \infty)$)* *as* $s \to \infty$

(74.7) *for each* $u > 0$

$$\lim_{s \to \infty} \sum \{|k(s; t+) - k(s; t-)|: \ 0 < t < u\} = 0$$

(74.8) *for each bounded Borel set W, and $k_1(s; t)$ the continuous part of k,*

$$\lim_{s \to \infty} \int_0^\infty ch\,(W; .)\, dk_1(s; .) = 0$$

Alternatively, (74.7; 74.8) can be replaced by:
(74.9) *for each $\{s_n\}$ strictly increasing to $+\infty$, and for each $u > 0$,*

$$V_1(u, \varepsilon, m) \equiv \sup V(k(s_n; .); \mathcal{A}; [0, \infty); W) \to 0$$

as $\varepsilon \to 0$ and $m \to \infty$, where the sup is over all $n \geqslant m$ and all sets $W \subseteq [0, u]$ with $e(W) \equiv \sum_{n=1}^\infty 2^{-n} V(k_1(s_n; .); \mathcal{A}; [0, \infty); W) < \varepsilon$.

In practice it is easier to test whether (74.7; 74.8) are obeyed. But (74.9) is added to go deeper into (74.8).

Proof. From Theorem 66.1 and (74.3), $k(s; t)$ is of bounded variation in t for each fixed s, and each finite subinterval of $t \geqslant 0$, so that

$$|y(f; s; u)|$$

$$\leqslant |k(s; 0)| \, |f(0)| + |k(s; u)| \, |f(u)| + \sup_{0 < t < u} |f(t)| \cdot V(k(s; .); \mathcal{A}; [0, u])$$

$$\leqslant \|f\|_\infty \{|k(s; 0)| + |k(s; u)| + V(k(s; .); \mathcal{A}; [0, u])\}$$

so that $y(f; s; u)$ is a continuous linear functional in the space of bounded Baire functions $f(t)$ with a limit as $t \to \infty$. As in Theorem 62.3, a similar proof shows that the space is complete; and hence is a Baire space, and there is a function $M_1(s)$, finite for each s, with

$$\lim_{u \to \infty} \sup y(f; s; u) \leqslant M_1(s) \cdot \|f\|_\infty$$

We now take numbers $0 = t_1 < t_2 < \ldots < t_n$ and a function $f_1(t)$ constant in $[t_m, t_{m+1}]$ $(m = 1, 2, \ldots, n-1)$, and zero elsewhere, and we obtain, as in Lemmas 66.1, 66.2, and using (74.3),

$$y(f; s; t_n) = k(s; t_{n-1}+) f_1(t_n) - \sum_{m=2}^{n-1} f_1(t_m) \{k(s; t_m+) - k(s; t_{m-1}+)\}$$

A suitable $f_1(t)$ is given by

$$f_1(t_m) = \operatorname{sgn} \{k(s; t_m+) - k(s; t_{m-1}+)\} \quad (m = 2, \ldots, n-1),$$

$$f_1(t_n) = 0: \quad \|f_1\|_\infty = 1$$

$$\sum_{m=2}^{n-1} |k(s; t_m+) - k(s; t_{m-1}+)| \leqslant M_1(s)$$

Being true for each sequence $0 = t_1 < t_2 < \ldots < t_n$, it follows that

$$V(k(s; t+); \mathcal{A}; [0, \infty)) \leqslant M_1(s)$$

giving (74.4), on use of (74.3). Thus the $y(f; s)$ is a continuous linear functional for each fixed s, with norm $M_2(s)$ satisfying

$$V(s) \leqslant M_2(s) \leqslant 2\{|k(s; 0)| + V(s)\} < \infty$$

By hypothesis, $\lim_{s \to \infty} y(f; s)$ exists, so that if we apply again Theorem 34.1 for a continuous s, we have (74.5). For (74.6) we take a function with jump 1 at t that is otherwise constant.

400

If (74.7) is false, there are a $u > 0$ and an $\varepsilon > 0$, with a sequence $\{s_n\}$, such that, for $n = 1, 2, \ldots$,

(74.10) $\qquad \sum \{|k(s_n; t+) - k(s_n; t-)|: \; 0 < t < u\} \geqslant \varepsilon$

The singularities of $k(s_n; t)$ in $(0, u)$, for $n = 1, 2, \ldots$, can be put in a sequence $\{w_m\}$, so that we can put

$$v_{nm} = k(s_n; w_m+) - k(s_n; w_m-)$$

Let $f_2(w_m) \neq 0$, and otherwise put $f_2 = 0$, so that $f_2(t) \to 0$ as $t \to \infty$, and by hypothesis

$$y(f_2; s_n) = -\sum_{m=1}^{\infty} f_2(w_m) v_{nm} \to 0$$

as $n \to \infty$. By (55.14) we have (55.15), which in this case contradicts (74.10). Hence (74.7) is true.

Now let $f_3(t) = 0$ for $t \geqslant u$, and a bounded Baire function in $t \geqslant 0$. Then by Theorem 39.3 and what has already been proved,

$$y(f_3; s) = -k(s; 0+) f_3(0) - \sum \{f_3(t) [k(s; t+) - k(s; t-)]: 0 < t < u\}$$

$$- \int_0^u f_3(t) \, dk_1(s; t) \to -f_3(0)$$

$$\lim_{s \to \infty} \int_0^u f_3(t) \, dk_1(s; t) = 0$$

For (74.8) we need only take u so large that $W \subseteq [0, u]$, and $f_3 = ch(W; .)$.

If $\{s_n\}$ is a sequence of s tending to infinity, and $u > 0$, we define the $e(W)$. Then

$$\left| \int_0^u ch(W; .) \, dk_1(s_n; .) \right| \leqslant \int_0^u ch(W; .) \, dV(k_1(s_n; .); \mathcal{A}; [0, \infty); .)$$

$$= V(k_1(s_n; .); \mathcal{A}; [0, \infty); W)$$

so that $k_1(s; .)$ is absolutely continuous relative to its variation, which in turn is absolutely continuous relative to $e(.)$. Hence by Henstock (1963c), p. 77, Theorem 34.5, we have, for some $g(s; .)$,

$$k_1(s; u) - k_1(s; t) = \int_t^u g(s; .) \, de(.)$$

$$\lim_{m \to \infty} \int_0^u ch(W; .) g(s_n; .) \, de(.) = 0$$

We now have the position of Theorem 70.3, in which (70.6) implies (70.8; 70.9), and we have a function $M(N; \varepsilon)$. But here we have a better position, since having found an $M(N(\varepsilon), \varepsilon)$, we can now use the fact that each

$$\int_0^u ch(W; .) |g(s_n; .)| \, de(.) \qquad (1 \leqslant n < N(\varepsilon))$$

is absolutely continuous relative to $e(.)$, and take smaller W to ensure that the integrals for $1 \leqslant n < N(\varepsilon)$ are in modulus less than $M(N(\varepsilon), \varepsilon)$, as well as the rest. By Henstock (1963c), pp. 60–1, Theorem 31.2, we have (74.9), for k_1 replacing k. To complete the result we have only to use (74.7), since a countable set is of e-variation zero.

To prove the sufficiency of the conditions, let $l = \lim\limits_{t \to \infty} f(t)$. Then

$$y(f; s; u) = k(s; u-)\{f(u)-l)\} - k(s; 0+)\{f(0)-l\}$$

$$- \int_0^u \{f(t)-l\} \, dk_1(s; t)$$

$$- \sum \{(f(t)-l)(k(s; t+) - k(s; t-)): 0 < t < u\}$$

$$|k(s; u-)(f(u)-l)| \leqslant \{V(s) + |k(s; 0+)|\} |f(u)-l| \to 0 \qquad (u \to \infty)$$

$$y(f; s) = k(s; 0+)((l-f(0)) + \sum \{(l-f(t))(k(s; t+) - k(s; t-)): t > 0\}$$

$$+ \int_0^\infty (l-f(t)) \, dk_1(s; t)$$

By (74.6) the first term tends to $l-f(0)$ as $s \to \infty$. Also, given $\varepsilon > 0$, there is a $u = u(\varepsilon) > 0$ with $|f(t)-l| \leqslant \varepsilon$ for $t \geqslant u$, so that

$$\left| \sum \{(l-f(t))(k(s; t+) - k(s; t-)): t \geqslant u\} + \int_u^\infty (l-f(t)) \, dk_1(s; t) \right|$$

$$\leqslant \varepsilon V(s)$$

For the rest we first use (74.7; 74.8), so that as $|l-f(t)| \leqslant B$, for some B,

$$\sum \{(l-f(t))(k(s; t+) - k(s; t-)): 0 < t < u\} \to 0 \qquad (s \to \infty)$$

Taking $-B = t_0 < t_1 < \ldots < t_n = B$, $t_m - t_{m-1} < \varepsilon \ (m = 1, \ldots, n)$, $f_4(t) = t_m \ (t_m \leqslant f(t) - l < t_{m+1})$

i.e.
$$t \in W_m \qquad (m = 0, 1, \ldots, n-1)$$
$$|f_4(t) + l - f(t)| < \varepsilon$$

Hence using (74.8) for the n sets $W_m \cap [0, u]$

$$\lim_{s \to \infty} \sup \left| \int_0^u (l - f(t)) \, dk_1(s; t) \right| \leq \varepsilon \lim_{s \to \infty} \sup V(s)$$

As $\varepsilon > 0$ is arbitrary we collect the results and have $y(f; s) \to l - f(0)$.

We now replace (74.7; 74.8) by (74.9). Then as a countable set has e-variation zero, (74.7) is obtained from (74.9). Thus we need only prove the last part. Since $l - f(t)$ is a bounded Baire function it is e-measurable, and so is equal to a continuous function in $[0, u]$, except in an open set W with $e(W) < \delta$. This is Lusin's theorem, and can be found, for example, in Saks (1937), p. 72 (7.1). The continuous function can be chosen to have the same bounds $\pm B$, and further, we can replace it by a function $f_5(t)$ with bounds $\pm B$ and constant in each interval $u_{r-1} < t \leq u_r$, for $r = 1, 2, \ldots, m$, where $0 = u_0 < u_1 < \ldots < u_m = u$. Then if $f_6 = l - f - f_5$, we can choose the u_r and the constants so that

$$|f_6(t)| < \varepsilon \quad (t \in [0, u] \backslash W), \quad |f_6(t)| \leq 2B \quad (t \in W)$$

$$\left| \int_0^u (l - f(t)) \, dk_1(s_n; t) \right| \leq \varepsilon V(s_n) + 2B \cdot V(k_1(s_n; t); \mathcal{A}; [0, u]; W)$$

$$+ \left| \sum_{r=1}^m f_5(u_r) (k_1(s_n; u_r) - k_1(s_n; u_{r-1})) \right|$$

For fixed $u > 0$ we use (74.6; 74.7) to obtain

$$k_1(s_n; t) = k(s_n; t-) - \sum \{k(s_n; w+) - k(s_n; w-) : 0 < w < t\}$$
$$\to 1(n \to \infty)$$

$$\lim_{n \to \infty} \sup \left| \int_0^u (l - f(t)) \, dk_1(s_n; t) \right|$$

$$\leq \varepsilon \lim_{n \to \infty} \sup V(s_n) + 2B \cdot \lim_{n \to \infty} \sup V(k_1(s_n; .); \mathcal{A}; [0, \infty); W)$$

As $e(W) < \delta$ and $\delta > 0$ is arbitrary, (74.9) shows that the last term is arbitrarily small. Hence as $\varepsilon > 0$ is arbitrary, we again have the

403

result, for each strictly increasing sequence $\{s_n\}$, tending to $+\infty$, and so for $s \to +\infty$.

Ex. 74.1. Let $k(t) = 1-t(0 \leqslant t \leqslant 1)$, $t-1(1 \leqslant t \leqslant 2)$, $1(t \geqslant 2)$, $k(n; t) = k(nt)$
Show that

$$e((0, u)) \equiv \sum_{n=1}^{\infty} 2^{-n} V(k(n; .); \mathcal{A}; [0, \infty); (0, u))$$

is continuous, so that $e((0, u)) \to 0$ as $u \to 0$. But for $nu \geqslant 2$, show that

$$V(k(n; .); \mathcal{A}; [0, \infty); (0, u)) = 2$$

This example does not satisfy the conditions of Theorem 74.1, and it shows that not all k, for which $k(s; m+) = a_n(u)$ in (55.22), satisfies the condition that $h(\mathbf{c}, u) \to \sum_{n=1}^{\infty} c_n$, when the latter exists, also satisfy Theorem 74.1.

75. The Summability of Laplace–Stieltjes Integrals

We now turn to the summability of Fourier, Fourier–Stieltjes, Laplace, and Laplace–Stieltjes integrals, respectively

$$\int_0^{\infty} e^{ist} f(t) \, dt, \quad \int_0^{\infty} e^{ist} \, df(t), \quad \int_0^{\infty} e^{-zt} f(t) \, dt, \quad \int_0^{\infty} e^{-zt} \, df(t)$$

Clearly the first two are equal to the second two on putting $s = iz$, while the third integral is included in the fourth. We could have chosen the Fourier–Stieltjes integral, but instead we take the Laplace–Stieltjes form, as in Henstock (1957b). Note that if f is constant except for jumps a_n at the integers,

$$\int_0^{\infty} e^{-zt} \, df(t) = \sum_{n=0}^{\infty} a_n e^{-nz}$$

a power series, so that we can expect the summability of the Laplace–Stieltjes integral to result formally from an exponential transformation of summability results for power series. The summability of

Dirichlet series also comes under this heading, since if f is constant except for jumps a_n at points λ_n,

$$\int_0^\infty e^{-zt}\, df(t) = \sum_{n=0}^\infty a_n \exp\left(-\lambda_n z\right)$$

The ordinary Dirichlet series has $\lambda_n = \log n$. Since e^{-zt} is continuous, if $f(t)$ of bounded variation, in $[o, u,]$ we have

$$F(z, u) = \int_0^u e^{-zt}\, df(t) = e^{-zu} f(u) - f(0) + \int_0^u ze^{-zt} f(t)\, dt$$

and $F(z, u,)$ has the same value as a generalized Riemann integral and as an integral by parts.

More generally, let $F(z, u)$ be an integral by parts. Let t be the associated point of an interval $[t, u]$. Then if g, h are functions of t, the integral element for the integral by parts

$$\int_0^w g\, dh, \quad \text{is} \quad \left[gh\right]_t^u - h(t)\{g(u) - g(t)\} = g(u)\{h(u) - h(t)\}$$

Similarly for a 'left-hand' interval. Thus to obtain the integral by parts we need only take the value of g at the *opposite* end of the interval from the associated point used in the generalized Riemann integration of *Ex. 43.3*, and the integral by parts is just another kind of generalized Riemann integral. It follows that if the integrals by parts

$$\int_0^u g(t)\, dh(t), \quad \int_0^u j(t)\, d\left\{\int_0^t g(t)\, dh(t)\right\}$$

exist, then by Theorem 44.11 the second is equal to the integral by parts

$$\int_0^u j(t) g(t)\, dh(t)$$

A first application gives, for all complex v, z,

$$(75.1) \qquad F(z, u) = \int_0^u e^{(v-z)t}\, d_t F(v, t)$$

$$= e^{(v-z)u} F(v, u) + (z - v) \int_0^u e^{(v-z)t} F(v, t)\, dt$$

405

Let re z and im z denote the real and imaginary parts of z, and let $R(r)$ be the half-plane re $z > r$. Then by (75.1), if $F(z) \equiv \lim\limits_{u \to \infty} F(z, u)$ exists at some point $z = v$, it exists for all $z \in R(\text{re } v)$ as

$$(75.2) \qquad F(z) = (z - v) \int_0^\infty e^{(v-z)t} F(v, t)\, dt$$

Thus the Laplace–Stieltjes integral is convergent in $R(\sigma)$ for some minimal $\sigma < +\infty$, and divergent at all points of re $z < \sigma$, if the integral is convergent for any z. Note that σ can be $-\infty$. The half-plane can be obtained by exponential transformation from a circle with centre the origin. The domain of z for $F(z)$ that corresponds to the principal star domain for a series, is defined as follows: A *horizontal set* is a closed set Z of complex numbers with the properties:

$(75.3) \quad$ if $\quad v \in Z, \quad$ then $\quad z \in Z \quad$ when im $z = $ im $v, \quad$ re $z \leqslant$ re v

$(75.4) \qquad\qquad\qquad 0 \in Z$

$(75.5) \qquad\qquad R(0) \cap Z$ is empty

$(75.6) \quad$ the section of Z by each line re $z = $ constant is bounded

By (75.3; 75.4), Z contains Z_0, the line im $z = 0$, re $z \leqslant 0$. For each Laplace–Stieltjes integral $F(z)$ we can define a real function $\alpha = \alpha(\beta)$ of the real number β, to be such that $F(z)$ can be continued analytically along re $z \geqslant \gamma$, im $z = \beta$, for all $\gamma > \alpha$, but for no $\gamma < \alpha$. Then $-\infty \leqslant \alpha \leqslant \sigma$ for all β. For a horizontal set Z we can now put

$$H(F; Z) \equiv \Big\backslash \bigcup_\beta (Z + (\alpha + i\beta))$$

The *principal horizontal domain of $F(z)$* is $H^* \equiv H(F; Z_0)$, consisting of lines λ parallel to the real axis, including such part of λ that lies to the right of all singularities on λ, or the whole of λ if no singularity on it. The value of F in H^* is that given by direct analytic continuation from the half plane of convergence of the integral for $F(z)$. The *partial horizontal domain of F, relative to Z, is $H(F; Z) \subseteq H^*$*.

For the summability of the Laplace–Stieltjes integrals F we replace the f of (74.2) by $F(z,.)$, considering the integral by parts

$$B(F; z, s) \equiv \int_0^\infty k(s; t)\, d_t F(z, t) = \int_0^\infty k(s; t) e^{-zt}\, df(t)$$

by a second application of the result with an integral as integrator. If Z is a horizontal set and p a fixed real number, we say that $k(s; t)$ is *efficient* $(Z; p)$ for a Laplace–Stieltjes integral $F(z)$ with half-plane of convergence $R(\sigma)$, if

(75.7) $B(F; z, s)$ is convergent for each $s \geqslant 1$ and each $z \in R(\sigma-p)$,

(75.8)   and as $s \to \infty$, $B(F; z, s)$ is uniformly convergent to $F(z)$ in each compact set contained in $H(F; Z) \cap R(\sigma-p)$.

We first consider (75.7) (see Henstock (1957b), p. 15, Theorem 1).

THEOREM 75.1. *If $k(s; t)$ is a finite function satisfying* (74.3), *then in order that $B(F; z, s)$ should exist for a fixed s, for $z \in R(\sigma-p)$, and for each Laplace–Stieltjes integral with half-plane $R(\sigma)$ of convergence, and with f, a Baire function bounded in each finite interval of $t \geqslant 0$, it is necessary and sufficient that*

(75.9) $M_1(q, s) \equiv V(e^{qt}k(s; t); \mathcal{A}; [0, \infty)) < \infty$ *(all $q < p$)*

Proof. For the necessity we need only use the second integral expression for $B(F; z, s)$, replacing k by $k \cdot e^{qt}$ in (74.4), for each $\sqrt{}q < p$. For if f is an arbitrary bounded Baire function, then $\sigma \leqslant 0$, and $-q = z \in R(\sigma-p)$, and $B(F; -q, s)$ must exist. The sufficiency then also follows easily; let z be fixed in $R(\sigma-p)$. Then there is a $q < p$ with re $z+q > \sigma$, so that

$$\lim_{t \to \infty} F(z+q, t) = F(z+q); \quad |e^{qt} k(s; t) - k(s; 0)| \leqslant M_1(q, s)$$

$$\int_u^V k(s; t) e^{-zt} \, df(t) = \int_u^V k(s; t) e^{qt} \, d_t\{F(z+q, t) - F(z+q)\}$$

$$= [k(s; t) e^{qt}\{F(z+q, t) - F(z+q)\}]_u^V$$

$$- \int_u^V \{F(z+q, t) - F(z+q)\} \, d_t(k(s; t) e^{qt})$$

$$\left| \int_u^V k(s; t) e^{-zt} \, df(t) \right|$$

$$\leqslant (|k(s; 0)| + M_1(q, s) + M_1(q, s)) \sup_{u \leqslant t \leqslant V} \{F(z+q, t) - F(z+q)\},$$

which shows that $B(F; z, s)$ exists in $R(\sigma - p)$, and also

(75.10)

$$|B(F; z, s)| \leqslant \{2M_1(q, s) + |k(s; 0)|\} \sup_{t > 0} \{F(z+q, t) - F(z+q)\}$$

It may happen that no singularity of $F(z)$ occurs on the boundary of the half-plane of convergence, as distinct from the position in regard to power series. For example, we can consider the special subclass S_r of f for which f is bounded as $t \to \infty$, but

$$\int_u^{u+1} |f(t)| \, dt = O\,(e^{-ru}) \qquad (u \to \infty)$$

For these functions, in general $\sigma = 0$, while no singularity occurs in $R(-r)$, since if

$$F_1(z, u) \equiv \int_0^u e^{-zt} \, d_t \left\{ \int_0^t f(v) \, dv \right\} = \int_0^u e^{-zt} f(t) \, dt$$

then by integration by parts, when $z \neq 0$,

(75.11) $$F(z, u) = e^{-zu} f(u) + z F_1(z, u) - f(0)$$

This is also true for $z = 0$. If $z \in R(0)$ we obtain

(75.12) $$F(z) = z F_1(z) - f(0), \quad F_1(z) \equiv \lim_{u \to \infty} F_1(z, u)$$

By analytic continuation this is true for all z in the principal horizontal domain of $F_1(z)$, which includes $R(-r)$ by the order relation on the integral of $|f|$. Thus F is regular in $R(-r)$. For this interesting subclass of Laplace–Stieltjes integrals we can give a useful theorem.

THEOREM 75.2. (*Henstock* (1957b) p. 16, Theorem 2). *If $k(s; t)$ is a finite Baire function satisfying (74.3; 75.9), and if $p > 0$ is fixed, then in order that for every r in $0 \leqslant r < p$, $k(s; t)$ is efficient in $R(-r)$ for each $f \in S_r$, it is necessary and sufficient that*

(75.13) $$k(s, t-) \to 1 \quad (t > 0), \quad k(s, t+) \to 1 \quad (t \geqslant 0) \quad as$$
$$s \to \infty, \quad fixed \; t$$

$$\lim_{s \to \infty} \sum \{e^{qt} |k(s, t+) - k(s, t-)|: t > 0\} = 0 \quad (each \; q < p)$$

(75.14)

408

(75.15) *for each $x \geqslant 0$, each Borel set W with $\mu(W \cap (u, u+1)) = \mathcal{O}(e^{-xu})$ $(u \to \infty)$ where $\mu(W)$ is the variation of W using $l(a, b) = b - a$, and each $q < \inf(p, x)$, we have the two conditions*

$$(75.16) \qquad \lim_{s \to \infty} \int_0^\infty ch(W; t)e^{qt} \, d_t k_1(s; t) = 0$$

$$(75.17) \qquad \int_0^\infty ch(W; t) \, e^{qt} \, d_t V(k_1(s; .); \mathcal{A}; [0, t])$$

$$\leqslant M_2(q, x) \left[1 + \sup_{u > 0} e^{xu} \mu(W \cap (u, u+1)) \right]$$

where $M_2(q, x)$ is finite and independent of W and of $s \geqslant s_0(q, x)$

Proof. The necessity of (75.13; 75.14) follow as usual, since if $f = 0$ except for a countable number of points, then $f \in S_r$ for all r. For (75.16; 75.17) under conditions (75.15), we note (75.12) and the hypotheses, so that

$$\int_0^\infty k(s; t) \, d(e^{qt}f(t)) = \int_0^\infty k(s; t) f(t) q e^{qt} \, dt + \int_0^\infty k(s; t) \, e^{qt} \, df(t)$$

$$\to F(-q) + q F_1(-q) = 0$$

$$(75.18) \qquad \int_0^\infty k(s; t) \, d(e^{qt}f(t)) \to 0 \qquad (s \to \infty)$$

$$[e^{qt}f(t) \, k(s; t)]_0^\infty = 0$$

$$\sum_{t > 0} e^{qt}f(t) (k(s; t+) - k(s; t-)) =$$

$$= \mathcal{O}\left(\sum_{t > 0} e^{qt} |k(s; t+) - k(s; t-)| \right) \to 0 \qquad (s \to \infty)$$

Hence if we integrate by parts in (75.18) we obtain

$$(75.19) \qquad \int_0^\infty e^{qt}f(t) \, dk_1(s; t) \to 0 \qquad (s \to \infty)$$

for each $q < \inf(p, r)$. To obtain (75.16) we put $f = ch(W; .)$, for $r = x$, and all W satisfying (75.15).

To obtain (75.17) we need Banach–Steinhaus type arguments,

noting that S_r is complete for the norm

$$\|f\| = \sup_{w>0} |f(w)| + \sup_{w>0} e^{rw} \int_w^{w+1} |f(t)| \, dt = \|f\|_\infty$$

$$+ \left\| e^{rw} \int_w^{w+1} |f(t)| \, dt \right\|_\infty$$

LEMMA 75.1. *If* $V(q) \equiv V(e^{qt}a(t); \mathcal{A}; [0, \infty)) < \infty$ *(all* $q < p$*), then*

$$|a(t)| \leqslant e^{-qt} V(q) \qquad (all\ q < p)$$

Proof. For each $q < x < p$, $e^{xu}a(u)$ tends to a limit, and so $e^{qu}a(u) \to 0$, as $u \to \infty$. The result then follows from

$$|e^{qu}a(u) - e^{qt}a(t)| \leqslant V(q)$$

on letting $u \to \infty$.

Continuing with the proof of Theorem 75.2, by (75.9) and Lemma 75.1, for each $q < x < p$, if

$$Y(f; q, s) \equiv \int_0^\infty e^{qt} f(t) \, dk_1(s; t)$$

$$= \int_0^\infty f(t) \, d\{e^{qt} k_1(s; t)\} - \int_0^\infty f(t) \, k_1(s; t) \, q e^{qt} \, dt,$$

$$|Y(f; q, s)| \leqslant \|f\|_\infty M_1(q, s) + \|f\|_\infty q \int_0^\infty e^{-xt} M_1(x, s) e^{qt} \, dt$$

$$\leqslant \|f\|_\infty \{M_1(q, s) + q M_1(x, s)/(x-q)\}$$

It follows that $Y(.; q, s)$ is a continuous linear functional in S_r, while by (75.19), $\lim\limits_{s \to \infty} Y(f; q, s) = 0$. Hence by the continuous variable form of Theorem 34.1, there is an $M_2(q, r)$ such that

$$(75.20) \quad |Y(f; q, s)| \leqslant M_2(q, r) \|f\| < \infty \qquad (s \geqslant s_0 = s_0(q, r))$$

Now, $k_1(s; .)$ is absolutely continuous relative to its variation, which we can denote by $V_1(s; .)$, and we have, for $u > t$,

$$k_1(s; u) - k_1(s; t) = \int_t^u g(s; .) \, dV_1(s; .),$$

$$V_1(s; u) - V_1(s; t) = \int_t^u |g(s; .)| \, dV_1(s; .)$$

so that by variational equivalence arguments, $|g(s;.)| = 1$ almost everywhere relative to $V_1(s;.)$. Thus we can take $|g(s;.)| = 1$ everywhere, and

$$Y(f; q, s) = \int_0^\infty e^{qt} f_1(t)\, dV_1(s; t), \quad f_1(t) \equiv f(t)\, g(s;.) \in S_r$$

All we now have to do is to substitute in (75.20) this result with

$$f_1(t) = ch(W; t), \quad \|f_1\| = 1 + \sup e^{ru}\mu \quad (W \cap (u, u+1))$$

To prove that the conditions are sufficient, we first take $z \in R(\sigma)$, Then Theorem 74.1, sufficiency, proves that $B(F; z, s) \to F(z)$. For (75.9) gives (74.4); (75.13) is (74.6); (75.14) gives (74.7); (75.16) gives (74.8). We do not have (74.5), but

(75.21) $$\lim_{s \to \infty} \sup M_1(q, s) < \infty \quad (each\ q < 0)$$

the effect of which is to ensure that if the integral for $F(z)$ is convergent at $z = v$ then $B(F; z, x) \to F(z)$ in $R(re\ v)$, but not necessarily at $z = v$. This result holds for all Laplace–Stieltjes integrals, and not just those with $f \in S_r$.

To prove that (75.21) follows from the conditions, we first take $x = 0$, $W = (0, \infty)$, in (75.17), so that for $q < 0$, $s \geqslant s_0\ (q, 0)$.

$$\int_0^\infty e^{qt}\, dV_1(s; t) \leqslant 2M_2(q, 0), \quad e^{qt} V_1(s; t) \leqslant 2M_2(q, 0),$$

$$|k_1(s; t)| \leqslant |k_1(s; 0)| + 2M_2(q, 0)\, e^{-qt},$$

$$|e^{qu} k_1(s; u) - e^{qt} k_1(s; t)| \leqslant e^{qu} |k_1(s; u) - k_1(s; t)|$$
$$+ |k_1(s; t)|\, (e^{qt} - e^{qu}) \quad (u > t),$$

$$\leqslant \exp(qu)\, [V_1(s;.)]_t^u + (|k_1(s; 0)|$$

$$+ 2M_2(\tfrac{1}{2}q, 0) \exp(-\tfrac{1}{2}qt))\, (\exp(qt) - \exp(qu)) \leqslant \int_t^u \exp(qv)\, dV_1(s; v)$$

$$+ (|k_1(s; 0)| + 2M_2(\tfrac{1}{2}q, 0)) \int_t^u \exp(-\tfrac{1}{2}qv)\, d(-\exp(qv))$$

411

From (75.13) and $k_1(s; 0) = k(s; 0+)$, we have for $q < 0$,

$$M_1(q, s) \leqslant 2M_2(q, 0) + 2\,|k(s; 0+)| + 4M_2(\tfrac{1}{2}q, 0)$$

$$\lim_{s \to \infty} \sup M_1(q, s) \leqslant 2M_2(q, 0) + 2 + 4M_2(\tfrac{1}{2}q, 0) < \infty$$

From (75.10; 75.21),
(75.22) $B(F; z, s)$ is uniformly bounded as $s \to \infty$, in each compact set contained in the half plane of convergence of the integral for $F(z)$.

We now show that
(75.23) if $f \in S_r$, then $B(F; z, s)$ is uniformly bounded in each compact set Y contained in $R(-r)$

This, with the convergence of $B(F; z, s)$ to $F(z)$ in $R(0)$, will give the convergence in $R(-r)$, by using Vitali's theorem on the convergence of a sequence of uniformly bounded analytic functions.

By Theorem 13.7, Y is at a positive distance from the half plane re $z \leqslant -r$, so that there is a q in $0 < q < r$ with $Y \subseteq R(-q)$. Let the integer n satisfy $n(r-q) > 1$, and let l be an integer in $qn-1 < l < rn-1$. From the definition of S_r, for numbers $A > 0$, $N > 0$,

(75.24) $$|f| \leqslant A, \qquad \int_u^{u+1} |f(t)|\, dt \leqslant ANe^{-ru}$$

Let W_{wn} be the set of t with

$$A \exp(-wt/n) \geqslant |f(t)| > A \exp(-(w+1)t/n);$$

$$W_1 \equiv \bigcup_{w \geqslant l+1} W_{wn}$$

In W_1, $f(t) = O\,[\exp(-wt/n)]$ for $w/n > q$, so that the Laplace-Stieltjes integral using $f(t)ch(W_1; t)$ will converge in $R(-q)$, and by (75.22) we need only take $w = 0, 1, \ldots, l$, and we have

$$A \exp(-(w+1)(t+1)/n)\, \mu(W_{wn} \cap (t, t+1))$$

$$\leqslant \int_t^{t+1} ch(W_{wn}; v)\, |f(v)|\, dv \leqslant ANe^{-rt}$$

412

$$\mu(W_{wn} \cap (t, t+1)) \leqslant N \exp((w+1)/n) \exp((w+1-rn)t/n)$$

$$\int_0^\infty e^{qt}\,|f(t)\,ch(/W_1;t)|\,dV_1(s;t) \leqslant \sum_{w=0}^{l} \int_0^\infty ch(W_{wn};t)\,e^{qt}Ae^{-wt/n}\,dV_1(s;t)$$

$$\leqslant \sum_{w=0}^{l} AM_2((q-w/n,\ r-(w+1)/n)[1+N\exp((w+1)/n)] < \infty$$

We have used (75.17), the result being true for $s \geqslant \sup\limits_{0 < w \leqslant l} s_0(q-w/n,$
$r-(w+1)/n)$ since $q-w/n < r-(w+1)/n$.

Let $f_2 = f \cdot ch(\backslash W_1;\,.)$, and let $F_2(z,\,.)$ be constructed from f_2. Then as in (75.11), and integrating by parts,

$$B(F_2;\,z,\,s) = -\int_0^\infty F_2(z,\,t)\,dk(s;\,t)$$

$$= -\int_0^\infty \{e^{-zt}f_2(t)-f_2(0)+zF_3(z,\,t)\}\,dk(s;\,t)$$

$$F_3(z,\,t) \equiv \int_0^t e^{-zw}\,d_w\left\{\int_0^w f_2(v)\,dv\right\} = \int_0^t -e^{-zw}\,d_w\left\{\int_w^\infty f_2(v)\,dv\right\}$$

$$= \int_0^\infty f_2(t)\,dt - z\int_0^t e^{-zw}\left\{\int_w^\infty f_2(v)\,dv\right\}dw$$

By (75.24) this is convergent as $t \to \infty$, absolutely and uniformly for $z \in R(-q)$. Hence, uniformly in the same set,

$$F_3(z,\,t) = F_3(z)+O(|z|\,e^{(q-r)t}), \quad F_3(z) \equiv \lim_{t \to \infty} F_3(z,\,t)$$

and substituting in $B(F_2;\,z,\,s)$, we have

$$B(F_2;\,z,\,s) = (-f_2(0)+zF_3(z))\,k(s;\,0)$$

$$-\int_0^\infty \{e^{-zt}f_2(t)+O(|z|^2\,e^{(q-r)t})\}\,dk(s;\,t)$$

and we obtain the result from (75.21) and the last computation using M_2.

We now turn to the general class of Laplace–Stieltjes integrals that are convergent in some half plane. In order to obtain a result like that of Theorem 56.3 for power series we have to impose an extra condition on k. Assuming k of bounded variation, we can

413

put

$$k_2(s; t) \equiv \partial k(s; t)/\partial t, \quad Q(s, z) \equiv \int_0^\infty e^{-zt} k_2(s; t) \, dt$$

Then k will be said to satisfy condition A_p if there are numbers $q < p$, with limit-point p, and to each such q there are an integer $n \geqslant 0$ and numbers $1 \leqslant r \leqslant 2$, $v \geqslant 0$, $s_0 \geqslant 0$, all depending on q, with

(75.25) $$\int_{|t| > v} |Q^{(n)}(s, -q+it)|^r \, dt \leqslant M_3(q) \qquad (s \geqslant s_0)$$

where $M_3(q)$ is independent of s, and where the differentiation of Q is relative to it.

THEOREM 75.3. (*Henstock (1957b), p. 23, Theorem 3*). *If k is finite and satisfies (74.3) and condition A_p, then in order that k should be efficient $(Z; p)$ for each Laplace–Stieltjes integral F with f a Baire function bounded in each finite interval of $[0, \infty)$, it is necessary and sufficient that (75.9) is true for all $s \geqslant 1$, $q < p$; that (75.13; 75.14; 75.16; 75.17) are all true; and that $Q(s, z) \to 0$ as $s \to \infty$, uniformly for z in each compact set contained in $R(-p) \backslash Z$.*

Proof. The necessity of (75.9) follows from Theorem 75.1, the necessity of (75.13; 75.14; 75.16; 75.17) from Theorem 75.2. For the last condition,

$$\frac{1}{z}(1 - e^{-zt}) = \int_0^t e^{-zv} \, dv, \quad \frac{1}{z} = \int_0^\infty e^{-zv} \, dv$$

the sole singularity of $1/z$ being at $z = 0$. By hypothesis and (75.9)

$$\int_0^\infty k(s; t) \, d_t \left\{ \frac{1 - e^{-zt}}{z} \right\} \to \frac{1}{z}, \quad \int_0^\infty k(s; t) \, de^{-zt} \to -1$$

$$-k(s; 0) - \sum_{t > 0} e^{-zt}(k(s; t+) - k(s; t-)) - \int_0^\infty e^{-zt} \, dk_1(s; t) \to -1$$

so that by (75.13; 75.14),

(75.26) $$\int_0^\infty e^{-zt} \, dk_1(s; t) \to 0 \qquad (s \to \infty)$$

uniformly in each compact set in $R(-p)\backslash Z$. Now let $W(s)$ be the set of variation zero that contains all the variation of

$$k_1(s; t) - \int_0^t k_2(s, v)\, dv$$

For a sequence $\{s_n\}$ of s tending to infinity, the set

$$W_2 \equiv \bigcup_{n=1}^{\infty} W(s_n)$$

is of variation zero, and $ch(W_2; t) \in S_r$ for all r. Further, for all $z \in R(0)$,

$$F_4(z, t) \equiv \int_0^t e^{-zv}\, dch(W_2; v) = e^{-zt}\, ch(W_2; t) - ch(W_2; 0)$$

$$F_4(z) \equiv \lim_{t \to \infty} F_4(z, t) = -ch(W_2; 0)$$

Hence by the sufficiency in Theorem 75.2, and (75.13; 75.14),

$$\int_0^\infty e^{-zt}\, dk_1(s_n, t) - \int_0^\infty e^{-zt} k_2(s_n, t)\, dt = \int_0^\infty e^{-zt}\, ch(W_2; t)\, dk_1(s_n; t)$$

$$= \int_0^\infty (ch(W_2; 0) + F_4(z, t))\, dk_1(s_n, t)$$

$$= -ch(W_2; 0)\, k_1(s_n; 0) - \sum_{t>0} F_4(z, t)\{k(s_n; t+)$$

$$-k(s_n; t-)\} - \int_0^\infty k(s_n, t)\, dF_4(z, t) \to -ch(W_2; 0) + ch(W_2; 0) = 0$$

as $n \to \infty$, and is uniformly bounded in each compact set contained in $R(-p)$. This is true for each sequence $\{s_n\}$ tending to infinity, and so is true as $s \to \infty$. Hence by (75.26), $Q(s, z) \to 0$ in the way given.

To prove the sufficiency, let Y be a compact set in $R(\sigma - p)$. Then we can find $q < p$ such that $Y \subseteq R(\sigma - q)$. By (75.1), for $q < x < p$, $F(z, t) = O(e^{xt})$ as $t \to \infty$, uniformly for $z \in Y$. Then from (75.9) taking $x < y < p$,

$$|k(s; t)\, F(z, t)| = O(e^{-yt} e^{xt}) = o(1) \qquad (t \to \infty)$$

By Theorem 75.1 the integral for $B(F; z, s)$ is convergent in Y. Thus

$$B(F; z, s) = -\int_0^\infty F(z, t) \, dk(s; t)$$

$$= -\sum_{t > 0} F(z, t)\{k(s; t+) - k(s; t-)\} - \int_0^\infty F(z, t) \, dk_1(s; t)$$

By (75.14) the first term is uniformly bounded in Y and tends to 0 there as $s \to \infty$. Further, following a proof similar to that involving W_2, we can easily show that

$$\int_0^\infty F(z, t) \, dk_1(s; t) - \int_0^\infty F(z, t) \, k_2(s; t) \, dt \to 0 \qquad (s \to \infty)$$

and is uniformly bounded in Y. Hence as $s \to \infty$,

$$B(F; z, s) = \mathbf{o}(1) + B^*(F; z, s),$$

$$B^*(F; z, s) \equiv -\int_0^\infty F(z, t) \, k_2(s; t) \, dt$$

We can replace f by any other Baire function f_3, provided that $f - f_3 \in S_p$. In particular, we can put

(75.27) $$f(t) = 0 \quad (0 \leqslant t \leqslant 1)$$

which is useful later. As for power series, we consider the integral

(75.28) $$G(z, s, w) \equiv \frac{1}{2\pi i} \int_{-w}^w \frac{F(z + it + q) \, Q(s, -it - q)}{t - iq} \, dt$$

We take re $(z + it + q) > \sigma$, re $z > \sigma - q$ (since t is real), and we can deal with $R(\sigma - p)$ on taking $q \to p-$, but in general we cannot go outside $R(\sigma - p)$. From (75.1), for $\varepsilon = \frac{1}{2}(\text{re } z + q - \sigma)$, $F(z, t) = O(e^{(q - \varepsilon)t})$. Hence by (75.2),

$$F(z + it + q) = (it + q) \int_0^\infty e^{-(it + q)v} F(z, v) \, dv$$

an absolutely convergent integral, and $e^{-qt} F(z, t)$ is bounded and in $L_2(0, \infty)$.

Also let $q+\delta < p$. Then by (75.9), and Lemma 75.1 for $q+\delta$,

$$e^{qt}|k_2(s;t)| \leqslant qe^{qt}|k(s;t)|+|qe^{qt}k(s;t)+e^{qt}k_2(s;t)|$$

$$\int_0^\infty e^{qt}|k_2(s;t)|\,dt \leqslant qM_1(q+\delta,s)/\delta+M_1(q,s) < \infty$$

and $e^{qt}k_2(s;t)$ is in $L_1(0,\infty)$, for each $s \geqslant 1$, $q < p$. Hence applying a Parseval theorem, Titchmarsh (1948), p. 94, Theorem 70, to the functions $e^{qt}k_2(s;t)$ and $e^{qt}F(z,-t)$, where $k_2(s;t)$ and $F(z,t)$ are defined to be zero in $t < 0$, we obtain the $(C,1)$ limit

$$(C,1)\ \lim_{w\to\infty}\ G(z,s,w)$$

$$\equiv \lim_{w\to\infty} \frac{1}{2\pi i}\int_{-w}^w \left(1-\frac{|t|}{w}\right)\frac{F(z+it+q)\,Q(s,-it-q)}{t-iq}\,dt$$

$$= \int_0^\infty F(z,t)\,k_2(s;t)\,dt = -B^*(F;z,s)$$

We now put $-v = it+q$, so that

$$(75.29) \qquad B^*(F;z,s) = \frac{1}{2\pi i}\int_\theta \frac{F(z-v)\,Q(s,v)}{v}\,dv\ (C,1)$$

for the path θ given by re $v = -q$, $-\infty < \text{im}\,v < \infty$.

As for the power series result, we can displace a finite part of θ to the right so that it surrounds Z and passes to the right of the origin, and yet is unaltered in $|\text{im}\,v| \geqslant \delta$, for some $\delta > 0$. For that finite part of θ we can let $w \to \infty$ and so use the calculus of residues on omitting $(1-|t|/w)$. Let φ be the rest of the path θ. Then as for power series, we obtain

$$B^*(F;z,s) \to F(z) - \lim_{s\to\infty}\lim_{w\to\infty}\frac{1}{2\pi i}\int_{\varphi\cap[-w,w]}\left(1-\frac{|\text{im}\,v|}{w}\right)$$

$$\cdot\frac{F(z-v)\,Q(s,v)}{v}\,dv$$

uniformly in Y. The rest of the argument is to show that the double limit exists uniformly, and is 0, and this is where we use the condition A_p. By (75.2),

$$\int_{-q-it}^{-q+iu} \frac{F(z-w)}{w}\,dw = \int_{-q-it}^{-q+iu}\left\{-\int_0^\infty e^{wv}F(z,v)\,dv\,dw\right\}$$

$$= \int_0^\infty \frac{F(z,v)}{v}\,e^{-qv}(e^{-itv}-e^{iuv})\,dv$$

The inversion is possible since the double integral is absolutely convergent. Using (75.27) we can let $t \to \infty$ with the Riemann–Lebesgue theorem *(Ex. 70.1)*, obtaining

$$\int_{-q-i\infty}^{-q+iu} \frac{F(z-w)}{w}\,dw = -\int_0^\infty \frac{F(z,v)}{v}\,e^{(-q+iu)\,v}\,dv$$

We can integrate n times between $-q-i\infty$ and $-q+iu$, replacing $F(z,w)/w$ by $F(z,w)/w^n$. Thus we integrate by parts n times,

$$\int_{-q+iw}^{-q+iu} \frac{F(z-v)}{v}\,Q(s,v)\,dv = [Q(s,v)\,F_{(1)}(z,v) - Q'(s,v)\,F_{(2)}(z,v) + \cdots$$

$$+ (-)^{n-1}Q^{(n-1)}(s,v)\,F_{(n)}(z,v)]_{v=-q+iw}^{v=-q+iu}$$

$$+ (-)^n\int_{-q+iw}^{-q+iu} Q^{(n)}(s,v)\,F_{(n)}(z,v)\,dv$$

where

$$F_{(o)}(z,v) \equiv \frac{F(z-v)}{v}, \quad F_{(m)}(z,v) = \int_{-q-i\infty}^{v} F_{(m-1)}(z,w)\,dw \quad (m \geqslant 1),$$

$$\lim_{u \to \infty} F_{(m)}(z, -q+iu) = 0$$

for $m = 1, 2, \ldots, n$, by the Riemann–Lebesgue theorem. Also as for $q+\varepsilon < p$,

$$e^{(q+\varepsilon)t}\,|k_2(s;t)| \in L^1(0,\infty),$$

$$|Q^{(m)}(s,-q+iu)| \leqslant \int_0^\infty t^m e^{qt}\,|k_2(s;t)|\,dt$$

$$= O\left(\int_0^\infty e^{(q+\varepsilon)t}\,|k_2(s;t)|\,dt\right) = O\,(1)$$

$$(m = 0, 1, \ldots, n-1; u \to \infty)$$

Hence from the integration by parts,

(75.30)
$$\int_{-q+iw}^{-q+i\infty} \frac{F(z-v)}{v} Q(s,v)\,dv = -Q(s,-q+iw)\,F_{(1)}(z,-q+iw) + \dots$$
$$+ (-)^n Q^{(n-1)}(s,-q+iw)\,F_{(n)}(z,-q+iw)$$
$$+ (-)^n \int_{-q+iw}^{-q+i\infty} Q^{(n)}(s,v)\,F_{(n)}(z,v)\,dv$$

By $Q \to 0$ and Cauchy's integrals we see that for fixed $w > 0$,

(75.31) $\quad Q^{(m)}(s,-q+iw) \to 0 \qquad (s \to \infty) \qquad (0 \leqslant m < n)$

Also the condition A_p shows that $Q^{(n)}(s,-q+it) \in L_r(v,\infty) \cap L_r(-\infty,-v)$. From the order relation on F,

$$\sup_{z \in Y} \int_0^\infty |t^{-n}F(z,t)\,e^{-kt}|^r\,dt < \infty \qquad (r > 0,\ k > \sigma - \mathrm{re}\ z)$$

Hence if $1 < r \leqslant 2$, with $1/r + 1/p = 1$, we have by Titchmarsh (1948), p. 96, Theorem 74 (4.1.2),

$$\sup_{z \in Y} \int_{-\infty}^\infty |F_{(n)}(z,-k+iu)|^\varrho\,du < \infty \qquad (k > \sigma - \mathrm{re}\ z)$$

Hence putting $k = q < p$, and using (75.30; 75.31), and condition A_p, with $w \geqslant v$,

$$\limsup_{s \to \infty} \left| \int_{-q+iw}^{-q+i\infty} \frac{F(z-v)}{v} Q(s,v)\,dv \right|$$
$$= \limsup_{s \to \infty} \left| \int_{-q+iw}^{-q+i\infty} Q^{(n)}(s,v)\,F_{(n)}(z,v)\,dv \right|$$
$$\leqslant \limsup_{s \to \infty} \left\{ \int_w^\infty |Q^{(n)}(s,-q+it)|^r\,dt \right\}^{1/r} \left\{ \int_w^\infty |F_{(n)}(z,-q+it)|^\varrho\,dt \right\}^{1/\varrho}$$
$$\leqslant M_3^{1/r}(q) \left\{ \int_w^\infty |F_{(n)}(z,-q+it)|^\varrho\,dt \right\}^{1/\varrho}$$

Similarly for the range $-q-i\infty$ to $-q-iw$.

For $r = 1$, $F_{(n)}(z,-q+it)$ is bounded in t, uniformly for $z \in Y$. A similar result follows in this case. Thus we have now completed the proof that $B^*(F; z, s) \to F(z)$, and so $B(F; z, s)\ F(z)\ (s \to \infty)$, for all $z \in R(\sigma - p) \cap H(F; z)$.

Ex.75.1. Transform the complex plane minus the line $v = \mathrm{re}\, v \geqslant 1$, into the plane minus the line $z = \mathrm{re}\, z \leqslant 0$ (e.g. $v = e^{-z}$, $v = 1-z$), and put $Q(s, z)E(s) = -E(s, v)$, where $E(v)$ is an integral (entire) function of Cooke (1950), p. 184, Theorem (8.2, III); p. 188, Theorem (8.3, I). Do any such functions satisfy the conditions of our Theorem 75.3?

Ex. 75.2. Alternatively, transform $\backslash Z$ into $|v| < 1$, $Q(s, z)$ into $Q_1(s, v)$, the latter tending to 0 as $s \to \infty$, uniformly in $|v| \leqslant 1-\varepsilon$, for each $\varepsilon > 0$. For example, consider $-v^s$, and put $v = (1+z)^{-1}$,

$$Q(s, z) = -(1+z)^{-s} = -\int_0^\infty e^{-zu} e^{-u} u^{s-1} \, du / \Gamma(s)$$

finding $a(s, w)$ as an integral from w to $+\infty$, and $a(n, w)$. Show that Q satisfies condition A_1 with $q < 1$, $n = 0$, $r = 1$, $s_0 = 2$, $v = 1$, Let Z be a horizontal set including $|z+1| \leqslant 1$, and show that the conditions of Theorem 75.3 hold. Compute $B(F; z, n)$ in relation to a Taylor series, (Henstock (1957b)).

Ex. 75.3. Let $\alpha > 0, \beta > 0, \xi > 0, \eta > 0, -\alpha - i\xi \notin Z, -\beta + i\eta \notin Z$, where Z is a horizontal set, and let Z_1 be a strip $-\xi \leqslant iz \leqslant \eta$, $\mathrm{re}\, z \geqslant -\max(\alpha, \beta)$. For each s let $J(s, z)$ be regular for $z \in Z_1$, apart from a simple pole at $z = 0$, with residue tending to -1 as $s \to \infty$. Further, let $J(s, z) \to 0$ as $s \to \infty$ uniformly for each compact set in $Z_1 \backslash Z$. If the Laplace–Stieltjes integral F is convergent in $R(\sigma)$, show that

$$F(z) = \lim_{s \to \infty} \frac{1}{2\pi i} \int_\gamma F(z-v) J(s, v) \, dv = \lim_{s \to \infty} \int_0^\infty k(s; t) \, dF(z, t)$$

uniformly for z in each compact set contained in $H(F; Z) \cap R(\sigma - \min(\alpha, \beta))$, where γ is the line from $-\alpha - i\xi$ to $-\beta + i\eta$, and where

$$k(s, t) \equiv \frac{1}{2\pi i} \int_\gamma e^{vt} J(s, v) \, dv$$

i.e. k is efficient $(Z; p)$ with $p = \min(\alpha, \beta)$. (Henstock (1957b), p. 29, Theorem 4).

Ex. 75.4. In *Ex. 75.3* show that $k(s; t)$ is an integral function in t of order less than 1, or of order 1, type $\leqslant \max(\alpha, \beta) + \max(\xi, \eta)$.

Ex. 75.5. If $k(s; t)$ is an integral function of t of order <1, or order 1, type r, show that for z in a suitable region,

$$k(s; t) = \sum_{n=0}^{\infty} k_n(s) t^n, \quad B(F; z, s) = \sum_{n=0}^{\infty} (-)^n k_n(s) F^n(z)$$

and B is regular in the domain formed by excluding all points from the complex plane that are within a distance $\leqslant r$ of some singularity or inaccessible point of F.

Ex. 75.6. In *Ex. 75.3*, show that the only singularities of $B(z^{-1}; z, s)$ are at $-\alpha - i\xi$, $-\beta + i\eta$, and for J_1 regular at those points, $B(z^{-1}; z, s) = J(s, z)(\log\{(z+\alpha+i\xi)/(z+\beta-i\eta)\})/(2\pi i) + J_1(s, z)$

Ex. 75.7. In *Ex. 75.3* show that $\alpha = \beta = p$, $\xi = \eta = \pi$, $J(s, z) = (1-e^z)^{-1}$. $K(s, e^{-z})$, $k(s, v) \equiv \sum_{n=0}^{\infty} k_n(s)v^n$, gives the power series result.

REFERENCES

Adams, C. R. and Morse, A. P. (1937). 'On the space (BV)', *Trans. Am. Math. Soc.*, 42, 194–205.

Agnew, R. P. (1939). 'Properties of generalized definitions of the limit', *Bull. Am. Math. Soc.*, 45, 689–730.

Agnew, R. P. (1946). 'Summability of power series', *Am. Math. Mon.*, 53, 251–9.

Alexandroff, P. and Hopf, H. (1935). *Topologie* I, Berlin.

Alexiewicz, A. (1948). *Colloquium Math.*, 1, 289–93.

Alexiewicz, A. (1950). 'On sequences of operations I', *Studia Math.*, 11, 1–30.

Appling, W. D. L. (1962a). 'Interval functions and the Hellinger integral', *Duke Math. J.*, 29, 515–20.

Appling, W. D. L. (1962b). 'Concerning non-negative valued interval functions', *Proc. Am. Math. Soc.*, 13, 784–8.

Appling, W. D. L. (1963). 'Infinite series and non-negative valued interval functions', *Duke Math. J.*, 30, 107–11.

Arzelà, C. (1889). 'Funzioni di linee', *Atti Accad. naz. Lincei Rc. (Cl. Sci. Fis. Mat. Nat.)* (4) 5_I, 342–8.

Arzelà, C. (1895). 'Sulle funzioni di linee', *Memorie R. Accad. Sci. Ist. Bologna (Cl. Sci. Fis. Mat.)*, (5) 5, 55–74.

Ascoli, G. (1883–4). 'Le curve limiti di una varietà data di curve', *Atti Accad. naz. Lincei Memorie (Cl. Sci. Fis. Mat. Nat.)*, (3) 18, 521–86.

Baire, R. (1899). 'Sur les fonctions de variables réelles', *Anneli Mat. Pura Appl.*, (3) 3, 1–122.

Banach, S. (1922). 'Sur les opérations dans les ensembles abstraits et leur application aux équations intégrales', *Fundam. Math.* 3, 128–81.

Banach, S. (1929a, b). 'Sur les fonctionnelles linéaires', *Studia Math.* 1, I (211–16), II (223–39).

Banach, S. (1930). 'Théorème sur les ensembles de première catégorie', *Fundam. Math.* 16, 395–8.

Banach, S. (1932). *Théorie des Opérations Linéaires*, (Reprinted, Chelsea, New York) Lwow.

Banach, S. and Steinhaus, H. (1927) 'Sur le principe de la condensation de singularités', *Fundam. Math.*, 9, 50–61.

Bary, N. (1964), *A Treatise on Trigonometric Series*, vol. 2. Authorized translation by M. F. Mullins, Pergamon, Oxford.

Besicovitch, A. S. (1932). *Almost Periodic Functions*, Cambridge University Press, London.

Bohnenblust, H. F. and Sobczyk, A. (1938). 'Extensions of Functionals on Complex Linear Spaces', *Bull. Am. Math. Soc.*, 44, 91–3.

Bohr H. (1909). 'Om en Udvidelse af en kendte Konvergenssaeting', *Nyt Tidsskr.*

Mat. (Copenhagen), (B) **20**, 1–4.

Bois-Reymond, P. du (1882). *Die allgemeine Functionentheorie* I, Tübingen.

Borel, E. (1898). *Leçons sur la Théorie des Fonctions*, Paris.

Borel, E. (1901). *Leçons sur les Séries Divergentes*, Paris.

Bourbaki, N. (1953). *Espaces Vectoriels Topologiques*, Ch. I–II, Hermann, Paris.

Bourbaki, N. (1958). I, Livre III. *Topologie Générale*, Ch. 9, 'Utilisation des nombres réels en topologie générale', 2nd éd., Hermann, Paris.

Bray, H. E. (1919). 'Elementary properties of the Stieltjes integral', *Ann. Math.* **20**, 177–86.

Buhl, A. (1925). 'Séries analytiques, sommabilité', *Mém. Sci. Math.*, *Fasciscule* VII, Paris.

Buniakowsky, V. (1859). 'Sur quelques inégalités concernant les intégrales ordinaires et les intégrales aux différences finies', *Mém. Acad. St. Petersburg*, (7) **1**, No. 9, 4.

Burkill, J. C. (1924a). 'Functions of intervals', *Proc. Lond. Math. Soc.*, (2) **22**, 275–310.

Burkill, J. C. (1924b). 'The expression of area as an integral', *Proc. Lond. Math. Soc.*, (2) **22**, 311–36.

Burkill, J. C. (1924c). 'The derivates of functions of intervals', *Fundam. Math.* **5**, 321–7.

Burkill, J. C. (1929). *J. Lond. Math. Soc.*, **4**, 127–32.

Cantor, G. (1872). 'Über die Ausdehnung eines Satzes aus der Theorie der trigonometrischen Reihen', *Math. Annln*, **5**, 123–32. (p. 129).

Cantor, G. (1879). 'Über unendliche lineare Punktmannigfaltigkeiten I', *Math. Annln*, **15**, 2.

Cantor, G. (1883a). 'Über unendliche lineare Punktmannigfaltigkeiten IV,' *Math. Annln*, **21**, 51.

Cantor, G. (1883b). 'Über unendliche lineare Punktmannigfaltigkeiten V,' *Math. Annln*, **21**, 590.

Cantor, G. (1884). 'Über unendliche lineare Punktmannigfaltigkeiten VI', *Math. Annln*, **23**, 471.

Carmichael, R. D. (1918–19). 'General aspects of the theory of summable series', *Bull. Am. Math. Soc.*, **25**, 97–131.

Cartan, H. (1940). 'Sur la mesure de Haar', *C. R. hebd. Séanc. Acad. Sci., Paris*, **211**, 759–62.

Cauchy, A. (1821). *Oeuvres*, sér. II, t. 3, p. 373, Gauthier-Villars, Paris, 1900.

Cooke, R. G. (1936). 'On mutual consistency and regular T-limits', *Proc. Lond. Math. Soc.*, (2) **41**, 113–25.

Cooke, R. G. (1937). 'An extension of some recent results on mutual consistency and regular T-limits', *J. Lond. Math. Soc.*, **12**, 98–105.

Cooke, R. G. and Barnett, A. M. (1948). 'The "right" value of the generalized limit of a bounded divergent sequence', *J. Lond. Math. Soc.*, **23**, 211–21.

Day, M. M. (1939). 'Regularity of function-to-function transformations', *Bull. Am. Math. Soc.*, **45**, 296–303.

Day, M. M. (1962). *Normed Linear Spaces*, Springer-Verlag, Berlin.

Denjoy, A. (1915). 'Mémoire sur les nombres dérivés des fonctions continues', *J. Math. Pures Appl.*,(7) **1**, 105–240.

Dienes, P. (1931) *The Taylor series*, Oxford University Press, London.

Dowidar, A. F. and Petersen, G. M. (1963). 'The distribution of sequences and summability', *Can. J. Math.*, **15**, 1–10.

Dunford, N. and Schwartz, J. T. (1958, 1963). *Linear Operators, Parts* I, II, Interscience, New York.

Ellis, R. (1957). 'A note on the continuity of the inverse', *Proc. Am. Math. Soc.*, **8**, 372–3.

Evans, G. C. (1927). 'The Logarithmic Potential', *Am. Math. Soc. Colloquium Publ.* 6, New York.

Fischer, E. (1907). 'Sur la convergence en moyenne', *C.R. hebd. Séanc. Acad. Sci. Paris*, 144, 1022–24.

Fuchs, L. (1958) *Abelian Groups*, Budapest.

Gál, I. S. (1951). 'Sur la méthode de résonance et sur un théorème concernant les espaces de type (B)', *Annls Inst. Fourier Univ. Grenoble* 3, 23–30.

Gál I. S. (1953). 'The principle of condensation of singularities', *Duke Math. J.* **20**, 27–35.

Garreau, G. A. (1951). 'A note on the summation of sequences of 0's and 1's', *Ann. Math.*, (2) **54**, 183–5.

Graves, R. E. (1951). 'Additive functionals on a space of continuous functions II', *Ann. Math.*, **54**, 275–85.

Haar, A. (1933). 'Der Massbegriff in der Theorie der kontinuierlichen Gruppen', *Ann. Math.*, **34**, 147–69.

Hadamard, J. (1903). 'Deux théorèmes d'Abel sur la convergence des séries', *Acta Math. Stokh.*, **27**, 177–83.

Hahn, H. (1922). 'Über Folgen linearer Operationen', *Mh. Math. Phys.*, **32**, 3–88.

Hahn, H. (1927). 'Über lineare Gleichungssysteme in linearen Räumen', *J. Reine Angew. Math.*, **157**, 214–29.

Halperin, I. and Nakano, H. (1953). 'Generalized l^p spaces and the Schur property', *J. Math. Soc., Japan*, **5**, 50–8.

Hardy, G. H. (1949). *Divergent Series*, Oxford University Press, London.

Hausdorff, F. (1957). *Set Theory*, English edn, Chelsea, New York.

Hellinger, E. (1907). *Die Orthogonalinvarianten Quadratischer Formen von unendlichvielen Variablen*, Dissertation, Göttingen.

Helly, E. (1921). 'Über lineare Funktionaloperationen', *Sber. Akad. Wiss. Wien (Math.-naturw.)*, **121**, (part IIa, numbers I to X), 265–97.

Henstock, R. (1947). 'The efficiency of matrices for Taylor series', *J. Lond. Math. Soc.*, **22**, 104–7.

Henstock, R. (1950). 'The efficiency of matrices for bounded sequences', *J. Lond. Math. Soc.*, **25**, 27–33.

Henstock, R. (1955a). 'Linear functions with domain a real countably infinite dimensional space', *Proc. Lond. Math. Soc.*, (3) **5**, 238–56.

Henstock, R. (1955b). 'The efficiency of convergence factors for functions of a continuous real variable', *J. Lond. Math. Soc.*, **30**, 273–86.

Henstock, R. (1956). 'Linear and bilinear functions with domain contained in a real countably infinite dimensional space', *Proc. Lond. Math. Soc.* (3) **6**, 481–500.

Henstock, R. (1957a). 'On Ward's Perron–Stieltjes integral', *Can. J. Math.*, **9**, 96–109.

Henstock, R. (1957b). 'The summation by convergence factors of Laplace–Stieltjes integrals outside their half plane of convergence', *Math. Z.* **67**, 10–31.

Henstock, R. (1961a). 'N-variation and N-variational integrals of set functions', *Proc. Lond. Math. Soc.*, (3) **11**, 109–33.

Henstock, R. (1961b). 'Definitions of Riemann type of the variational integrals', *Proc. Lond. Math. Soc.*, (3) **11**, 402–18.

Henstock R. (1963a). 'Difference-sets and the Banach–Steinhaus theorem', *Proc. Lond. Math. Soc.* (3) **13**, 305–21.

Henstock, R. (1963b). 'Tauberian theorems for integrals', *Can. J. Math.*, **15**, 433–9.

Henstock, R. (1963c). *Theory of integration*, Butterworths, London.

Henstock, R. (1964). 'The integrability of functions of interval functions', *J. Lond. Math. Soc.*, **39**, 589–97.

Henstock, R. and Macbeath, A. M. (1953). 'On the measure of sum-sets (I) The theorems of Brunn, Minkowski, and Lusternik', *Proc. Lond. Math. Soc.* (3) **3**, 182–94.

Hildebrandt, T. H. (1964). Mathl Rev., **28**, Review 1274.

Hill, J. D. (1936). 'A theorem in the theory of summability', *Bull. Am. Math. Soc.*, **42**, 225–8.

Hill, J. D. (1942). 'Some properties of summability', *Duke Math. J.*, **9**, 373–81.

Hill, J. D. (1944). 'Some properties of summability II', *Bull. Am. Math. Soc.*, **50**, 227–30.

Hill, J. D. (1945). 'Summability of sequences of 0's and 1's', *Ann. Math.*, (2) **46**, 556–62.

Hill, J. D. (1951). 'Note on a theorem in summability', *Proc. Am. Math. Soc.*, **2**, 372–3.

Hölder, E. (1889), 'Über einen Mittelwertsatz', *Nachr. Akad. Wiss. Göttingen. (Math. Phys.)* 38–47.

Iyer, V. G. (1948). 'On the space of integral functions I', *J. Indian Math. Soc.*, (2) **12**, 13–30.

Iyer, V. G. (1950). 'On the space of integral functions II', *Q. Jl Math.*, (2) **1**, 86–96.

Jessen, B. (1934). 'The theory of integration in a space of an infinite number of dimensions', *Acta Math., Stockh.*, **63**, 249–323.

Kakutani, S. (1936). 'Über die Metrization der topologischen Gruppen', *Proc. Imp. Acad. Japan*, **12**, 82–84.

Kalman, J. A. (1958). 'On the inequality of Ingham and Jessen', *J. Lond. Math. Soc.*, **33**, 306–11.

Kaloujnine, L. (1947). 'Sur les groupes abéliens primaires sans éléments de hauteur infinie', *C. R. hebd. Séanc. Acad. Sci., Paris*, **225**, 713–15.

Kantorovitch, L. (1931). 'Sur la convergence de la suite des polynômes de S. Bernstein en dehors de l'intervalle fondamental', *Izv. Akad. Nauk S.S.S.R.*, (7) **8**, 1103–15.

Kelley, J. L. (1955). *General Topology*, Van Nostrand, New York.

Keogh, F. R. (1960). 'Some generalizations of the Riemann–Lebesgue theorem', *J. Lond. Math. Soc.*, **35**, 283–93.

Kestelman, H. (1947). 'On the functional equation $f(x+y) = f(x)+f(y)$', *Fundam. Math.*, **34**, 144–7.

Kojima, T. (1917). 'On generalized Toeplitz's theorems on limit and their applications', *Tôhoku Math. J.*, **12**, 291–326.

Kojima, T. (1918). *Tôhoku Math. J.*, **14**, 64–79.

Kojima, T. (1920). *Tôhoku Math. J.*, **20**, 37–45.

Kuratowski, C. (1930). *Fundam. Math.*, **16**, 390.

Kurepa, S. (1956). 'Convex functions', *Glasn. Mat.-fiz. Astr. Hrv. Prirodosl Društ.* **11**, 89–94.

Lebesgue H. (1902). 'Intégrale, longueur, aire', *Annali Mat. Pura Appl.*, (3) **7**, 231–359.

Lebesgue H. (1909). 'Sur les intégrales singulières', *Annls Fac. Sci. Univ. Toulouse*, Série 3, **1**, 25–117.

Lee, P. Y. (1965). 'Integrals involving parameters', *J. Lond. Math. Soc.*, **40**, 338–344.

Lee, P. Y. (1966). 'A note on some generalizations of the Riemann–Lebesgue Theorem', *J. Lond. Math. Soc.*, **41**, 313–7.

Lindenbaum, A. (1926). 'Sur les espaces métriques', *Fundam. Math.*, **8**, 211.

Lorentz, G. G. (1947). 'Über Limitierungsverfahren, die von einem Stieltjes-Integral abhängen', *Acta Math.*, **79**, 255–72.

Lorentz, G. G. (1955). 'Borel and Banach properties of methods of summation', *Duke Math. J.*, **22**, 129–41.

Lusin, N. (1912). *Intégrale et série trigonométrique*, (in Russian), Moscow.

Lusin, N. (1927). 'Sur les ensembles analytiques', *Fundam. Math.*, **10**, 1–95.

McGrotty, J. J. (1962). 'A theorem on complete sets', *J. Lond. Math. Soc.*, **37**, 338–40.

McGrotty, J. J. (1965). 'On a generalization of the Riemann-complete integral'.

Mazurkiewicz, S. (1931). 'Sur les fonctions non dérivables', *Studia Math.*, **3**, 92–4.

Mehdi, M. R. (1964). 'On convex functions', *J. Lond. Math. Soc.*, **39**, 321–6.

Minkowski, H. (1896). *Geometrie der Zahlen*, I. pp. 115–17, Leipzig.

Moore, E. H. (1915). 'Definition of limit in general integral analysis', *Proc. Natn. Acad. Sci. U.S.A.*, **1**, 628.

Moore, E. H. (1935). *General Analysis* I, Part II, Mem. Amer. Philos. Soc. Philadelphia.

Moore, E. H. and Smith, H. L., (1922). 'A general theory of limits', *Am. J. Math.* **44**, 102–21.

Nakano, H. (1951). *Topology and Linear Topological Spaces*, Maruzen Co., Tokyo.

Nikodym, O. (1925). 'Sur une propriété de l'opération A', *Fundam. Math.*, **7**, 149–54.

Ostrowski, A. (1929). 'Über die Funktionalgleichung der Exponentialfunktion und verwandte Funktionalgleichungen', *Jber. Dt. MatVerein*, **38**, 54–62.

Parker, S. T. (1950). 'Convergence factor and regularity theorems for convergent integrals', *Duke Math. J.*, **17**, 91–110.

Perron, O. (1920). 'Zur Theorie der divergenten Reihen', *Math. Z.*, **6**, 158–60 and 286–310.

Pettis, B. J. (1950). 'On continuity and openness of homomorphisms in topological groups', *Ann. Math.*, (2) **52**, 293–308.

Rademacher, H. (1922). 'Einige Sätze über Reihen von allgemeinen Orthogonalfunktionen', *Math. Annln*, **87**, 112–38.

Rappoport, S. I. (1949). 'On certain transformations of summation formulas', *Mat. Sb.*, (2) **24**, (66), 87–100.

REFERENCES

Riesz, F. (1907). 'Sur les systèmes orthogonaux de fonctions', *C. R. hebd. Séanc. Acad. Sci., Paris*, **144**, 615–19.

Riesz, F. (1909). 'Sur les opérations fonctionnelles linéaires', *C. R. hebd. Séanc. Acad. Sci. Paris*, **149**, 974–7.

Rogers, C. A. (1946). 'Linear transformations which apply to all convergent sequences and series', *J. Lond. Math. Soc.*, **21**, 123–8; 'Addendum to "Linear transformations..." ', *ibid.*, 182–5.

Saks, S. (1933). 'On some functionals', *Trans. Am. Math. Soc.*, **35**, 549–56.

Saks, S. (1937). 'On some functionals II', *Trans. Am. Math. Soc.*, **41**, 160–170.

Saks, S. (1937). *Theory of the Integral*, 2nd English edn, Warsaw.

Sargent, W. L. C. (1948). 'On the integrability of a product', *J. Lond. Math. Soc.*, **23**, 28–34.

Sargent, W. L. C. (1950). 'On linear functionals in spaces of conditionally integrable functions', *Q. Jl Math.*, (2) **1**, 288–98.

Sargent, W. L. C. (1952). *J. Lond. Math. Soc.*, **27**, 401–13.

Sargent, W. L. C. (1953). 'On some theorems of Hahn, Banach, and Steinhaus', *J. Lond. Math. Soc.*, **28**, 438–51.

Sargent, W. L. C. (1955). 'On the transform $y_z(s) = \int_0^\infty x(t) k_s(t) \, dt$', *J. Lond. Math. Soc.*, **30**, 401–16.

Schur, J. (1920). 'Über lineare Transformation in der Theorie der unendlichen Reihen', *J. Math. (Crelle)*, **151**, 79–111

Schwarz, H. A. (1885). *Gesammelte Mathematische Abhandlungen*, Band I, p. 251 (Springer, Berling, 1890).

Sierpiński, W. (1929). 'Sur une opération sur les familles d'ensembles', *C. R. Séanc. Soc. Sci. Varsovie (Spraw. Posied. Tow. nauk. Warsz.)*, **22**, 163–7.

Silverman, L. L. (1913). 'On the definition of the sum of a divergent series', *Univ. Missouri Studies*, Math. Series I, 1–96.

Silverman, L. L. (1916). 'On the notion of summability for the limit of a function of a continuous variable', *Trans. Am. Math. Soc.*, **17**, 284–94.

Sobczyk, A. (1941). 'Projections in Minkowski and Banach spaces', *Duke Math. J.*, **8**, 78–106.

Soukhomlinoff, G. A. (1938). 'Über Fortsetzung von linearen Funktionalen in linearen komplexen Räumen und linearen Quaternionräumen', *Mat. Sb.*, (45), **3**, 353–8 (Russian; German summary).

Souslin, M. (1917). 'Sur une définition des ensembles mesurables B sans nombres transfinis', *C. R. hebd. Séanc. Acad. Sci., Paris*, **164**, 88–91.

Steinhaus, H. (1911). 'Remarks on the generalization of the idea of limit', (in Polish), *Pr. mat.-fiz.*, **22**, 121–34.

Takenaka, S. (1922). 'A general view of the theory of summability, I', *Tohoku Math. J.*, **21**, 193–221.

Tamarkin, J. D. (1935). 'On the notion of regularity of methods of summation', *Bull. Am. Math. Soc.*, **41**, 241–3.

Tatchell, J. B. (1953). 'On some integral transforms', *Proc. Lond. Math. Soc.*, (3) **3**, 257–66.

Titchmarsh, E. C. (1948). *Introduction to the Theory of Fourier Integrals*, 2nd edn, Oxford University Press, London.

Toeplitz, O. (1911). 'Über allgemeine lineare Mittelbildungen', *Pr. mat.-fiz.*, **22**, 113–20.

REFERENCES

Tolstov, G. (1939). 'Sur l'intégrale de Perron', *Mat. Sb.*, **5**, (47), 647–60.

Tychonoff, A. (1929). 'Über die topologische Erweiterung von Räumen', *Math. Annln*, **102**, 544–61.

Tychonoff, A. (1935). 'Über einen Funktionenraum', *Math. Annln*, **111**, 762–6.

Urysohn, P. (1925). 'Über die Machtigkeit der zusammenhängen Mengen', *Math. Annln*, **94**, 262–95.

Von Neumann, J. (1936). 'The uniqueness of Haar's measure', *Mat. Sb.*, *1*, 721–34.

Weil, A. (1937). 'Sur les espaces a structure uniforme et sur la topologie générale, *Actual. Scient. Ind.*, **551**,

Weil, A. (1940). *L'intégration dans les groupes topologiques et ses applications*, Hermann, Paris.

Weston, J. D. (1957a). 'On the comparison of topologies', *J. Lond. Math. Soc.*, **32**, 342–54.

Weston, J. D. (1957b). 'The principle of equicontinuity for topological vector spaces', *Proc. Univ. Durham Phil. Soc.*, **13**, series A(science)1

Weyl, H. (1916). 'Über die Gleichverteilung von Zahlen mod. Eins', *Math. Annln*, **77**, 313–52.

Whitney, H. (1957). *Geometric Integration*,

Widder, D. V. (1941). *The Laplace Transform*, Princeton University Press, Princeton.

Young, W. H. (1912). 'On classes of summable functions and their Fourier series', *Proc. R. Soc.*, (A) **87**, 225–9.

Young W. H. and Young, G. C. (1915). 'On the reduction of sets of intervals', *Proc. Lond. Math. Soc.*, **14** (2), 111–30.

Zaanen, A. C. (1953). *Linear Analysis*, Amsterdam.

Zygmund, A. (1959). *Trigonometric Series*, 2nd edn, vol. 1, Cambridge University Press, London.

ADDITIONAL REFERENCES

Burkill, J. C. (1932). 'The approximately continuous Perron integral', *Math. Z.*, **34**, 270–278.

Chan, K. M. (1967). 'The equivalence of Henstock's two definitions of the Riemann-complete integral', *J. Lond. math. Soc.*, **42**, 349–350.

Cooke, R. G: (1950). Infinite matrices and sequence spaces, Macmillan, London

Cooke, R. G. (1953). Linear Operators, Macmillan, London.

Dienes, P. (1913). Lecons sur les singularités des fonctions analytiques, Paris.

Henstock, R. (1960c). 'The equivalence of generalized forms of the Ward, variational, Denjoy–Stieltjes, and Perron–Stieltjes integrals', *Proc. Lond. math. Soc.*, (3) **10**, 281–303.

Kolmogoroff, A. (1929). 'Über des Gesetz des interierten Logarithmus', *Math. Ann.*, **101**, 126–135.

Kuratowski, C. (1952). Topologie. Monografie matematyczne, Warsaw.

Kurzweil, J. (1957). 'Generalized ordinary differential equations and continuous dependence on a parameter', *Czech. math.*, **7** (82), 418–446.

Loomis (1953). An introduction to abstract harmonic analysis, Van Nostrand, New York.

429

ADDITIONAL REFERENCES

Maddox, I. J. (1967). 'On theorems of Steinhaus type', *J. Lond. math. Soc.*, **42**, 239–244.

Okada, Y. (1925). 'Über die Annäherung analytischer Funktionen', *Math. Z.*, **23**, 62–71.

Pratt, J. W. (1960). 'On interchanging limits and integrals', *Ann. Math. Statistics*, **31**, 74–77.

Ray, K. D. (1962–65). 'On some properties of ratio sets', *Ann. Univ. Ferrara Sez.*, VII (N.S.) **11**, 45–49.

Steinhaus, H. (1919). 'Sur les distances des points des ensembles de mesure positive', *Fundam. Math.*, **1**, 93-104.

Fau Dyk Tin and Silov, G.E. (1966). 'Quadratic functionals in a space with gaussian measure' (in Russian), *Uspehi Mat. Nauk.*, **21**, 226–229.

NOTATION INDEX

431

432

433

GENERAL INDEX

435

GENERAL INDEX

Jessen, B., 248, 320
Join, 6

Kalman, J. A., 202
Kaloujnine, L., 122
Kantorovitch, L., 184
Karták, K., 221
Kelley, J. L., 2, 42, 58, 68
Keogh, F. R., 393
Kestelman, H., 158, 199
K-matrix, 275
Kojima, T., 275, 278
Kolmogoroff, A., 2, 252–260, 325
Kuratowski, C., IX, 50
Kurepa, S., 158
Kurzweil, J., 221

Laplace–Stieltjes integral, 404
Law of the iterated logarithm, 2,
    252–260
Lebesgue, H., IX, 1–3, 28, 186, 194,
    198, 206, 221, 237–8, 380, 382, 384
Lebesgue space L, 350–358
Lee, P. Y., X, 244, 246, 395–7
Left-translation-invariance, 123
Limit-point, 28
Lindenbaum, A., 42
Linear combination, 173
Linear dependence, 173
Linear independence, 173
Linear manifold, 173
Linear space, 172
Linear subspace, 173
Linear topological space, 176
Linear vector space, 172
Littlewood, J. E., 366
Local base, 37
Locally compact, 59
Locally complete, 66
Locally finite, 42
Locally half-compact, 73
Locally half-complete, 73
Locally semi-compact, 62
Locally semi-complete, 66
Loomis, IX
Lorentz, G. G., 377–8, 395–6

Lower bound, 32
Lower sum, 186
Lusin, N., 77, 221, 403

Macbeath, A. M., 160, 197
McCrudden, M., 221
McGrotty, J. J., X, 220
Maddox, I. J., X, 279, 300
Majorized convergence, 238
Mapping, 5
Mazur, S., 96, 100
Mazurkiewicz, S., 342
Meager, 44
Measurability, 244
Measure, 3
Meet, 6
Mehdi, M. R., 15, 131, 157–9
Member, 4
Metric, 39
Metric topology, 39
Minimal difference sequence, 121
Minimal θ-sequence, 16
Minkowski, H., 203
Module, 7
Modulus topology, 28
Moment, 287
Monotone convergence, 238
Monotone increasing, 108
Moore, E. H., 32–3, 220, 340, 398
Moore–Smith convergence, 32–3
Morse, A. P., 50
Multiplicative functional, 125, 127
μ-measurable, 110
Mutually disjoint, 7

Nakano, H., 202
Neighbourhood, 26
Nikodym, O., 50, 80
Non-meager, 44
Non-negative definite, 127
Non-overlapping, 213
Norm (function), 163
Norm (group), 15, 141
Normal, 206
Normal space, 36
Normed linear space, 178
Norm-homogeneous, 180

438